Addison-Wesley

Pre-Algebra

A Transition to Algebra

Phares G. O'Daffer

Stanley R. Clemens

Randall I. Charles

Addison-Wesley Publishing Company

Menlo Park, California Reading, Massachusetts New York Don Mills, Ontario

Wokingham, England Amsterdam Bonn Sydney Singapore Tokyo Madrid San Juan

Acknowledgments

Illustration Acknowledgments
Nea Bisek
Susan Iannone

Photo Acknowledgments
2 Gene Stein/West Light
3 Craig Aurness/West Light
6 Phillip Wallick/ The Stock Market
21 Robert Wagoner/The Stock Market
24 Wayland Lee*/Addison-Wesley Publishing Company
29 Timothy O'Keefe/Bruce Coleman Inc.
34 Rob Nelson/Stock Boston
38 David Madison/Bruce Coleman Inc.
39 Wayland Lee*/Addison-Wesley Publishing Company
48 David Madison/Bruce Coleman Inc.
58 Spencer Swanger/Tom Stack & Associates
60 Lee Foster/Bruce Coleman Inc.
76 Guy Motil/West Light
77 Larry Lee/West Light
99 Wayland Lee*/Addison-Wesley Publishing Company
116 Tom McCarthy/The Stock Market
124 Bob Daemmrich/Stock Boston
130 David Madison/Bruce Coleman Inc.
131 David Stoecklein/The Stock Market
145 Anthony Edgeworth/The Stock Market
148 Chuck O'Rear/West Light
150 Henley & Savage/The Stock Market
152 Wayland Lee*/Addison-Wesley Publishing Company
160 William Warren/West Light
162 David Madison/Bruce Coleman Inc.
163 Wayland Lee*/Addison-Wesley Publishing Company
165 James Blank/Stock Boston
169 Lee Foster/Bruce Coleman Inc.
175 Focus on Sports
180 Bob McKeever/Tom Stack & Associates
186 Carroll Seghers/The Stock Market
187 Ted Mahieu/The Stock Market
190 Pierre Kopp/West Light
192 Bob Burch/Bruce Coleman Inc.
198 Wayland Lee*/Addison-Wesley Publishing Company
208 Focus on Sports
209 Gabe Palmer/The Stock Market
212 Wendell Metzer/Bruce Coleman Inc.
215 Gabe Palmer/The Stock Market
216 Craig Aurness/West Light
218 Sepp Seitz/Woodfin Camp & Associates
220 Greg Vaughn/Tom Stack & Associates
224 The Far Side, Copyright 1990 Universal Press Syndicate Reprinted with permission. All Rights Reserved.
230 Greg Vaughn/Tom Stack & Associates
231 Martin Rogers/Stock Boston
245 Lawrence Migdale/Stock Boston
251 Animals, Animals
254 Brian Parker/Tom Stack & Associates
260 Frank Oberle/Bruce Coleman Inc.
261 Stephen Frisch*
269 Tom Bean/The Stock Market
278 Gale Zucker/Stock Boston
281 Kathleen Culbert-Aguilar*
298 James W. Kay/Bruce Coleman Inc.
303 Wayland Lee*/Addison-Wesley Publishing Company
317 Wayland Lee*/Addison-Wesley Publishing Company
320 The Image Bank
340 Tim Schultz/Bruce Coleman Inc.
344 Jon Feingersh/The Stock Market
348 Tom Martin/The Stock Market
353 Charles Gupton/Stock Boston
359 Wayland Lee*/Addison-Wesley Publishing Company
372 David Madison/Bruce Coleman Inc.
374 Wayland Lee*/Addison-Wesley Publishing Company
380 Wayland Lee*/Addison-Wesley Publishing Company
385B Wayland Lee*/Addison-Wesley Publishing Company
406 Winnie Denker/The Stock Market
413T Brian Parker/Tom Stack & Associates
434 NASA
444 Wayland Lee*/Addison-Wesley Publishing Company
450 Craig Aurness/West Light
460 Eric Simmons/Stock Boston
471 B. Bachmann/Stock Boston
476 Ted Horowitz/The Stock Market
486 Paul Mozell/Stock Boston
513 John Gerlach/Tom Stack & Associates
515 Wilson Goodrich/Tom Stack & Associates
517 Guy Motil/West Light
524 David Stoecklein/The Stock Market
528 Stephen Frisch*
540 Bob Daemmrich/Stock Boston
551 Wayland Lee*/Addison-Wesley Publishing Company
551B Chris Knutson*
552 Wayland Lee*/Addison-Wesley Publishing Company
557 Bob Abraham/The Stock Market

*Photographs provided expressly for the publisher

All other photographs taken by Janice Sheldon expressly for the publisher.

ISBN 0-201-28520-7

7 8 9 10—DO—95 94 93

Contents

Chapter 1

Expressions and Equations: Addition and Subtraction

Chapter 2

Expressions and Equations: Multiplication and Division

Chapter 3

Integers

Chapter 4

Decimals

Chapter 5

Number Theory

Chapter 6

Rational Numbers: Addition and Subtraction

Chapter 7

Rational Numbers: Multiplication and Division

Chapter 8

Equations and Inequalities

Chapter 9

Graphs of Equations and Inequalities

Chapter 10

Ratio, Proportion, and Percent

Chapter 11

Applying Percent

Chapter 12

Equations in Geometry

Chapter 13

Area and Volume Formulas

Chapter 14

Probability, Statistics, and Graphs

Chapter 15

Square Roots and Special Triangles

Appendix

1 Expressions and Equations: Addition and Subtraction

The biplanes performed for a total of 54 minutes at yesterday's air show. If their first performance lasted 26 minutes, how long did their second performance last?

1-1 Variables and Expressions

Objective To evaluate numerical and algebraic expressions.

Application

When the air inside a hot-air balloon was heated, the balloon rose 300 meters from the ground. When the burner was turned off and the air cooled, the balloon dropped 50 meters. After rising another 100 meters, the pilot wanted to know the present altitude of the balloon.

Understand the Ideas

The solution to the application can be found by using the **numerical expression** $(300 - 50) + 100$. A numerical expression is a name for a number. To **evaluate** a numerical expression, find the number it represents. When an expression includes **parentheses** ( ), do the operation inside the parentheses first.

Example 1

Find the altitude of the balloon in the **application** above.

Solution $(300 - 50) + 100$ Do the operation inside the parentheses first. $300 - 50 = 250$

$= 250 + 100$

$= 350$ Complete the calculation. $250 + 100 = 350$

The present altitude of the balloon is 350 meters.

Try This Evaluate.

a. $16 - 7$ **b.** $8 + (17 - 9)$ **c.** $(27 + 6) - 19$

d. A second balloon rose 450 meters, descended 125 meters, rose 250 meters, and then descended 125 meters. Evaluate $(450 - 125) + (250 - 125)$ to find its present altitude.

A calculator can be used to evaluate an expression. To add 87 to a number, you can describe the process like this.

Enter a number [+] 87 [=]

If the number is 58, the result is 145. If the number is 287, the result is 374. To describe this process for any number, we use the **variable** n and write $n + 87$.

A **variable** is a symbol or letter, such as n, that reserves a place for a number. An expression such as $n + 87$ that contains at least one variable is called an **algebraic expression.** To evaluate an algebraic expression, replace each variable with a number, or value, and evaluate the numerical expression that results.

Example 2

Evaluate $n + 87$ for $n = 9$.

Solution $n + 87$

$9 + 87$ Replace the variable n with the number 9.

$= 96$

Try This Evaluate. **e.** $32 - x$ for $x = 8$ **f.** $a + (13 - 8)$ for $a = 6$

An algebraic expression may contain more than one variable.

Example 3

Evaluate $(a + b) - 10$ for $a = 8$ and $b = 9$.

Solution $(a + b) - 10$

$(8 + 9) - 10$ Replace a with 8 and b with 9.

$= 17 - 10 = 7$

Try This Evaluate. **g.** $c - (c - d)$ for $c = 17$ and $d = 4$

Class Exercises

What letter is used as a variable? What number replaces it? Evaluate.

1. $x + 5$
$3 + 5$ **2.** $5 + a$
$5 + 7$ **3.** $12 - b$
$12 - 8$ **4.** $r - 7$
$9 - 7$

Discuss the Ideas

5. Do the following instructions make sense? If so, evaluate the expression. If not, tell why. Evaluate $a + (5 + b)$ for $a = 6$ and $b = 6$.

Exercises

Practice and Apply

Evaluate each numerical expression.

1. $49 + 9$ **2.** $45 - 10$ **3.** $(36 - 8) + 5$

4. $43 - (6 + 7)$ **5.** $(19 + 9) - 10$ **6.** $(35 + 4) + 7$

Evaluate each numerical expression.

7. $(11 + 12) - 13$ **8.** $33 - (22 + 10)$ **9.** $28 + (19 - 4)$

Evaluate each algebraic expression.

10. $b - 13$ for $b = 17$

11. $n + 5$ for $n = 7$

12. $16 - a$ for $a = 7$

13. $(x - 9) + 8$ for $x = 75$

14. $8 + (6 + c)$ for $c = 53$

15. $(e - 5) - 9$ for $e = 64$

16. $x - 8$ for $x = 12$, for $x = 14$, and for $x = 76$

Evaluate each expression for $a = 5$, $b = 8$, and $c = 9$.

17. $(c - b) + 26$

18. $(b + b) - 8$

19. $(29 + 57) + (c - a)$

20. $(c + a) - (12 - 4)$

21. $(a + b) - (17 - 8)$

22. $(13 - c) + (14 - b)$

23. $(12 - a) + (8 - a)$

24. $(8 + b) + (c - b)$

25. While riding in a hot-air balloon, Susan recorded temperatures at various heights for a science project. When she began, the temperature was 70°F. Her first reading showed a decrease of 3° and the second reading showed another decrease of 8°. Evaluate the expression $(70 - 3) - 8$ to find the new temperature.

26. The amount of fencing needed for a rectangular rabbit pen with width of 5 ft can be found by evaluating the expression $(L + 5) + (L + 5)$ for a given length, L. Find the amount of fencing needed for a rectangular rabbit pen with length 7 ft.

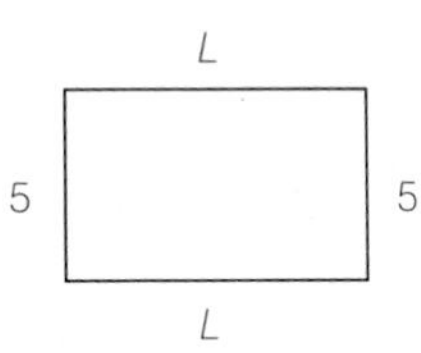

27. The perimeter of a triangle is found by adding the length of each side. Evaluate the expression $a + b + c$ for $a = 3$ cm, $b = 6$ cm, and $c = 8$ cm to find the perimeter of this triangle.

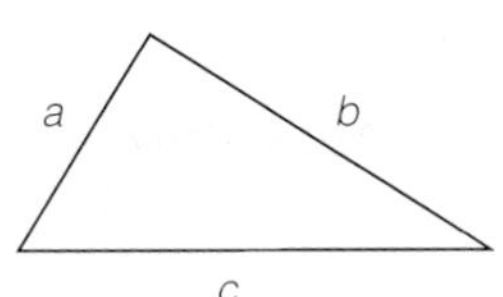

Extend and Apply

Evaluate each expression for $w = 47$, $x = 56$, $y = 94$, and $z = 123$.

28. $(w + x) + (z - y)$

29. $(z - x) - (y - w)$

Copy and complete each table, evaluating the algebraic expression for the numbers given.

	n	$n + n - 1$
	5	$5 + 5 - 1 = 9$
30.	10	
31.	9	
32.	20	

	x	y	$x + x - y$
	8	7	$8 + 8 - 7 = 9$
33.	7	6	
34.	9	8	
35.	6	9	

The altitude of a hot air balloon is the total distance it has risen (R) minus the total distance it has lowered (L), or $R - L$. Find the altitude of the balloon for each set of data below.

36. Rise 450 ft, Lower 125 ft, Rise 256 ft, Lower 98 ft

37. Rise 365 ft, Lower 160 ft, Lower 88 ft, Rise 289 ft

Use Mathematical Reasoning

38. Choose numbers for a, b, and c so that $c - b = a$. Do this three times with different numbers. Does $a + b = c$ each time?

39. What is the value of the next expression in this pattern if $n = 9$?
$n + 1, n + 3, n + 6, n + 10, n + 15$

40. Find replacements for x and y so that $x + y = 16$ and $x - y = 2$.

Mixed Review

Add or subtract. **41.** 221 − 96 **42.** 178 − 65 **43.** 7,841 − 538
44. 1,240 − 141 **45.** 14,326 − 2,134 **46.** 30,001 − 5,642
47. 50,129 + 11,297 **48.** 3,590 + 7,246

Calculator Activity

Use the memory keys on a calculator to evaluate expressions.
The M+ key adds the displayed number to the total in the memory.
The M− key subtracts a number from the total in the memory.
Use the MR key to display the total in the memory.
Evaluate $936 - (a - b)$ for $a = 342$ and $b = 178$.

342 [−] **178** [=] [M+] — Find the difference in parentheses and store it in memory.

936 [−] [MR] [=] **772** — Then subtract the difference in the memory from 936.

Use the calculator memory keys to evaluate each expression.

1. $5{,}392 - (x + y)$ for $x = 849, y = 768$

2. $4{,}238 + (c - d)$ for $c = 6{,}982, d = 748$

3. $3{,}479 - (a - b)$ for $a = 1{,}603, b = 479$

4. $965 + (p - q + 467)$ for $p = 640, q = 398$

1-2 Patterns and Variables

Objective To write a rule that represents the relationship between two numbers.

Explore

For the triangles below, each side is 1 unit long and the *perimeter* (distance around) is 3 units. The triangles are pushed together to form a 4-sided larger figure whenever possible. With 2 triangles, the perimeter of the new figure is 4 units. Copy and complete the table below. Make or draw triangles and look for patterns.

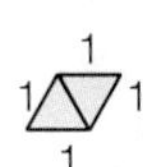

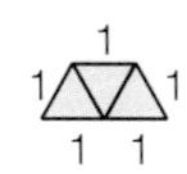

No. of triangles	1	2	3	4	5	6
Perimeter	3	4	5			

Understand the Ideas

In the previous lesson you saw that a variable can be used to reserve a place for a number in an expression like $x + 8$. In this section you will see another important way that a variable can be used.

In the Explore above, you can find a rule that tells how to find the perimeter of the larger figure when you know the number of triangles. The rule is, "To find the perimeter, add 2 to the number of triangles."

Example 1

Look for a pattern. Copy and complete the table to describe the pattern. Write a rule that tells how to get a number in the bottom row.

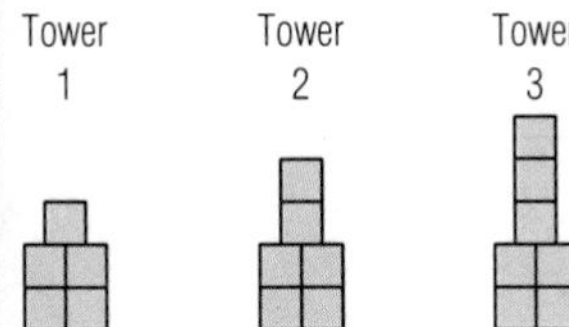

Tower no.	1	2	3	4	5	. . .	20
No. of blocks	5	6	7				

Solution

Tower no.	1	2	3	4	5	6	. . .	20
No. of blocks	5	6	7	8	9	10		24

Each number in the bottom row is 4 more than the number above it.

Rule: To get the number of blocks in the bottom row, add 4 to the tower number above it in the top row.

Try This

Look for a pattern. Copy and complete the table to describe the pattern. Write a rule that tells how to get a number in the bottom row.

a.

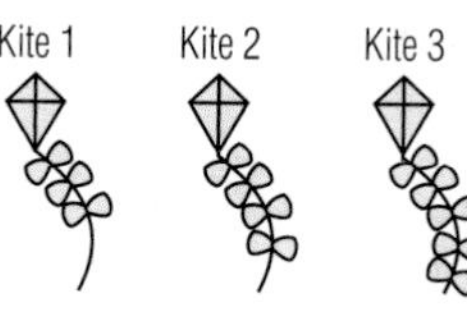

Kite no.	1	2	3	4	5	...	20
No. of bows	3	4	5				

Since the numbers in the top row of a table vary, we can use a **variable** to help us write a rule that tells how to get a number in the bottom row for a given number in the top row.

Example 2

Copy the table. Look for number patterns to complete the table. Use the variable to write a rule that tells how to get a number in the bottom row.

5	6	7	8	10	...	20	...	x
1	2	3						

Solution

5	6	7	8	10	20	x
1	2	3	**4**	**6**	**16**	$\mathbf{x - 4}$

To get a number in the bottom row, subtract 4 from the number in the top row.

Try This Copy the table. Look for number patterns to complete the table. Use the variable to write a rule that tells how to get a number in the bottom row.

b.

8	10	12	14	16	30	n
5	7	9	11			

c.

2	4	6	8	10	20	p
11	13	15				

Class Exercises

Look for patterns and give the missing numbers.

1. 4, 7, 10, 13, ___ , ___

2. 0, 5, 10, 15, ___ , ___

Discuss the Ideas

3. Jared said that the numbers in the bottom row in Try This a. increase by 1 each time. Dee said Jared's pattern wouldn't help much if you needed to find the number that would be below 1,000. Do you agree? Explain your decision.

Exercises

Practice and Apply

Look for a pattern. Copy and complete the table to describe the pattern. Write a rule that tells how to get a number in the bottom row.

1\. 1st 2nd 3rd

Design no.	1	2	3	4	5	. . .	10
No. of blocks	4	5	6				

2\. 1st 2nd 3rd

Design no.	1	2	3	4	5	. . .	10
No. of balls	7	8	9				

Look for number patterns. Copy and complete the table. Use the variable to write a rule that tells how to get a number in the bottom row.

3\.

10	20	30	40	50	x
20	30	40			

4\.

25	50	75	100	125	u
5	30	55			

Extend and Apply

Use the rule given to complete the table.

5\.

5	10	15	20	25	n
					$n - 4$

6\.

7	11	15	19	23	x
					$x + 11$

7\. What is the total one-day rental fee at these different car rental agencies if they each have a $13 per day insurance fee?

Agency	Ace	Bump-n-Run	Oldies	Just Rust	Bent Over
Basic fee	$18	$32.95	$12.50	$23.75	$38
Total charges					

Use Mathematical Reasoning

8\. If x is a number in the sequence, how can you find the next two numbers in the sequence? 5, 8, 11, 14, 17, 20, 23

Mixed Review

Evaluate. **9.** $(34 - 18) + 25$ **10.** $64 - (23 + 11)$ **11.** $(10 + 24) - 7$

Evaluate for $x = 5, y = 7, z = 9$. **12.** $(x + y) - z$ **13.** $(z - y) + x$

1-3 Problem Solving: Writing Expressions

Translating Phrases to Algebraic Expressions

Objective To translate a verbal phrase to a numerical or algebraic expression.

Verbal phrases that suggest addition or subtraction can be translated into numerical or algebraic expressions.

Example 1

Joe said, "My \$5 hourly pay has been increased by \$3." Write a numerical expression for "5 increased by 3".

Solution $5 + 3$ The phrase "increased by 3" suggests adding 3.

Try This Write as a numerical expression.

a. 6 less than 10 **b.** the sum of 8 and 7

c. My \$9 allowance decreased by \$2.

The phrase "5 increased by 3" is translated to the numerical expression $5 + 3$. To translate the phrase "a number increased by 3," use a variable to replace "a number" and write the algebraic expression $n + 3$.

Number	Number increased by 3	
5	$5 + 3$	"5 increased by 3"
10	$10 + 3$	"10 increased by 3"
n	$n + 3$	"a **number** increased by 3"

Example 2

Write as an algebraic expression. "a number decreased by 4"

Solution $n - 4$ Think of a specific number, say 6. "6 decreased by 4" is $6 - 4$, so "a number decreased by 4" is $n - 4$.

Try This Write as an algebraic expression.

d. a number plus 5 **e.** a number decreased by 8

f. 7 more than a number **g.** 5 less than a number

Example 3

Write as an expression. Jeff has \$68. How much will he have if:

a. he earns 43 dollars? **b.** he earns x dollars?

c. he spends 29 dollars? **d.** he spends y dollars?

Solution

a. he earns 43 dollars? $68 + 43$

b. he earns x dollars? $68 + x$ Think about a number, write a variable.

c. he spends 29 dollars? $68 - 29$

d. he spends y dollars? $68 - y$ Think about a number, write a variable.

Try This Write as an expression. Tina's house is 23 years old. How old:

h. will it be in 9 years? **i.** will it be in y years?

j. was it 14 years ago? **k.** was it t years ago?

Class Exercises

Tell whether the phrase suggests addition or subtraction.

1. The sum of **2.** decreased by **3.** minus

4. plus **5.** increased by **6.** make it less

7. added to **8.** subtracted from **9.** a total of

Discuss the Ideas

10. Work together to make up a paragraph involving the earning, saving, and spending of money. Use as many of the phrases in Exercises 1–9 above as you can.

Exercises

Practice and Apply

Write as a numerical expression.

1. the sum of 8 and 6 **2.** the difference of 12 and 4

3. 7 more than 9 **4.** 3 less than 10

5. 6 increased by 7 **6.** 14 decreased by 5

7. 8 added to 12 **8.** 12 subtracted from 15

Write as an algebraic expression.

9. the sum of x and 6 **10.** 4 taken away from t

11. 7 more than n **12.** 3 less than a number

13. 8 added to r **14.** 12 subtracted from z

15. y decreased by 5 **16.** x more than 16

17. the difference of s and 9 **18.** the sum of a number and 8

19. 6 more than a number **20.** a number increased by 11

21. 16 added to a number **22.** a number decreased by 56

Write an expression for each question.

Beth weighs 45 kg. How much will she weigh:

23. after she gains 7 kg?

24. after she gains n kg?

25. after she loses 4 kg?

26. after she loses y kg?

Todd earned $75 by washing cars. How much money will he have:

27. after he earns 45 dollars more?

28. after he earns x dollars more?

29. after he buys some $37 shoes?

30. after he spends d dollars?

Extend and Apply

The letter n represents an even number $0, 2, 4, 6, 8, \ldots$.

Write an algebraic expression for:

31. the whole number just after n.

32. the whole number just before n.

33. the even number just after n.

34. the even number just before n.

Use Mathematical Reasoning

35. Choose two variables and write an algebraic expression for their sum. Write an expression for the difference of the same two variables. Find values for the variables that have a sum of 31 and difference of 3.

36. Look for a pattern in this sequence: $1, 1, 2, 3, 5, 8, 13, 21, 34, 55, \ldots$ Let a represent a number in the sequence and b represent the next number after a. Write an algebraic expression for the next number in the sequence after b.

Mixed Review

Evaluate. **37.** $850 + 143$ **38.** $248 - (20 + 28)$ **39.** $46 - (9 - 6)$

Evaluate for $s = 136$ and $s = 312$. **40.** $70 + (s - 86)$ **41.** $1000 - (s + s)$

42. $(s + 20) + (s - 53)$ **43.** $(500 - s) - (450 - s)$

Mental Math

You can use compensation to find certain sums and differences mentally.

- To find $752 - 398$, think "$752 - 400$ is 352. I subtracted 2 too much, so I'll add it back. The difference is $352 + 2$, or 354."
- To find $645 + 296$, think "$645 + 300$ is 945. I added 4 too much, so I'll subtract it. The sum is $945 - 4$, or 941."

Use compensation to find each sum or difference mentally.

1. $642 - 299$ **2.** $8{,}546 - 3{,}998$ **3.** $874 - 549$

4. $387 + 497$ **5.** $4{,}638 + 2{,}995$ **6.** $529 + 348$

1-4 Properties of Addition

Objective To use the basic properties of addition to write an algebraic expression equivalent to a given algebraic expression.

Understand the Ideas

The **whole numbers** are the numbers 0, 1, 2, 3, 4, 5, . . . The basic properties for addition of whole numbers can make computation with numerical expressions easier. You can also use the properties to write **equivalent** expressions. Two algebraic expressions are equivalent if (and only if) they have the same value for any number that replaces the variable.

You can change the order in which two numbers are added and the sum will stay the same. The diagram below shows this with sets of dots.

Mark dots on a card.

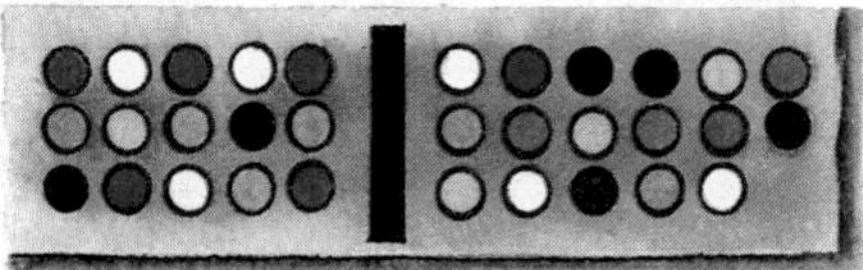

Flip the card horizontally

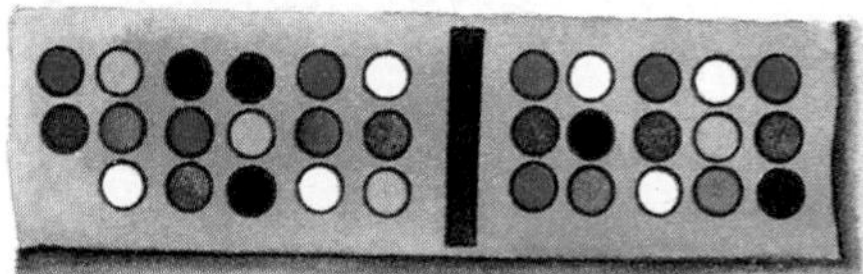

$$15 + 17 = 17 + 15$$
$$32 = 32$$

Variables can be used to state this property for all whole numbers.

Commutative Property of Addition

A change in the order in which two whole numbers are added does not change their sum.

For all whole numbers a and b, $a + b = b + a$

Example 1

Use the Commutative Property to write an equivalent expression for $n + 5$.

Solution $5 + n$ $\quad$ $5 + n$ has the same value as $n + 5$ for any number that replaces n.

Try This Use the Commutative Property to write an equivalent expression.

a. $45 + x$ **b.** $a + 5{,}138$ **c.** $479 + t$

You can change the way whole numbers are grouped for addition and the sum will stay the same. The following diagram shows this with sets of dots.

Mark dots, place a strip.

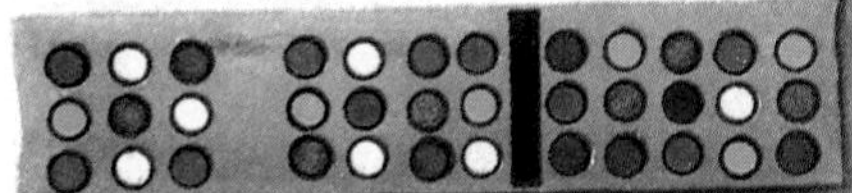

Move the strip to change grouping.

$(9 + 12) + 15 \quad = \quad 9 + (12 + 15)$

Variables can be used to state this property for all whole numbers.

Associative Property of Addition

A change in the grouping of whole numbers for addition does not change the sum.

For all whole numbers a, b, and c, $a + (b + c) = (a + b) + c$

Example 2

Use the Associative Property to write an equivalent expression.
$(x + 57) + 43$

Solution $x + (57 + 43)$ — $x + (57 + 43)$ has the same value as $(x + 57) + 43$ for any number that replaces x.

Try This Use the Associative Property to write an equivalent expression.

d. $(n + 145) + 68$ **e.** $125 + (75 + a)$

Zero is called the **additive identity** because when it is added to a number, the result is that same number. For example, $689 + 0 = 689$.

Identity Property of Addition

The sum of an addend and zero is the addend.

For every whole number a, $a + 0 = a \quad 0 + a = a$

When zero is subtracted from a number, the result is that same number: $a - 0 = a$. When a number is subtracted from itself, the result is zero: $a - a = 0$.

Example 3

Use the Identity Property to write an equivalent expression for $x + 0$.

Solution x — x has the same value as $x + 0$ for any number that replaces x.

Try This Write an equivalent expression.

f. $0 + t$ **g.** $a + 0$ **h.** $z - 0$ **i.** $n - n$

Class Exercises

Name the property shown by each number sentence.

1. $8 + 23 = 23 + 8$
2. $18 + (2 + 9) = (18 + 2) + 9$
3. $47 + 0 = 47$
4. $(14 + 6) + 15 = 14 + (6 + 15)$

Discuss the Ideas

5. Give some real-world situations that demonstrate the Commutative Property.

Exercises

Practice and Apply

Use the Commutative Property to write an equivalent expression.

1. $137 + b$
2. $c + 236$
3. $507 + y$

Use the Associative Property to write an equivalent expression.

4. $(a + 4) + 16$
5. $(z + 16) + 34$
6. $38 + (12 + r)$

Use the Identity Property to write an equivalent expression.

7. $x + 0$
8. $0 + y$
9. $a - a$

Write an equivalent expression and name the property you used.

10. $n + 7$
11. $y + 0$
12. $(n + 7) + 3$
13. $57 + x$
14. $p + 23$
15. $0 + (x + y)$
16. Each employee at Expressions Sport Shop received a bonus of \$100. An announcement expressed this as $100 + s$, where s is a person's salary. Using the Commutative Property, express this in an equivalent way.
17. During the first year of operation, an airport's average noise level was recorded at d decibels. The next year the noise level increased by 30 decibels and the following year by 35 decibels. Write an equivalent expression for $(d + 30) + 35$ and name the property you used.

Extend and Apply

18. Are the Commutative Property and the Associative Property true for subtraction of whole numbers? Give examples supporting your answer.
19. **Write to Learn** Ephie discovered the **Rearrangement Property for Addition** and wrote the following: $a + b + c = (a + b) + c = (a + c) + b = (b + c) + a$. Write a paragraph explaining the property.

Use the Rearrangement Property and look for **compatible numbers** to compute mentally.

20. $(98 + 75) + 25$

21. $(975 + 492) + 25$

22. $64 + 9 + 36 + 11 + 3 + 79 + 97$

23. $55 + 9 + 24 + 45 + 11$

Use Mathematical Reasoning

This "clock" can be used to find "clock sums." For example, $3 \oplus 2 = 1$, because two hours after pointing to 3 o'clock, the hand would point to 1 o'clock.

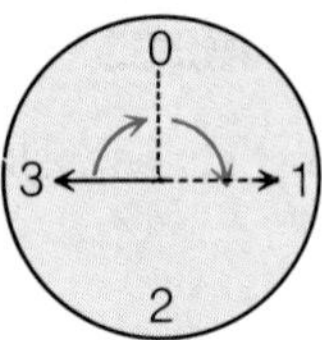

Find each clock sum. Do you think the operation $\oplus$ is commutative?

24. $2 \oplus 1$ **25.** $2 \oplus 2$ **26.** $2 \oplus 3$ **27.** $3 \oplus 3$

Mixed Review

Evaluate. **28.** $(45 - 18) - 16$ **29.** $23 + 49 + 85$ **30.** $65 + 25$

Evaluate for $b = 12$, $c = 13$. **31.** $b + c$ **32.** $c - b$

Write the word name. **33.** 2,017 **34.** 452 **35.** 6,906

Numbers to Algebra

A generalization that can be made about numbers can be expressed with variables. Check to see if the number examples are true. Then see how the variables are used to express the generalization.

Numbers	Algebra
$(35 + 49) + 15 = (35 + 15) + 49$ $(75 + 89) + 25 = (75 + 25) + 89$ $(148 + 97) + 52 = (148 + 52) + 97$	**For whole numbers a, b, and c,** $(a + b) + c = (a + c) + b$

Give two more number examples, then copy and complete the generalization.

Number Examples	Generalization
$(50 + 6) + (30 + 7) = (50 + 30) + (6 + 7)$ $(40 + 9) + (60 + 8) = (40 + 60) + (9 + 8)$ $(200 + 52) + (600 + 48) = (200 + 600) + (52 + 48)$	**For whole numbers a, b, c, and d,** $(a + b) + (c + d) =$ ___ ? ___

1-5

Understanding Equations

Objective To use balance scales and counters to understand equality and equations.

Explore

Scales A and B are balanced. The same objects are shown on the scales below. Decide which of the scales below are balanced.

Understand the Ideas

An **equation** is a mathematical sentence that uses an equal sign to state that two expressions represent the same number or are equivalent. An equation may or may not include a variable. Because both sides of a true equation represent the same number, you can use a balance scale to model equations.

$7 + 2 = 9$

The expression on the left side names the same number as the expression on the right side

Example

Write an equation for this balance scale. Find the number of counters in the bag.

Solution $n + 3 = 9$

6 counters are covered

6 counters must be in the bag for the scale to be balanced.

Try This **a.** Suppose the number of counters on each side of the scale above is increased by one. Write an equation for the scale and tell how many counters are in the bag.

Class Exercises

Discuss the Ideas

1. The objects on these scales are the same as on A and B in the Explore. Are the scales balanced? Discuss why or why not.

Exercises

Practice and Apply

Write an equation for each balance scale. How many counters are in the bag?

1. 

2. 

3. 

4. A geologist can find the weight of a rock using a balance scale and 1 kg weights. Write an equation for the scale and find the weight of the rock.

Extend and Apply

Draw or think about a balance scale and find the number of counters for n.

5. $n + 8 = 12$
6. $n + 6 = 13$
7. $n + 8 = 15$
8. $n + 6 = 9$
9. $15 = n + 7$
10. $18 = n + 9$
11. $20 = 12 + n$
12. $15 = 9 + n$

Use Mathematical Reasoning

13. Write an equation for this balance scale and tell how many counters are in each bag.

Mixed Review

Evaluate. **14.** $54 - (13 + 8)$ **15.** $128 - 47 - 18 - 6$

16. $(32 + 7) - (76 - 37)$

1-6 More About Equations

Objective To solve an equation for a replacement set that is given.

Understand the Ideas

An equation that contains only numbers can be either true or false. For example, $24 + 6 = 30$ is true, but $24 + 6 = 31$ is false. An equation that contains at least one variable is an **open sentence** and is neither true nor false. For example, $x + 6 = 30$ is neither true nor false because x has not been replaced with a number.

The set of numbers from which you can select replacements for the variable is called the **replacement set.** A replacement for a variable that makes an equation true is called a **solution** of the equation. You can **solve** an equation by finding all of its solutions. The collection of all the solutions is called the **solution set** of the equation.

When the replacement set contains only a few numbers, you can solve the equation by trying all of the numbers.

Equation (or open sentence)

$x + 3 = 12$

Replacement Set

$\{0, 1, 2, 3, 4, 5, 6, 7, 8, 9, 10\}$

True equation

$9 + 3 = 12$

Solution Set $\{9\}$

Solution 9

Example 1

Solve $x + 38 = 42$ for the replacement set $\{1, 2, 3, 4, 5, 6\}$.

Solution

$x + 38 = 42$

$1 + 38 = 42$ (false) — Replace the variable x with each number in the replacement set.

$2 + 38 = 42$ (false)

$3 + 38 = 42$ (false)

$4 + 38 = 42$ (true) ✓ — The number that makes the equation true is the solution. $x = 4$

$5 + 38 = 42$ (false)

$6 + 38 = 42$ (false)

Try This Solve the equation for the replacement set $\{0, 2, 4, 6\}$.

a. $51 - n = 45$ **b.** $b + 79 = 81$

c. $31 = 27 + y$ **d.** $17 - a = 17$

Example 2

Solve the equation $x - 8 = 16$ for the replacement set $\{23, 25, 27\}$.

Solution

$x - 8 = 16$

$23 - 8 = 16$ (false) Replace the variable x with each number in the replacement set.

$25 - 8 = 16$ (false)

$27 - 8 = 16$ (false) No number in the replacement set makes the equation true.

There is no solution.

Try This Solve the equation for the replacement set given.

e. $n + 15 = 45$ $\{31, 32, 33\}$ **f.** $x + 5 = 2$ $\{0, 1, 2, 3\}$

Class Exercises

Is the value given for the variable a solution to the equation?

1. $n + 5 = 12, n = 8$? **2.** $9 + p = 13, p = 4$?

Discuss the Ideas

3. How would you describe a replacement set with an unlimited number of numbers for which the equation $2n = 25$ has no solution?

Exercises

Practice and Apply

Solve the equation for the replacement set given.

1. $z + 8 = 17$ $\{7, 8, 9, 10\}$ **2.** $11 - s = 7$ $\{1, 2, 3, 4, 5\}$

3. $31 = 28 + x$ $\{0, 2, 4\}$ **4.** $12 + n = 20$ $\{2, 4, 6, 8, 10\}$

5. $z + 34 = 187$ $\{150, 151, 152\}$ **6.** $y - 37 = 241$ $\{277, 278\}$

Extend and Apply

Describe the solution set. The replacement set is the set of all whole numbers.

7. $n + 4 = 0$ **8.** $x + 5 = 5 + x$ **9.** $y - y = 0$ **10.** $a + a = a$

Use Mathematical Reasoning

11. Write an equation with no solution. Replacement set: all odd numbers.

Mixed Review

Write as a numerical expression. **12.** 12 added to 7 **13.** 7 minus 6

1-7 Solving Equations: Using Mental Math or Guess, Check, Revise

Objective To use mental math or Guess, Check, Revise to solve equations.

Understand the Ideas

When the replacement set for an equation is the set of all whole numbers, it is impossible to try every number to find the solution. If an equation involves small or compatible numbers and a single operation, it often can be solved mentally.

Sometimes the *cover-up* method shown here can help you find the solution. Cover the variable with your finger or a pencil and think about what number could be covered to make a true equation.

Example 1

Find the number of bowling pins knocked down when 6 are left standing by mentally solving the equation $6 + p = 10$.

Solution $6 + p = 10$ Think: What number added to 6 gives 10?

$p = 4$

Check $6 + 4 = 10$ Mentally substitute 4 for p in $6 + p = 10$.

$10 = 10$ ✓ The equation is true, so 4 is a solution.

Try This Solve and check mentally.

a. $25 + n = 75$ **b.** $12 - b = 8$ **c.** $y - 6 = 2$

d. Find the number of bowling balls that have been taken from a rack of 50 balls when 20 are left by mentally solving the equation $50 - n = 20$.

For some equations, you may not think of the solution on the first try. The strategy **Guess, Check, Revise** can help you find a solution. When the equations contain larger numbers, a calculator is helpful.

Example 2

Use Guess, Check, Revise, to solve the equation $923 - x = 346$.

Solution Try 565. Guess 565.

$923 - 565 = 358$ Check your guess. 565 is too small.

Try 577. Revise your guess. Guess 577.

$923 - 577 = 346$ It checks.

$x = 577$ 577 is a solution.

Try This Use Guess, Check, Revise to solve.

e. $73 + n = 121$ **f.** $c - 267 = 837$ **g.** $942 - b = 275$

Class Exercises

The solution of the equation $6 + x = 10$ is "the number that adds to 6 to give 10." Describe the solution of each equation.

1. $n + 5 = 13$ **2.** $4 + c = 20$ **3.** $x - 5 = 12$

Discuss the Ideas

4. When using Guess, Check, Revise to solve equations, are there any techniques you could use to reduce the number of guesses you make when finding the solution? Use these equations to think about and explain your techniques. **a.** $n + 289 = 724$ **b.** $n - 348 = 753$

Exercises

Practice and Apply

Solve and check mentally. The replacement set is all whole numbers.

1. $n + 2 = 8$ **2.** $a + 4 = 9$ **3.** $7 + x = 9$

4. $x - 8 = 9$ **5.** $c - 5 = 6$ **6.** $b - 10 = 8$

7. $a - 19 = 2$ **8.** $120 = p + 70$ **9.** $0 = n - 13$

Use Guess, Check, Revise, and a calculator to solve.

10. $x - 27 = 56$ **11.** $a + 43 = 201$ **12.** $39 + m = 157$

13. $394 - c = 239$ **14.** $z + 239 = 934$ **15.** $311 + n = 1{,}962$

16. $501 - b = 284$ **17.** $y - 426 = 701$ **18.** $932 - g = 689$

19. In a bowling game, find the number of frames that have been bowled when 7 frames are left by mentally solving the equation $c + 7 = 10$.

20. When \$3 tax is added to the price of a shirt, the total cost is \$40. Mentally solve the equation $p + 3 = 40$ to determine the price of the shirt.

21. A factory worker wanted to complete 20 computer circuit boards by the end of the day. By lunch time he had completed 13. Find how many more boards he needs to complete by mentally solving the equation $x + 13 = 20$.

22. To solve the equation $y + y + 3 = 15$, Maria's first guess was $y = 6$. Was she correct?

Extend and Apply

For all whole numbers, a, b, and c, if $a - b = c$, then $a = c + b$. Use this relationship to rewrite each equation with the variable by itself on one side. Then use a calculator and solve for the variable.

23. $x - 638 = 7{,}247$ **24.** $y - 3{,}514 = 9{,}672$ **25.** $6{,}079 = z - 2{,}346$

26. After giving away 2,575 campaign buttons, a politician had 4,925 left. Solve the equation $b - 2{,}575 = 4{,}925$ to find how many she had at the beginning of her campaign.

27. The population of a city increased by 5,689 during a certain year, making a total of 157,743. Solve the equation $p + 5{,}689 = 157{,}743$ to find the population before the increase.

28. During non-prime time, a television commercial cost \$235,650. This was \$195,750 less than its cost during prime time. Solve the equation $p - 195{,}750 = 235{,}650$ to find the cost of the commercial during prime time.

29. After Leslie had flown enough miles to receive two free tickets, she flew an extra 5,478 miles. Her total mileage was 81,453. Solve the equation $m + 5{,}478 = 81{,}453$ to find the number of miles she had to fly to win two free tickets.

30. **Write Your Own Problem** Think about situations such as travel, salaries, populations, or others of your choice and write a problem that can be solved by solving the equation $n + 9{,}648 = 16{,}432$. Solve your problem. Then give it to a classmate to solve.

Use Mathematical Reasoning

31. These 3 equations have the same solution. Find the solution. Look for a pattern and write two more equations that have the same solution.

$$x + 2 = 5$$
$$x + 5 = 8$$
$$x + 8 = 11$$

Use your calculator and the idea suggested in the box below to solve the equations. Note that if a number has been subtracted in the equation, you can undo this operation by adding.

1. In the equation below 346 has been *added* to a number x to give 923.

$x + 346 = 923$

2. Undo the operation in the equation. Start with 923 on your calculator and *subtract* 346 to find the number x, 577.

32. $n + 479 = 1{,}235$ **33.** $b - 567 = 494$ **34.** $c + 5{,}926 = 13{,}415$

35. $y - 8{,}319 = 437$ **36.** $r + 3{,}643 = 9{,}008$ **37.** $t - 54{,}876 = 6{,}795$

Mixed Review

Evaluate. **38.** $b + 45$ for $b = 55$ **39.** $35 - (7 + x)$ for $x = 8$

40. Use the Commutative Property to rewrite $28 + y$.

Solve the equation for the replacement set {10, 15, 20}. **41.** $y - 5 = 15$

Computer Activity

This computer program helps you to practice Guess, Check, Revise with equations of the form $x + A = B$.

```
10 REM GUESS, CHECK, AND REVISE
20 LET AB = INT(RND(1)*100)
30 LET B = INT (RND(1)*100)
40 IF B < AB THEN 20
50 PRINT "SOLVE X +";AB; "="; B
60 PRINT
70 INPUT "TYPE IN YOUR ANSWER "; X
80 IF X = B - AB THEN GOTO 110
90 PRINT "NO, TRY AGAIN:": INPUT X
100 GOTO 80
110 PRINT "YOU GOT IT!!!"
120 END
```

1. Run the program to practice your equation solving.
2. Change lines 50 and 80 to solve an equation of the form $x - A = B$.

1-8 Solving Equations: Using Addition and Subtraction

Objective To use addition or subtraction to solve equations involving whole numbers.

Understand the Ideas

Although some simple equations can be solved mentally, other methods are useful with equations that have larger numbers or more operations. Two ideas are used in solving equations involving addition or subtraction. The first is that addition and subtraction can undo each other because they are **inverse operations.**

Subtraction can undo addition	Addition can undo subtraction
$10 + 9 - 9 = 10$	$10 - 9 + 9 = 10$
$n + 9 - 9 = n$	$n - 9 + 9 = n$

The second idea is that an equation is like a balanced scale. A scale will stay balanced if you add the same amount to both sides or take away the same amount from both sides. For example, scale A below is balanced. Scale B will be balanced when a block is added to each side, and scale C will be balanced when two blocks are taken from each side.

The properties of equality state this idea for equations.

Addition and Subtraction Properties of Equality

You can add or subtract the same number on both sides of an equation and the two sides will remain equal.

For all numbers a, b, and c, if $a = b$, then $a + c = b + c$
and if $a = b$, then $a - c = b - c$

The following examples use balance scales to help you understand the process for solving equations.

Example 1

Write an equation for the balance scale. Think about the scale to solve the equation.

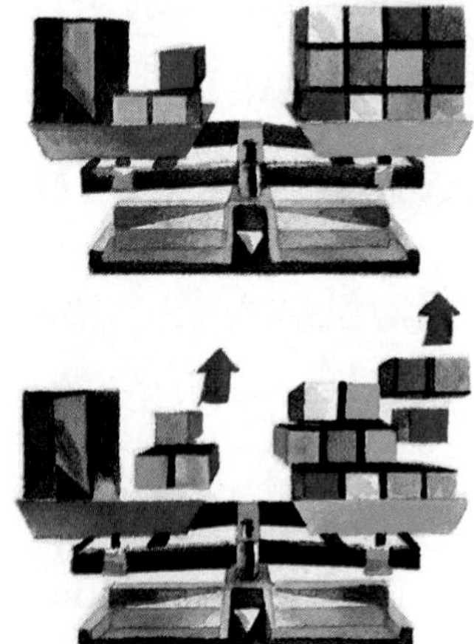

Solution

$x + 3 = 12$ Let x be the number of blocks in the bag.

$x + 3 - \mathbf{3} = 12 - \mathbf{3}$ Remove 3 blocks from each side.

$x = 9$ The bag holds 9 blocks.

Try This

a. Write and solve an equation for this scale.

The examples above suggest the following steps for solving equations.

> **Rule** **Solving Equations Using Addition and Subtraction**
>
> **1.** Decide which operation has been applied to the variable.
>
> **2.** Use the inverse of this operation, adding or subtracting the same number on both sides of the equation.

The following examples show how to use these steps to solve equations.

Example 2

Solve and check. $n + 89 = 134$

Solution $n + 89 = 134$ You need to get the variable by itself.

$n + 89 - \mathbf{89} = 134 - \mathbf{89}$ To undo adding 89, subtract 89 from both sides.

$n = 45$

Check $45 + 89 = 134$ Replace n with 45.

$134 = 134$ ✓ The solution is 45.

Try This

Solve and check. **b.** $x + 77 = 394$ **c.** $123 = x + 87$

Example 3

Solve and check. $x - 89 = 176$

Solution $x - 89 = 176$ — You need to get the variable by itself.

$x - 89 + \mathbf{89} = 176 + \mathbf{89}$ — To undo subtracting 89, add 89 to both sides.

$x = 265$

Check $265 - 89 \stackrel{?}{=} 176$ — Replace x with 265.

$176 = 176 \checkmark$ — The solution is 265.

Try This Solve and check.

d. $m - 76 = 158$ **e.** $146 = y - 89$

Class Exercises

Give the inverse of each operation.

1. adding 58 **2.** subtracting 97 **3.** subtracting 29

Name the operation that would be used to solve the equation.

4. $x + 19 = 56$ **5.** $n - 28 = 56$ **6.** $98 = b - 35$

Discuss the Ideas

7. A 2-ton truck hauling some corn weighed 6,275 pounds on a scale. Do you think the equation $c - 4{,}000 = 6{,}275$, where $c =$ the weight of the corn, describes this situation? Explain your reasoning.

Exercises

Practice and Apply

In Exercises 1–3, write an equation for the balance scale. Think about the scale to solve the equation.

1.

2.

3.

Solve and check.

4. $n + 38 = 84$ **5.** $x + 56 = 92$ **6.** $a + 47 = 85$

7. $y + 29 = 92$ **8.** $c + 76 = 154$ **9.** $n + 67 = 282$

10. $y - 69 = 145$ **11.** $x - 58 = 139$ **12.** $y - 77 = 229$

13. $c - 167 = 85$ **14.** $n - 258 = 197$ **15.** $c - 376 = 488$

16. Tai weighs x pounds, Minh weighs 70 pounds, and their father weighs 158 pounds. When the two boys sit on one end of a seesaw it balances if their dad sits on the other end. Write an equation for the balanced seesaw.

17. In order to wrestle in the 128 pound division, Artemio needed to lose 5 pounds. Solve the equation $w - 5 = 128$ to find Artemio's current weight.

Extend and Apply

Solve and check.

18. $x + (157 + 29) = 342$ **19.** $a - (104 - 78) = 28$

20. $(358 + 76) + y = 500$ **21.** $(56 + 87) - b = 17$

22. Write and solve an equation in which the sum is 2,475 and the addend 1,697 is added to a number represented by the variable n.

Use Mathematical Reasoning

In a magic square, the sum of the numbers in each row, column, and diagonal is the same.

x	**2**	14
12	**9**	y
n	**16**	7

↓
27
(Sum)

23. Write and solve equations as needed to find x, y, and n.

24. Andy had more nickels than dimes, and more dimes than pennies. Can you tell the value of his 6 coins?

25. Use the variables a and b to complete this generalization about solving equations of the type $x - a = b$ for x: $x =$ ___?___

26. A block box with three missing blocks balances 9 blocks.

   a. Write an equation for this situation.

   b. Suppose you put the 3 blocks back in to make a full "x box". How many blocks would you have to add to the right side to keep the scale balanced?

   c. What is the weight of the blocks in the full "x box"? What is the solution to your equation in part a?

Mixed Review

Write as an algebraic expression. **27.** 125 added to a number

Evaluate. **28.** $927 + 386$ **29.** $400 - 157$ **30.** $98 + 837 + 369$

Solve mentally and check. **31.** $n + 5 = 11$ **32.** $y - 6 = 10$

1-9 Estimating

Objective To estimate whole number sums and differences by using rounding or front-end estimation.

Application

Three years ago, the Garcias bought a camper with an odometer reading of 16,329. Now the odometer reads 38,647. They want to know about how many miles they have driven the camper.

Understand the Ideas

It is often useful to **estimate** to find an approximate answer to a problem or to see if an answer found with a calculator makes sense. There are several ways to estimate sums and differences of whole numbers. One way is called **estimating using rounding.**

Rule Estimating Using Rounding

- Round the numbers to the desired place.
- Compute with the rounded numbers to find the estimate.

Example 1

Find about how far the Garcias have driven their camper in the **application** above by rounding to the nearest thousand and estimating the value of the variable. $n = 38{,}647 - 16{,}329$

Solution

$$\begin{array}{r} 39{,}000 \\ -16{,}000 \\ \hline 23{,}000 \end{array}$$

Round 38,647 to 39,000.
Round 16,329 to 16,000.

The Garcias have driven their camper about 23,000 miles.

Try This Round to the nearest thousand and estimate the value of the variable. **a.** $a = 9{,}586 + 4{,}299$ **b.** $76{,}953 - 5{,}466 = y$

Front-end estimation is another useful technique for estimating sums and differences. It is most often used when the numbers have the same number of digits.

Rule Front-end Estimation

- Add (or subtract) the first digits to get a rough estimate.
- Adjust your estimate by using the remaining digits and looking for numbers that are compatible.

Example 2

Use front-end estimation to estimate the value of the variable.
$3{,}527 + 7{,}969 + 5{,}493 = n$

Solution Rough Estimate: 15,000 — Add the "front-end" digits. **3**,527 + **7**,969 + **5**,493 is about **15** thousand.

Adjusted Estimate: 17,000 — Look at the other digits, 3,**527** + 7,**969** + 5,**493**, for compatible numbers. **527** + **493** is about 1,000. **969** is about 1,000. Increase the estimate by 2,000.

Try This Use front-end estimation to estimate.

c. $347 + 598 + 754 = x$ **d.** $r = 8{,}802 - 2{,}319$

Class Exercises

Round to the place indicated.

1. 658 (ten) **2.** 864 (hundred) **3.** 6,523 (thousand)

Discuss the Ideas

4. Tanya's moped had an odometer reading of 5,493 when she bought it and 7,114 when she sold it. She used front-end estimation to estimate the number of miles (m) she rode the moped, $m = 7{,}114 - 5{,}493$. Do you think she arrived at an overestimate or an underestimate? Explain.

Exercises

Practice and Apply

Round to the nearest ten and estimate the value of the variable.

1. $59 + 87 = x$ **2.** $92 - 58 = b$ **3.** $94 + 78 = y$

4. $z = 149 - 62$ **5.** $s = 263 + 695$ **6.** $e = 865 - 243$

Round to the nearest hundred and estimate the value of the variable.

7. $n = 725 + 487$ **8.** $1{,}248 - 519 = x$ **9.** $z = 938 + 694$

Round to the nearest thousand and estimate the value of the variable.

10. $y = 8{,}399 + 6{,}508$ **11.** $12{,}778 - 7{,}499 = c$

Use front-end estimation to estimate the value of the variable.

12. $873 + 449 + 628 + 858 = y$ **13.** $2{,}543 + 7{,}986 + 4{,}478 = x$

14. $9{,}704 - 6{,}218 = x$ **15.** $875{,}652 + 925{,}468 = y$

16. The Bison's football team had good attendance for their first three games of the year. Use front-end estimation to estimate the attendance, a, if $a = 9{,}214 + 8{,}904 + 6{,}721$.

Extend and Apply

17. The first owner of a car drove it for 56,478 miles. The second owner put 37,517 miles on it. Estimate the total mileage, to the nearest thousand miles.

18. A number, rounded to the nearest thousand, is 6,000. What letters on the number line below could show the position of this number?

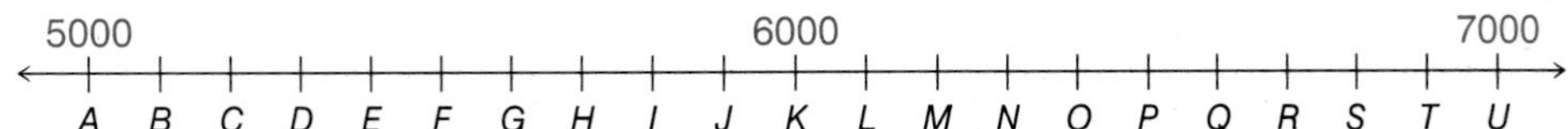

19. A used-car salesperson says that a car has been driven about 70,000 miles. If this number has been rounded to the nearest ten thousand, what is the greatest number of miles the car could have been driven? What is the smallest?

20. Determine Reasonable Answers Tell whether the answer given for the following problem is reasonable. If it is not reasonable, explain why.

A bike trip around the mainland of the United States covered 12,092 miles. A trip directly from the west coast to the east coast covered 2,964 miles. How much longer was the trip around the mainland? Answer: The mainland trip was 10,932 miles longer.

Use Mathematical Reasoning

21. Estimate the sum of the whole numbers from 1 to 25. Use a calculator to check your estimate.

22. Whole numbers in order, such as 8, 9, and 10, are called **consecutive** whole numbers. Find 3 consecutive whole numbers whose sum is 111.

Mixed Review

23. Use the Associative Property to rewrite $(78 + 65) + 135$.

Write as an algebraic expression. **24.** a number decreased by 650

Solve and check. **25.** $65 - x = 38$ **26.** $48 + y = 93$

27. $n + 37 = 129$ **28.** $x - 54 = 207$

Add or subtract. **29.** 1,295 + 1,128 **30.** 5,007 − 3,985

31. 22,423 + 10,525 **32.** 13,254 + 8,098 **33.** 500,821 − 39,827

1-10 Problem Solving: Applications

Buying a Car

Objective To use the Problem-Solving Checklist to solve applied problems.

When solving a word problem, you can use the six guidelines in this Problem-Solving Checklist.

Sample Problem The dealer deducts $325 from the base list price of a Cyclone 500 for a special sale. If the car cost the dealer $8,627, what is the dealer's profit?

Problem-Solving Checklist

- Understand the **Situation**
- Find the Needed **Data**
- **Plan** the Solution
- **Estimate** the Answer
- **Solve** the Problem
- **Check** the Answer

Price List Cyclone 500	
Base List Price:	$9,614
Extra Options, List Price:	
Air Conditioner	$690
Cruise Control	$167
Rear Defrost	$151
Tinted Glass	$118
PinStripe	$84
AM/FM Stereo Radio	$220
Power Steering	$250
Automatic Transmission	$527
Selling Price:	$11,821

Note that the price list shows the customer's cost. The customer's "base list price" equals the dealer's cost plus the dealer's profit.

Understand the *Situation*

Read the problem carefully and decide what question is asked.

You are asked to find the amount of profit the dealer makes on the sale price.

Find the Needed *Data.*

Decide what information is needed to solve the problem.

You can look at the data chart to find that the base list price is $9,614.

Plan the Solution.

Choose a strategy that will help you solve the problem.

To *include* the discount on the base price choose *subtraction*. To compare the sale price with the dealer's cost, use *subtraction* again.

Estimate the Answer

Choose an estimation method and find an answer close to the original answer.

The base price − the discount is about $9,300. The dealer's cost is about $8,600. The profit is about $700.

9,300
8,600
1900

Solve the Problem

Complete the reasoning or computation needed to find the answer.

Subtract the discount of $325 from the base list price of $9,614 then subtract the dealer's cost, $8,627.

(9,614 − 325) − 8,627 = 662

The total dealer's profit is $662.

Check the Answer

Reread the problem. Does your answer seem reasonable?

The dealer's cost was about $8,600. If the discount and a profit of about $700 was added, the base list price would be about $9,600. The answer is reasonable.

Problems

Solve. Use the data on p. 32.

1. What is the total cost of the extra options for the Cyclone 500?
2. The extra options actually cost the dealer $1,375. How much profit would the dealer make on the extra options?
3. The dealer's profit is the difference between the total dealer's cost and the total listed selling price. What is the dealer's profit for the Cyclone 500 with all the extra options?
4. The dealer is willing to make only $380 profit on the sale of the Cyclone 500. What will be the selling price with all the extra options?
5. What would the total cost be if a customer chose all the options and paid the full selling price plus a sales tax of $591?
6. Suppose the dealer reduced the selling price by $450 and then the buyer decided to have the car rustproofed at a cost of $234. What would the total cost be before the addition of sales tax?
7. Which two extra options could a customer omit to save about $400?
8. **Data Search** Find the listed selling prices of two of your favorite cars. By how much do the prices of these cars differ?

What's Your Decision?

You need a new car and have chosen the Cyclone 500. You can afford to spend only $10,500 plus tax. The dealer will not reduce the listed selling price. If you buy the car, which extra options will you choose?

1-11 Problem Solving: Strategies

Guess, Check, Revise

Objective To solve nonroutine problems, using the strategies Choose the Operations or Guess, Check, Revise.

In Section 1-10 you had to decide which operations to use to solve a problem. This strategy is called **Choose the Operations.** Think about what operations are needed to solve the following problem.

Sample Problem A television costs $469. You could pay in cash, or choose an installment plan with a $95 down payment and 24 installments totaling $456. How much more would you pay on the installment plan?

To solve the problem, you might plan to use the operation of addition first, then subtraction.

$95 + 456 = 551$ The television costs $551 on the installment plan.

$551 - 469 = 82$ You would pay $82 more on the installment plan.

You need to use other strategies for word problems that cannot be solved by simply choosing the operations. For some you can guess a solution, check the guess, and use what you learned to revise the guess. This strategy is called **Guess, Check, Revise.**

Sample Problem A soccer ball and soccer shoes cost a total of $59. If the shoes were $15 more than the ball, what did each cost?

The chart below shows how you might use the Guess, Check, Revise strategy to find the solution to this problem.

Guess	Check	Revise
First Guess **Ball: $20**	Shoes: $20 + $15 = $35 Total Cost: $20 + $35 = $55	55 is less than 59. Revise guess up. **Revised guess, $25**
Second Guess **Ball: $25**	Shoes: $25 + $15 = $40 Total Cost: $25 + $40 = $65	65 is more than 59. Revise guess down. **Revised guess, $22**
Third Guess **Ball: $22**	Shoes: $22 + $15 = $37 Total Cost: $22 + $37 = $59	This is correct!

The ball cost $22 and the shoes cost $37.

Problem-Solving Strategies

Choose the Operations	Make a Table	Make an Organized List
Guess, Check, Revise	Look for a Pattern	Use Logical Reasoning
Draw a Diagram	Write an Equation	Work Backward
	Simplify the Problem	

Problems

Solve, using one or more of the strategies shown above.

1. Denise scored 6 more points in this week's basketball game than she scored in last week's game. She scored a total of 30 points in the two games. How many points did she score in each game?
2. Mrs. Gentry sold 36 more computers in August than she did in July. She sold one more computer in September than she sold in August. In September, she sold 55 computers. How many did she sell in the three months?
3. Eric is 9 years old. In 4 years his father will be 13 years older than twice what Eric's age will be then. How old is Eric's father now?
4. While playing darts, Raul noticed that if he reversed the two digits of his score, it would produce Linda's score. Linda's score was a multiple of 9 and only 9 more than Raul's score. What were their scores? (Note: multiples of nine are $0, 9, 18, 27, 36, \ldots$)
5. Will is one year older than Phil and Phil is one year older than Gil. The sum of their ages is 75. How old is each?

Group Decision Making

6. Work in a group. Discuss and decide.

Situation Your dog is lost and you want to run an ad in the classified section of your local newspaper. You can afford to spend $50 on the ad and a reward. How much can you offer for the reward?

Guidelines for Planning

- **Formulate Problems** you will need to solve.
- Discuss **Assumptions** you will make and **Data** you will need.

a. What decision or decisions do you need to make in this situation?
b. Formulate problems you need to solve to make the decision(s).
c. List any assumptions you need to make to arrive at a decision.
d. What data, if any, do you need to collect to make a decision?
e. Write a paragraph summarizing what your group did, what decisions you made, and why. Then write the ad.

Extend Key Ideas

Logical Reasoning and Venn Diagrams

The words *and, or, not,* and *if-then* are used to express ideas in **logical reasoning.** A **Venn Diagram** is a drawing used to show logical relationships among members of sets. The set members can be numbers, people, cards, or any other elements. The Venn Diagrams below show some relationships.

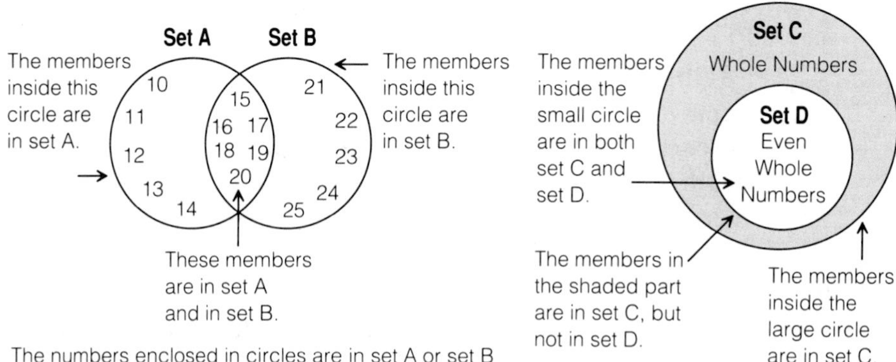

Refer to the Venn Diagrams above for Exercises 1–7. List the numbers in:

1. both set A ***and*** set B.

2. set B, but ***not*** in set A.

3. set A, but ***not*** in set B.

4. set A ***or*** set B.

5. List the smallest five numbers that are in set C, but ***not*** in set D.

6. Are there any numbers that are in set D, but ***not*** in set C?

7. ***If*** a number is in set D, ***then*** what can you conclude?

Make a Venn Diagram to show: Set A = brown-haired people.
Set B = green-eyed people. Describe the people in:

8. both set A ***and*** set B.

9. set A, but ***not*** set B.

10. set B, but ***not*** set A.

11. ***neither*** set A ***nor*** set B.

Make a Venn Diagram to show: Set C = people from the United States.
Set D = people from Texas.

12. A person is in set C, but ***not*** in set D. What can you conclude?

13. A person is ***not*** in set D. What can you conclude?

14. A person is ***not*** in set C. What can you conclude?

Chapter 1 Review/Test

Understanding

True or false?

1-1 **1.** To evaluate $n + 6 + n$, replace the first n by 2 and the second n by 3.

1-6 **2.** An equation always has exactly one solution.

1-4 **3.** The Associative Property is about changing the grouping of addends.

1-4 **4.** Addition is the inverse operation of multiplication.

1-8 **5.** To solve for x in $x - 23 = 19$, add 23 to both sides.

Skills

1-1 Evaluate each numerical or algebraic expression.

6. $17 - (3 + 6)$ **7.** $(25 - 5) + 4$ **8.** $(16 - 7) + 5$

9. $13 - (x + 7)$ for $x = 2$ **10.** $r - k$ for $r = 7$ and $k = 2$

1-3 Write as an algebraic expression.

11. 5 more than p **12.** v decreased by 4 **13.** 7 added to a number

1-4 Use basic properties. Write an equivalent expression.

14. $t + 0$ **15.** $(n + 5) + 4$ **16.** $6 + y$

1-6 1-7 1-8 Solve the equations. A replacement set is given for Exercise 17. For the others, the replacement set is the set of whole numbers.

17. $x + 9 = 12$ $\{1, 2, 3, 4\}$ **18.** $s - 6 = 4$ **19.** $67 = g + 14$

1-9 Round to the nearest hundred (h) or thousand (t) to estimate the value of the variable.

20. $4{,}679 + 3{,}525 = a$ (t) **21.** $1{,}386 - 235 = w$ (h)

22. Use front-end estimation to estimate n where $n = 143 + 993 + 245$.

Applications

1-8 **23.** A balanced diet and exercise helped Fred lose 26 pounds. He now weighs 143 pounds. How much did he weigh before his weight loss? Write an equation to describe this situation.

1-11 **24.** In a hockey game, the Jets scored 5 more goals than the Lasers. The teams scored a total of 9 goals. How many goals did each team score?

1-9 **25.** When Tom bought tires for his car, the odometer read 34,843. Now the odometer reads 63,140. Round to the nearest thousand and estimate how many miles, m, Tom has driven on these tires.
$m = 63{,}140 - 34{,}843$

2 Expressions and Equations: Multiplication and Division

There are 10 hurdles in the 400-meter hurdle race. If Maurice ran 5 heats of this race at his last track meet, how many hurdles did he jump over?

2-1 Evaluating Expressions: Order of Operations

Objective To evaluate an expression involving all four operations with or without grouping symbols.

Explore

Some calculators are programmed to follow the order of operation rules. With others, you must know these rules and enter the computations into the calculator in the order in which they should be performed.

Enter the operations below in order. Describe the rules your calculator follows to produce its final displayed number.

1. $8 + 4 \div 2$
2. $15 - 5 \times 3$
3. $4 \times 6 - 4 + 2$
4. $8 \times 2 - 9 + 3$
5. $9 + 12 \div 3 - 2$
6. $8 + 24 \div 8 - 2 \times 3$

Understand the Ideas

Grouping symbols, such as parentheses ( ) and brackets [ ] are used in numerical expressions to indicate the order in which operations should be done. The fraction bar, which serves as a division symbol, is also a grouping symbol. When no grouping symbols are given, we need a rule for the order of operations.

The table below shows how grouping symbols are used when you want to designate a special order of operations. Notice that the operations multiplication and division can be written in several ways. When you see $9 \cdot 8$ or $9(8)$, it means 9×8. When you see $72/8$ or $\frac{72}{8}$ it means $72 \div 8$.

Expression	Meaning of grouping symbols	Results
$(9 + 6) \div 3$	*Parentheses* indicate that addition is to be done first.	$15 \div 3 = 5$
$7 - [(6 + 9) \div 5]$	*Inner parentheses* indicate that addition is to be done first. The division inside the *brackets* is to be done next.	$7 - [15 \div 5]$ $7 - 3 = 4$
$\frac{9 + 3}{3 \cdot 2}$	The *fraction bar* indicates that the addition above and the multiplication below are to be done before dividing.	$\frac{12}{6} = 12 \div 6 = 2$

The following order of operations rule ensures that everyone will get the same answer when no grouping symbols are given.

Rule Order of Operations

First do all multiplying and dividing in order from left to right.

Then do all adding and subtracting in order from left to right.

Example 1

Evaluate. $[18 + (4 \cdot 6)] \div 7$

Solution

$[18 + (4 \cdot 6)] \div 7$ Look for the inside grouping symbols. Compute $4 \cdot 6$ first.

$= [18 + 24] \div 7$ Next do the operation in the outer pair of grouping symbols. Compute $18 + 24$.

$= 42 \div 7 = 6$

Try This Evaluate. **a.** $27 \div (5 + 4)$ **b.** $23 - [(56 + 7) \div 9]$

Example 2

Evaluate. $8 \cdot 2 + 45 \div 9$

Solution

$8 \cdot 2 + 45 \div 9$ Multiply and divide from left to right. First compute 8×2.

$= 16 + 45 \div 9$ Then compute $45 \div 9$.

$= 16 + 5 = 21$ Next add and subtract from left to right. Compute $16 + 5$.

Try This Evaluate. **c.** $5 + 4 \cdot 7$ **d.** $16 + 30 \div 3 \cdot 2$

Like numerical expressions, algebraic expressions involving multiplication and division can be written in several ways. For example, $\mathbf{9 \times s}$ can be written $\mathbf{9 \cdot s}$, $\mathbf{9(s)}$, or $\mathbf{9s}$. An expression such as $\mathbf{7 \times a \times b}$ is most often written $\mathbf{7ab}$. The expression $\mathbf{y \div 3}$ can be written $\mathbf{\frac{y}{3}}$.

Example 3

Evaluate $x(7 + y)$ for $x = 9$ and $y = 3$.

Solution

$x(7 + y)$ Replace x with 9 and y with 3. Add within the parentheses first.

$9(7 + 3)$ Remember that 9(10) means 9×10.

$= 9(10) = 90$

Try This Evaluate for $a = 5$ and $b = 8$. **e.** $3(a + 5)b$ **f.** $8 + \left(\frac{ab}{40}\right)$

Example 4

Evaluate. $\frac{x + 7}{6}$ for $x = 47$

Solution $\frac{x + 7}{6}$

$\frac{47 + 7}{6}$ Replace x with 47. Do the operations above the fraction bar first.

$= \frac{54}{6}$

$= 9$

Try This Evaluate. **g.** $\frac{7 + 9}{z + 6}$ for $z = 10$ **h.** $\frac{3y + 9}{2y}$ for $y = 9$

Class Exercises

Which operation would you do first?

1. $5 + 3 \cdot 2$
2. $(7 + 4) \cdot 6$
3. $(36 - 32) \div 4$
4. $48 - 24 \div 6 \cdot 2$
5. $15 - 8 \div 2$
6. $7 + 6 \cdot 3 - 3$

Discuss the Ideas

7. A student said she used the "My Dear Aunt Sally" rule for deciding upon the order of operations in an expression. Discuss what she might have meant. Then create a phrase like hers that you could use.

Exercises

Practice and Apply

Evaluate each numerical expression.

1. $13 + (54 \div 9)$
2. $[9 + (9 \cdot 7)] \div 8$
3. $[48 \div (32 - 26)] \cdot 12$
4. $16 - 7 \cdot 2$
5. $9 \cdot 4 \div 2$
6. $12 + 9 \cdot 3 - 28$
7. $96 \div 4 - 3 \cdot 5$
8. $54 + 24 \div 3 - 30$
9. $36 \div 3 + 4 \cdot 5 - 3$

Evaluate each algebraic expression.

10. $\frac{54}{b}$ for $b = 6$
11. $4bc$ for $b = 16, c = 17$
12. $(18 + 7)ab$ for $a = 2, b = 5$
13. $6y - 2y$ for $y = 24$
14. $\frac{a}{b}$ for $a = 945, b = 9$
15. $\frac{3cd}{6}$ for $c = 18, d = 25$
16. $n(n) + 2$ for $n = 8$
17. $12(52 - p)$ for $p = 47$
18. $\frac{43 - t}{9}$ for $t = 7$
19. $\frac{5a}{b + 4}$ for $a = 9, b = 1$

20. Ellen invested \$400 for 2 years at 6% interest. Find the amount of money in her account at the end of the second year by evaluating the expression $400[100 + (6)(2)] \div 100$.

Extend and Apply

Copy and complete each table.

	a	b	$6a - b$
	3	3	$6(3) - 3 = 15$
21.	5	30	
22.	9	4	

	x	y	$x \div 3 + y \div 3$
	6	9	$6 \div 3 + 9 \div 3 = 5$
23.	12	18	
24.	24	45	

Find the final answer without writing down intermediate answers.

25. Evaluate. $959 \div 7 - 16 \cdot 8$ **26.** Simplify. $24 \cdot 57 + 1{,}424 \div 89$

Use Mathematical Reasoning

27. Use each of the numbers 2, 4, 6, 8, and 12 exactly once, with any operation signs and grouping symbols you wish, to write an expression for the smallest possible whole number.

28. Use the digits for this year with any grouping symbols and operations to write expressions for the whole numbers from 0 to 10.

Mixed Review

Solve mentally. **29.** $120 + n = 135$ **30.** $80 = 105 - m$

Write as an expression. **31.** x less than 27 **32.** x more than 12

Round to the nearest hundred and estimate the sum. **33.** 3,647 + 2,891

Calculator Activity

If your calculator does not follow the order of operation rules, you can use the memory keys to help you enter the operations in the correct order. To find $832 \div 8 + 3 \times 26$, enter the following.

832 [÷] 8 [M+] 3 [×] 26 [M+] [MR]

When you do this, the calculator divides 832 by 8 and stores the result in its memory. Then it multiplies 3 times 26 and adds this to the number already in the memory. Finally it displays the sum.

The [M−] key can be used when you want to subtract from the number in the memory. Use the memory keys on a calculator to do these calculations.

1. $56 + 9 \cdot 57$ **2.** $84 - 240 \div 16$ **3.** $832 \div 8 + 4 \cdot 26$

4. $254 - 19 \cdot 13 + 68$ **5.** $16 + 4 \cdot 7 - 36 \div 9$

2-2

More Patterns and Variables

Objective To write a rule that represents the relationship between two numbers.

Application

Many ticket agencies have tables showing the total cost for a given number of tickets. When orders are placed, the agent can read the total from the table without computing.

Understand the Ideas

In Chapter 1 you used a variable to express the relationship between two quantities. Those relationships involved addition or subtraction. Here you will explore relationships involving multiplication or division.

Example

Look for a pattern. Copy and complete the table referred to in the **application**. Write a rule that tells how to get a number in the bottom row.

No. of tickets	5	10	15	20	25	30	x
Cost (dollars)	30	60	90				

Solution

No. of tickets	5	10	15	20	25	30	x
Cost (dollars)	30	60	90	120	150	180	$6x$

Rule: Multiply the number of tickets by 6 to get the total cost.

Try This Look for a pattern. Copy and complete the table. Write a rule that tells how to get the cost when you know the number of tickets.

a.

Raffle tickets	10	20	30	40	50	60	n
Cost (dollars)	5	10	15				

b.

No. in class	12	18	23	30	41	45	p
Cost (dollars)	84	126	161				

Class Exercises

Look for patterns to tell the missing numbers.

1.

20	40	60	80	100
5		15		25

2.

2	4	6	8	10
	20	30	40	

Discuss the Ideas

3. When a student saw the table in Class Exercise 1, she said "You just count by 5's to get the numbers in the bottom row." What other relationship could she discover to help her quickly give the number in the bottom row below 1000 in the top row if the table were extended?

Exercises

Practice and Apply

Look for patterns. Copy and complete the table. Write a rule that tells how to get the number in the bottom row.

1.

3	9	15	24	x
1	3	5		

2.

3	8	11	17	m
12	32	44		

3.

15	25	40	65	p
105		280		

4.

78	144	198	282	k
13		33		

5. The total cost to leave a dog in a kennel depends on the number of days. Look for a pattern and complete the table at right. Write a rule for finding the cost, given the number of days.

No. of days	3	5	6	7	x
Cost (dollars)	18	30		42	

Extend and Apply

Use the rule given to copy and complete the table.

6.

3	5	7	9	p
				$6p$

7.

32	64	128	264	x
				$\frac{x}{8}$

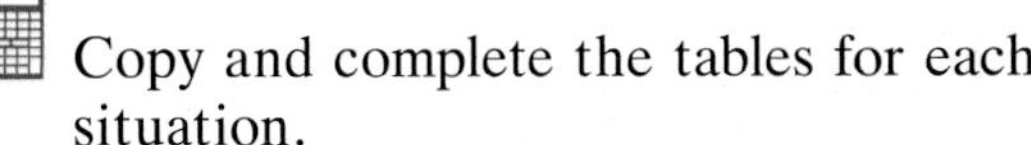

Copy and complete the tables for each situation.

8. The length and width of rectangular flower boxes are related in a particular way. The table below shows several of the pots made by Pete's Pots. Write a rule that tells how to find the width of a flower box if you know the length. (All measurements are in inches.)

	L	W
Pot #1	36	12
Pot #2	48	16
Pot #3	60	20
Pot #4	72	24

9. Tickets for a baseball game differ in price depending on the location. Copy and complete the table at the right. Write a rule for each kind of ticket that tells how to find the cost for any number of tickets.

	Number of tickets				
	1	2	3	5	10
Main level		\$22		\$55	
Upper deck			\$30		\$100
Outfield		\$14			

10. Tickets for an amusement park cost \$9.00 each. The expression $9n$ gives the total cost for n tickets. Make a table showing the cost for 1 through 10 tickets.

Use Mathematical Reasoning

11. To find the bottom number in the table below you need to use both multiplication and addition. Copy and complete the table. Write a rule that tells how to get a number in the bottom row.

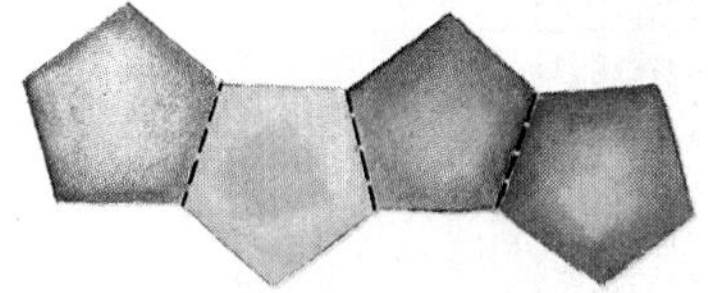

Number of pentagons	1	2	3	4	5	x
Perimeter	5	8	11			

Mixed Review

Solve and check. **12.** $x - 35 = 74$ **13.** $56 = y + 18$ **14.** $123 + t = 300$

Evaluate for $m = 12$ and $n = 5$. **15.** $8mn$ **16.** $(23 - 6)n$ **17.** $4m + 6n$

Solve. **18.** A car that regularly sold for a base price of \$12,075 was being sold with a rebate of \$1,075. What was the cost of the car after the rebate, not including tax and other charges?

2-3 Problem Solving: Writing Expressions

Translating Phrases to Algebraic Expressions

Objective To translate a verbal phrase to a numerical or algebraic expression.

Verbal phrases that suggest multiplication or division can be translated to numerical or algebraic expressions.

Example 1

The number of days in nine weeks is the product of 9 and 7. Write "the product of 9 and 7" as a numerical expression.

Solution 9×7 The phrase "the product of" suggests multiplying the two numbers.

Try This Write as a numerical expression.

a. the quotient of 24 and 6

b. twice 8

c. 12 multiplied by 7

d. Pay for 3 hours work at $4 per hour is 3 times 4.

The phrase "9 times 7" translates to the numerical expression 9×7. To translate the phrase "9 times a number" use a variable and write the algebraic expression $9n$. Study the following pattern.

number	9 times the number	
7	9×7	"9 times 7"
10	9×10	"9 times 10"
n	$9n$	"9 times a **number**"

Example 2

Write an algebraic expression for "a number divided by 6."

Solution $\frac{n}{6}$ Think of a specific number, say 24. "24 divided by 6" is $\frac{24}{6}$, so "a number divided by 6" is $\frac{n}{6}$.

Try This Write as an algebraic expression.

e. the product of 6 and a number

f. double a number

g. the quotient of a number and 5

A phrase may suggest a combination of operations, as in the following example.

Example 3

Write an algebraic expression for "6 less than twice a number."

Solution $2n - 6$ "6" less than suggests subtracting 6.

Try This Write as an algebraic expression.

h. 5 increased by twice a number **i.** 7 times the sum of a number and 4

Example 4

Write as an expression.

Rita earned $24. How much will she have if:

a. she earns 7 times as much? **b.** her earnings are divided by n?

Solutions

a. she earns 7 times as much? 24×7

b. her earnings are divided by n? $24 \div n$ Think about a number, write a variable.

Try This Write as an expression.

Ellis sold 84 calendars last month. What if: **j.** his sales are doubled?

k. his sales are divided by 4? **l.** he sells s times as many?

Class Exercises

Tell whether the phrase suggests multiplication or division.

1. the product of **2.** divided by **3.** the quotient of

4. doubled **5.** multiplied by **6.** halved

Discuss the Ideas

7. Work together to make up sentences about the real world that use each of the words or phrases in Class Exercises 1–6. Make up a paragraph that includes all six phrases.

Exercises

Practice and Apply

Write as a numerical expression.

1. the product of 8 and 7 **2.** 45 divided by 15 **3.** twice 46

4. 6 multiplied by 7 **5.** 48 shared among 4 **6.** 7 times 9

Write as an algebraic expression.

7. the product of a number and 9 **8.** the quotient of a number and 8

9. a number divided by 5

10. double a number

11. 35 increased by twice a number

12. 12 less than twice a number

13. 1 less than a number divided by 10

14. 8 times the sum of 18 and a number

15. 24 less than 3 times a number

16. 5 times a number, plus 4

Write an expression for each question.

There are 36 cars in the garage. How many will there be when there are:

17. 9 times as many?

18. y times as many?

19. the number of cars divided by 4?

20. the number of cars divided by n?

Kristy sold 48 calculators in one week. How many will she sell when:

21. her sales are multiplied by 4?

22. her sales are multiplied by x?

23. her sales are divided by 12?

24. her sales are divided by z?

Extend and Apply

The expression $2n + 1$ represents an odd number such as $1, 3, 5, 7, 9, \ldots$

Write an algebraic expression for:

25. the even numbers that come just before and just after $2n + 1$.

26. the odd numbers that come just before and just after $2n + 1$.

Use Mathematical Reasoning

27. Communicate In a soccer game, the Eagles scored 7 points more than the Cougars. If the Cougars had scored 3 times as many points, they would have scored 3 points more than the Eagles. How many points did each team score? Explain how you solved this problem.

28. Look for a pattern in the equations below.

$1 = \mathbf{1}$ Sum of the first **1** odd number

$1 + 3 = \mathbf{4}$ Sum of the first **2** odd numbers

$1 + 3 + 5 = \mathbf{9}$ Sum of the first **3** odd numbers

Write an algebraic expression for the sum of the first n odd numbers. Use it to find the sum of the first 100 odd numbers.

Mixed Review

Solve and check. **29.** $n - 163 = 291$ **30.** $x + 62 = 157$

Solve for the replacement set given. **31.** $c + 16 = 42 \ \{24, 25, 26, 27\}$

32. Use the Associative Property to rewrite $(x + 7) + 3$.

2-4 Basic Properties of Multiplication

Objective To use the basic properties of multiplication to write an algebraic expression that is equivalent to a given algebraic expression.

Understand the Ideas

The basic properties of multiplication and division can be used to write equivalent expressions.

You can change the order in which two numbers are multiplied and their product will stay the same. For example, $32 \times 15 = 15 \times 32$. The diagram below gives a way to show changing order with dot cards.

Mark dots on a card.

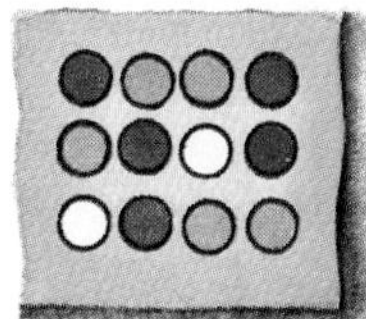

Rotate the card 90°.

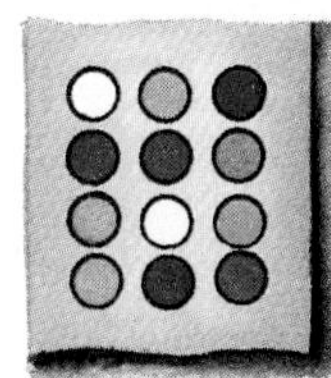

$3 \times 4 \quad = \quad 4 \times 3$

For larger numbers, you can test this idea with a calculator by finding a pair of products such as $436 \times 275 = 119{,}900$ and $275 \times 436 = 119{,}900$. With variables, this property can be stated for all whole numbers.

Commutative Property of Multiplication

A change in the order in which two numbers are multiplied does not change their product.

For all whole numbers a and b, $ab = ba$

Example 1

Use the Commutative Property to write an expression equivalent to $5y$.

Solution $y(5)$ $y(5)$ has the same value as $5y$ for any number that replaces y.

Try This Use the Commutative Property to write an equivalent expression. **a.** xy **b.** $z(6)$ **c.** $24p$

You can change the way three numbers are grouped for multiplication and the product stays the same. The following diagram gives a way to show this with sets of dots.

Mark dots on a card. Use 2 divider strips.

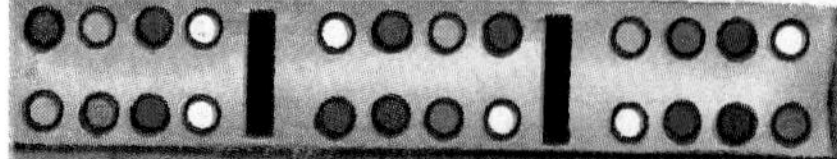

Now use a different divider strip.

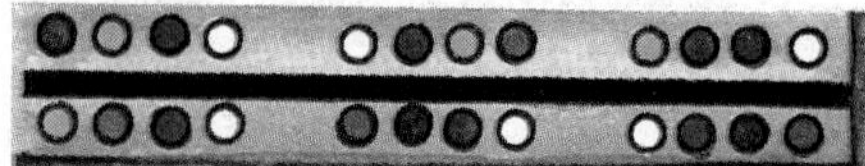

$$(2 \times 4) \times 3 = 2 \times (4 \times 3)$$

For larger numbers, such as 17, 25, and 4, you can test this idea with a calculator by finding $(17 \times 25) \times 4 = 1700$, and $17 \times (25 \times 4) = 1700$. With variables, this property can be stated for all whole numbers.

Associative Property of Multiplication

A change in the grouping of three whole numbers for multiplication does not change the product.

For all whole numbers ***a***, ***b***, and ***c***, $a(bc) = (ab)c$

Example 2

Use the Associative Property to write an expression equivalent to $6(4n)$.

Solution $(6 \cdot 4)n$ $(6 \cdot 4)n$ has the same values as $6(4n)$ for any number that replaces n.

Try This Use the Associative Property to write an equivalent expression.

d. $(n \cdot 12)7$ **e.** $25(4a)$ **f.** $(6a)b$

The number 1 is called the **Multiplicative Identity** because when it is multiplied by a number, the result is that same number: $49 \times 1 = 49$.

Identity Property of Multiplication

The product of a factor and one is the factor.

For all whole numbers ***a***, $a(1) = a$ $1(a) = a$.

Any number divided by 1 equals that same number: $a \div 1 = a$.
Any number divided by itself equals one: $a \div a = 1$.

The number 0 also has special properties. When any number is multiplied by 0, the product is always 0: $6 \times 0 = 0$.

Zero Property of Multiplication

The product of any number and zero is zero.

For all whole numbers ***a***, $a(0) = 0$ $0(a) = 0$

When 0 is divided by another number, the quotient is always 0: $\mathbf{0 \div a = 0}$. But when you consider dividing by 0 and checking possible quotients, strange things happen, as shown below.

$? \leftarrow 0 \times ? = 0$ $0\overline{)0}$ Any number would check.	$? \leftarrow 0 \times ? = 9$ $0\overline{)9}$ No number would check.

For these reasons, **division by 0 is not permitted.**

Example 3

Use the Zero or Identity Property to write an equivalent expression.

a. $0 \cdot x$ **b.** $1 \cdot x$

Solution **a.** 0 $0 \cdot x = 0$ for any number that replaces x.

b. x $1 \cdot x = x$ for any number replacing x.

Try This Use the Zero or Identity Property to write an equivalent expression.

g. $0 \cdot t$ **h.** $1n$ **i.** $p(0)$

The diagrams below use dot cards to show another important property.

Mark dots on a card.
Use horizontal dividers.

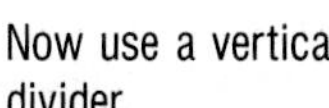

Now use a vertical divider.

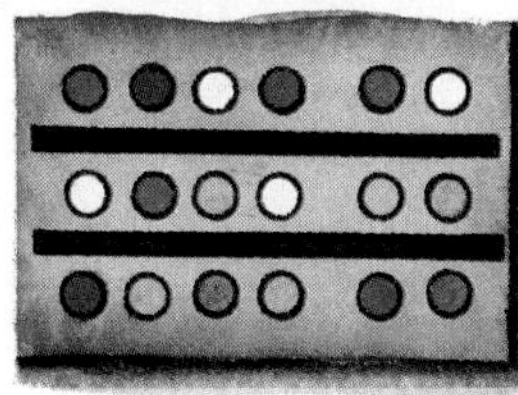

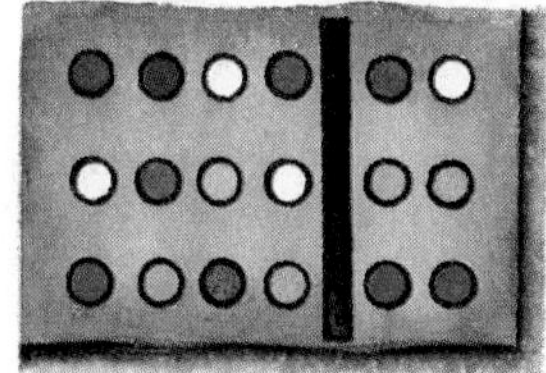

$3 \times (4 + 2) = (3 \times 4) + (3 \times 2)$

By rotating the cards, this idea is shown below in reverse order.

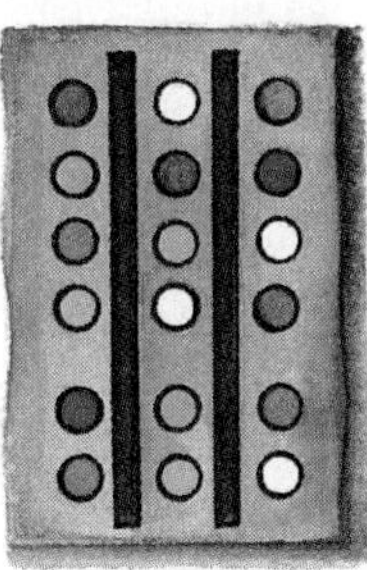

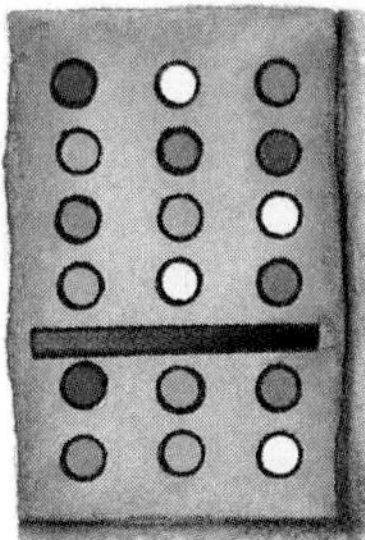

$(4 + 2) \times 3 = (4 \times 3) + (2 \times 3)$

Each diagram suggests that you can add first and then multiply or you can multiply first and then add. The answer is the same.

Using numbers you see that $9 \cdot (10 + 6) = 9 \cdot 10 + 9 \cdot 6$. The result is the same whether the two numbers are added first and their sum is multiplied by 9, or the products are found first and then added.

$9 \cdot (10 + 6)$	$9 \cdot 10 + 9 \cdot 6$
$9 \cdot (16)$	$90 + 54$
144	144

This important property ties multiplication and addition together.

Distributive Property of Multiplication Over Addition

When two numbers have been added and then multiplied by a factor, the result will be the same when each number is multiplied by the factor and the products are then added.

For whole numbers ***a*, *b*, and *c*,** $a(b + c) = ab + ac$
$(b + c)a = ba + ca$

Example 4

Use the Distributive Property to write an expression equivalent to $5(x + y)$.

Solution $5x + 5y$ $5(x + y)$ has the same value as $5x + 5y$ for any numbers that replace the variables.

Try This Use the Distributive Property to write an equivalent expression.

j. $6(r + 4)$ **k.** $(5 + 3)n$

The Distributive Property can be very useful when doing computations mentally. For example, when finding $59 \cdot 96 + 59 \cdot 4$, it helps to know that when there is a sum of two products with a common factor, you can add the other factors first and then multiply. $59 \cdot (96 + 4)$ is easy to calculate mentally.

Example 5

Find $48 \cdot 86 + 52 \cdot 86$ mentally.

Solution

Think: $(48 + 52) \cdot 86$ Use the Distributive Property.
$100 \cdot 86 = 8{,}600$ $48 \cdot 86 + 52 \cdot 86 = (48 + 52) \cdot 86$

Try This Use the Distributive Property to calculate mentally.

l. $27 \cdot 8 + 27 \cdot 2$ **m.** $992 \cdot 58 + 8 \cdot 58$ **n.** $354 \cdot 46 + 354 \cdot 54$

Class Exercises

Name the property shown by each equation. Do not compute.

1. $12 \times 0 = 0$

2. $17 \times 8 = 8 \times 17$

3. $16 \times (3 \times 5) = (16 \times 3) \times 5$

4. $1 \times 26 = 26$

5. $83 \times 14 = 14 \times 83$

6. $6 \times (12 + 7) = 6 \times 12 + 6 \times 7$

Discuss the Ideas

7. A student started with $(ab)c$, used the Associative Property to write the equivalent expression $a(bc)$ and then used the Commutative Property to write the equivalent expression $a(cb)$. Describe how you could start with $a(cb)$ and write equivalent expressions to get to the expression $(ca)b$.

Exercises

Practice and Apply

Use the Commutative Property to write an equivalent expression.

1. $y(4)$ **2.** $9x$ **3.** cd **4.** $x(28)$

Use the Associative Property to write an equivalent expression.

5. $(n \cdot 3)8$ **6.** $(y \cdot 7)13$ **7.** $8(5 \cdot a)$ **8.** $50(4n)$

Use the Zero or Identity Property to write an equivalent expression.

9. $1y$ **10.** $0 \cdot s$ **11.** $y \div y$ **12.** $0 \div m$

Use the Distributive Property to write an equivalent expression.

13. $4(x + 3)$ **14.** $8(s + 7)$ **15.** $y(6 + 9)$ **16.** $(n + 4)3$

Use the Distributive Property and solve mentally.

17. $26(6) + 26(4)$ **18.** $38(57) + 38(43)$ **19.** $64(56) + 36(56)$

20. The distance covered in t seconds by a cheetah running 35 yards/second can be represented by the expression $35(t)$. Use the Commutative Property to write an equivalent expression for $35(t)$.

21. The perimeter of this swimming pool can be represented by the expression $2(L + 12)$. Use the Distributive Property to write an equivalent expression.

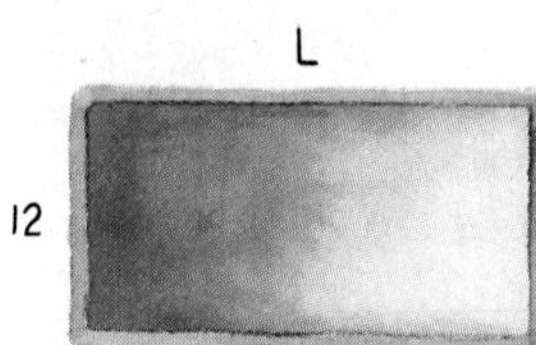

Extend and Apply

22. Evaluate $(12a)b$ and $12(ab)$ for $a = 7$ and $b = 3$. Are the values equal?

23. Evaluate $a(7 + b)$ and $7a + ab$ for $a = 9$ and $b = 6$. Are the values equal?

Use basic properties to solve the equations.

24. $8n = 13(8)$

25. $8(16 + 24) = 8(16) + 8m$

26. $(54 \cdot 36)23 = 54(b \cdot 23)$

27. $8(4x) = (8 \cdot 4)100$

28. Evaluate $a(b - c)$ for $a = 7$, $b = 14$, and $c = 8$.
Evaluate $ab - ac$ for the same numbers.
Try some other whole numbers for a, b, and c. When would a Distributive Property involving multiplication with subtraction be true?

29. Choose values for a, b, and c to show that a Distributive Property for addition over multiplication, $a + (b \cdot c) = (a + b) \cdot (a + c)$, does not hold true for all whole numbers.

Use Mathematical Reasoning

30. Suppose the symbol @ represents the operation "doubleadd" so that $3 @ 4 = 2(3) + 4 = 10$. That is, double the first number and add the second. Give examples to show that neither the Commutative nor the Associative Properties hold true for this operation.

Mixed Review

Use paper and pencil to find the product or quotient. **31.** 376×23

32. 236×43 **33.** 95×307 **34.** 119×45 **35.** 472×11

36. $8586 \div 53$ **37.** $513 \div 27$ **38.** $1848 \div 56$ **39.** $1292 \div 76$

Numbers to Algebra

When an expression has the same number as a factor in each addend, a reversed form of the Distributive Property, $\boldsymbol{ab + ac = a(b + c)}$ may be used to write an equivalent expression that is a product.

Check the number examples to see that they are true.

This property is used to **factor** algebraic expressions.

Numbers	**Algebra** (factored form)
$\mathbf{4} \cdot 3 + \mathbf{4} \cdot 5 = \mathbf{4}(3 + 5)$	$4b + 4c = 4(b + c)$
$\mathbf{6} \cdot 5 + \mathbf{6} \cdot 7 = \mathbf{6}(5 + 7)$	$6x + 6y = 6(x + y)$
$\mathbf{5} \cdot 8 + \mathbf{5} \cdot 4 = \mathbf{5}(8 + 4)$	$5m + 5n = 5(m + n)$

Use the Distributive Property to factor each expression.

1. $2a + 2b$
2. $5y + 5z$
3. $6n + 6(7)$
4. $8s + 16$
5. $3p + np$
6. $ax + az$

2-5 Simplifying Algebraic Expressions

Objective To use the associative and distributive properties to simplify algebraic expressions.

Explore

Choose a number for n and find expressions in the box below that have the same value when n is replaced by the number. See if the expressions have the same value using other numbers for n. Write equations stating that the expressions are equivalent.

$4(3n)$	$3n + 4n$	$7 + n$	$12nnnn$
$n + (4 + 3)$	$12nn$	$4n + 3n$	$(4 + 3)n$
$7n$	$12n - 5n$	$(3 + n) + 4$	$12n$

Understand the Ideas

To **simplify an algebraic expression,** you replace it with a simpler equivalent expression. An expression in its simplest form does not contain parentheses. For example, the table to the right suggests that $6n$ has the same value as $3(2n)$ for every number.

n	1 2 3...
$3(2n)$	6 12 18...
$6n$	6 12 18...

You can use the basic properties to simplify algebraic expressions.

Example 1

Use the Associative Property of Multiplication to simplify. $3(2n)$

Solution $3(2n) = (3 \cdot 2)n$ $(3 \cdot 2)n$ has the same value as $3(2n)$ for any value of n.

$= 6n$

Try This Simplify. **a.** $5(6x)$ **b.** $9(7b)$ **c.** $12(8y)$

Example 2

Use the Associative Property of Addition to simplify. $(x + 7) + 6$

Solution $(x + 7) + 6 = x + (7 + 6)$ $x + (7 + 6)$ has the same values as $(x + 7) + 6$ for any value of n.

$= x + 13$

Try This Simplify. **d.** $(n + 24) + 8$ **e.** $(z + 13) + 7$

The parts of an algebraic expression that are separated by an addition or subtraction sign are called **terms**. The expression $4x + 2y - 3$ has three terms.

$$\underbrace{4x}_{\text{term}} + \underbrace{2y}_{\text{term}} - \underbrace{3}_{\text{term}}$$

terms

Terms with the same variable factors are called **like terms.** $2n$ and $3n$ are like terms, but $4x$ and $2y$ are unlike terms because their variable factors, x and y, are different.

To simplify expressions with addends that are like terms, you can **combine like terms.** The pattern in the table below suggests that $2n + 3n$ can be simplified to $5n$. A method of simplifying the algebraic expression $2n + 3n$ using a reverse form of the distributive property is also shown below.

Look for a Pattern or **Use the Distributive Property**

n	$2n + 3n$	$5n$
1	5	5
2	10	10
3	15	15
⋮	⋮	⋮

$$\begin{aligned} b\,a + c\,a &= (b + c)a \\ \downarrow\downarrow \quad \downarrow\downarrow \quad &\quad \downarrow \quad \downarrow\downarrow \\ 2\,n + 3\,n &= (2 + 3)n \\ &= 5n \end{aligned}$$

Example 3

Use the Distributive Property to simplify by combining like terms.
$5x + 8x$

Solution $5x + 8x = (5 + 8)x$ $(5 + 8)x = 5x + 8x$ for any number replacing x.
$= 13x$

Try This Combine like terms.

f. $6n + 5n$ **g.** $25b + 15b$ **h.** $37z + 4z$ **i.** $x + 5x$

Class Exercises

Name the property that could be used to simplify the expression.

1. $5(4x)$ **2.** $(n + 9) + 6$ **3.** $7(5 \cdot b)$

4. $6y + 9y$ **5.** $(c \cdot 5)7$ **6.** $12c + 17c$

7. $8 + (9 + r)$ **8.** $23t + 1t$ **9.** $6(2n)$

Discuss the Ideas

10. How would you convince someone that the expression $3a + 2b$ cannot be simplified to $5ab$?

Exercises

Practice and Apply

Use the Associative Property of Multiplication to simplify.

1. $13(16c)$ **2.** $5(3 \cdot s)$ **3.** $8(6p)$ **4.** $6(10 \cdot n)$

Use the Associative Property of Addition to simplify.

5. $(z + 45) + 25$ **6.** $(n + 18) + 5$ **7.** $(y + 135) + 68$

Use the Distributive Property to simplify by combining like terms.

8. $9p + 7p$ **9.** $7a + 5a$ **10.** $5a + 36a$ **11.** $86c + 37c$

12. The number of cubic inches of water contained in this aquarium can be expressed as $12(15h)$. Use the Associative Property to simplify the expression.

Extend and Apply

Use the basic properties as needed to simplify each expression.

13. $(5 + y) + 9$ **14.** $5(3x + 4x)$ **15.** $7(x + 8)$ **16.** $\frac{6a + 4a}{7a + 3a}$

Use Mathematical Reasoning

17. **Communicate** Nancy sold tickets to the school play. Compared to the number she sold on Monday, Tuesday's number was double, Wednesday's was triple, and Thursday's was quadruple. If Nancy sold a total of 80 tickets, how many did she sell each day? Write an explanation of how you solved this problem.

18. Try this "number trick": choose a number; add 7; subtract 2; multiply by 2; subtract 10; divide by 2. What is the result? Choose a variable to express the number and write an algebraic expression to help explain why this works.

Mixed Review

Write as an algebraic expression. **19.** 9 less than 6 times a number

Solve and check. **20.** $x - 19 = 6$ **21.** $304 = x - 24$

Mental Math

Because of the Distributive Property, you can find products such as 3(24) by **breaking apart** 24 and thinking "3(20) plus 3(4), or 60 + 12. The product is 72." Break apart numbers to find each product mentally.

1. 2(34) **2.** 3(26) **3.** 4(23) **4.** 5(33) **5.** 6(43) **6.** 7(24)

2-6 Solving Equations: Using Mental Math or Guess, Check, Revise

Objective To solve simple equations mentally.

Application

A 5 hour raft trip covered a distance of 35 km. The guide wanted to find the average speed for the trip.

Understand the Ideas

An equation that involves small numbers and a single operation, either multiplication or division, can often be solved mentally.

The *cover-up* method, described in Chapter 1, can help you think about a solution. Study the following.

$6n = 24$

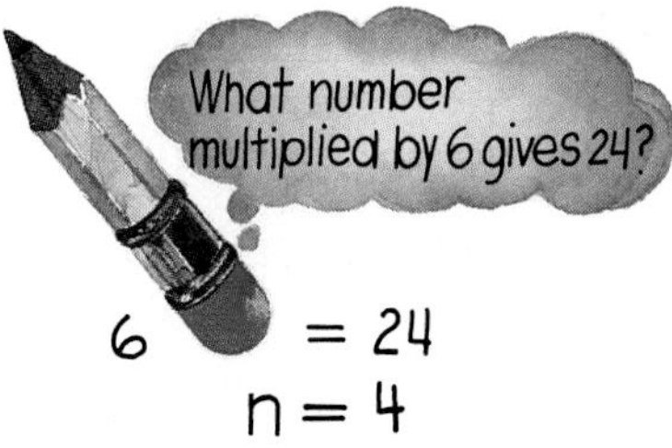

$\frac{n}{6} = 3$

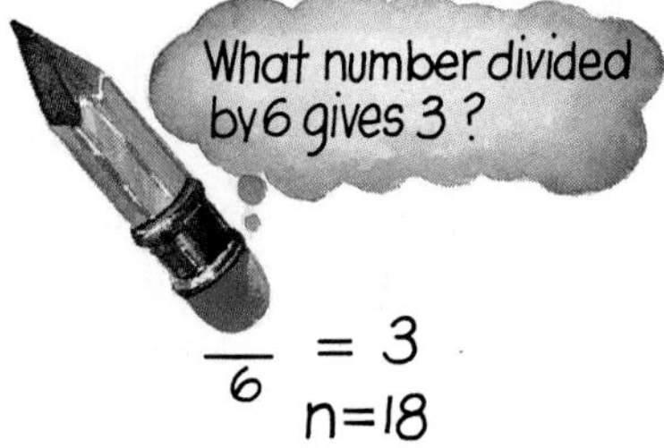

Example 1

Find the average speed for the raft trip in the **application** by solving $5n = 35$ mentally. Check your solution.

Solution $5n = 35$ Think: what number multiplied by 5 gives 35?
$n = 7$

Check $5(7) \stackrel{?}{=} 35$ Mentally substitute 7 for n in the equation.
$35 = 35$ ✓ The equation is true, so 7 is a solution.

The average speed of the raft was 7 km/h.

Try This Solve and check mentally.

a. $\frac{x}{4} = 9$ **b.** $56 = 7r$ **c.** $9 = \frac{c}{3}$

d. Find the average weight of the 6 people on the raft by solving $6w = 900$ mentally.

The Guess, Check, Revise strategy can also be used to solve equations that involve multiplication or division. When the equations contain larger numbers, a calculator is helpful.

Example 2

Use Guess, Check, Revise and a calculator to solve the equation $36x = 468$.

Solution		
	Try 11.	Guess 11.
	36 [×] 11 [=] 396	Check your guess. Too small.
	Try 13.	Revise your guess. Guess 13.
	36 [×] 13 [=] 468	It checks.
	$x = 13$	13 is a solution.

Try This Use Guess, Check, Revise to solve.

e. $n \div 14 = 26$ **f.** $42c = 966$ **g.** $38 = \frac{n}{16}$

Class Exercises

The solution of the equation $6x = 42$ is "the number that multiplied by 6 gives 42." Describe the solution of each of these equations.

1. $\frac{n}{5} = 9$ **2.** $4c = 20$ **3.** $\frac{x}{7} = 4$

Discuss the Ideas

4. Bill challenged Jan to make up an equation that had more than one solution. He agreed that she could use the variable more than once in the equation. Create an equation that she might have made up.

Exercises

Practice and Apply

Solve and check mentally.

1. $8b = 72$ **2.** $4a = 28$ **3.** $\frac{x}{8} = 9$ **4.** $\frac{b}{10} = 8$

5. $240 = 8x$ **6.** $10 = \frac{n}{3}$ **7.** $100 = 5y$ **8.** $250 = 10x$

9. $3 = \frac{p}{70}$ **10.** $350t = 700$ **11.** $125z = 250$ **12.** $\frac{r}{1{,}000} = 3$

Use Guess, Check, Revise to solve.

13. $24x = 312$ **14.** $\frac{n}{12} = 18$ **15.** $47n = 423$ **16.** $t \div 27 = 36$

Extend and Apply

17. For all whole numbers a, b, and c, if $\frac{a}{b} = c$, then $a = c \cdot b$. Use this relationship to rewrite each equation with the variable by itself on one side. Then solve for the variable.

a. $\frac{x}{28} = 42$ **b.** $\frac{n}{24} = 53$ **c.** $\frac{z}{125} = 17$

18. An amusement park director divided the total attendance for a two-week period by 14 to find that the average daily attendance was 8,654. Solve the equation $\frac{t}{14} = 8{,}654$ to find the total two-week attendance.

19. A detective divided her earnings for an 8-week case by 8 to find that her average weekly salary had been \$4,535. Solve the equation $\frac{a}{8} = 4{,}535$ to find the total amount she earned.

20. **Suppose** In Exercise 19 suppose the case took 9 weeks. Write an equation and use it to find out how much the detective earned.

Use Mathematical Reasoning

21. Find numbers for x and y that make both $x \cdot y = 144$ and $x \div y = 4$ true.

22. The product of the ages of a teenager and her mother was 784. The sum of their ages was 70. What was the quotient of their ages?

Mixed Review

Evaluate each expression. **23.** $(9 - 6) \cdot 3$ **24.** $21 \div 7 - 6 \div 3$

Solve and check. **25.** $x + 71 = 90$ **26.** $27 = x - 14$ **27.** $x + 26 = 53$

Estimation

Since the addends in the sum $598 + 613 + 587$ cluster around 600 you can use **clustering** to estimate this sum as 3×600, or 1,800. Use clustering to estimate the following sums.

1. $275 + 314 + 326$ **2.** $923 + 879 + 894$

3. $1{,}232 + 1{,}187 + 1{,}199$ **4.** $708 + 674 + 719 + 697$

2-7 Solving Equations: Using Multiplication and Division

Objective To use multiplication and division to solve equations involving whole numbers.

Understand the Ideas

Although some simple equations can be solved mentally, other methods are useful with equations that have larger numbers or more operations. Two ideas are used to solve equations involving multiplication and division. The first is that multiplication and division are inverse operations, and each can be used to undo the other.

Division can undo multiplication.	Multiplication can undo division.
$\frac{4 \cdot 8}{4} = 8$	$\frac{8}{4} \cdot 4 = 8$
$\frac{4 \cdot n}{4} = n$	$\frac{n}{4} \cdot 4 = n$

The second idea is that an equation is like a balanced scale. Whatever is done to one side must also be done to the other side in order for the scale to remain balanced. Scale A below is balanced. Scale B is the result of multiplying the blocks on each side of scale A by 3 and is balanced. Scale C is the result of dividing the blocks on each side of scale A in half and is balanced.

The following properties of equality state this idea for equations.

Multiplication and Division Properties of Equality

You can multiply or divide by the same number on both sides of the equation and the two sides will remain equal.
For all numbers a, b, and c, if $a = b$, then $ac = bc$

and, when $c \neq 0$, if $a = b$, then $\frac{a}{c} = \frac{b}{c}$

Example 1

Write an equation for the balance scale. Think about the scale to solve the equation.

Solution

$2n = 6$

$\frac{2n}{2} = \frac{6}{2}$ Divide the number of blocks on each side in half.

$n = 3$ The n box balances 3 blocks.

Try This **a.** Write an equation for the balance scale. Think about the scale to solve the equation.

To solve an equation, you need to change it into an equation with the variable by itself on one side. The following steps use the idea of inverse operations and the properties of equality to help you do this.

Rule **Solving Equations Using Multiplication and Division**

1. Decide which operation has been applied to the variable.
2. Use the inverse of this operation, multiplying or dividing by the same number on both sides of the equation.

Example 2

Solve and check. $4n = 72$

Solution $4n = 72$

$\frac{4n}{4} = \frac{72}{4}$ To undo multiplying by 4, divide by 4.

$n = 18$ Divide both sides by 4 so they remain equal.

Check $4 \cdot 18 \stackrel{?}{=} 72$ Replace n with 18 in $4n = 72$.

$72 = 72$ ✓ The solution is 18.

Try This Solve and check. **b.** $6x = 78$ **c.** $192 = 8n$

Example 3

Solve and check. $\frac{n}{4} = 26$

Solution $\frac{n}{4} = 26$

$\frac{n}{4} \cdot 4 = 26 \cdot 4$ To undo dividing by 4, multiply by 4.

$n = 104$ Multiply both sides by 4 so they remain equal.

Check $\frac{104}{4} \stackrel{?}{=} 26$ Replace n with 104 in $\frac{n}{4} = 26$.
$26 = 26$ ✓ The solution is 104.

Try This Solve and check. **d.** $\frac{n}{6} = 12$ **e.** $4 = \frac{x}{8}$

Class Exercises

Name the operation that would be used to solve the equation.

1. $27c = 513$ **2.** $125 = z \div 94$ **3.** $35 = \frac{y}{16}$

Discuss the Ideas

4. Tim separated some beans into 9 piles. When he put one pile on the scale, it weighed 18 ounces. He said he could solve the equation $9n = 18$ to find the weight of the beans he had at the beginning. Do you agree? Explain.

Exercises

Practice and Apply

In Exercises 1–3, write an equation for the balance scale. Think about the scale to solve the equation.

1.

2.

3.

Solve and check.

4. $6y = 48$ **5.** $2c = 98$ **6.** $9n = 99$ **7.** $4c = 68$

8. $\frac{a}{36} = 54$ **9.** $\frac{b}{75} = 28$ **10.** $\frac{c}{38} = 69$ **11.** $\frac{y}{54} = 183$

12. $432 = 36b$ **13.** $38 = \frac{y}{38}$ **14.** $527 = 31n$ **15.** $23 = \frac{c}{35}$

16. A store advertised a sale: "three sweaters for \$72." To find the average cost of a sweater, solve the equation $3s = 72$.

Extend and Apply

17. Write and solve an equation in which m is divided by 9 and the quotient is 5.

18. Write and solve an equation in which the product is 612, one factor is 3, and the other factor is represented by the variable n.

Solve and check.

19. $(32 + 45)n = 231$ 20. $(54 - 9) = 15y$ 21. $\frac{a}{27(3)} = 24 + 36$

22. $\frac{x}{3 \cdot 18} = 4$ 23. $(126 \div 9) = \frac{z}{5}$ 24. $266 = (46 - 8)p$

Use Mathematical Reasoning

25. Use inverse operations to find n in this flow chart.

Start with n	⟶	Subtract: 1492	⟶	Multiply by 6	⟶	Add 282	⟶	End with 1986

26. A block box only $\frac{1}{3}$ full balances 4 blocks.

a. Write an equation about this situation.

b. Suppose you multiplied the number of blocks in the box by 3 to make a full box. What would you have to do to the right side to keep the scale balanced?

c. How many blocks are in a full box? What is the solution to your equation in part a?

Mixed Review

Write as an expression 27. 13 added to the product of 6 and 9

Solve and check. 28. $n - 36 = 17$ 29. $41 + x = 63$

Computer Activity

This program can be used to create a distance chart. It uses the formula *distance* = *rate* × *time*. Time (T) is measured in hours.

```
10 REM MILEAGE CHART
20 INPUT "ENTER RATE"; R
30 PRINT "RATE","TIME","DISTANCE"
40 FOR T = 1 TO 15
50 D = R * T: PRINT R,T,D
60 NEXT T
70 END
```

1. Run the program 3 times, using rates of 45, 50, and 55.
2. Suppose you are going on a trip that is 550 miles long. How long would it take at each rate? Are these times reliable? What could make them change?

2-8 Problem Solving: Applications

Keeping Physically Fit

Objective To solve word problems involving whole numbers.

A calorie is a heat unit that can measure the food energy taken in and used by the body. Average calorie amounts used by activities are shown in the table at right. Calorie needs are shown below.

To keep your weight the same take in 15 calories per pound of your weight, per day.

To gain a pound take in 3500 extra calories.

To lose a pound use 3500 extra calories.

Calorie Use

Activity	Calories per minute
Running	14
Bicycling	11
Swimming	9
Tennis	7
Bowling	5

Problems

Use the information given above to solve. Decide whether to use **pencil and paper, mental math, estimation,** or a **calculator** to find the answer. Use each of these techniques at least once.

1. How many calories would you use by swimming for 30 minutes?
2. Do you use more or less than 460 calories by bicycling for 45 minutes?
3. How many calories would you use by running for 1 hour and 5 minutes?
4. How many minutes would you have to run to use 350 calories?
5. How many more calories would you use by running than by playing tennis for 55 minutes?
6. An athlete weighs 129 pounds. Will she gain or lose weight if she eats 15 calories per pound of weight and uses a total of 2000 calories daily?
7. During one month, Enrique took in 31,576 fewer calories than he needed to keep his weight the same. How many pounds did he lose?
8. **Data Search** How many calories do you need each day to maintain your weight?

What's Your Decision?

Suppose you want to lose 10 pounds by either running or swimming. How will you do it and how long will it take?

2-9 Evaluating Formulas

Objective To evaluate formulas.

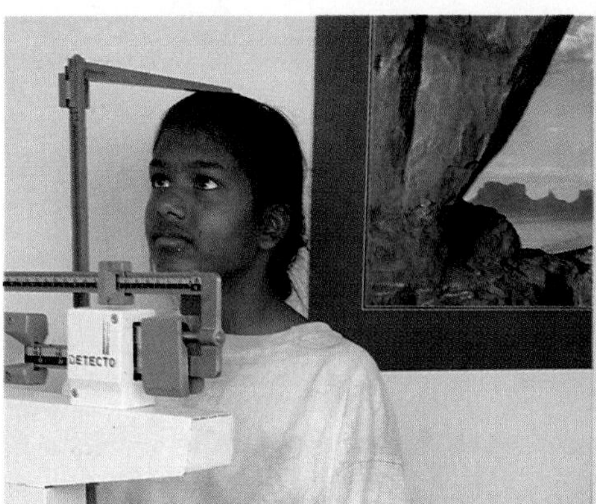

Application

A health report gave a formula to help readers decide if their weights were about right for their heights. Hindola wanted to use the formula to predict her weight.

Understand the Ideas

A **formula** is an equation that shows a relationship between two or more variables. The formula $\boldsymbol{W} = 5\boldsymbol{H} - 190$ expresses the relationship between a person's height in inches ($\boldsymbol{H}$) and a predicted weight in pounds ($\boldsymbol{W}$).

Example

In the application, Hindola's height is 60 inches. Evaluate the formula $W = 5H - 190$ to predict her weight in pounds.

Solution $W = 5H - 190$

$W = 5(60) - 190$ Replace the variable H with 60.

$W = 110$ Evaluate the resulting numerical expression.

Hindola's weight should be about 110 pounds.

Try This **a.** Evaluate the formula above for $H = 65$

b. Predict Dara's weight. His height is 72 inches.

Class Exercises

Evaluate mentally. **1.** $95 - ab$ for $a = 9, b = 7$

2. $R + 23$ for $R = 45$ **3.** $A + B$ for $A = 199, B = 78$

Discuss the Ideas

4. Test the formula $H = 22p$ where H is your height in cm and p is length of your index finger in cm. Is the formula accurate? Explain.

Exercises

Practice and Apply

Evaluate the formula for the values given.

1. $W = 5H - 190$ for $H = 66$
2. $S = 16t + 64$, for $t = 12$
3. $P = S - 38$ for $S = 124$
4. $D = 16r - 57$ for $r = 6$
5. $P = 2L + 76$ for $L = 98$
6. $A = 3rr$ for $r = 9$
7. Formula: $D = r \cdot t$ where D is distance in miles, r is rate in mi/hour, and t is time of ride in hours. Find how far Jenny rode her bicycle in 3 hours at 17 mi/hour.
8. Formula: $S = p - d$. Find the sale price (S) of a television when the regular price (p) is $325 and the discount ($d$) is $48.
9. Formula: $W = 6h + e$. Find Brian's total wages (W) when he works 37 hours (h) and his overtime pay (e) is $58.

Extend and Apply

For Exercises 10–14, copy and complete the table.

Formula: $T = t - \frac{a}{300}$ where T is Temperature in degrees Celsius at an altitude in meters (a) when the ground temperature in degrees Celsius is (t).

	10.	**11.**	**12.**	**13.**	**14.**
a	900	1200	2,400	4,800	6,000
t	20	20	20	20	20
T					

15. Formula: $W = 5000d(d + 1)$ where W is weight in thousands of pounds that a rope with diameter (d) in inches will hold without breaking. Make a table showing values of W for $d = 1, 2, 3, 4,$ and 5.

Use Mathematical Reasoning

16. **Write to Learn** Test the formula $S = 3F - 24$. S = shoe size and F = length of foot in inches. Make a table to show your data, then write a paragraph that answers the question, "Is the formula accurate?"
17. The formula for finding the total points scored in a youth basketball game is $P = 2g + f$, in which P is the total points scored, f is the number of free throws and g is the number of field goals. Write a formula for finding the number of field goals when the total points scored and the number of free throws are known.

Mixed Review

Solve and check. **18.** $m \div 19 = 11$ **19.** $23t = 437$

Write as an algebraic expression. **20.** the sum of 37 and a number

2-10 Estimating

Objective To use rounding or compatible numbers to estimate with whole numbers.

Application

An airline pilot knew that his average speed during a 9-hour flight was 425 mi/h. He wanted to estimate the number of miles flown.

Understand the Ideas

You have used rounding to estimate sums and differences. You can also use rounding to estimate products and quotients.

Example 1

In the application above, distance(d) = rate × time, so $d = 425 \cdot 9$. Use rounding to estimate the value of the variable d.

Solution $425 \cdot 9$ Round 425 to 400. Replace 9 with 10.

$400 \cdot 10 = 4{,}000$

The estimated value for d is 4,000. The trip was about 4,000 miles long.

Try This Estimate the value of the variable by rounding.

a. $876 \cdot 79 = n$ **b.** $x = 2{,}449 \div 79$

When rounding to estimate a quotient does not result in an easy division, you can choose a compatible number that makes the division easier.

Example 2

Estimate the value of the variable by choosing a compatible number.
$1{,}419 \div 28 = c$

Solution $1{,}400 \div 30$ Round the numbers.

$1{,}500 \div 30 = 50$ Choose a number compatible with 30.

Try This Estimate. **c.** $738 \div 9 = t$ **d.** $m = 1{,}694 \div 37$

Class Exercises

Choose a number compatible with the divisor and estimate the quotient.

1. $1{,}100 \div 60$ **2.** $2{,}300 \div 40$ **3.** $1{,}300 \div 60$ **4.** $4{,}600 \div 90$

Discuss the Ideas

5. When you estimate the value of $2{,}598 \div 63$ by rounding and then choosing a compatible number for the larger number, do you get an overestimate or an underestimate? Explain your reasoning.

Exercises

Practice and Apply

Estimate the value of the variable by rounding.

1. $28 \cdot 82 = x$ **2.** $93 \cdot 57 = y$ **3.** $n = 78 \cdot 19$

4. $b = 54 \cdot 995$ **5.** $n = 513 \cdot 289$ **6.** $89 \div 29 = c$

7. $243 \div 57 = z$ **8.** $3{,}984 \div 832 = n$ **9.** $s = 724 \div 89$

Estimate the value of the variable by choosing a compatible number.

10. $342 \div 7 = s$ **11.** $294 \div 58 = y$ **12.** $n = 653 \div 8$

13. $d = 372 \div 55$ **14.** $2{,}438 \div 53 = c$ **15.** $2{,}652 \div 68 = d$

16. The school play was attended by 196 people at a cost of $6 per person. Estimate the total amount of money made by rounding to estimate the value of the variable in $t = 196 \cdot 6$.

Extend and Apply

Estimate, then compute the value of the variable in Exercises 17–19.

17. $p = 58 \cdot 94 \cdot 75$ **18.** $z = (1848 \div 56) \cdot 98$ **19.** $x = (684 \cdot 423) \div 12$

20. A store sold 96 regular tires at an average price of $56 a tire and 28 snow tires at an average price of $79 per tire. Estimate the total sales.

21. Estimate the number of flight hours logged by a pilot who made six 895-mile trips at an average speed of 618 mi/hour.

Use Mathematical Reasoning

22. Mrs. Ward rounded her monthly salary to the nearest hundred and arrived at an estimate of $40,800 for her yearly salary. Describe her actual monthly salary as accurately as possible.

Mixed Review

Solve and check. **23.** $169 = \frac{b}{13}$ **24.** $61 = x - 24$ **25.** $19a = 304$

Evaluate the formula $M = 6w + 12$ for: **26.** $w = 9$ **27.** $w = 3$

2-11 Data Collection and Analysis

Conducting a Survey

Objective To conduct a survey and interpret the data.

A **survey** is a technique for collecting data involving fact or opinion. Completed surveys are often used to present information which can help make decisions. Conducting a survey involves the following steps:

- **Choose** the topic or issue to be surveyed.
- **Plan** the questions to be asked.
- **Ask** the questions and collect the data.
- **Organize** and **interpret** the data.
- **Present** the findings.

Work with a group to conduct the following survey. Follow the procedures suggested.

Survey Topic

Colors of high-top sneakers that are most popular among students of your age group

Planning the Survey

- Decide what colors of high-top sneakers you will consider.
- Make a ***questionnaire*** you can give to students. List all of the colors of sneakers you will consider. Decide how students indicate their favorite color or colors on the questionnaire.
- Suppose you cannot give the questionnaire to all students at your grade level. Decide which students will be your ***sample***—that is, the ones to whom you will give the questionnaire.

1. If you went to the store to buy a new pa
sneakers, what color would be your 1st

☐ black ☐ blue

☐ white ☐ red

Collecting Data

- Give the questionnaire to the sample you selected.

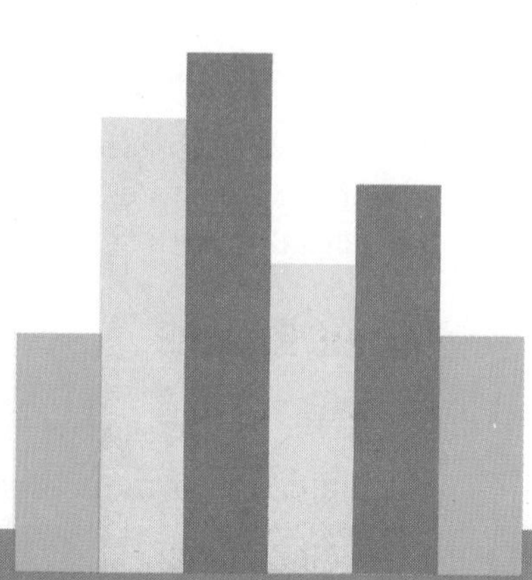

Organizing the Data

- Make and complete a ***frequency table,*** like the one below, to record the ***data*** from your survey.

Sneaker Color	1st choice	2nd choice	3rd
white	卌 II	卌	
black			

- Make and complete a ***bar graph,*** like the one below, to show the data pictorially.

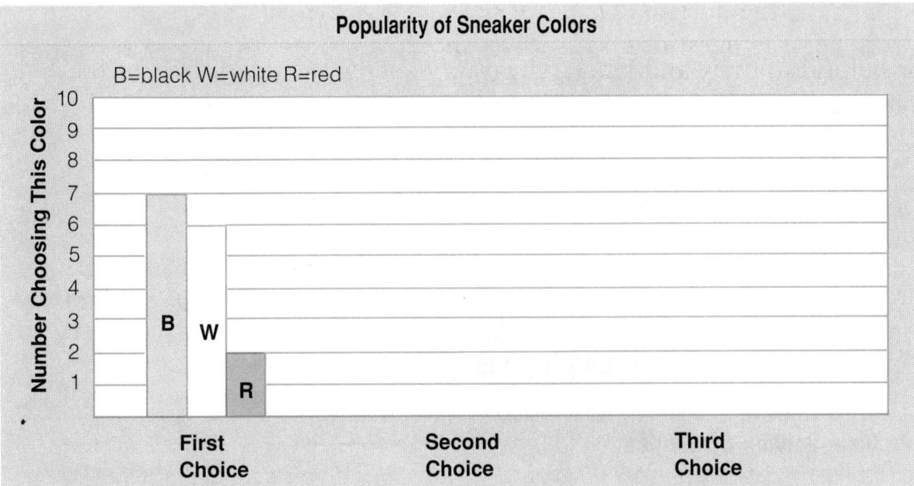

Interpreting the Data

- What color of high top sneakers was chosen most? least?
- Do you think there is any doubt about which 2 colors of sneaker are most popular? Give reasons to support your answer.

Presenting Your Findings

- Write a letter to a sneaker company that summarizes the findings from your survey. Use the frequency table and the graph in your letter. Include recommendations for the manufacturing of their sneakers with regard to color.

Project

Work in a group to choose a survey topic of your own and conduct a survey at your school. In general, follow the procedure above, but make your own decisions about how to best organize the data and to present the findings.

2-12 Problem Solving: Strategies

Draw a Diagram

Objective To solve nonroutine problems, using the strategy Draw a Diagram and other strategies learned so far.

The problem-solving strategy called **Draw a Diagram** can often help you better understand a problem situation and give you a start toward a solution.

Sample Problem The head of a tropical fish is $\frac{1}{3}$ as long as its midsection. Its tail is as long as its head and midsection combined. The total length of the fish is 48 cm. How long is each part of the fish?

It is helpful to draw and label a diagram to show the conditions of the problem.

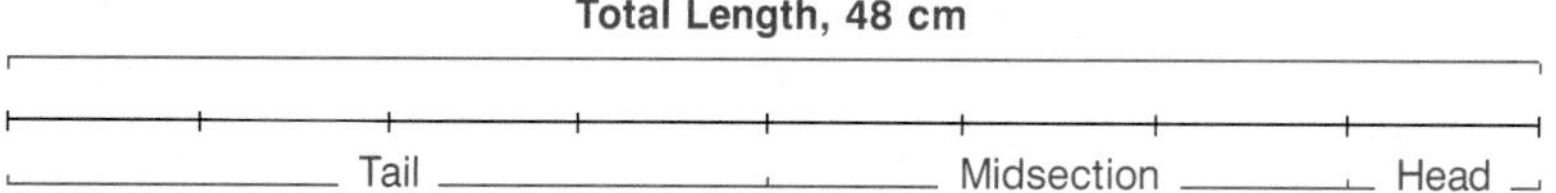

The diagram shows that 8 equal segments make up the 48 cm. Each segment must be 6 cm long, so the head is 6 cm long, the midsection is 18 cm long, and the tail is 24 cm long.

Problem-Solving Strategies

Choose the Operations	Make a Table	Make an Organized List
Guess, Check, Revise	Look for a Pattern	Use Logical Reasoning
Draw a Diagram	Write an Equation	Work Backward
	Simplify the Problem	

Problems

Solve using one or more of the strategies shown above.

1. The tail of a salamander is three times as long as its midsection. Its head is $\frac{1}{2}$ as long as its midsection. If the total length of the salamander is 27 cm, how long is its tail?

2. Joliet is 564 km from Canton. A bus started at Canton and drove 248 km towards Joliet. A jeep started at Joliet and drove 216 km towards Canton. How far apart were the two vehicles at the end of these trips?

3. A ball is dropped from the top of a wall 16 feet high. Each time it hits the ground it bounces half as high as its previous bounce. If the ball is caught just as it bounces 1 foot high, how far has it traveled?

4. Kiyoko scored her test by multiplying the number of problems correct by 3 and subtracting 1 for each of the 16 problems she missed. She answered twice as many problems correctly as the number she missed. How many problems were on the test? What was her score?

5. Sam's class took twice as long as Mark's class to build a homecoming float. Mark's class took 8 hours longer than Randy's class. The total number of hours spent by all classes was 60. How long did it take each class to build its float?

6. Mr. Ashby sold 37 small carved wooden whistles for $5 each, and his last 5 large whistles for $25 each. How many more small whistles will he have to sell to reach a sales total of $500?

7. An astronaut completed a 152-km trip around a crater on the moon in 4 hours of traveling time in a moon buggy. She plans to make a 114-km trip at the same speed around another crater and stop for 1 hour along the way to explore on foot. How long will this take?

8. A construction engineer wants to make a tunnel that is 10 meters long. Each hour the drilling tool goes in 5m, but as the engineer rests, the tunnel caves in and the drilling tool slides back 4 m. At this rate, how many hours will it take the engineer to finish the tunnel?

Group Decision Making

9. Work in a group. Discuss and decide.

Situation Your class is to make punch for a school party. The following punch recipe makes about 3 quarts: 1 46-oz can of fruit punch, 1 package of cherry juice drink, 1 qt of ginger ale, 2 cups of water. How much will it cost to serve about 120 people?

> **Guidelines for Planning**
>
> ■ **Formulate Problems** you will need to solve.
> ■ Discuss **Assumptions** you will make and **Data** you will need.

a. What decision or decisions do you need to make in this situation?

b. Formulate problems you need to solve to make the decision(s).

c. List any assumptions you need to make to arrive at a decision.

d. What data, if any, do you need to collect to make a decision?

e. Write a paragraph summarizing what your group did, what decisions you made, and why.

Extend Key Ideas

Discovering Number Patterns

An important part of mathematical reasoning is the ability to make conjectures, or guesses, about patterns that might occur in numerical situations. Arrays of dots can help you find the next triangle or square number, as shown below.

Triangle Numbers

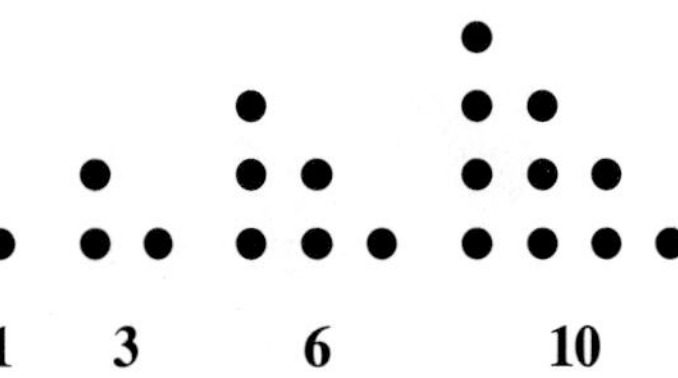

Square Numbers

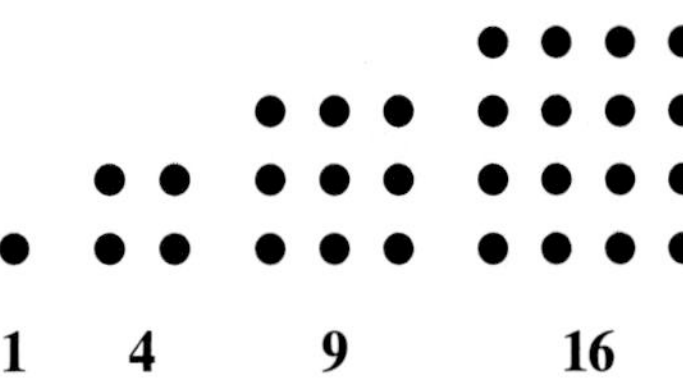

A useful technique for discovering new patterns and relationships is to ask **What if...** questions. For example, what if we draw lines to separate dots in our arrays? What conjecture can you make about the relationship between triangle and square numbers?

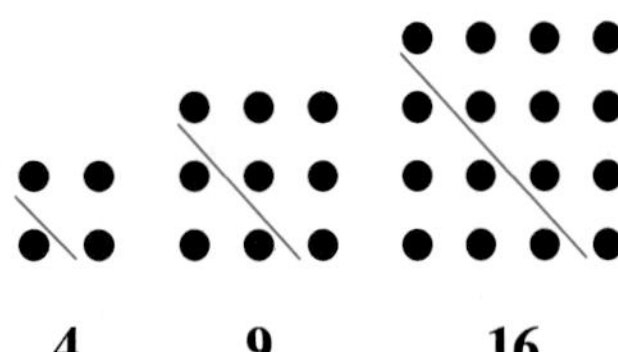

Work in groups to make and test some conjectures about these patterns.

1. Make conjectures about the square and triangle numbers.

2. Make a conjecture about the sum of the first n odd numbers.

$$1 + 3 = 2 \times 2$$
$$1 + 3 + 5 = 3 \times 3$$
$$1 + 3 + 5 + 7 = 4 \times 4$$

3. Make a conjecture about "pyramid sums".

$$1 + 2 + 1 = 2 \times 2$$
$$1 + 2 + 3 + 2 + 1 = 3 \times 3$$
$$1 + 2 + 3 + 4 + 3 + 2 + 1 = 4 \times 4$$

4. Make a conjecture about the sum of the first n counting numbers.

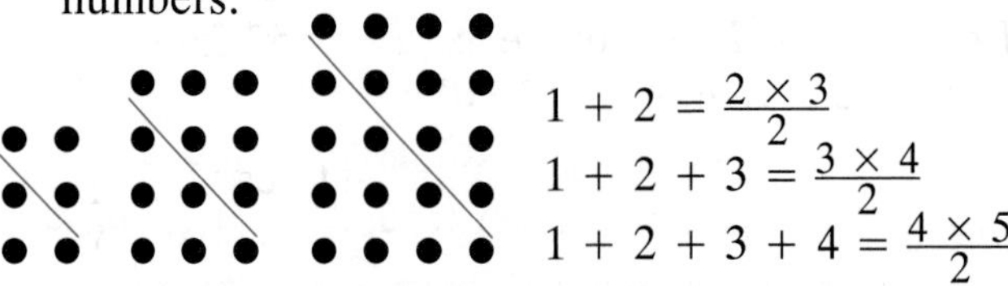

$$1 + 2 = \frac{2 \times 3}{2}$$
$$1 + 2 + 3 = \frac{3 \times 4}{2}$$
$$1 + 2 + 3 + 4 = \frac{4 \times 5}{2}$$

Chapter 2 Review/Test

Understanding

True or false?

2-1 **1.** The fraction bar serves as a division symbol and as a grouping symbol.

2-2 **2.** You can use a variable to write a rule that tells how to get a number in a given pattern of numbers.

2-4 **3.** $17 \times 0 = 0$ is an example of the Identity Property.

2-7 **4.** To get the variable x alone in $\frac{x}{7} = 8$, divide by 8.

2-10 **5.** When rounding to estimate a quotient does not result in an easy division, you can choose a compatible number that makes the division easier.

Skills

2-1 Evaluate each numerical or algebraic expression.
2-9

6. $16 \div (2 + 6)$ **7.** $3 \cdot 8 + 7 \cdot 4$ **8.** $9 + [(3 + 7) \div 2]$

9. $D = 9t$ for $t = 5$ **10.** $\frac{6m}{4}$, for $m = 8$ **11.** $a(a - 6)$ for $a = 8$

2-3 Write as an algebraic expression.

12. twice f **13.** 6 divided by r **14.** 13 less than twice a number

2-5 Simplify using the Associative or Distributive Property.

15. $(n + 7) + 5$ **16.** $15(2v)$ **17.** $r(2 + 5)$ **18.** $2z + 3z$

2-6 Solve and check.
2-7

19. $8n = 32$ **20.** $\frac{y}{7} = 8$ **21.** $6z = 78$ **22.** $\frac{b}{6} = 19$

2-10 Use rounding to estimate the value of the variable. Choose compatible numbers as needed.

23. $394 \cdot 28 = m$ **24.** $5776 \div 19 = c$ **25.** $8122 \div 23 = h$

Applications

2-9 Solve.
2-12

26. Formula: $A = lw$, where l is the length of a rectangle, w is the width, and A is the area. The width of a new teen center dance floor is 43 feet. The area of the floor is 2,322 square ft. Can a 52 foot banner be put on the wall along the length of the floor?

27. Four cars are parked in a parking garage. The white car is 7 spaces to the right of the blue car and 3 spaces to the right of the silver car. The silver car is 11 spaces to the left of the red car. How many spaces away from the blue car is the red car?

3 Integers

When Lance got to Mt. Bachelor this morning, the temperature was 12°F. After snowboarding for 2 hours, the temperature was −3°F. What was the change in temperature?

3-1 Integers

Objective To give integers for points on the number line, to find the absolute value of an integer, and to compare integers.

Application

In football, each play begins with the ball at the line of scrimmage. After the first play, the ball was 7 yards behind the line. After the second play, the ball was 8 yards ahead of the line. The coach wanted to use a diagram to show this.

Understand the Ideas

On the number line, the whole numbers to the right of 0 are called the **positive integers.** If you choose any positive integer, say **4,** there is a number opposite it on the left side of 0 that is the same distance from 0 as 4. This number is written $^{-}4$ and read as "negative four."

Numbers such as 4 and $^{-}4$ are called **opposites.** The opposite of 0 is 0. The set of all opposites of the positive integers are called the **negative integers.** The complete set of **integers** consists of the positive integers, the negative integers, and 0.

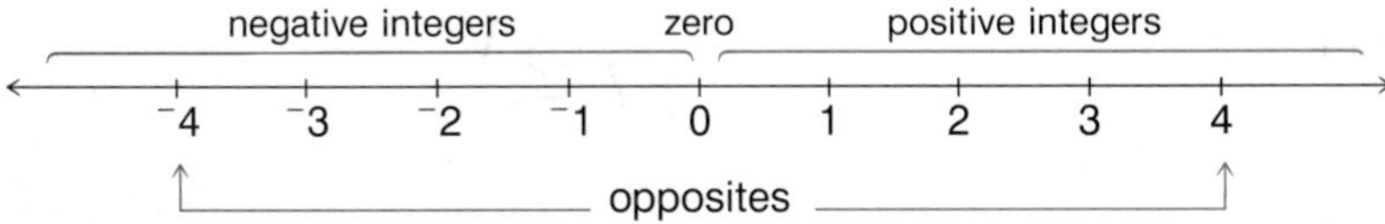

Sometimes it is useful to represent "the opposite of an integer." We use a minus sign that is not raised to indicate "the opposite of."

The *opposite of 4* is written as -4.
The *opposite of* $^{-}4$ is written $-(^{-}4)$.

Example 1

Give an integer for point A on this number line to show the location of the ball after the first play in the **application** above.

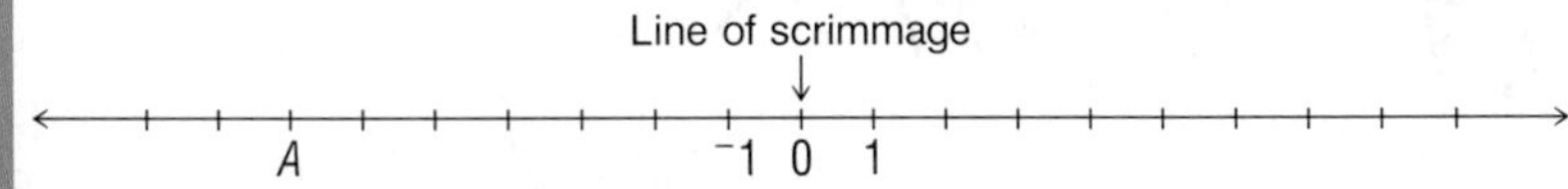

Solution $^{-}7$ Point A is 7 units to the left of 0 on the number line.

Try This

a. Draw a number line. Show the line of scrimmage and the location of the ball after the second play described in the application. Give an integer for this location.

The **absolute value** of an integer is the number of units the integer is from 0 on the number line.

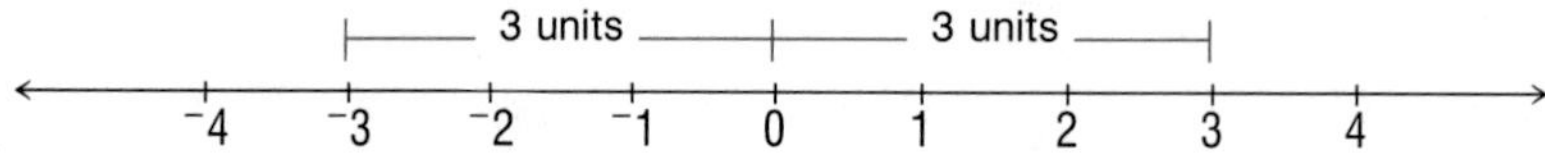

The absolute value of 3 is written $|3|$.

Since 3 is 3 units from 0, $|3| = 3$.
Since $^-3$ is 3 units from 0, $|^-3| = 3$.

Whether a number is positive or negative, its absolute value is always a positive number.

Example 2

Find the absolute value. $|^-7|$

Solution $|^-7| = 7$ $^-7$ is 7 units from 0 on the number line.

Try This Find the absolute value.

b. $|9|$ **c.** $|^-85|$

As with whole numbers, the integer farther to the right on the number line is the greater number. The symbols > (greater than) and < (less than) express inequalities.

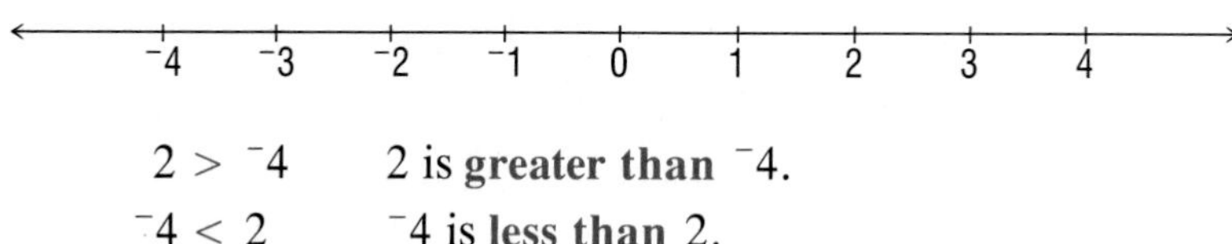

$2 > {}^-4$ 2 is **greater than** $^-4$.
$^-4 < 2$ $^-4$ is **less than** 2.

To order a set of integers, you need to compare each integer to the others in turn.

Example 3

Use the symbols < or > to order from least to greatest. $^-8, 5, ^-2$

Solution $^-8 < {}^-2 < 5$ $^-8$ is farthest to the left on the number line. $^-2$ is next, and 5 is farthest to the right, so $^-8 < {}^-2$ and $^-2 < 5$.

Try This Use the symbols < or > to order from least to greatest.

d. $6, ^-8, ^-16$ **e.** $|^-6|, 9, 0, ^-3$

Class Exercises

Give the integer suggested by the situation. Give the opposite of that integer.

1. a gain of \$9 **2.** 900 ft below sea level **3.** 4° below zero

4. decrease by 7 kg **5.** 6 s before blastoff **6.** lose 4 points

Discuss the Ideas

7. Describe the opposite of each situation above. What are some other everyday situations that suggest an integer and its opposite?

Exercises

Practice and Apply

Give the integer for each point on the number line.

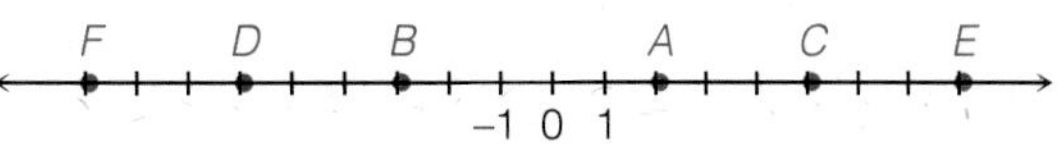

1. *A* **2.** *B* **3.** *C* **4.** *D* **5.** *E* **6.** *F*

Give the absolute value.

7. $|5|$ **8.** $|{}^-9|$ **9.** $|123|$ **10.** $|{}^-15|$ **11.** $|{}^-36|$

Use the symbols < or > to order from least to greatest.

12. $2, {}^-21$ **13.** ${}^-7, 0, 7$ **14.** ${}^-1, {}^-6, 4$

15. ${}^-23, 8, {}^-24$ **16.** ${}^-2, |{}^-3|, {}^-1, |4|$ **17.** ${}^-13, 12, |{}^-18|, 6, {}^-4$

18. In theory, the volume of a gas would equal zero when it reached a temperature of ${}^-273$°C. To find the number of degrees this is below 0°, find the absolute value of $|{}^-273|$.

19. The coldest temperatures recorded in four different cities were 5°C, ${}^-4$°C, ${}^-1$°C, and ${}^-6$°C. Use the symbols < or > to order the temperatures from least to greatest.

Extend and Apply

For Exercises 20–23, give the integer for the point on the number line.

20. 27 units to the right of 0 **21.** 124 units to the left of 0

22. 20 units to the right of ${}^-2$ **23.** 16 units to the left of 4

24. What integer is the opposite of $|{}^-8|$?

25. Give the integer represented by $-({}^-8)$.

26. Find 2 values for x that make the equation $|x| = 5$ true.

27. A weather forecaster recorded morning (*M*), afternoon (*A*), evening (*E*), and night (*N*) temperatures on a number line. Use integers to give each temperature.

N E M A
-5 0 5

Complete the following.

28. The opposite of a positive integer is a ______ integer.

29. The opposite of a negative integer is a ______ integer.

30. The integer ___ is neither positive nor negative.

31. The absolute value of a nonzero integer is always a ______ integer.

32. The opposite of the opposite of a negative integer is a ______ integer.

33. A positive number is ______ than any negative number.

Use Mathematical Reasoning

Find the next 3 numbers in each pattern by thinking about the number line.

34. 16, 9, 2, ___, ___, ___

35. $^{-}13$, 2, 17, ___, ___, ___

36. $^{-}8$, $^{-}4$, 0, ___, ___, ___

37. 13, 7, 1, ___, ___, ___

38. If you were to fold a piece of notebook paper in half twice and make a straight cut across the corner with only folded edges, what would the cut-off piece look like when unfolded? Try it; then draw a picture to show the results.

Mixed Review

Solve and check. **39.** $\frac{x}{221} = 16$ **40.** $56 = m - 133$ **41.** $24w = 3144$

Estimate the value of the variable. **42.** $t = \frac{(83 \cdot 28)}{17}$

Simplify. **43.** $3n - n$ **44.** $11(9x)$ **45.** $26a + 7a$ **46.** $\frac{t}{t}$

Evaluate. **47.** $5 \cdot 4 - \frac{36}{9}$ **48.** $\frac{12 + 6}{10 - 7}$ **49.** $5 \cdot 1 \cdot 1$

Basic Property Update

The basic properties for whole number operations are also true for integer operations.

Identity Properties

For every integer a, $a \cdot 1 = 1 \cdot a = a$ $a + 0 = 0 + a = a$

Commutative Properties

For all integers a and b, $a + b = b + a$ $a \cdot b = b \cdot a$

Associative Properties

For all integers a and b,
$(a + b) + c = a + (b + c)$ $(a \cdot b) \cdot c = a \cdot (b \cdot c)$

Distributive Property

For all integers a, b, and c, $a(b + c) = ab + ac$

These properties of integers follow from the basic properties.

$a - 0 = a$ $a - a = 0$ $a \cdot 0 = 0$

$0 \div a = 0$ $a \div 1 = a$ $a \div a = 1$

3-2 Adding Integers

Objective To add integers.

Explore

Yellow counters represent positive integers, and red counters represent negative integers. When red and yellow counters are paired, they cancel each other and both are removed!

Complete several rows of a table like the one below by putting the same kind of counters in each of two piles, combining the piles, and removing pairs of counters when possible. Talk about some rules you might invent for adding integers.

First Pile Second Pile

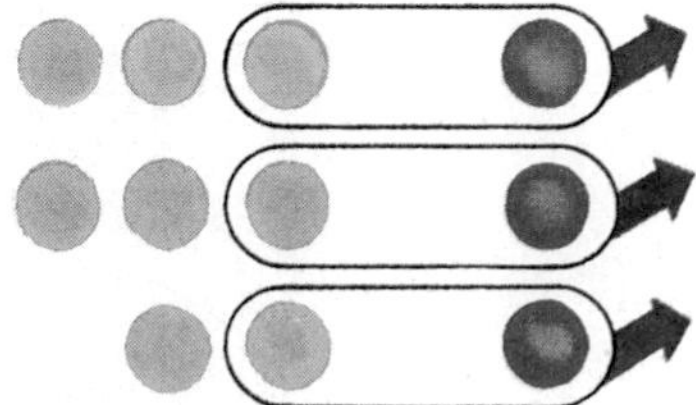

First Pile	Second Pile	Combined Pile	Equation
8	$^-3$	5	$8 + {}^-3 = 5$

Understand the Ideas

The following example shows how to use counters to find an integer sum. Yellow counters represent positive integers and red counters represent negative integers.

Example 1

Find the sum. $^-9 + 5$

Solution

$^-9 + 5 = {}^-4$

Lay out 9 red counters ($^-9$).

Lay out 5 yellow counters (5).

Combine the counters. Remove red-yellow pairs. There are four red counters left. The sum is $^-4$.

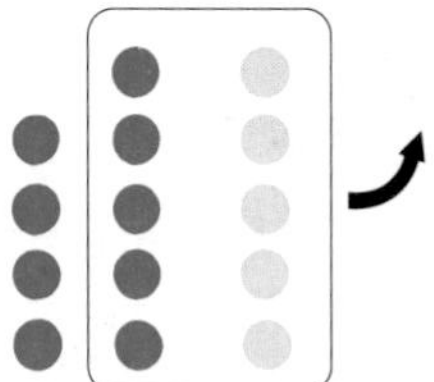

Try This Find these sums using counters.

a. $^-6 + {}^-5$ **b.** $^-4 + 7$ **c.** $6 + ({}^-8)$ **d.** $6 + 9$

The idea that different colored counters cancel each other out suggests the following property for adding integers.

Inverse Property of Addition (Opposites Property)

The sum of any integer and its opposite is zero.

For every integer a, $a + (-a) = 0$ and $-a + a = 0$

You can also use arrows on the number line to find integer sums.
Adding a *positive integer* is shown by an arrow to the *right*.
Adding a *negative integer* is shown by an arrow to the *left*.

Example 2

Use the number line to find $3 + (^-7)$.

Solution

$3 + (^-7) = {}^-4$ Start at the first number, 3. To add negative 7, move to the left 7 units. The ending point, $^-4$, is the sum.

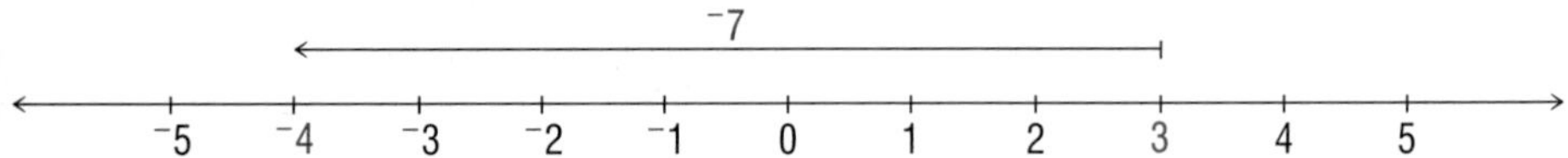

Try This Draw and use a number line to find these sums.

e. $^-5 + (^-8)$ **f.** $^-4 + 6$ **g.** $7 + (^-3)$

The following rule explains how to find the sum of any two integers.

Rule **Adding Integers**

To add integers with like signs,
- Add their absolute values.
- Give the sum the sign of the integer addends.

To add integers with unlike signs,
- Find the difference of their absolute values.
- Give the difference the sign of the integer addend with the greater absolute value. If the difference is zero, omit the sign.

Example 3

Find the sum. **a.** $^-2 + {}^-3$ **b.** $^-6 + 4$

Solutions

a. $^-2 + {}^-3 = {}^-5$ $|^-2| + |^-3| = 5$ Since both original addends are negative, the sum is negative. $^-5$.

b. $^-6 + 4 = {}^-2$ $|^-6| - |4| = 2$. Since $|^-6|$ is larger than $|4|$, the sum is negative, $^-2$.

Try This Find the sum. **h.** $^-14 + {}^-16$ **i.** $35 + 29$

j. $^-34 + {}^-26$ **k.** $^-4 + 6$ **l.** $25 + {}^-9$

Example 4

Evaluate. $n + 8$ for $n = |^{-}24|$

Solution $n + 8$

$|^{-}24| + 8$ Replace n with $|^{-}24|$.

$= 24 + 8$ $|^{-}24| = 24$

$= 32$

Try This Evaluate.

m. $^{-}9 + x$ for $x = |^{-}11|$

n. $a + b$ for $a = |^{-}24|$ and $b = 36$

Class Exercises

Tell whether the sum will be positive, negative, or zero.

1. $9 + 5$ **2.** $^{-}6 + ^{-}7$ **3.** $^{-}8 + ^{-}5$ **4.** $5 + ^{-}14$

5. $^{-}9 + ^{-}7$ **6.** $^{-}7 + 3$ **7.** $^{-}6 + 6$ **8.** $^{-}7 + 12$

Discuss the Ideas

9. Which model, counters or the number line, do you find most helpful in understanding how to find the sum of two integers? Why?

Exercises

Practice and Apply

Find each sum. Use counters for 1–4. Use a number line for 5–8.

1. $5 + (^{-}7)$ **2.** $9 + (^{-}4)$ **3.** $^{-}3 + (^{-}7)$ **4.** $^{-}7 + 2$

5. $10 + (^{-}8)$ **6.** $^{-}8 + 4$ **7.** $9 + (^{-}3)$ **8.** $^{-}3 + (^{-}6)$

9. $^{-}3 + 11$ **10.** $^{-}8 + 14$ **11.** $^{-}5 + 13$ **12.** $^{-}9 + 25$

13. $3 + (^{-}12)$ **14.** $17 + (^{-}8)$ **15.** $^{-}24 + 0$ **16.** $^{-}26 + (^{-}23)$

17. The stock price of Ball Foods Corporation lost \$6 on Monday and gained \$4 on Tuesday. Use a number line and find $^{-}6 + (4)$ to find the total gain or loss.

18. On Wednesday, Phil earned 10 points extra credit. On Friday, his teacher deducted 3 points for not having his homework completed. Find $10 + (^{-}3)$ to determine the total number of points Phil earned for the week.

Evaluate each expression.

19. $n + (^{-}5)$ for $n = ^{-}7$ **20.** $^{-}13 + x$ for $x = 35$

21. $r + (^{-}45)$ for $r = 71$ **22.** $x + (^{-}24)$ for $x = 16$

Extend and Apply

Find each sum.

23. $25 + |^-12 + {}^-15|$

24. $(43 + {}^-29) + ({}^-43 + 29)$

25. On the first down, Jerry's football team gained 6 yards. On the second down it lost 14 yards. On the third down it gained 16 yards. If it lost 13 yards on the fourth down, what was its total gain or loss?

26. The temperature was recorded at 15° C. It then rose 8°, fell 6°, rose 12°, and fell 23°. What was the temperature after these changes?

27. In the first game Janet bowled 10 points above her average and in the second game she bowled 16 points below her average. Find the total number of pins she was from her average after the second game.

Use Mathematical Reasoning

28. Add mentally. $^-57 + 46 + 178 + (^-45) + 199 + 58 + (^-178)$

29. This proof uses basic properties to show that $^-5 + 8 = 3$.

$^-5 + 8$	
$= {}^-5 + (5 + 3)$	Substitute 5 + 3 for 8.
$= ({}^-5 + 5) + 3$	Associative Property
$= 0 + 3$	Additive Inverse Property
$= 3$	Zero Property

Write a proof for $9 + (^-4) = 5$.

Mixed Review

Solve mentally and check. **30.** $4m = 24$ **31.** $\frac{c}{5} = 7$ **32.** $n - 2 = 18$

Order from least to greatest. Use inequality symbols. **33.** $^-6, 4, 0, 1, {}^-1$

Connections Numbers to Algebra

In algebra, $-n$, which means "the opposite of n," is negative when n is replaced with a positive integer, but it is positive when n is replaced with a negative integer.

$-n$	Replace n with 5.	$-n$	Replace n with $^-5$.
-5		$-{}^-5$	
$^-5$	The result is a negative integer.	5	The result is a positive integer.

Complete each statement.

1. If $n = 8$, then $-n =$ ___ .

2. If $n = {}^-9$, then $-n =$ ___ .

3. If $n = {}^-24$, then $-n =$ ___ .

4. If $n = 45$, then $-n =$ ___ .

3-3 Subtracting Integers

Objective To subtract integers.

Understand the Ideas

You can use yellow (+) and red (−) counters to subtract integers. Remember that a yellow and a red counter can be paired to cancel each other out. Because of this you can also include a yellow-red pair of counters whenever you wish and not change the result. The following diagram shows how this idea can help you take 2 red counters away from 5 yellow counters.

Start with 5 yellow counters

Add 2 yellow-red pairs.

Now take away 2 red counters.

Notice that taking away red counters has the effect of increasing the number of yellow counters. Also, taking away yellow counters has the effect of increasing the number of red counters. This idea can help you understand how to subtract integers.

Example 1

Subtract. $7 - (^{-}3)$

Solution

$7 - (^{-}3) = 10$ Lay out 7 yellow counters.
Lay out 3 yellow-red pairs.

Take away 3 red counters.

Try This Subtract. **a.** $8 - (^{-}3)$ **b.** $^{-}3 - (^{-}2)$ **c.** $2 - (^{-}5)$

Example 2

Subtract. $^{-}3 - 5$

Solution

$^{-}3 - 5 = {}^{-}8$ Lay out 3 red counters.
Lay out 5 yellow-red pairs.

Take away 5 yellow counters.

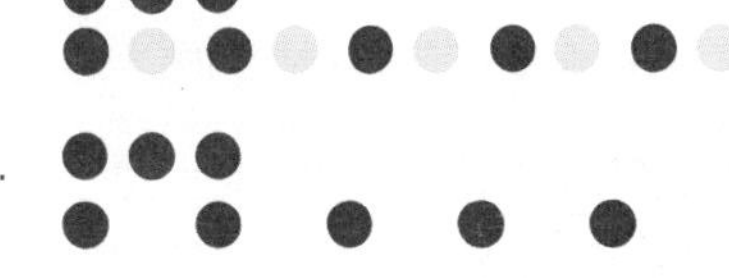

Try This Subtract. **d.** $^{-}6 - 2$ **e.** $^{-}4 - 9$ **f.** $2 - 8$

You can also use the number line to understand how to subtract integers. These number lines show that subtracting an integer and adding the opposite of the integer produce the same result.

5 + (⁻2) or 5 − 2

−1 0 1 2 3 4 5 6 7

Adding ⁻2 is the same as subtracting 2.

5 + 2 or 5 − (⁻2)

−1 0 1 2 3 4 5 6 7

Adding 2 is the same as subtracting ⁻2.

This suggests the following rule.

Rule Subtracting Integers

To subtract an integer, add its opposite.

For all integers a and b, $a - b = a + (-b)$

You learned earlier in this chapter that −5 represents "the opposite of five" and that ⁻5 (with raised sign) represents the integer "negative five." Since −5 and ⁻5 name the same number, either can be used to represent that integer. Beginning with the following examples, a minus sign that is not raised will always be used to represent a negative integer.

Example 3

Subtract. $-5 - 8$

Solution $-5 - 8$

$= -5 + (-8)$ Subtracting 8 is the same as adding −8.

$= -13$

Try This Subtract.

g. $2 - 7$ **h.** $-4 - 6$ **i.** $-8 - 3$ **j.** $15 - 9$

Example 4

Subtract. $7 - (-4)$

Solution $7 - (-4)$

$= 7 + 4$ Subtracting −4 is the same as adding 4.

$= 11$

Try This Subtract.

k. $9 - (-3)$ **l.** $4 - (-10)$ **m.** $-9 - (-2)$

Example 5

Evaluate. $-8 - n$ for $n = -5$

Solution $-8 - (-5)$ Replace n with -5.

$= -8 + 5 = -3$

Try This Evaluate.

n. $x - (-7)$ for $x = -13$ **o.** $-9 - b$ for $b = -15$

A calculator can also be used to add and subtract integers. A negative number can be entered into the calculator by first entering a whole number such as 8 and then pushing the *change sign* key [+/−] to change the displayed number to its opposite.

Example 6

Use a calculator to subtract. $-67 - (-289)$

Solution 67 [+/−] [−] 289 [+/−] [=] 222

Try This Use a calculator. **p.** $23 - (-7)$ **q.** $86 + (-123)$

Class Exercises

Rewrite each subtraction expression as an addition expression.

1. $8 - 4$ **2.** $3 - 9$ **3.** $-2 - 7$ **4.** $-11 - 6$

Discuss the Ideas

5. How could you use a checking account model to explain the statement "subtracting a negative is the same as adding a positive."?

Exercises

Practice and Apply

Subtract using counters.

1. $8 - (-3)$ **2.** $5 - (-7)$ **3.** $-2 - (-6)$ **4.** $-9 - (-4)$

5. $3 - 7$ **6.** $-4 - 2$ **7.** $-6 - 9$ **8.** $-7 - 7$

Subtract.

9. $9 - 3$ **10.** $8 - 12$ **11.** $4 - 10$ **12.** $9 - 13$

13. $1 - 7$ **14.** $-3 - 11$ **15.** $-6 - 8$ **16.** $-12 - 5$

17. $-8 - 14$ **18.** $-20 - 6$ **19.** $4 - (-9)$ **20.** $6 - (-15)$

21. $17 - (-8)$ **22.** $24 - (-10)$ **23.** $7 - (-7)$ **24.** $-3 - (-12)$

Evaluate.

25. $n - 9$ for $n = -6$ **26.** $-7 - n$ for $n = 14$ **27.** $12 + n$ for $n = -18$

28. $n + (-6)$ for $n = 11$ **29.** $n - (-11)$ for $n = 5$ **30.** $n - (-9)$ for $n = 9$

Add or subtract using the [+○−] key on your calculator.

31. $258 + (-689)$ **32.** $-9674 + 6739$ **33.** $-783 - (-975)$

34. One day the nation's high temperature was 75°F. The low temperature was −8°F. To find the difference between these temperatures, subtract $75 - (-8)$.

35. Danny had \$348 in his checking account. He wrote a check for \$402. Use a calculator and find 348−402, to determine his new balance.

Extend and Apply

Simplify.

36. $5 - (-6) - |-20|$ **37.** $-8 - (-2) - |-7|$

38. $-13 - (-7) + (-5)$ **39.** $(-5 - 3) + (-9) - (-15)$

40. $-6 + (-9 - 12)$ **41.** $7 - |-8 + 13| + (-5)$

42. Evaluate the formula $P = I - E$ to find the Profit (P) when Income (I) = \$85,654 and Expenses (E) = \$92,472.

43. Replace a and b with integers to show that $a - b = b - a$ is not true for all integers.

44. Replace a, b, and c with integers to show that $(a - b) - c = a - (b - c)$ is not true for all integers.

45. Death Valley is 282 ft below sea level. Mt. Whitney is 14,494 ft above sea level. How much higher is the elevation of Mt. Whitney than the elevation of Death Valley?

46. **Write to Learn** Write a paragraph explaining how to subtract integers.

Use Mathematical Reasoning

47. In a magic square, the sum of the numbers in each row, column, and diagonal is the same. Find the missing numbers in this magic square. The magic sum is −2.

4	−6		
−7		2	
	−3	−8	
		5	−5

48. An elevator went up 6 floors, down 9 floors, down 12 more floors, up 8 floors, and down 4 floors. It stopped on the 43rd floor. On what floor did it start?

Mixed Review

Solve and check. **49.** $8y = 216$ **50.** $t + 163 = 204$

Find the sum. **51.** $-5 + 3$ **52.** $5 + (-3)$ **53.** $-5 + (-3)$

3-4 Solving Integer Equations: Using Models

Objective To use models to solve equations involving integers.

Explore

Use yellow counters (positive integers) and red counters (negative integers) on an equation chart to show each of the situations below.

Discuss how you can add counters to each side of the equation chart to get the n card by itself on one side. Remember that red and yellow counters cancel each other and can be removed. Add counters, remove canceled counters and decide how many counters are under each n card.

A 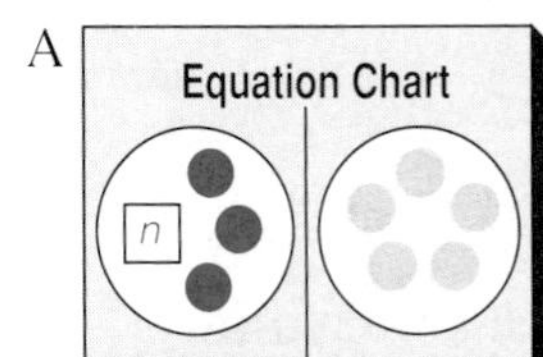

B 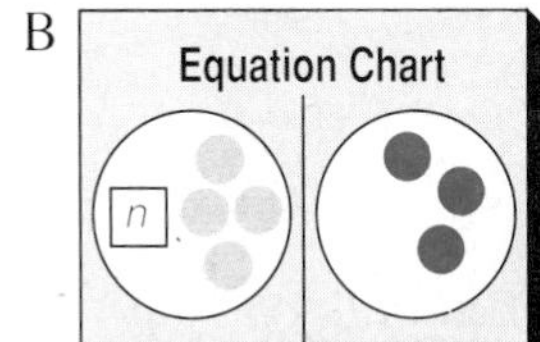

C 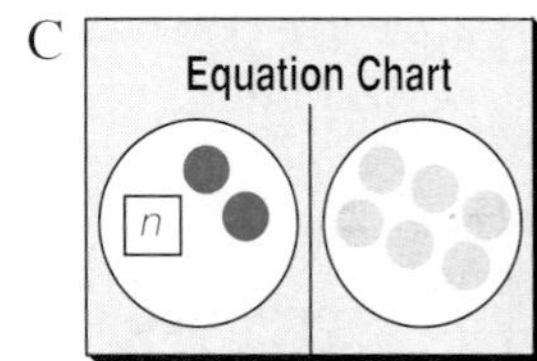

Understand the Ideas

This example shows how to use an equation chart and counters to solve an equation that contains integers.

Example

Use an equation chart and counters to show this equation, then find n. $n + (-2) = 6$

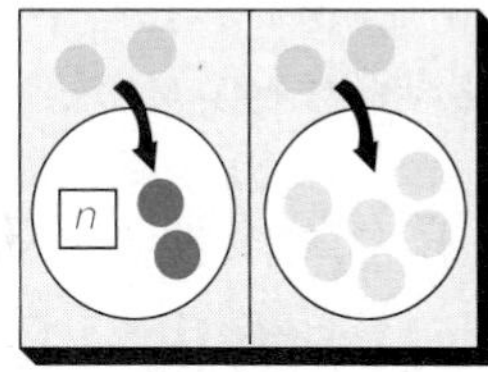

Solution $n = 8$ Put 2 yellow counters on each side of the chart. This keeps the chart balanced. Remove yellow-red pairs.

Try This Use an equation chart and counters to show these equations, then find n. **a.** $n + (3) = -5$ **b.** $n + (-4) = -7$

348

Class Exercises

Discuss the Ideas

These equations describe counters on an equation chart. Describe the left and right sides of the chart. To find n, how many and what kind of counters would you add to both sides of the chart?

1. $n + (-2) = 7$ **2.** $n + 3 = -5$ **3.** $n + (-1) = -9$

Exercises

Practice and Apply

Use an equation chart and counters to show these situations. Add counters to each side and remove canceled pairs to find n.

1. 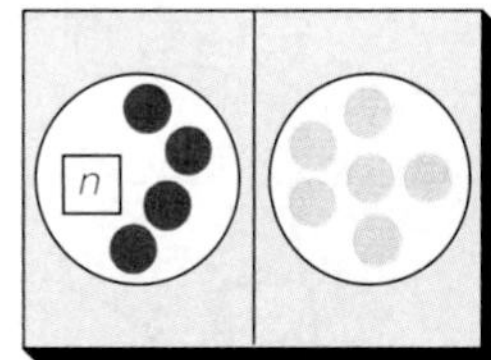

2. 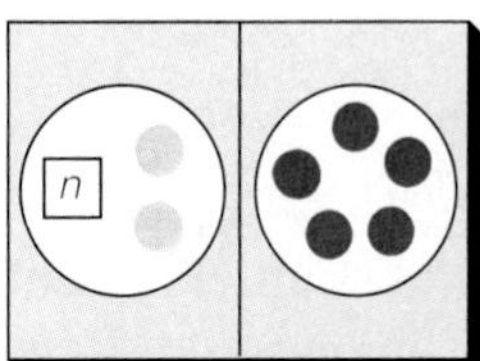

Use an equation chart and counters to show these equations. Add counters and remove canceled pairs to find the number for n in each equation.

3. $n + (-6) = -2$ **4.** $n + 4 = -9$ **5.** $n + (-6) = (-3)$

6. $n + (-2) = 7$ **7.** $-3 = n + 6$ **8.** $8 = (-4) + n$

9. Phil's puppy, tied to a helium balloon that reduced his weight by 3 pounds, weighed 12 pounds. Solve the equation $w + (-3) = 12$ to find the puppy's weight without the balloon.

Extend and Apply

Think about or use a chart and counters to find the number for n.

10. $n + (-8) = 12$ **11.** $n + 6 = -13$ **12.** $n + 14 = -6$

13. $n + (-6) = 6$ **14.** $n + 7 = -9$ **15.** $12 = n + (-4)$

16. Jodi scored -8 in the 5th round of a game. When this was added to her score on the first 4 rounds, the result was 20. Choose the correct equation and solve it to find her score on the first 4 rounds.

a. $s - (-8) = 20$ **b.** $s + (-8) = 20$ **c.** $5(-8) + s = 4(20)$

Use Mathematical Reasoning

17. What equation does this chart represent? If counters and an n-card are available, how can you change only the left side of the chart to make it show an addition equation? Describe how you can use the chart to find the number for n.

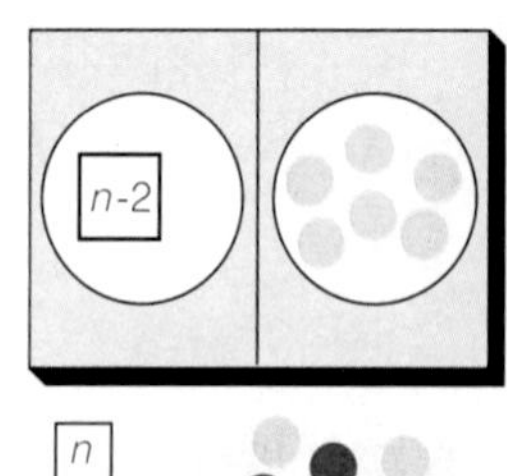

Mixed Review

18. Use the symbols < or > to order -8, $|6|$, 5, and 0 from least to greatest.

Simplify. **19.** $4n - 11n$ **20.** $5(7a)$ **21.** Evaluate $n + 4$ for $n = -5$

3-5 Solving Integer Equations: Using Addition and Subtraction

Objective To use addition and subtraction to solve equations involving integers.

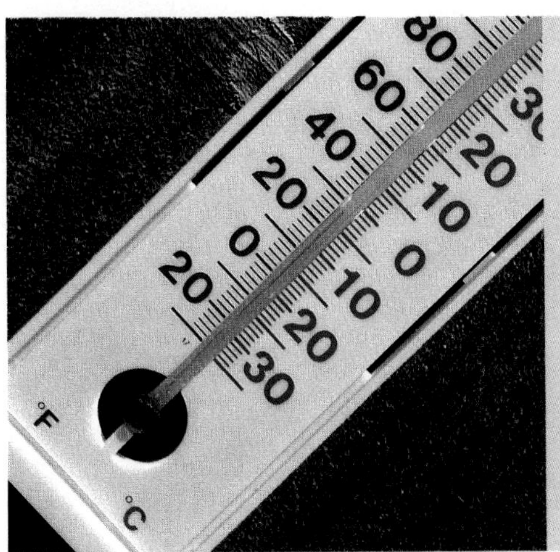

Application

If the temperature increased 34°F to reach a high of 28°F, you could solve the equation $t + 34 = 28$ to find the original temperature.

Understand the Ideas

To solve integer equations such as $t + 34 = 28$ or $x - 18 = -35$, you need to get the variable by itself on one side of the equation. The following steps show you how to use the ideas of inverse operations or the additive inverse property and the properties of equality to do this.

Rule **Solving Equations Using Addition and Subtraction**

- Decide which operation (addition or subtraction) has been applied to the variable.
- Using the inverse operation or the additive inverse property, add or subtract the same number on both sides of the equation.

Examples 1 and 2 show how to use inverse operations and the same steps you used with whole number equations to solve integer equations.

Example 1

Find the original temperature in the **application** by solving $t + 34 = 28$. Check your solution.

Solution

$t + 34 = 28$	You need to get the variable by itself on one side.
$t + 34 - 34 = 28 - 34$	To undo adding 34, subtract 34 from both sides of the equation so they remain equal. (Subtraction Property of Equality)
$t = -6$	

Check $-6 + 34 \stackrel{?}{=} 28$ Replace t with -6 in $t + 34 = 28$.

$28 = 28 \checkmark$ The solution is -6.

The original temperature was $-6°$F.

Try This Solve and check. **a.** $x + 19 = -47$ **b.** $-42 = y + 76$

c. The temperature decreased by 19°F to reach a level of $-6°$F. Find the original temperature by solving $t - 19 = -6$.

Example 2

Solve and check. $x - 18 = -35$

Solution
$$x - 18 = -35$$
$$x - 18 + 18 = -35 + 18$$
$$x = -17$$

To undo subtracting 18, add 18 to both sides so they remain equal. (Addition Property of Equality.)

Check $-17 - 18 \stackrel{?}{=} -35$ Replace x with -17 in $x - 18 = -35$.

$-35 = -35 \checkmark$ The solution is -17.

Try This Solve and check. **d.** $b - (-15) = 43$ **e.** $n - 29 = -45$

Since subtracting an integer is the same as adding the opposite integer, an equation that can be solved by subtracting can also be solved by using the Additive Inverse Property.

Example 3

Solve and check. $n + (-25) = 46$

Solution
$$n + (-25) = 46$$
$$n + (-25) + 25 = 46 + 25$$
$$n = 71$$

To undo adding -25, use the Additive Inverse Property and add the opposite of -25, or 25. $-25 + 25 = 0$

Check $71 + (-25) \stackrel{?}{=} 46$ Replace n with 71 in $n + (-25) = 46$.

$46 = 46 \checkmark$ The solution is 71.

Try This Solve and check. **f.** $a + (-17) = -75$ **g.** $43 = p + (-26)$

Class Exercises

To solve, what integer would you add to or subtract from each side?

1. $x + 19 = -48$ **2.** $n - 28 = -56$ **3.** $-379 = x + (-85)$

Discuss the Ideas

4. A student said, "You can always solve an integer equation by adding the same number to each side." Do you agree? Explain with examples.

Exercises

Practice and Apply

Solve and check.

1. $n + 27 = -84$
2. $x + 97 = 42$
3. $a + 157 = -96$
4. $y - (-75) = 60$
5. $x - 158 = 42$
6. $c - 63 = -441$
7. $-278 = n + (-69)$
8. $-263 = n - 45$
9. $-274 = a + 37$
10. While hiking in a valley, Lorena hiked to a spot 228 ft. above Lookout Rock. The new spot was 134 ft. above sea level. Solve the equation $a + 228 = 134$ to find the altitude of Lookout Rock.

Extend and Apply

Solve and check.

11. $x + (-74 + 39) = 546$
12. $a - (-72 + 78) = 17$
13. Write and solve an equation with sum -75, one addend -16, and the other addend represented by the variable n.

Use Mathematical Reasoning

14. When $n + n + n + n$ is evaluated, the result is 9 less than n. Find n.
15. If 5 cards are moved from stack A to stack B, both stacks will contain 12 cards. How many cards were in each stack to begin with? Draw a diagram and explain your solution.

Mixed Review

Add or subtract. **16.** $7 - (-2)$ **17.** $-9 - (-2)$ **18.** $-4 + (-1)$

Write as an algebraic expression. **19.** twice the sum of 7 and a number

Mental Math

You can find the sum of any number of positive integers in order, starting with 1, by multiplying the last number by the number that follows it and dividing by 2. Study the pattern and complete the generalization.

$$1 + 2 = 2(3) \div 2$$
$$1 + 2 + 3 = 3(4) \div 2$$
$$1 + 2 + 3 + 4 = 4(5) \div 2$$
$$1 + 2 + 3 + 4 + \ldots + n = \underline{\quad} ? \underline{\quad}$$

Find each sum mentally.

1. $1 + 2 + 3 + 4 + 5 + 6 + 7$
2. $1 + 2 + 3 + 4 + 5 + 6 + 7 + 8 + 9$

The positive integers from **3.** 1 through 20 **4.** 1 through 99

3-6 Problem Solving: Skills

Choosing a Calculation Method

Objective To decide if you need an exact answer or an estimate, and to select an appropriate calculation method.

Develop a Plan

When you are developing a plan to solve a problem, there are two questions you need to answer.

- Do I need an exact answer or an estimate?
- If I need to compute, should I use mental math, paper-and-pencil, or a calculator?

Decide When to Estimate

Mrs. Leong recorded the amount of time her computer telephone modem was connected to a computer data service. The charge per minute was different at different times during the day.

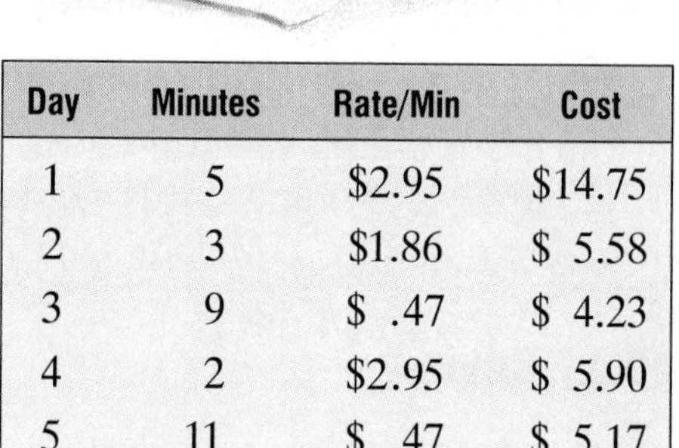

Day	Minutes	Rate/Min	Cost
1	5	$2.95	$14.75
2	3	$1.86	$ 5.58
3	9	$ .47	$ 4.23
4	2	$2.95	$ 5.90
5	11	$ .47	$ 5.17

Sample Problem 1 Mrs. Leong wanted to keep her 5-day cost under $40. Was she able to do this?

Solution

An estimate is all that is needed to decide if a total is over or under a benchmark. Estimate the answer to the question.

Sample Problem 2 Mrs. Leong wanted to record the total modem cost for the 5 days in her budget. What was the total cost?

Solution

An exact answer is needed because a budget requires actual expenses. Use a calculator to find the total cost.

Choose a Calculation Method

Once you know you need an exact answer, you need to select an appropriate calculation method. Try mental math first. If mental math is not appropriate, then decide between paper and pencil and a calculator.

Sample Problem 3 Mrs. Leong wants to know exactly how many minutes she used the computer data service. What method would you use to compute the answer?

Solution

The numbers are small and the sum of the first four is compatible with the fifth. Use mental math to find the total.

Problems

Indicate whether you need an exact answer or an estimate. Solve the problem and state which calculation method you used.

1. The table shows the record of MWA stock for a five-day week. What was the price at the end of each day? By how much did the stock increase or decrease during the week

Day	Opening Price	Increase or Decrease	Closing Price
1	45	−2	____
2	____	+4	____
3	____	+1	____
4	____	−3	____
5	____	−6	____

2. Mr. Caisley bought 500 shares of MWA stock at the end-of-week closing price. About how much did he pay for the stock?

3. What would it cost for a family of two adults and three children to see the play?

4. How much income was made from ticket sales on each of the days? How much in all?

5. Were more adult tickets or childrens tickets sold? About how many more?

School Play Ticket Information
Adults $6.50 Children: $3.50

Day	Adult Tickets Sold	Childrens Tickets Sold	Income
1	126	89	____
2	97	106	____
3	145	138	____
4	194	176	____

6. How many more adult tickets were sold on day 4 than on day 1?

7. The lowest temperature in the continental United States one day was −45°. That same day the lowest temperature in the Soviet Union was −120°. How much lower was the low temperature in the Soviet Union?

8. **Think About Your Solution** In how many ways can you make change for a 50¢ piece without using pennies?
   - **a.** Solve.
   - **b.** Write your answer in a complete sentence.
   - **c.** Name the strategy or strategies you used to solve this problem.

3-7 Problem Solving: Applications

Keeping Checkbook Records

Objective To solve problems involving checkbook records.

A **checking account** at a bank or savings and loan company allows a customer to write checks to pay bills or get needed cash. To keep money in the account, the customer makes deposits.

A deposit of money to an account is called a **credit (+)**. A payment (check) or withdrawal is called a **debit (−)**. The **balance** is the amount of money in the account at a given point. The balance changes after each withdrawal, payment, or deposit. If an account's debits are greater than its credits, the balance that remains is less than zero and the account has been **overdrawn.** The customer must keep an accurate record of all account **transactions,** or activities.

NUMBER	DATE	DESCRIPTION OF TRANSACTION	PAYMENT DEBIT (−)		T	(−)FEE (IF ANY)	DEPOSIT CREDIT (+)		BALANCE	
									$125	00
126	2/9	Terry's Service Station	$ 79	00						
	2/9	Deposit from Salary					215	00		
127	2/11	Record Land	48	00						
128	2/14	Cancer Research Donation	125	00						
	2/15	Transfer from Savings					575	00		
129	2/15	Food Mart	56	00						
130	2/17	Snapit Camera Shop	279	00						

Problems

Solve Problems 1–4, using the transaction record above. For Problems 5–8, decide whether to use **pencil and paper, mental math, estimation,** or a **calculator** to find the answer. Use each of these techniques at least once.

1. The amount of money in the account before check number 126 is shown in the balance column. What is the balance after check number 126 is written?

2. What is the new balance following the deposit on 2/9?

3. What is the new balance following: check number 128? the deposit on 2/15?

4. What is the new balance following: check number 129? check number 130? Check your answers by writing credits as positive integers and debits as negative integers and finding their sum.

5. A customer wrote a check for $79, wrote a check for $156, made a deposit of $275, and wrote a check for $398. If the balance before these transactions was $517, what was the balance after the transactions?

6. Decide whether or not this checking account has been overdrawn: beginning balance: $1353: check for $798; check for $206; deposit of $449; check for $747.

7. A checking account with a beginning balance of $150 had debits of $1250 and credits of $900. By how much was it overdrawn?

8. A checking account had a beginning balance of $435. Deposits were made in the amount of $1196. Checks were written in the amount of $1952. Three of these checks were written when the account was overdrawn. The bank fee for overdrawn checks is $12 per check. How much must be deposited to pay the fee and bring the balance up to $400?

9. **Data Search** Find a record form for a checking account. Make up a beginning balance, then 3 checks and 2 deposits. Fill out the record form for the transactions and find the ending balance.

What's Your Decision?

At the National Bank you can choose between the two types of non-interest checking accounts shown below.

Regular Account		Zero Balance Account
Account Balance	**Fee for Writing Checks**	
Below $100	$6/month	Annual fee of $24
$100–$200	$5/month	plus $0.20 for each check
$200–$300	$4/month	
$300–$400	$3/month	
Over $400	No charge	

You want to open a checking account, and expect to write no more than 10 checks per month. You usually keep a little over $100 in your account. Would you choose a Regular Account or a Zero Balance Account? Why?

3-8 Multiplying Integers

Objective To multiply integers.

Explore

Put 2 handfuls of counters in a bag. Use counters and follow the directions below. Copy and complete the equations.

Talk about the rules you might create for multiplying integers.

ACTION 1: PUTTING IN 2 COUNTERS (+2)

Do Action 1 three times. → $+3(+2) = \square$ ← Does the bag have more (+) or less (−) counters? How many more or less?

Do the opposite of Action 1 three times. → $-3(+2) = \square$ ← Does the bag have more (+) or less (−) counters? How many more or less?

ACTION 2: TAKING OUT 2 COUNTERS (−2)

Do Action 2 three times. → $+3(-2) = \square$ ← Does the bag have more (+) or less (−) counters? How many more or less?

Do the opposite of Action 2 three times. → $-3(-2) = \square$ ← Does the bag have more (+) or less (−) counters? How many more or less?

Understand the Ideas

You can use number properties and patterns to help you decide how to multiply integers. For example, you can use repeated addition to show that the product of a positive integer and a negative integer is a negative integer.

$$3(-2) = (-2) + (-2) + (-2) = -6$$

The equation pattern below, in which the product increases by 2 each time, suggest that $-3(-2) = 6$.

$$3(-2) = -6$$
$$2(-2) = -4$$
$$1(-2) = -2$$
$$0(-2) = 0$$
$$-1(-2) = 2$$
$$-2(-2) = 4$$
$$-3(-2) = 6$$

These ideas can be summarized as follows. Multiplying a number by a negative number is the opposite of multiplying it by a positive number. For example,

2(4) is 8, so −2(4) would be the opposite of 8, or −8.

2(−4) is −8, so −2(−4) would be the opposite of −8, or 8.

The ideas above suggest these procedures for multiplying integers.

Rule Multiplying Integers

Find the product of the absolute values. Then use the following rules for determining the sign.

- The product of two positive integers is positive.
- The product of two negative integers is positive.
- The product of a positive integer and a negative integer is negative.

Example 1

Find the product. −6(−4)

Solution −6(−4) = 24 The product of two negative integers is a positive integer.

Try This Find the product. **a.** 9(6) **b.** −7(−8) **c.** −9(−5)

Example 2

Find the product. −8(5)

Solution −8(5) = −40 A positive times a negative integer is a negative integer.

Try This Find the product.

d. −5(4) **e.** 6(−8) **f.** 9(−4) **g.** −7(3)

A calculator can be used to test the rules above for multiplying integers. Remember that pushing the change-sign key [+○−] after entering a whole number changes it to a negative number.

Example 3

Use a calculator to multiply. −46(−168)

Solution

46 [+○−] [×] 168 [+○−] [=] [7728]

Try This Use a calculator to find these products.

h. 23(−47) **i.** −89(126) **j.** −145(−472) **k.** −17(−36)(−67)(−39)

Class Exercises

Tell whether the product is positive or negative.

1. 6(3) **2.** −7(4) **3.** −6(−9) **4.** 5(−9)
5. −8(−3) **6.** −2(−17) **7.** −12(15) **8.** 24(−45)

Discuss the Ideas

9. Artemio said, "I know that 3(−2) = −6 because (−2) + (−2) + (−2) = −6. Now 3(−2) and −3(−2) can't both be −6, so −3(−2) must equal 6." Do you agree? Why or why not?

Exercises

Practice and Apply

Find the product.

1. 9(7) **2.** −5(−3) **3.** −4(−8) **4.** 8(6)
5. −9(−4) **6.** −6(−8) **7.** −7(−2) **8.** −3(−8)
9. 7(8) **10.** −6(−7) **11.** 9(−5) **12.** −8(7)
13. −7(0) **14.** −1(8) **15.** −9(9) **16.** 6(−5)

Find the products using the [+○−] key on your calculator.

17. −956(498) **18.** −853(−32)(−46) **19.** 535(−726)(−43)

20. A stock's average change in price per month over a 4-month period was −3. To find the total change in price, find the product 4(−3).

21. Over a 5-day period the water level in Duane's swimming pool decreased 4 inches each day. Find the number Duane used to record the total change in water level by finding the product 5(−4).

22. Bill removes 6 bushels of corn each day from his main supply to feed his cattle. Find the number Bill used to record the change in his main supply in one week by finding the product −6(7).

23. When doing the calculations for an astronomy problem, Dr. Shapiro knew her solution would check out if the sum of 20(−5,000) and (−20)(−5,000) is 0. Show that the sum is 0.

Extend and Apply

24. Find the product. Is the number of negative factors even or odd? Is the product positive or negative?

a. 2(−3)(−4)(−5) **b.** (−5)(−6)(−2)(−1)

25. Choose between positive and negative to complete the following.

a. The product of an odd number of negative factors is __?__

b. The product of an even number of negative factors is __?__

Find the product.

26. $7(-4)(6)(-3)(-2)$

27. $-36(-25)(-4)(-2)(-3)(-1)$

Evaluate each expression.

28. $-3n$ for $n = 47$

29. $15(z + 6)$ for $z = -23$

30. $-12pq$ for $p = 32$ and $q = -9$

31. $4a - 3b$ for $a = -5, b = 7$

32. Show that $2b + 3b$ has the same value as $5b$ when $b = 4$, $b = -8$, and $b = -34$. What property does this show?

33. Show that $-9(a + 25)$ has the same value as $-9a + (-9)(25)$ when $a = -9$, $a = 12$, and $a = -24$.

34. The formula $s = -4(y \div 10) + 1{,}020$ has been used to predict the record time (s) in seconds, for the mile run in a chosen year (y). Evaluate the formula for $y = 1990$.

35. The air temperature decreases 7°C for each kilometer of increase in altitude. If the temperature was 0°C at one altitude, what would the temperature be outside an airplane flying 4 km above this altitude?

36. **Communicate** Solve the following problem. Then discuss your solution and compare it with the solutions of others in your group. Decide as a group which solution to present to the class.

Mindy tripled the temperature reading on a cold day and the result was 6 less than the original temperature. How could this be possible? What was the original temperature?

Use Mathematical Reasoning

37. Find the pattern and give the next 3 integers in each sequence.

a. $3, -6, 6, -12, 9, -18,$ ___, ___, ___.

b. $6, 2, -2, -6,$ ___, ___, ___.

Mixed Review

Solve and check. **38.** $r + 23 = -36$ **39.** $m + 19 = 12$ **40.** $25t = 1075$

Estimate the value of the variable. **41.** $503 \div 9 = a$ **42.** $19 \times 49 = a$

Mental Math

Because of the Commutative and Associative Properties, you can choose any pair from among 3 factors ***a*, *b*,** and ***c*** to multiply first. That is, $(ab)c = (bc)a = (ac)b$. Choosing **compatible numbers** makes it easier to find products mentally. Choose compatible numbers to find each product mentally.

1. $4(687)(250)$

2. $68(50)(20)$

3. $20(579)(-5)$

4. $-674(385)(0)$

5. $96(4)(25)$

6. $250(127)(40)$

3-9 Dividing Integers

Objective To find integer quotients.

Understand the Ideas

The relationship between multiplication and division can be used to find the quotient of two integers.

factor	factor		product		product		factor		factor
$4 \cdot$	6	$=$	24	$\rightarrow$	$24 \div$		6	$=$	4
$4 \cdot$	(-6)	$=$	-24	$\rightarrow$	$-24 \div$		-6	$=$	4
$-4 \cdot$	6	$=$	-24	$\rightarrow$	$-24 \div$		6	$=$	-4
$-4 \cdot$	(-6)	$=$	24	$\rightarrow$	$24 \div$		-6	$=$	-4

The equations above suggest the following procedure.

Rule **Dividing Integers**

To divide integers, find the quotient of their absolute values. Then use the following rule for determining the sign:

- The quotient of two positive integers is positive.
- The quotient of two negative integers is positive.
- The quotient of a positive and a negative integer is negative.

Example 1

Find the quotient. $-35 \div (-7)$

Solution $-35 \div (-7) = 5$ The quotient of two negative integers is positive. This checks, since $5(-7) = -35$.

Try This Find the quotient.

a. $30 \div 6$ **b.** $-45 \div (-9)$ **c.** $\frac{-72}{-8}$

Example 2

Find the quotient. $-32 \div 4$

Solution $-32 \div 4 = -8$ The quotient of two integers with unlike signs is negative. This checks, since $-8(4) = -32$.

Try This Find the quotient.

d. $-48 \div 8$ **e.** $\frac{20}{-4}$ **f.** $40 \div (-5)$

Class Exercises

Check each quotient by multiplying. Is it correct?

1. $35 \div (-5) = -7$
2. $-18 \div 6 = 3$
3. $24 \div 8 = 3$

Discuss the Ideas

4. Explain why the quotient of two negative integers is positive.

Exercises

Practice and Apply

Find the quotient.

1. $56 \div 8$
2. $-24 \div (-8)$
3. $-20 \div (-4)$
4. $81 \div 9$
5. $-36 \div 4$
6. $42 \div (-7)$
7. $-64 \div 8$
8. $72 \div (-9)$
9. $45 \div (-5)$
10. $36 \div 6$
11. $-48 \div (-8)$
12. $-90 \div 10$
13. $9 \div (-1)$
14. $0 \div (-12)$
15. $-66 \div (-11)$
16. $30 \div (-5)$
17. Over a 4-month period, the total change in the average high temperature was −32°F. To find the average change per month, find $-32 \div 4$.
18. Aaron missed 21 points on his last 3 math tests. Find the average number of points he missed on each test by finding $-21 \div 3$.

Extend and Apply

Simplify.

19. $(-6)(4) \div (-8)$
20. $-40 \div (-8) - 9$
21. $-56 \div (2 - 10)$
22. Does $a \div (b + c)$ have the same value as $a \div b + a \div c$ when $a = -48$, $b = 12$, and $c = -4$?

Find the quotient. Use the change-sign key. Check by estimating.

23. $5{,}239{,}374 \div (-6958)$
24. $\dfrac{-1024(-75)}{-32}$
25. $\dfrac{-94 + 1886}{-108 + 164}$

Use Mathematical Reasoning

26. Find integers a and b for which $a + b = 6$ and $a \div b = -4$.
27. Half an integer is five more than the integer. What is the integer?
28. The temperature rose at the rate of 3°F per hour to reach 0°F at noon. At what earlier time had the temperature been −21°F?

Mixed Review

Solve and check. **29.** $y - 63 = 14$ **30.** $w - (-4) = 61$ **31.** $24r = 384$

Simplify. **32.** $12(9c)$ **33.** $112w + 13w$ **34.** $(9 + t) + 4$

Patterns and Inductive Reasoning

Objective: To use inductive reasoning to make generalizations about geometric figures.

Group Activity Three roads intersect, as shown at the right, to enclose an equilateral triangular piece of land. Mr. Ortega wants to build a factory on the land where the sum of the distances, $a + b + c$, to the three roads is the smallest. Where should he build the factory?

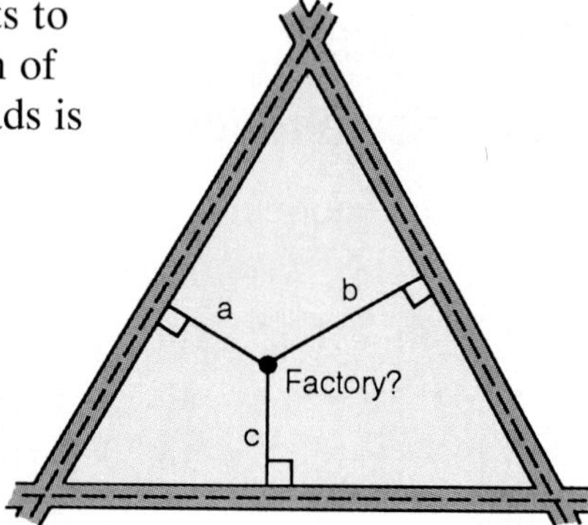

Draw a large equilateral triangle, pick several locations for the factory, and measure the distances a, b, and c to the nearest millimeter. Write a paragraph describing your results.

The process of observing that something happens in every case you check, and concluding that it will probably happen in every case is called **inductive reasoning.**

In the activity above, you can observe a pattern in the sums of the measures. After trying a few more cases and thinking about the situation, it seems reasonable that the pattern will continue. The steps in this process are shown here.

Inductive Reasoning

Step 1 You observe that something is true for every case you check, and seems reasonable.

Step 2 Conclude that it is probably true for all other cases, and state a generalization.

When you use inductive reasoning, remember that even though a generalization is true for every case you have checked, you have not *proved* that it is true for all cases. Deductive reasoning or other methods are used to prove generalizations true.

Apply Mathematical Reasoning

1. Draw a quadrilateral and connect the midpoints on the sides. Repeat this for several different quadrilaterals. Make a conjecture about the figure formed by the segments that connect the midpoints. Explain your conjecture to the other members of your group.

3-10 Solving Integer Equations: Using Multiplication and Division

Objective To use multiplication and division to solve equations involving integers.

Application

If quick-freezing for 7 minutes lowers the temperature 91°C, you can solve the equation $7d = -91$ to find the temperature change per minute.

Understand the Ideas

To solve integer equations involving multiplication or division, you can use the same steps you used with whole number equations.

- Decide which operation (multiplication or division) has been applied to the variable.
- Use the inverse operation, multiplying or dividing both sides of the equation by the same number.

Example 1

What is the temperature change per minute in the **application**? Solve $7d = -91$ to decide.

Solution

$$7d = -91$$

$$\frac{7d}{7} = \frac{-91}{7}$$ To undo multiplying by 7, divide by 7 on both sides.

$$d = -13$$

Check $7(-13) \stackrel{?}{=} -91$ Replace d with -13 in $7d = -91$

$-91 = -91$ ✓ The solution is -13.

The temperature change is -13°C per minute.

Try This Solve and check. **a.** $-4x = 68$ **b.** $-182 = 7n$

c. Solve $8c = -120$ to find the temperature change per minute for an item whose temperature dropped 120° when quick-frozen for 8 minutes.

Example 2

Solve and check. $\frac{n}{-4} = 17$

Solution

$$\frac{n}{-4} = 17$$ To undo dividing by -4, multiply by -4 on both sides.

$$\frac{n}{-4}(-4) = 17(-4)$$

$$n = -68$$

Check

$$\frac{-68}{-4} \stackrel{?}{=} 17$$ Replace n with -68 in $\frac{n}{-4} = 17$.

$$17 = 17 \checkmark$$ The solution is -68.

Try This Solve and check. **d.** $\frac{a}{6} = -72$ **e.** $25 = \frac{x}{-8}$

The following property of -1 is useful when solving equations such as $-n = 24$. It allows us to rewrite $-n = 24$ as $n = -24$.

Property of −1

The product of -1 and a number is the opposite of the number.

For each number n, $\mathbf{-1n = -n}$, and $\mathbf{-n = -1n}$

Class Exercises

Check. Is the given number a solution to the equation?

1. $-3c = 18, c = 6$? **2.** $8 = \frac{b}{-3}, b = -24$? **3.** $\frac{x}{-9} = -9, x = 81$?

Discuss the Ideas

4. How can you find 5 equations that have the same solution as $-12n = 60$?

Exercises

Practice and Apply

Solve and check.

1. $-8y = 96$ **2.** $2b = -86$ **3.** $-7n = -105$ **4.** $-b = 72$

5. $-4z = 92$ **6.** $8c = -272$ **7.** $-14a = -168$ **8.** $-23y = 161$

9. $\frac{n}{17} = -9$ **10.** $\frac{b}{-26} = 7$ **11.** $\frac{r}{-31} = -6$ **12.** $\frac{t}{36} = -8$

13. $\frac{a}{18} = -15$ **14.** $\frac{a}{-29} = 13$ **15.** $\frac{x}{46} = -11$ **16.** $\frac{y}{-54} = -13$

17. A marathon runner might burn 150 calories (−150) per mile. To find an integer representing a person's calorie usage during a 26-mile marathon, solve the equation $\frac{x}{26} = -150$.

18. Over the past 3 weeks, Carlin City's water supply has decreased an average of 543 gallons (−543) per week. To find the total number of gallons lost, solve the equation $\frac{w}{3} = -543$.

Extend and Apply

Solve and check.

19. $(-16 + 25)b = 162$ **20.** $\frac{x}{(-12)(-16)} = -8$ **21.** $(235 - 421) = -31d$

22. Write and solve an equation in which the product is −518, one factor is −7, and the other factor is represented by the variable n.

23. A football team lost an average of 12 yards (−12) a play for a total loss of 72 yards (−72). How many plays were run?

Use Mathematical Reasoning

24. Find the solutions to these equations and look for a pattern. Write the next 3 equations in the pattern. $2a = -2$, $3a = -6$, $4a = -16$, $5a = -40$, $6a = -96$

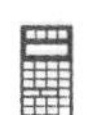

Use estimation and a calculator to find two solutions to each.

25. $n \cdot n = 1369$ **26.** $n \cdot n = 4624$ **27.** $n \cdot n = 18{,}769$

Mixed Review

Solve and check. **28.** $30x = 210$ **29.** $t - 26 = 14$ **30.** $m \div 12 = 18$

Multiply. **31.** $9(-2)$ **32.** $-9(-12)$ **33.** $11(-1)$ **34.** $-1(-11)$

Computer Activity

The following program can be used to balance a checkbook. Enter a withdrawal as a negative number.

```
10 REM CHECKING ACCOUNT
20 INPUT "ENTER BEGINNING BALANCE:"; BALANCE
30 INPUT "ENTER DEPOSIT(+) OR WITHDRAWAL(-):"; X
40 LET BALANCE=BALANCE+X
50 INPUT "ANOTHER ENTRY (Y/N)?"; R$: PRINT
60 IF R$="Y" THEN 30
70 PRINT "YOUR NEW BALANCE IS:"; BALANCE
80 END
```

1–7. Use the program to solve the problems on page 97.

3-11 Problem Solving: Writing Equations

Translating Sentences into Equations

Objective To translate verbal statements into equations.

To translate a verbal statement into an equation, read the verbal statement carefully, thinking about the meaning of each phrase. Then decide what the variable will represent. Notice how the following statement about numbers translates directly to an equation.

Verbal Statement **A number** increased by 5 gives the sum 23.

Equation $n + 5 = 23$

Sometimes the translation is less direct.

Verbal Statement $6 less than the **cost of the hat** is $17.

Equation $h - 6 = 17$

Example 1

Choose the equation that best represents this statement:
The $45 cost of the baseball glove is 5 times the cost of the ball.

i. $45 = 5 + b$ **ii.** $45 = 5b$ **iii.** $b - 5 = 45$

Solution $45 = 5b$ "5 times" translates to 5b.

Try This **a.** Choose the equation that best represents this statement:
The number of people divided by 9 gives 12 teams.

i. $n \div 9 = 12$ **ii.** $n \div 12 = 9$ **iii.** $9 \div n = 12$

Example 2

Write an equation. A number increased by 8 is 23.

Solution Let n = a number First decide what the variable represents.

$n + 8 = 23$ "a number increased by 8" translates to $n + 8$.
"is" translates to "=".

Try This Write an equation. **b.** A number decreased by 9 gives 54.
c. The sum of a number and 47 is -112.

Class Exercises

Give an algebraic expression for the phrase.

1. three times a number

2. 6 more than a number

3. a number divided by -17

4. the product of 9 and a number

5. a number decreased by 5

6. the quotient of a number and 8

Discuss the Ideas

7. How would you make each phrase above into a complete sentence that can be represented by an equation? Give each equation.

Exercises

Practice and Apply

Choose the equation that best represents the verbal statement.

1. 55 times the number of hours is 220. **a.** $55 + h = 220$ **b.** $55h = 220$

2. 16 more than my age is 29. **a.** $29 - 16 = a$ **b.** $a + 16 = 29$

3. The number of weeks divided by 4 is 8. **a.** $n \div 4 = 8$ **b.** $8 \div 4 = n$

4. The bill decreased by \$9 is \$54. **a.** $54 - b = 9$ **b.** $b - 9 = 54$

5. The difference of the rate and \$5 is \$24. **a.** $24 - r = 5$ **b.** $r - 5 = 24$

6. The number of teams times 5 is 75. **a.** $5t = 75$ **b.** $n + 5 = 75$

Translate the statement into an equation. Write the equation.

7. 17 less than a number is 101.

8. The quotient of a number and -8 is 216.

9. 56 more than a number is 104.

10. The difference of a number and 9 is 47.

11. A number n divided by 25 is -12.

12. 57 added to a number gives a total of 123.

13. 9 times a number is -171.

14. The sum of a number and -73 is 145.

15. 17 less than a number is 15.

16. A number increased by 45 gives 77.

17. Six times the number of days is 91.

18. The price decreased by \$29 is \$258.

19. \$9 more than the total restaurant bill is \$72.

20. A number increased by 56 produces a total of 124.

21. 34 multiplied by a number produces the product 272.

22. 28 is the result of multiplying -4 by a number.

23. The difference between the cost of the car and \$600 is \$19,820.
24. 369 items divided into boxes of 3 gives the number of boxes.
25. The present temperature increased by 19 degrees gives a reading of 56 degrees.
26. The difference of my new salary and my present \$24,500/yr salary gives a \$1175 raise.
27. \$375 is the result of decreasing the price of the television set by \$49.
28. When the number of students in our school was increased by 27, there were 406 students.
29. This year's \$12 student fees are \$5 more than the cost of last year's student fees.
30. When the money was divided evenly among 3 charities, each received \$150.
31. The 67 points scored by our team was 18 points less than the other team's score.
32. The product of our average weight and the 24 students in our class was 2,040 lbs.

Extend and Apply

Write a statement that describes each equation.

33. $x + 9 = 23$ **34.** $\frac{p}{4} = 9$ **35.** $-8c = 72$ **36.** $16 - n = 7$

37. $p + 12 = 65$ **38.** $b - 24 = 43$ **39.** $\frac{m}{12} = 5$ **40.** $65 = 5n$

Write and solve an equation. Tell what the solution represents.

41. A pair of running shoes cost 9 times as much as a pair of \$6 socks.
42. When the number of employees at a company was increased by 8, there were 56 employees.
43. LeRon caught 17 fewer fish this year than the 89 fish he caught last year.
44. When Pedro divided his \$270 prize evenly among his cousins, each got \$30.

Use Mathematical Reasoning

45. The sum of 5 times x and 7 times y is 110. Translate into an equation. Find integers x and y that make the equation true.
46. Write and solve an equation for "the sum of 3 page numbers in a row in a book is 828."

Mixed Review

Solve and check. **47.** $m + 19 = -31$ **48.** $14c = 434$ **49.** $\frac{z}{6} = -6$

Divide. **50.** $\frac{56}{-8}$ **51.** $\frac{-18}{-6}$ **52.** $\frac{-169}{13}$ **53.** $\frac{-324}{-9}$

3-12 Problem Solving: Strategies

Make a Table, Look for a Pattern

Objective To use the strategies Make a Table, Look for a Pattern, and other strategies learned so far to solve nonroutine problems.

Problem-solving strategies called **Make a Table** and **Look for a Pattern** are helpful when solving problems involving numerical relationships. Consider the following problem.

Sample Problem A secret agent was hired for a special assignment that would take exactly 14 days. He could choose to be paid one of the following two ways. Under payment plan A, he would receive $6000 for the job. Under payment plan B, his employer would put $1 into a safe for the first day and increase the amount in the safe to $2 the second day, $4 the third day, $8 the fourth day, and so on, doubling the amount in the safe each day. At the end of the assignment, the agent could claim the contents of the safe. Which payment plan should the agent choose?

Solution

To find the amount for payment plan B, you can use the data in the problem to begin a **table.** The red numbers show the data given in the problem. Look for a **pattern** to help extend the table and provide new information.

Day	Number of dollars in the safe
1	**1**
2	**2**← 2
3	**4**← 2(2)
4	**8**←2(2) (2)
5	16
6	32
.	.
.	.
.	.
14	?

Notice that the numbers in the second column are found by multiplying 1 less factor of two than the number for the day. On day **4** there were **3** factors of 2, or 2(2) (2), dollars in the safe. So on day **14** there would be **13** factors of 2, or 8192 dollars in the safe.

Payment plan A: $6000. Payment plan B: $8192. The agent should choose plan B.

Problem-Solving Strategies

Choose the Operations	**Make a Table**	Make an Organized List
Guess, Check, Revise	**Look for a Pattern**	Use Logical Reasoning
Draw a Diagram	Write an Equation	Work Backward
	Simplify the Problem	

Problems

Solve using one or more of the Problem-Solving strategies.

1. Nina started a computer users club. On the first day, she was the only member. Each day after that, one more member joined than on the previous day. What was the membership of the club after 30 days?
2. A generous millionaire had an unusual plan for giving away her money. Beginning on her birthday, she would give away $1 the first day, $3 the second day, $5 the third day, and so on. How much money would she have given away after 100 days?
3. Scientists send the following sequence of "beeps" into outer space: 1, 1, 2, 3, 5, 8, 13, 21, 34. They hope that intelligent life will receive these signals and send return signals that continue the sequence. What are the next 5 numbers of "beeps" that would be sent back?
4. A sandwich shop has 3-legged stools and 4-legged chairs at its tables. There are 31 seats and 104 legs all together. How many of the seats are stools and how many are chairs?
5. Emilio said, "A 1-year-old dog is 7 'dog years' old. My dog is 6 years old in regular years. If you change my age into dog years, I am 49 dog years older than my dog's age in dog years. How old am I?"
6. Suppose it takes newborn rabbits two months to mature and produce a new pair of rabbits. After that, they produce a new pair of rabbits on the first day of each month. If you started on January 1 with a pair of newborn rabbits and no rabbits died, how many pairs of rabbits would you have on July 1?
7. George had 12 cherry trees. On January 1, 1780, he cut down 2 of the trees. On December 31, 1780, he planted 1 tree. Each year on the same dates he did the same things. On what date did he first have no cherry trees in his yard?

Group Decision Making

8. Work in a group. Discuss and decide.

Guidelines for Planning

- **Formulate Problems** you will need to solve.
- Discuss **Assumptions** you will make and **Data** you will need.

Situation For your birthday you want to take three of your friends bowling and then out for pizza. You need to know how much it will cost.

a. What decision or decisions do you need to make in this situation?
b. Formulate problems you need to solve to make the decision(s),
c. List any assumptions you need to make to arrive at a decision.
d. What data, if any, do you need to collect to make a decision?
e. Write a paragraph summarizing what your group did, what decisions you made, and why.

Extend Key Ideas

Sequences

A **sequence** is a set of numbers in a particular order. The numbers in a sequence are called **terms** of the sequence. The table below shows the sequence **1, 3, 5, 7, 9, . . .** The numbers in the top row show the *order* of the terms. The *first* term is 1, the *second* term is 3, the *third* term is 5, and so on. The general rule for finding a particular term of the sequence is called the **rule for the *n*th term.**

Number of the term	1st	2nd	3rd	4th	5th	6th	7th	8th	. . .	*n*th	
Terms of the sequence	1	3	5	7	9	11	13	15		$2n - 1$	Rule for the *n*th term

To find the 9th, 10th, and 11th terms of the sequence above, you would replace the variable in the rule for the *n*th term by the number of the term you want to find.

Rule $2n - 1$: $2(\mathbf{9}) - 1 = 17$, $2(\mathbf{10}) - 1 = 19$, $2(\mathbf{11}) - 1 = 21$

The **9**th, **10**th, and **11**th terms of the sequence are **17, 19, 21.**

1. The rule for the *n*th term of a sequence is $\frac{n(n+1)}{-2}$. Write the first five terms.
2. The rule for the *n*th term of a sequence is $n(n) - 1$. Give the 8th term of the sequence. Give the 25th term of the sequence.
3. Find the rule for the *n*th term of this sequence: 1, 4, 9, 16, 25, 36, 49, . . .
4. Find the rule for the *n*th term of this sequence: −3, −7, −11, −15, −19, −23, −27, . . .
5. The *n*th term of a sequence is 0 when *n* is even and 1 when *n* is odd. Write the first eight terms of this sequence.
6. Write the next five terms in the **Fibonacci sequence**: 1, 1, 2, 3, 5, 8, 13, 21, 34, . . .
7. Square any term of the sequence in Exercise 6. Then find the product of the term preceding and the term following that term. What do you discover?
8. Estimate how many of the first 25 Fibonacci numbers are even. Extend the sequence to check your guess.

Chapter 3 Review/Test

Understanding

True or false? (Exercises 1–4)

3-1 **1.** The complete set of integers consists of the negative integers and 0.

3-1 **2.** $|-6| = -|6|$

3-3 **3.** Subtracting a number gives the same result as adding its opposite.

3-8 **4.** The product $-4(-5)$ is the opposite of product $4(5)$.

3-9 **5.** What would you do to get the variable by itself on one side in $\frac{n}{-3} = 24$?

Skills

3-1 **6.** Use inequality symbols. Order from least to greatest. $7, 5, -8$

3-2 Find the sum or difference.
3-3

7. $-3 + 8$ **8.** $7 + (-1)$ **9.** $-3 - 2$ **10.** $16 - (-5)$

Evaluate.

11. $-4 - r$ for $r = -7$ **12.** $a + b - 5$ for $a = 8$ and $b = -3$

3-5 Solve and check.

13. $s - 17 = -34$ **14.** $-37 = z + 56$ **15.** $v - (-28) = -77$

3-8 Find the product or quotient.
3-9

16. $5(-4)$ **17.** $-6(8)$ **18.** $-48 \div (-6)$ **19.** $24 \div (-3)$

3-10 Solve and check.

20. $-84 = 4s$ **21.** $-6x = 36$ **22.** $\frac{t}{5} = -40$ **23.** $-c = -22$

3-11 **24.** Write an equation for "24 less than a number x is 12."

Applications

Solve.

3-7 **25.** Fred represented deposits in his checking account with positive numbers and withdrawals with negative numbers. The following shows one week's activity in his account, which began the week with a balance of \$175: +25, −50, +125, −75, −60. What was the balance in the account at the end of the week?

3-12 **26.** Gino noticed that there was 1 microbe on his microscope slide when he checked on the first day. On the 2nd day there were 4, on the third day there were 9, and on the 4th day there were 16. If this pattern continues, how many microbes should Gino expect on the 12th day?

Cumulative Review

1-3 2-3 Write an algebraic expression for each phrase.

1. g added to 9 **2.** k decreased by 3 **3.** the sum of v and 10

4. half of m **5.** y times 7 **6.** 9 divided by w

Write an expression for each question.

Wendy has 16 records. How many will she have if

7. she gives away r records? **8.** she buys b more records?

2-1 Simplify.

9. $28 \div (3 + 4)$ **10.** $2 + [(7 + 2) \div 3]$ **11.** $4 \cdot 5 + 3 \cdot 9$

1-1 2-1 3-2 Evaluate each algebraic expression.

12. $s + 2$ for $s = 9$ **13.** $(4 + 8) - c$ for $c = 10$

14. $f - g$ for $f = 5, g = 1$ **15.** $8k$ for $k = 8$

16. $\frac{2x}{z}$ for $x = 8, z = 4$ **17.** $n(m + 6)$ for $n = 2, m = 3$

18. $y + (-10)$ for $y = 2$ **19.** $35 + b$ for $b = -10$

20. $-4 - t$ for $t = 5$ **21.** $-7 - x$ for $x = 3$

22. $\frac{7w}{2}$ for $w = 4$ **23.** $3(10 - c)$ for $c = 5$

2-4 Use the Commutative Property to write an equivalent expression.

24. $y(6)$ **25.** pq **26.** $12 + z$

2-4 Use the Associative Property to write an equivalent expression.

27. $20(8p)$ **28.** $(5f)n$ **29.** $(y + 2) + 9$

2-5 Use the Distributive Property to simplify.

30. $3(c + 4)$ **31.** $a(8 + 9)$ **32.** $(7 + b)8$

2-5 Use the Associative Property for multiplication to simplify.

33. $2(5 \cdot t)$ **34.** $6(4k)$ **35.** $15(2d)$

2-5 Use the Distributive Property to simplify by combining like terms.

36. $g + 7g$ **37.** $3v + 3v$ **38.** $25p + 50p$

3-3 3-8 3-9 Compute.

39. $3 - 7$ **40.** $-12 \cdot 8$ **41.** $18 \div (-9)$

2-2 **42.** Copy and complete the table. Write a rule that tells how to find the cost given the number of posters purchased.

Number of posters	2	3	4	5	6	x
Cost ($)	5	8	11	14	?	?

4 Decimals

In her last gymnastics competition, Ellen Kwan scored a 5.75 on the floor exercise, a 5.45 on the balance beam, and a 5.8 on the uneven parallel bars. What was her combined score?

4-1 Decimals and Place Value

Objectives To understand decimal notation and place value; to compare and order decimals.

Explore

- These blocks represent a number. A small cube represents one unit.
  a. How many hundreds are there?
  b. How many tens?
  c. How many ones?

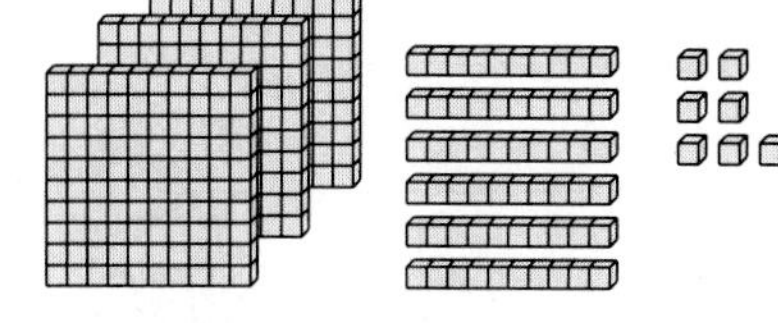

- Suppose the large square block represents one unit. What number do these blocks represent?

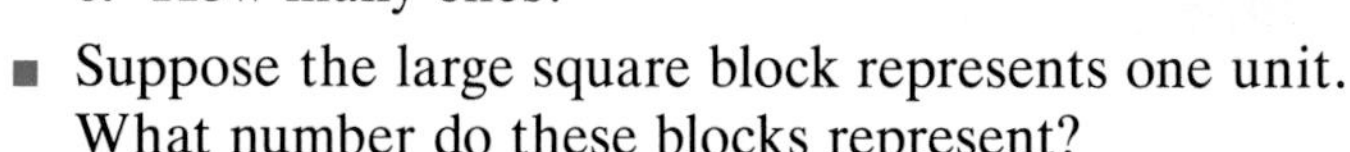

- Represent these numbers with blocks: **a)** 4.7 **b)** 2.61

Understand the Ideas

Numbers are represented in the decimal system by using the digits 0 through 9 and grouping by tens. The value of each digit in a decimal depends on its place. The chart below shows the **place value** names for the decimals 24.5 and 6.263.

thousands	hundreds	tens	ones	decimal point	tenths	hundredths	thousandths	
1,000	100	10	1		$\frac{1}{10}$	$\frac{1}{100}$	$\frac{1}{1000}$	
		2	4	.	5			twenty four and five tenths
			6	.	2	6	3	six and two hundred sixty-three thousandths

Example 1

Write the number represented by these blocks if the large cube represents one unit.

Solution 2.436

Try This

a. Write the number represented by these blocks if the large square block represents one unit.

Example 2

Write **3**(100) + **1**(10) + **3**(1) + **4**$\left(\frac{1}{10}\right)$ + **7**$\left(\frac{1}{100}\right)$ as a decimal.

Solution 313.47

Try This Write as a decimal.

b. $4(100) + 7(10) + 9\left(\frac{1}{100}\right) + 3\left(\frac{1}{1,000}\right)$

This decimeter ruler models a number line. The unit is divided into ten equal parts. The mark that represents 0.7 dm is shown.

Compare this with the number line shown below. The segment from 0 to 1 is also divided into ten equal spaces. Point A, which is at the end of the seventh space, represents the number seven tenths and can be named by the decimal 0.7. To find the number represented by point B, you can blow up the number line between 0.7 and 0.8. Then split that region into ten parts. You can now see that point B represents seventy-seven hundredths, or 0.77.

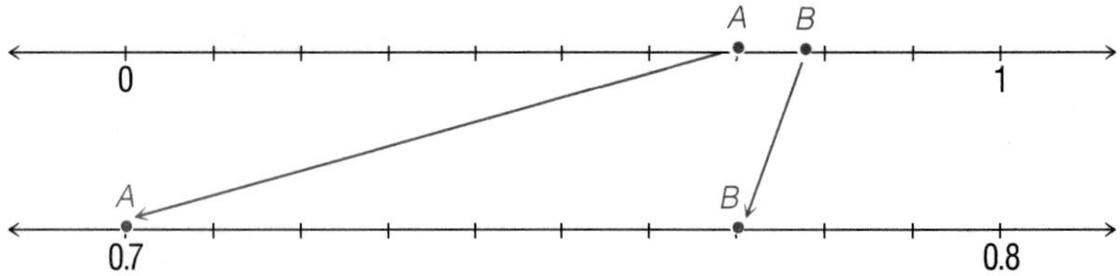

Positive numbers represented by decimals are shown to the right of zero on the number line, and negative numbers represented by decimals are shown to the left of zero.

Example 3

Give the decimal names for points A and B.

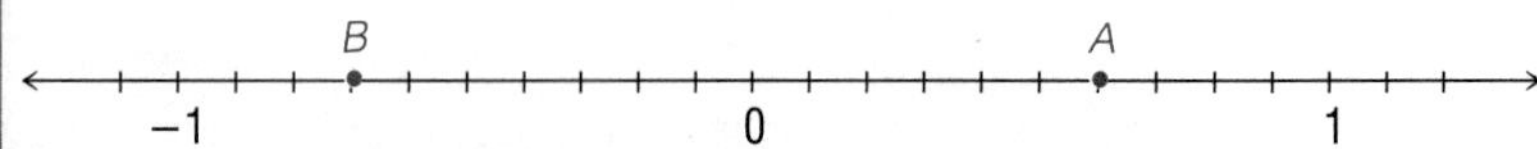

Solution point $A = 0.6$ Point A is at the end of the sixth of 10 equal spaces between 0 and 1.

point $B = -0.7$ Point B is at the end of the seventh of 10 equal spaces between 0 and -1.

Try This

Give the decimal name for point A.

c.

A

−2.8 −2.7

d.

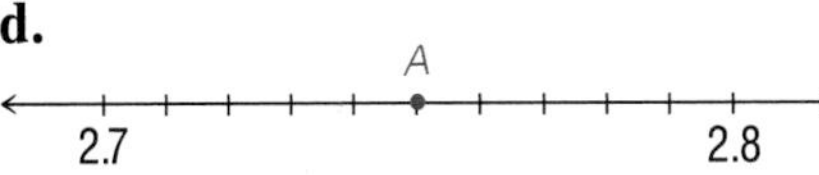

The number farther to the right on the number line is the greater number. To compare the decimals without a number line, start on the left, find the first place in which the digits are not equal, and compare the digits.

Example 4

Write $>$, $<$ or $=$ for □. 19.31 □ 19.23

Solution $19.31 > 19.23$ Start on the left. The tenths place is the first place in which the digits are not equal. Since $3 > 2$, $19.31 > 19.23$.

Try This

Write $>$, $<$, or $=$ for each □.

e. 47.14 □ 47.13 **f.** −7.003 □ −7.03 **g.** 18.06 □ 18.060

Class Exercises

Read each decimal.

1. 8.3 **2.** 45.8 **3.** 390.1 **4.** 7.64 **5.** 35.18

6. Which is greater, 8.23 or 8.1? **7.** Which is less, 12.7 or 12.69?

Discuss the Ideas

8. Our decimal system is based upon grouping by tens. Why do you think early man grouped by tens instead of some other number, such as fours or twelves?

Exercises

Practice and Apply

Write a decimal number represented by these tiles when the large cube is one unit.

1.

2.

Write as a decimal.

3. $5(100) + 4(10) + 7\left(\frac{1}{10}\right) + 6\left(\frac{1}{100}\right)$

4. $3(100) + 4(1{,}000) + 7(1) + 5\left(\frac{1}{10}\right)$

5. $7(100) + 8(1) + 7\left(\frac{1}{100}\right) + 4(10)$

6. $5\left(\frac{1}{10}\right) + 8(10) + 6\left(\frac{1}{100}\right) + 7(1{,}000)$

7. $8(1) + 7(10) + 5(100) + 3\left(\frac{1}{10}\right)$

8. $4\left(\frac{1}{100}\right) + 0(10) + 0(1) + 4(100)$

Give the decimal name for point A.

9. A — 0 — 1

10. A — 0.6 — 0.7

11. 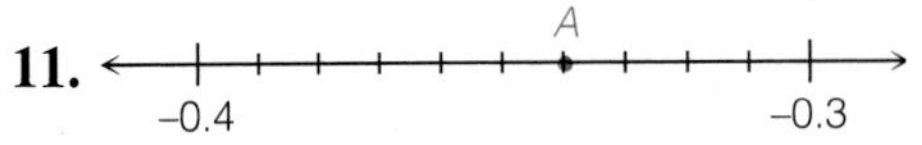

12. A — 5.21 — 5.22

Write >, <, or = for each □.

13. 6.93 □ 6.930

14. 1.01 □ 1.101

15. −4.658 □ −4.685

16. 4.1 □ 4.100

17. 7.001 □ 7.010

18. −14.3 □ −14.29

Extend and Apply

Write the numbers in order from least to greatest.

19. 3.7, 3.07, 3.069

20. 0.004, 0.039, 0.0041

21. 6.101, 6.010, 6.0101

22. 4.01, 4, 4.001

23. −5.404, −5.044, −5.040

24. −0.001, −0.101, −0.011, −0.01

Write two decimal replacements for x that make the sentence true.

25. $0.4 < x < 0.5$

26. $12.3 > x > 12.03$

27. $-7.6 > x > -7.601$

28. Sarah used a micrometer to measure the thickness of a piece of paper. She found its thickness was halfway between 0.18 millimeters and 0.19 millimeters. How thick was the piece of paper?

29. **Find the Missing Data** Tell what data is needed to solve this problem. Jack bought 3 new CD's that regularly sell for $12.99. One of them was on sale. He paid $2.22 in tax. How much change did he receive from the two $20 bills he gave the store clerk?

Use Mathematical Reasoning

30. Use only the digits 0 and 1 to write four decimals that are >0 and <1.

31. Use only the digits 5 and 6 to write four decimals that are >5 and <6.

32. **Communicate** Write a paragraph that explains how our monetary system is a decimal system.

Mixed Review

Solve and check. **33.** $\frac{x}{13} = -17$ **34.** $-24n = -360$ **35.** $16t = -400$

Evaluate for $x = 6$. **36.** $9x - 2$ **37.** $\frac{-36}{x}$ **38.** $-6x - 2$

4-2 Estimating Using Rounding

Objective To round decimals and estimate decimal sums and differences.

Application

A computerized gasoline pump records gallon amounts to the third decimal place. The attendant rounds the number of gallons to the nearest tenth before writing a receipt.

Understand the Ideas

When working with decimals, you sometimes need an estimate rather than an exact answer. The procedure for rounding decimals is given below.

Rule Rounding Decimals

Look at the digit to the right of the place to which you are rounding.

- If it is less than 5, do not change the digit in the place to which you are rounding.
- If it is 5 or more, add 1 to the digit in the place to which you are rounding.

Replace the digits to the right of this place with zeros, or drop them if they are to the right of the decimal point.

Example 1

Round 3.814 gallons to the nearest tenth, as the attendant did in the **application.**

Solution 3.8 3.**8**14 Since $1 < 5$, leave the 8 unchanged. Drop the digits to the right of the 8.

The attendant wrote 3.8 gallons on the receipt.

Try This Round.

a. 7.087 to the nearest hundredth. **b.** 0.925 to the nearest tenth

c. 11.673 gallons to the nearest tenth.

Example 2

Round 593.679 to the nearest hundredth.

Solution 593.68 593.679 Since 9 > 5, round 7 up to 8 and drop the digits to the right.

Try This Round.

d. 73.484 to the nearest tenth. **e.** 0.253 to the nearest hundredth.

You can use rounding with decimals to make estimates.

Rule Estimating Using Rounding

- Round each decimal.
- Compute with the rounded decimals.

Example 3

Estimate the value of n by rounding. $n = 505.3 + 294.8$

Solution $500 + 300 = 800$ Round 505.3 to 500. Round 294.8 to 300.

The estimated value of n is 800.

Try This Estimate the value of x by rounding.

f. $x = 21.71 + 11.29$ **g.** $x = 352.92 - 147.19$

Class Exercises

To round to the indicated place, would you increase the digit in that place or leave it unchanged?

1. 3.578, tenths **2.** 5.294, hundredths **3.** 32.925, tenths

Discuss the Ideas

4. Explain why the following information is exact or rounded.

a. There are 5 people in the Tso family.

b. Texas covers an area of 267,300 square miles.

Exercises

Practice and Apply

Round to the nearest whole number.

1. 146.73 **2.** 93.48 **3.** 34.61 **4.** 8.499 **5.** 999.99

Round to the nearest tenth.

6. 23.78 **7.** 1.725 **8.** 76.39 **9.** 8.294 **10.** 4.286

Round to the nearest hundredth.

11. 4.5869 **12.** 5.497 **13.** 3.0089 **14.** 9.896 **15.** 0.999

Estimate the value of the variable by rounding.

16. $n = 218.6 + 101.2$ **17.** $x = 24.5 - 10.3$

18. $y = 18.603 + 21.2218$ **19.** $z = 125.3 + 34.8$

20. In 1979, the Voyager space probes passed Jupiter.
a. Which space probe came closer to Jupiter?
b. Round the distances to the nearest ten thousand kilometers.

Space Probe	Minimum Distance from Jupiter (km)
Voyager 1	275,960
Voyager 2	645,560

21. Round to the nearest tenth.
a. The length of a hummingbird is 8.27 cm.
b. In one day, bamboo can grow as much as 0.86 m.

Extend and Apply

22. Find four numbers that, when rounded to the nearest tenth, result in 23.5.

23. Use front-end estimation to estimate the sum. 5.53 + 9.48 + 7.24 + 8.77

24. Use estimation to decide which is the better buy: 5 bars of soap for $1.98 or 3 bars of the same soap for $1.10.

25. Keiko and Sara need to buy 80 hot dogs for a class picnic. They can buy packages of 8 hot dogs for $1.05 or packages of 10 hot dogs for $1.53. Use estimation to decide which is the better buy.

Use Mathematical Reasoning

Look for a pattern. Give the next three numbers.

26. $1, 1, 2, 3, 5, 8, 13, 21, \ldots$

27. $0.001, 0.1, 0.101, 0.201, 0.302, 0.503, 0.805, 1.308, \ldots$

28. $-0.03, 0.1, -0.13, 0.26, -0.49, 0.88, -1.63, 3.00, \ldots$

Mixed Review

Solve and check. **29.** $-36m = 648$ **30.** $t - 26 = -8$ **31.** $\frac{w}{-9} = 14$

Simplify. **32.** $6t - 8t$ **33.** $6(-12)m$ **34.** $-9 + x + 3$

Mental Math

When multiplying mentally with decimals, it is often helpful to use the Distributive Property to "break apart" numbers. To find 3 × 2.3, think "3 × 2 is 6 and 3 × 0.3 is 0.9, a total of 6.9."

Use the Distributive Property to find each product mentally.

1. 3 × 9.25 **2.** 4 × 5.25 **3.** 5 × 3.02 **4.** 2 × 7.05 **5.** 4 × 3.6

4-3 Adding and Subtracting with Decimals

Objective To compute decimal sums and differences.

Application

An 800-meter relay team had individual times of 21.83 seconds, 22.81 seconds, 22.93 seconds, and 21.12 seconds. The time for the team is the sum of the four decimals.

Understand the Ideas

To add or subtract with decimals, align the decimal points and add or subtract as with whole numbers. Place the decimal point in the sum or difference, in line with the other decimal points.

Example 1

Add 21.83 + 22.81 + 22.93 + 21.12 to find the time for the team in the application.

Solution

$$\begin{array}{r} \overset{2}{2}1.83 \\ 22.81 \\ 22.93 \\ +21.12 \\ \hline 88.69 \end{array}$$

Write the numbers vertically, aligning the decimal points, and add.

Place the decimal point in the answer.

The time for the relay team is 88.69 seconds.

Try This Add.

a. 34.28 + 259.3 **b.** 46.08 − 2.485

Example 2

Add. −5.3 + 2.7

Solution −5.3 + 2.7 = −2.6 Find the difference in absolute values. Since −5.3 has the larger absolute value, the sum is negative.

Try This Add.

c. −17.4 + 75.3 **d.** −3.8 + (7.9 − 3.7)

Example 3

Evaluate. $v - 7.62$ for $v = 6.1$

Solution

$$v - 7.62$$
$$6.1 - 7.62$$
$$= 6.1 + (-7.62) = -1.52$$

Try This Evaluate.

e. $w - 7.65 + 4.8$ for $w = -2.1$ **f.** $z - 3.9 + 9.31$ for $z = 8.63$

To evaluate an expression like the one in Example 3 for many different values of the variable v it is helpful to use a calculator. Store the constant 7.62 in memory using the key sequence [ON/AC] 7.62 [M+].

Then the sequence 6.1 [−] [MR] [=] would give the solution to Example 3.

Class Exercises

Place the decimal point and read the answer.

1. $3.2 + 6.7 = 99$ **2.** $9.51 + 1.3 = 1081$ **3.** $63.7 - 1.2 = 625$

Discuss the Ideas

4. The second relay team finished 0.5 min behind the winning time of 96.1 s. Explain why the second place team did not finish in 96.6 seconds.

Exercises

Practice and Apply

Add or subtract.

1. $35.82 + 12.3$ **2.** $9.73 + (-3.7)$ **3.** $2.81 + (9.73 - 3.7)$

4. $254.87 - 73.62$ **5.** $-48.52 - 73.36$ **6.** $-38.15 + 8.24 + 17.28$

7. $35.9 - 24.8$ **8.** $71.05 - 39.23$ **9.** $4.98 + (2.89 + 0.82)$

10. $973.2 - 48.38$ **11.** $21.03 - (-19.128)$ **12.** $398.237 - 59.83$

Evaluate.

13. $75.92 - y$ for $y = 35.1926$ **14.** $(u - 45.2) + 21.04$ for $u = -97.2$

15. $x - 93.2 + 17.3$ for $x = -0.36$ **16.** $(45.23 + v) + 38.3$ for $v = -17.5$

17. A cross-country course has an uphill section of 0.82 km, a flat section of 1.3 km, a downhill section of 1.1 km, and a wooded section of 1.05 km. How long is the course?

Extend and Apply

18. Evaluate $a - (b - c)$ and $(a - b) - c$ for $a = 12.5$, $b = 5.3$, and $c = 1.4$. Are the two expressions equivalent?

19. A company that makes stereo components had profits, in millions, for the year of \$5.62 on speakers and \$4.38 on turntables. It had losses of \$0.21 on headphones and \$1.03 on amplifiers. What was its net profit?

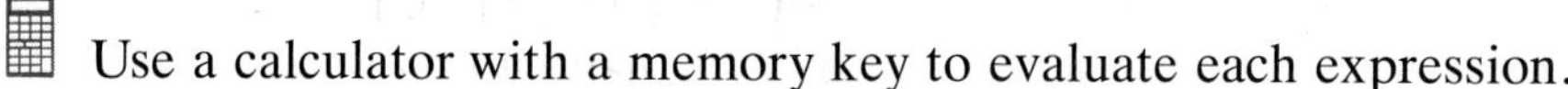

Use a calculator with a memory key to evaluate each expression.

20. $x - 2.73$ for $x = 7.9$, $x = 9.32$, and $x = 17.21$

21. $(12.5 - x) + 3.8$ for $x = 5.1$, $x = 7.92$, and $x = 3.3$

22. Communicate Explain how you can use compensation to find this difference mentally. $68.73 - 25.99$

Use Mathematical Reasoning

Copy each problem and find the missing digits.

23.
$$\begin{array}{r} 6\square.7 \\ -46.\square \\ \hline 14.8 \end{array}$$

24.
$$\begin{array}{r} 6\square\square.92 \\ -231.\square 5 \\ \hline 384.77 \end{array}$$

25. You can fly from one city to another and then return by train for a total travel time of 7.5 hours. To fly both ways would take a total of 2.5 hours. How long would it take to go both ways by train?

Mixed Review

Solve and check. **26.** $m - 36 = -15$ **27.** $33r = -594$ **28.** $\frac{x}{-26} = 18$

Evaluate for $n = 3$. **29.** $6n \div 9$ **30.** $-3n + 11$ **31.** $12n \div (-6)$

Connections Numbers to Algebra

In the Chapter 1 Numbers to Algebra, you saw that if a, b, c, and d represent whole numbers, then $(a + b) + (c + d) = (a + c) + (b + d)$. You can use this idea to simplify both numerical and algebraic expressions.

Numbers	Algebra
$(17 + 14) + (3 + 16)$ $= (17 + 3) + (14 + 16)$ $= 20 + 30 = 50$	$(2a + 3b) + (5a + 6b)$ $= (2a + 5a) + (3b + 6b)$ $= 7a + 9b$

Use the idea above to simplify each expression.

1. $(3x + 4y) + (4x + 2y)$ **2.** $(4a + 3b) + (7a + 6b)$

4-4 Solving Decimal Equations: Using Addition and Subtraction

Objective To solve decimal equations involving addition and subtraction.

Understand the Ideas

To solve decimal equations involving addition and subtraction, you can use the same steps you used to solve integer equations.

Example 1

Solve and check. $x + 0.21 = 7.32$

Solution

$x + 0.21 = 7.32$	Get the variable by itself on one side.
$x + 0.21 - \mathbf{0.21} = 7.32 - \mathbf{0.21}$	To undo adding 0.21, subtract 0.21 from both sides.
$x = 7.11$	

Check

$7.11 + 0.21 \stackrel{?}{=} 7.32$	Replace x with 7.11 in $x + 0.21 = 7.32$.
$7.32 = 7.32 \checkmark$	The solution is 7.11.

Try This Solve and check.

a. $x + 2.39 = -14.85$ **b.** $s + 4.287 = 6.24$

Example 2

Solve and check. $x - 0.01 = 4.35$

Solution

$x - 0.01 = 4.35$	Get the variable by itself on one side.
$x - 0.01 + \mathbf{0.01} = 4.35 + \mathbf{0.01}$	To undo subtracting 0.01, add 0.01 to both sides.
$x = 4.36$	

Check

$4.36 - 0.01 \stackrel{?}{=} 4.35$	Replace x with 4.36 in $x - 0.01 = 4.35$.
$4.35 = 4.35 \checkmark$	The solution is 4.36.

Try This Solve and check.

c. $x - 2.39 = 14.85$ **d.** $x - 5.92 = -2.813$

Class Exercises

Tell what operation you would use to solve the equation.

1. $x - 0.78 = 3.7$ **2.** $x + 8.92 = 13.5$ **3.** $y + 19.3 = 31$

Discuss the Ideas

4. Which of these equations doesn't belong? Explain.

a. $x + 0.5 = 3.1$ **b.** $z - 0.5 = 3.1$ **c.** $0.5 + y = -6.31$

Exercises

Practice and Apply

Solve and check.

1. $y + 0.05 = 7.95$
2. $z + 17.5 = 46.82$
3. $u + 0.99 = 5.72$
4. $x - 12.3 = -6.28$
5. $x + 29.6 = 142.8$
6. $x - 29.6 = -14.3$
7. $u + 1.53 = -26.91$
8. $v - 23.7 = -7.41$
9. $z + 0.5 = -5.03$
10. $x - 23.4 = 345.61$
11. $x - 5.05 = -4.38$
12. $x - 4.32 = 145.8$
13. A ferret weights 0.5 lb more than a guinea pig. Solve the equation $f - 0.5 = 1.54$ to find the weight of a ferret. How much does a guinea pig weigh?

Extend and Apply

Solve and check.

14. $-84.02 + z = 46.3$
15. $-46.3 = z + 84.02$
16. $(x - 5.2) + 0.47 = 25.84$
17. $32.7 + x + 25.2 = 124.8$
18. Write and solve an equation with sum of 35.82, one addend of 13.08, and the other addend represented by the variable y.

Use Mathematical Reasoning

19. Find values for x and y that solve both equations: $x + y = 1.5$ and $x - y = 0.5$.
20. The numbers in each row, column, and diagonal of this magic square have the same sum. Write equations for finding the values of w, x, y, and z.

1.6	0.2	x	1.3
w	1.1	1.0	0.8
0.9	0.7	0.6	y
0.4	z	1.5	0.1

Mixed Review

Compute. **21.** $120 - (65 \cdot 12) \div 15$ **22.** $15 + 8 \cdot 6 - 12$

Solve and check. **23.** $16m = -384$ **24.** $r - 16 = -4$

Mental Math

You can "break apart" numbers to add or subtract decimals mentally. For example, to find $9.45 + 11.55$, think "$9 + 11$ is 20 and $0.45 + 0.55$ is 1. The sum is 21."

Find each sum or difference by breaking apart the numbers.

1. $7.35 + 9.65$
2. $23.95 + 9.05$
3. $45.85 - 5.40$
4. $96.89 - 46.80$

4-5 Problem Solving: Applications

The Metric System

Objective To solve problems involving metric units.

The metric system of measurement uses the meter (m) as the basic unit of length, the liter (L) as the basic unit of capacity, and the gram (g) as the basic unit of mass.

A series of prefixes is used with the basic units. The table below shows how each prefix corresponds to a decimal place value.

kilo-	hecto-	deka-	--	deci-	centi-	milli-
1000 thousands	100 hundreds	10 tens	1 ones	0.1 tenths	0.01 hundredths	0.001 thousandths

When a prefix is attached to one of the basic units, a new unit is created. Look at the table below. Multiply a unit by 0.1 to obtain the unit on its right. Multiply a unit by 10 to obtain the unit on its left.

← larger **Metric Units of Length** smaller →						
kilometer (km)	**hecto**meter (hm)	**deka**meter (dkm)	meter (m)	**deci**meter (dm)	**centi**meter (cm)	**milli**meter (mm)
1000 m	100 m	10 m	1 m	0.1 m	0.01 m	0.001 m

The basic units of length, capacity, and mass are related to one another.

A cube with edges the *length* of one **decimeter** has the *capacity* of one **liter.** The *mass* of one liter of water is 1 **kilogram.**

Sample Problem A common dimension of camera film is 35 mm. How many meters is that?

Solution

$$35 \text{ mm} = 35 \times 1 \text{ mm}$$
$$= 35 \times 0.001 \text{ m}$$ Substitute 0.001 m for 1 mm.
$$= 0.035 \text{ m}$$

35 millimeters is the same as 0.035 meters.

Problems

Solve.

1. How many kilometers long is a 1500-meter race?
2. A man's waist size might be 90 cm. How many meters is that?
3. If the width of the palm of your hand is 0.8 dm, how wide is it in centimeters?
4. A football field is about 90 m long. How long is it in decimeters? In dekameters?
5. A penny is about 19 mm in diameter. How many centimeters is that?
6. A building is 12.34 meters long. How long is it in centimeters?
7. A stack of five pennies is about 1 cm high. Approximately how many millimeters thick is one penny?
8. If a person's stride is 50 cm long, how many strides equal one kilometer?
9. How many millimeters are there in one kilometer?
10. A thimble has a capacity of about 2 milliliters. What is the approximate mass of the water contained by a full thimble? (1 liter = 1 kilogram)
11. **Data Search** Weigh a milk carton full of water to find the mass of the water in grams. Approximately how many liters does the milk carton hold?

What's Your Decision?

To find the mass of water in a swimming pool, would you prefer to know the number of liters or the number of gallons it holds?

One dm^3 has a capacity of 1 liter.

4-6 Multiplying with Decimals

Objectives To estimate decimal products by rounding; to compute decimal products.

Explore

Multiplication of decimals can be represented on graph paper. The large square represents one unit and one small square represents 0.01.

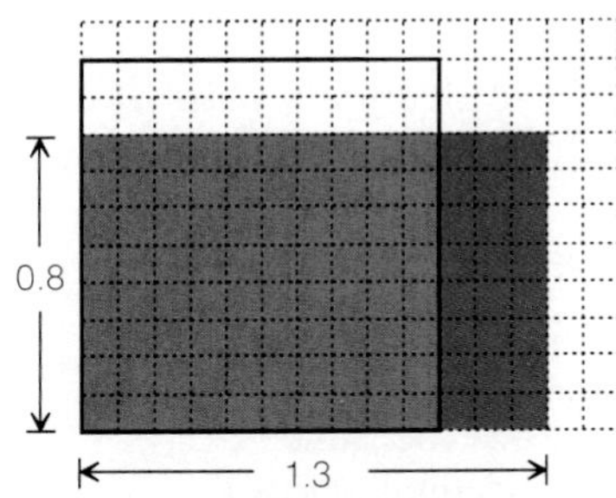

The shaded rectangle represents 0.8×1.3.

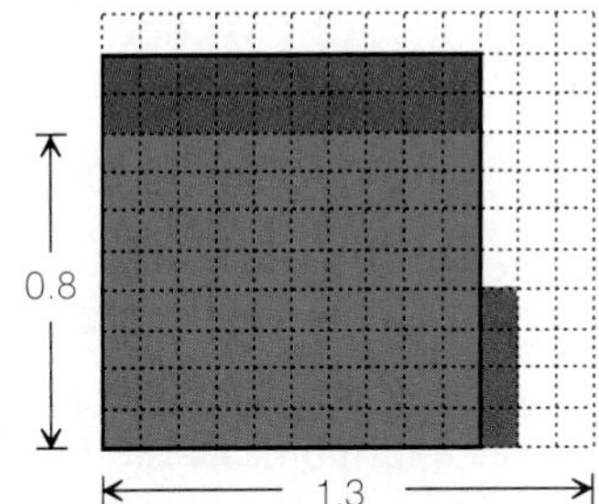

Rearrange shaded squares to show the product represents 1.04.

Represent each product on graph paper using the procedure shown above.

a. 1.3×2.4 **b.** 0.8×1.2 **c.** 1.7×1.9

Understand the Ideas

You can estimate the product of two decimals by rounding each decimal to the nearest whole number.

Example 1

Casey was preparing for her next mountain expedition and buying supplies. She wanted to buy 19.5 meters of rope priced at \$1.89 per meter. She had \$40. Estimate the cost of the rope by rounding $19.5 \times \$1.89$. Did Casey have enough money?

Solution

$19.5 \times \$1.89$

20×2 Round 19.5 to 20 and round 1.89 to 2.

$= 40.00$ Multiply.

$19.5 \times \$1.89$ is about \$40.00.

Since we rounded both numbers up, we know that Casey had enough money to pay for the rope.

Try This Estimate the product by rounding.

a. 9.8×12.1 **b.** 186.2×5.3

c. 19.2×43.9 **d.** 493.6×39.4

Sometimes you need an exact answer rather than an estimate. The steps for multiplying decimals with paper and pencil are given below.

The *sign* of the product of two decimals is determined in the same way as the sign for an integer product. The product of two decimals with like signs is positive. The product of two decimals with unlike signs is negative.

Rule Multiplying with Decimals

- Multiply as with whole numbers.
- Place the decimal point in the product so that it has the same number of decimal places as the total number of decimal places in the factors.
- Determine the sign of the product, as with integers.

Example 2

Multiply. $1.02 \times (-0.36)$

Solution

$$\begin{array}{r} 1.02 \\ \times\, 0.36 \\ \hline 612 \\ 306 \\ \hline 0.3672 \end{array}$$

Since the sum of the decimal places in the factors is 4, the product has 4 decimal places.

-0.3672 The product of a positive and a negative number is negative.

Try This Multiply.

e. 4.12×2.1 **f.** $-7.3 \times (-0.02)$

Sometimes you need to write zeros to the left of the calculated number in order to place the decimal point.

Example 3

Use a calculator to evaluate. $3.12v + 1.5$ for $v = 2.1$

Solution

$3.12(2.1) + 1.5$ Replace v with 2.1.

3.12 [×] 2.1 [+] 1.5 [=] 8.052

Try This Evaluate.

g. $3.89t - 7.2$ for $t = 4.3$

h. $7.41s + 3.87$ for $s = -2.7$

Class Exercises

Place the decimal point mentally and read the answer.

1. $3.46 \times 57.9 = 200334$

2. $146.2 \times 0.013 = 19006$

3. $12 \times 17.32 = 20784$

4. $29.83 \times 0.0035 = 0104405$

Discuss the Ideas

Decide whether the statement is always, sometimes, or never true.

5. The product of two numbers whose decimal form is 0.xxx is a number less than one. (the x's represent digits.)

6. The product of 12.3 and a number of the form 0.xxx is less than 10.

Exercises

Practice and Apply

Estimate the product by rounding.

1. 19.8×5.25

2. 8.1×4.5

3. 3.9×0.75

4. 399.6×20.03

5. 25.2×9.8

6. 996.8×37.5

Multiply.

7. 18.9×0.01

8. $4.01 \times (-0.32)$

9. $-34.6 \times (-0.1)$

10. 16.32×1.03

11. -4.38×0.08

12. 196.3×0.01

13. -84.6×-3.05

14. 0.193×100

15. 21.3×0.481

16. Darrell walks at the rate of 5.8 feet per second. How far does he walk in 5 seconds?

17. A vehicle travels at the rate of 23.4 m/s. How far does it travel in 2.03 seconds?

Use a calculator to evaluate these expressions.

18. $4.81w + 8.2$ for $w = 8.3$

19. $93.45y - 19.3$ for $y = 18.4$

20. $-12.3z + 5.3$ for $z = 9.3$

21. $34.5 - 3.2k$ for $k = 9.86$

Extend and Apply

Estimate the product, then compute.

22. 23.2×1.08

23. 0.515×0.02

24. 7.3×0.003

25. $2.3 + (3.2 \times 5.3)$

26. $4.2(1.3 + 6.7)$

27. $5.9(2.1 + 8.3)$

The relationship between temperature in degrees Fahrenheit (°F) and temperature in degrees Celsius (°C) is given by the formula $F = 1.8C + 32$. Evaluate the formula to find F for each value of C.

28. $C = 0°$ **29.** $C = 17°$ **30.** $C = 37°$

31. The hottest temperature ever recorded in North America was 56.7°C, in Death Valley. Use the formula above to find the temperature in degrees Fahrenheit.

32. A record was set by a driver in a three-wheeled car that averaged 157.19 miles per gallon while using 2.871 gallons of fuel. How many miles (to the nearest tenth) did the car travel?

Use Mathematical Reasoning

33. Leslie, Beth, Rafael, and Jason are joining Casey on a mountain climb. In how many different orders can the five climbers tie themselves to the safety rope if Casey is always the lead member of the party?

34. A mountain climb has four routes from the base camp to the first campsite, two routes from there to the second campsite, and one route from there to the peak. How many different routes are there to the peak?

Mixed Review

Simplify. **35.** $46c - 3c$ **36.** $35 + (m + 6)$ **37.** $7(-9k)$

Evaluate for $a = 6$, $b = 4$, $c = 2$. **38.** $a + b - c$ **39.** $2(a - c) + b$

Order from least to greatest. Use inequality symbols. **40.** 1.04, 1.4, 0.14

Computer Activity

The following program will print a table of equivalent Celsius and Fahrenheit temperatures.

```
10 REM CONVERSION PROGRAM
20 PRINT "DEGREES CELSIUS","DEGREES FAHRENHEIT"
30 FOR C=-10 TO 40
40 LET F=1.8*C+32
50 PRINT C,F
60 NEXT C
70 END
```

1. Use the table to check Exercises 28–30 above.

2. Alter the program so it can be used to answer Exercise 31.

3. Explain why there are no negative numbers in the Fahrenheit column.

4-7

Dividing with Decimals

Objective To estimate decimal quotients by rounding and choosing compatible numbers; to compute decimal products.

Application

A university charges \$5,789.40 for tuition, fees, room, and board for the school year. A student is permitted 12 monthly payments. What is the amount of the payment each month? When Sonya plans her monthly budget, she uses an estimate. But when she writes a check to the university, she will need an exact answer.

Understand the Ideas

When estimating, use the symbol $\approx$, which means "is approximately equal to."

Example 1

Round and choose compatible numbers to estimate Sonya's monthly bill in the **application.** $5{,}789.40 \div 12$

Solution $5{,}789.40 \div 12$

$\approx 5{,}800 \div 12$ — Round 5,789.40 to 5,800.

$\approx 5{,}500 \div 11$ — Change 5,800 to 5,500 and 12 to 11 to get compatible numbers for division.

≈ 500 — $5{,}789.40 \div 12 \approx 500$.

Sonya can estimate her monthly university budget as \$500.

Try This Round and choose compatible numbers to estimate.

a. $25.20 \div 8.10$ **b.** $46.30 \div 5.91$

You will often need an exact answer rather than an estimate. When the divisor is a whole number, place the decimal point in the quotient directly above the decimal point in the dividend.

Example 2

Divide to find the exact amount of Sonya's monthly check to the university in the **application.** $5789.40 \div 12$

Solution

$$\begin{array}{r} 482.45 \\ 12\overline{)5789.40} \\ \underline{48} \\ 98 \\ \underline{96} \\ 29 \\ \underline{24} \\ 54 \\ \underline{48} \\ 60 \\ \underline{60} \\ 0 \end{array}$$

Since the divisor is a whole number, place the decimal point in the quotient directly above the decimal point of the dividend.

Sonya will write a check to the university for $482.45 each month.

Try This Divide. **c.** $382.5 \div 18$ **d.** $223.2 \div 24$

When the decimal point is moved one place to the right in both dividend and divisor, the same quotient results.

$$\begin{array}{r} 3. \\ 2.0\overline{)6.0} \end{array} \qquad \begin{array}{r} 3. \\ 20.\overline{)60.} \end{array}$$

This supports the following procedure for dividing with decimals.

Rule Dividing with a Decimal Divisor

- Move the decimal point the same number of places to the right in both divisor and dividend until the divisor is a whole number.
- Divide.
- Determine the sign as you would for division with integers.

Example 3

Divide. $-0.0483 \div 2.1$

Solution

$$\begin{array}{r} 0.023 \\ 2.1\overline{)0.0483} \\ \underline{42} \\ 63 \\ \underline{63} \end{array}$$

Move the decimal point in both the divisor and the dividend and place the decimal point one place to the right. In the quotient, annex a zero.

-0.023 The quotient is negative since divisor and dividend have unlike signs.

Try This Divide.

e. $0.0045 \div 1.8$ **f.** $-1.353 \div 4.1$ **g.** $0.0315 \div 0.7$ **h.** $33.37 \div 4.7$

Class Exercises

Place the decimal point in the quotient mentally and read it.

1. $29.61 \div 9 = 329$ **2.** $16.3 \div -5 = -326$ **3.** $104.4 \div 6 = 174$

Discuss the Ideas

4. When one decimal is divided by another decimal, is the quotient sometimes, always, or never a whole number?

Exercises

Practice and Apply

Round and choose compatible numbers to estimate.

1. $23.72 \div 4.9$
2. $37.2 \div 5.78$
3. $121.4 \div 40.3$

Divide.

4. $33.58 \div 73$
5. $-0.4611 \div 53$
6. $6.201 \div 53$
7. $1.6758 \div 21$
8. $129.89 \div 31$
9. $87.99 \div (-21)$
10. $10.4 \div (-0.02)$
11. $109.5 \div 0.05$
12. $-131.58 \div (-8.6)$
13. $4.42 \div 1.3$
14. $-51.3 \div (-1.9)$
15. $2.88 \div 0.18$
16. An employer determines that he must withhold \$1,810.50 for an employee's annual income tax. Approximately how much will be withheld each of 12 months? (Estimate mentally.)
17. The employee in Exercise 16 is paid every 2 weeks. The payroll clerk must determine exactly how much to withhold for income taxes from each of 26 paychecks. Divide \$1,810.50 by 26 to find the amount withheld.

Extend and Apply

Estimate an answer, then divide.

18. $(4.63 + 25.5) \div 2.3$
19. $(24.7 \div 6.5) + 4.53$
20. $(1.3 + 1.82) \div 2$

Evaluate.

21. $x \div 7.5$ for $x = 12$
22. $x \div 2.25$ for $x = 72$
23. $x \div 3.5$ for $x = 14$

Use Mathematical Reasoning

Find the pattern in the quotients and write the next equation.

24.
$1.21 \div .11 = \underline{?}$
$12.321 \div 1.11 = \underline{?}$
$123.4321 \div 11.11 = \underline{?}$

25.
$0.05 \div .99 = \underline{?}$
$0.08 \div .99 = \underline{?}$
$0.123 \div .999 = \underline{?}$

Mixed Review

Solve and check. **26.** $n + 0.65 = 1.7$ **27.** $r - 0.83 = -1.26$

Evaluate for $m = 1.63$. **28.** $m - 19.09$ **29.** $1.27 - m$ **30.** $3.2 + m$

Write as an algebraic expression. **31.** 0.95 added to a number

32. Two less than half a number **33.** The quotient of 8.3 and a number

4-8 Problem Solving: Writing Equations

Writing Equations to Solve Problems

Objective To solve word problems by writing equations.

You can use the Problem-Solving Checklist as a guide for solving problems when your plan involves the strategy **Write an Equation.**

Problem-Solving Checklist
Writing Equations

Understand the Situation/Find the Needed Data
What do you need to find? Can you show the data in the problem?
Plan the Solution/Estimate the Answer
Can you use a variable to represent an unknown number?
Can you represent other conditions in terms of the variable?
What is equal in the problem? Can you write and solve an equation?
What is a reasonable estimate for the answer?
Solve the Problem/Check the Answer
Does the solution of the equation check?
What is the answer to the question in the problem?
Does the answer seem reasonable?

Example

Find the solution by writing and solving an equation. Check your answer.

Karla was running in a 26 km marathon. A friend held up a sign saying, "Only 8 km more to run." How far has Karla run?

Solution

You need to find how many kilometers Karla has run so far.

26 km
Start — Karla — 8 km — Finish

Draw a diagram to show the data.

Let d = the distance Karla has run.

Choose a variable to represent what you want to find.

$$d + 8 = 26$$
$$d + 8 - 8 = 26 - 8$$
$$d = 18$$

The distance Karla has run plus 8 km is equal to the total distance of the race. Write and solve an equation.

Check $18 + 8 \stackrel{?}{=} 26$ Check the equation solution.

$26 = 26\ \checkmark$ The equation solution checks.

Karla has run 18 km. 18 km and 8 km is 26 km. The answer is reasonable.

Try This Find the solution by writing and solving an equation.

a. Any student who sells 25 yearbooks wins a radio. Karen needs to sell 6 more yearbooks to win a radio. How many has she sold so far?

Class Exercises

Discuss the Ideas

Answer **a** through **e** for each problem.

a. What are you trying to find?

b. What are the important data?

c. What will the variable represent?

d. What is equal in the problem?

e. What is the equation?

1. A salesman sold $3,440 worth of merchandise. This was half his goal for the month. What was his goal?

2. After Mr. and Mrs. Wong gave their children 45 rare coins, they had 129 left in their collection. How many coins were in their original collection?

Exercises

Practice and Apply

Choose the equation or equations that can be used to solve each problem.

1. Lupe can start driving in 3 years. If the driving age is 16, how old is Lupe now?

a. $a + 3 = 16$ **b.** $a - 3 = 16$ **c.** $16 - 3 = a$

2. Phil saves $2 from his allowance each week. How many weeks will he have to save to buy a $36 skateboard?

a. $\frac{w}{2} = 36$ **b.** $2w = 36$ **c.** $2 + w = 36$

Find the solution by writing and solving an equation.

3. A movie was set in a year 16 years before the year 2005. In what year was it set?

4. A theater sold $789 worth of tickets. Each ticket cost $3. How many tickets did the theater sell?

5. Mr. Bolt sold 17 fewer cars than Ms. Johnson sold. Mr. Bolt sold 53 cars. How many cars did Ms. Johnson sell?

6. A sweater costs $24.75. Dana needs $8.50 more to buy the sweater. How much money does Dana have now?

7. A runner's time was 4.52 seconds more than the school's record. The runner's time was 29.32 seconds. What was the school's record?

8. Barry spent $3.75 of his allowance. He had $4.25 left. How much was his allowance?

Extend and Apply

9. Elaine earns \$4.25 an hour as a part-time clerk at a grocery store. Last week, she earned \$85.75, which included a \$5 bonus. How many hours did she work last week?

10. A number of people signed up for a recreation program. When 17 more enrolled the next day, 15 groups of 8 people could be formed. How many people signed up the first day?

11. Find the Missing Data Tell what data is needed to solve the problem. The local real estate property tax each year is 0.0102 times the appraised value of your property. How much property tax did Mr. Jordan pay for his movie theater?

Use Mathematical Reasoning

12. Write a word problem that could be solved using the equation.

a. $x + 15 = 43$ **b.** $5x = 115$

Mixed Review

Solve and check. **13.** $t - 1.863 = -2.1$ **14.** $m + 3.6 = 8$

Evaluate for $a = 1.5, b = 2.0$. **15.** $2a - b$ **16.** ab **17.** $a + b - 8$

Round to the nearest whole number and estimate the product. **18.** 9.2(0.89)

Calculator Activity

Some calculators have a Cons key that can be used for repeated multiplication by the same factor. The key sequence × 3 Cons makes 3 the repeating factor, as shown in the example below.

× 3 Cons	Display
4 Cons	12
6 Cons	18
9 Cons	27

This key sequence completes the problems $3 \cdot 4$, $3 \cdot 6$, and $3 \cdot 9$, with the answers displayed after each press of the Cons key.

A store owner is raising all prices by the factor 1.05. Use the constant multiplier key to find the new prices for the current prices given. Round prices to the nearest cent, if necessary.

1. 72.85 **2.** 92.60 **3.** 126.98 **4.** 361.89

4-9 Solving Decimal Equations: Using Multiplication and Division

Objective To solve decimal equations involving multiplication and division.

Application

In a diving competition, each dive is assigned a level of difficulty between 1.0 and 3.8. Each judge rates the dive on a scale of 0 to 10, with 10 being a perfect dive. The judge's score is then multiplied by the level of difficulty to give the total score for the dive.

Understand the Ideas

Many problems are solved by first writing an equation. If the equation has a variable that has been multiplied by a decimal, divide both sides of the equation by that decimal.

Example 1

In the **application,** Hyunsun scored a 27.58 on a dive with a 2.8 level of difficulty. Solve and check the equation $2.8r = 27.58$ to find the judge's rating of her dive.

Solution

$$2.8r = 27.58$$

$$\frac{2.8r}{\mathbf{2.8}} = \frac{27.58}{\mathbf{2.8}}$$ To undo multiplying by 2.8, divide by 2.8 on both sides.

$$r = 27.58 \div 2.8$$

$$r = 9.85$$

Check $2.8(9.85) \stackrel{?}{=} 27.58$ Replace r with 9.85 in $2.8r = 27.58$.

$$27.58 = 27.58 \checkmark$$

The judge gave Hyunsun a score of 9.85 on her dive.

Try This Solve and check.

a. $1.5x = 225$ **b.** $0.05x = -46$

To solve an equation in which the variable has been divided by a decimal, multiply both sides of the equation by that decimal.

Example 2

Solve and check. $\frac{x}{2.15} = -1.4$

Solution

$$\frac{x}{2.15} = -1.4$$

$$\frac{x}{2.15}(2.15) = -1.4(2.15)$$ To undo dividing by 2.15, multiply by 2.15 on both sides.

$$x = -3.01$$ Unlike signs result in a negative product.

Check $\frac{-3.01}{2.15} \stackrel{?}{=} -1.4$ Replace x with -3.01 in $\frac{x}{2.15} = -1.4$

$-1.4 = -1.4$ ✓ The solution is -3.01.

Try This Solve and check.

c. $\frac{x}{0.14} = 5.2$ **d.** $\frac{z}{-3.2} = 5.8$

Class Exercises

To solve, would you multiply or divide in the first step?

1. $\frac{x}{2.1} = 5.98$ **2.** $-8.21y = 5.7$ **3.** $23.5z = 8.3$

4. $19.6 = 3.5w$ **5.** $\frac{u}{7.1} = -83.5$ **6.** $-19.7 = \frac{z}{-3.9}$

Discuss the Ideas

7. When solving an equation like $2.5x + 7.5 = 28.5$, how do you decide what operation to perform in the first step of the solution?

Exercises

Practice and Apply

Solve and check.

1. $2.1x = 11.13$ **2.** $0.15z = 0.24$ **3.** $1.41y = -9.87$

4. $\frac{w}{6.5} = 7.2$ **5.** $\frac{z}{8.3} = -2.3$ **6.** $\frac{w}{3.2} = 48$

7. $-4.5x = 67.5$ **8.** $\frac{y}{1.7} = -3$ **9.** $3.6z = -43.2$

10. $-0.002u = -576.4$ **11.** $1.005x = 20.1$ **12.** $\frac{x}{-0.09} = 81$

13. $\frac{u}{4.98} = -1.2$ **14.** $\frac{-x}{0.55} = 0.2$ **15.** $\frac{y}{-5.4} = 3.2$

16. Greg scored 31.04 for a dive with a 3.2 level of difficulty. Solve the equation $3.2j = 31.04$ to find the judge's score for his dive.

17. A van is traveling at a speed of 66 ft/s. Solve the equation $66s = 303.6$ to find out how many seconds it will take the van to travel 303.6 feet.

Extend and Apply

Decide whether you will use paper and pencil or a calculator. Then solve and check these equations.

18. $-321.3 = 5.1x$

19. $-306.9 = 17.05x$

20. $21 = 67.2z$

21. $\frac{-u}{12.5} = -1.4$

22. $-0.91 = \frac{u}{1.2}$

23. $4.3 = \frac{x}{3.7}$

24. $(1.4 + 3.6)x = 15.5$

25. $\frac{x}{4.2} = 5.8 + 21.3$

26. $\frac{z}{8.5 - 2.3} = 25.4$

Write and solve an equation.

27. A number is multiplied by 1.2 and results in the product 264.

28. A number is divided by 3.4 and results in the quotient 25.3.

29. Write a word problem that could be solved using the equation $6.5x + 7.25 = 104.75$.

Use Mathematical Reasoning

Use inverse operations to find the missing number in each flow chart.

30. Start with ? ⟶ Multiply by 1.2 ⟶ Add 4.3 ⟶ End with 7.9

31. Start with 2.3 ⟶ Add 4.6 ⟶ Multiply by ? ⟶ End with 36.57

32. Write the equation whose solution is found by following the flow chart in Exercise 30.

33. Write the equation whose solution is found by following the flow chart in Exercise 31.

34. **Communicate** Write a flow chart similar to the ones in exercises 30 and 31 that can be used to find the solution to the equation $2.6(x - 4.8) = 12.6$. Then explain to a classmate how you figured it out.

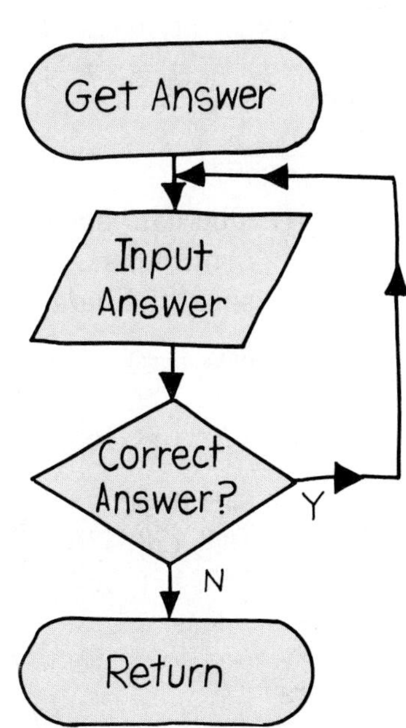

Mixed Review

Evaluate for $x = 1.5, y = 3.6$. **35.** $2x - 2y$

36. xy **37.** $2x + y$

Solve and check. **38.** $m + 1.04 = 3.1$

39. $-12k = 144$

Round to the nearest tenth and estimate the value of x. **40.** $9.02 + x = 1.49$

4-10 Data Collection and Analysis

Stem-and-Leaf Diagrams

Objective To construct and interpret stem-and-leaf diagrams.

A **stem-and-leaf diagram** is a method of displaying numerical data that shows all of the original numbers and has the visual impact of a tally. A stem-and-leaf diagram is easy to construct, easy to read, and is a useful means of comparing data.

Making a Stem-and-Leaf Diagram

Here is how to construct a stem-and-leaf diagram for the data at the right. To make the diagram, we split each numeral into two parts, a stem and a leaf. In this diagram, the stem numbers are tens digits and the leaf numbers are ones digits. The weights in the bottom row, 37, 35, 39, 38, 39, 38, and 37 are read by putting the stem number with each of the leaf numbers.

Weights in Kilograms of Boys and Girls in a Class	
Boys' Weights	**Girls' Weights**
41, 37, 35, 46, 50, 44, 40, 41, 45, 37, 39, 43, 45, 38, 51, 45	50, 39, 51, 50, 49, 48, 47, 38, 46, 52, 45, 49, 53, 47, 52, 52

Stem	Leaf
5	0, 1, 0, 1, 0, 2, 3, 2, 2
4	1, 6, 4, 0, 1, 5, 3, 5, 5, 9, 8, 7, 6, 5, 9, 7
3	7, 5, 7, 9, 8, 9, 8

Project

1. The data below shows student heights in centimeters. Make a stem-and-leaf diagram to show the data. Use 2-digit stem numbers.

   Boys' Height
   156, 139, 164, 149, 147, 176, 134, 153, 172, 163, 168, 138, 170, 157, 155, 145

   Girls' Height
   164, 128, 136, 147, 129, 136, 145, 161, 149, 171, 164, 173, 165, 173, 156, 159

2. A **ranked** stem-and-leaf diagram has numbers in order from least to greatest. Rank the stem-and-leaf diagram you made in problem 1.

Making Stem-and-Leaf Diagrams with Two Sets of Data

A stem-and-leaf diagram can also be used to display and compare two sets of data. This diagram shows the weight data from the previous page separated into weights for boys and girls. The stem numbers are in the center columns. The leaf numbers are in the outside columns.

Boys		Girls
0, 1	5	0, 1, 0, 2, 3, 2, 2
1, 6, 4, 0, 1, 5, 3, 5, 5	4	9, 8, 7, 6, 5, 9, 7
7, 5, 7, 9, 8	3	9, 8

Project

3. Make a stem-and-leaf diagram to display and compare the heights of boys and girls in a class. Use the height data given on the previous page.

Interpreting the Diagrams

- Here is one interpretation someone might make from the diagram on the previous page: The largest group of weights are in the 40s.
- Here is one interpretation someone might make from the diagram at the top of this page: The average girls' weight is in the upper 40s.

Work in groups to generate as many observations as possible about the two diagrams. Discuss your observations and compare them with the observations of other groups.

Project

4. Explain how the diagrams suggest each of the interpretations above.
5. Look at your diagrams for heights and make some statements that interpret the data. Explain your interpretations.
6. Make stem-and-leaf diagrams for the heights and weights of the students in your class. Use the diagrams to make statements that interpret the data.

4-11 Problem Solving: Strategies

Simplify the Problem

Objective To solve nonroutine problems, using the strategy "Simplify the Problem" and other strategies learned so far.

Solving some problems can be quite difficult if you try to find the solution using the numbers given in the problem. The strategy **Simplify the Problem** can help. To simplify, substitute smaller numbers. Then solve the simplified problem, and use your solution to it to help you solve the original problem.

Sample Problem Ms. Corelli needs to install phone lines for a political convention. She has to install lines connecting each committee chairperson's desk with each of the others' desks. Ten desks are to be connected in all. A separate phone line is needed for each connection so people won't listen in on conversations. How many phone lines should Ms. Corelli install?

To solve, try **simplifying** the problem. Suppose there were only 2 desks, rather than 10, that needed phone lines. You could draw a **diagram.**

If there were 2 desks, 1 line would be needed.

With 3 desks, 3 lines would be needed.

With 4 desks, 6 lines would be needed.

Recording the results from these simpler problems in a **table** helps you see a **pattern.** The difference in the number of lines needed increases by 1 each time.

Number of Desks	2	3	4	5	6	7	8	9	10
Lines needed	1	3	6	10	15	21	28	36	45

2 3 4 5 6 7 8 9

A total of 45 lines is needed to connect the 10 desks.

Problem-Solving Strategies

Choose the Operations	Make a Table	Make an Organized List
Guess, Check, Revise	Look for a Pattern	Use Logical Reasoning
Draw a Diagram	Write an Equation	Work Backward
	Simplify the Problem	

Problems

Solve.

1. A major company gave a large financial gift to a university. The plan was that $1 million would be given to the university the first year. In each of the following years, the university would receive an amount that was double the amount it received the previous year. What was the total amount of the gift through 12 years?
2. A 100-km bicycle race was held on roads near a large city. Markers were placed at the starting line of the race, at the finish line, and at every 10 km in between. How many markers were used for this race?
3. In a basketball game, the Giants beat the Lions by 25 points. The coach of the Lions said, "If we had scored twice as many points, we would have beaten the Giants by 14 points." What was the final score?
4. A boat was having engine trouble. Each day, it could go forward 20 miles. At night, it had to rest its engines and would drift back 5 miles. At this rate, how many days would it take the boat to get 100 miles from its starting point?

Group Decision Making

5. Work in a group. Discuss and decide.

Situation: Your sister is on a soccer team. The coach asked you to take the team's picture and make a 5 × 7 print for each of the 15 members of the team. He will pay you $5 an hour for your time and whatever expenses are involved. You want to find out how much this will cost the coach.

Guidelines for Planning

- **Formulate Problems** you will need to solve.
- Discuss **Assumptions** you will make and **Data** you will need.

a. What decision or decisions do you need to make in this situation?

b. Formulate problems you need to solve to make the decision(s).

c. List any assumptions you need to make to arrive at a decision.

d. What data, if any, do you need to collect to make a decision?

e. Write a paragraph summarizing what your group did, what decisions you made, and why.

Extend Key Ideas

The Binary System and the Computer

A microcomputer that has an 8-bit microprocessor processes information that is coded in strings of 8 digits of zeros and ones.

A digital computer uses only two digits, 0 and 1, to code information. Numbers are represented by a place value system called the **binary system.**

As in the decimal system, each digit in the binary system has a place value. The first seven place values are shown in red below.

Binary Place Value	64	32	16	8	4	2	1
Binary Number	1	1	0	1	1	0	1

The base 10 number represented by the binary number 1101101 is found by multiplying the digit in each place by its place value and adding together all the values.

$$\begin{aligned}(1101101)_2 &= 1(64) + 1(32) + 0(16) + 1(8) + 1(4) + 0(2) + 1(1)\\ &= 109\end{aligned}$$

Find the base 10 number represented by each binary number.

1. 1011 **2.** 1101 **3.** 110111

4. 100011 **5.** 1010111 **6.** 11001

Chapter 4 Review/Test

Understanding

True or False?

4-1 **1.** To decide which number is smaller, 48.072 or 48.009, start at the right and compare the 2 and the 9.

4-4 **2.** To solve $x - 3.2 = 5$ first add 3.2 to both sides of the equation.

4-6 **3.** The product 2.39×14.5 will have three digits to the right of the decimal point because in the problem 2.39×14.5 there are a total of three decimal places in the factors.

4-7 **4.** You can find $25.32 \div 1.8$ by changing the problem to $2532 \div 18$.

4-9 **5.** To solve the equation $\frac{x}{3.15} = 25.2$ begin by dividing both sides of the equation by 3.15.

Skills

4-1 Write as a decimal.

6. $1(10) + 5(1) + 3\left(\frac{1}{10}\right)$

7. $4(100) + 6\left(\frac{1}{100}\right) + 8\left(\frac{1}{10}\right)$

4-2 Estimate the value of x by rounding.

8. $33.89 - 19.25 = x$

9. $x = 415.2 + 75.5$

10. $x = 391.37 - 106.93$

11. $59.82 + 16.05 = x$

4-3 Evaluate.

12. $41.35 - d$ for $d = 9.16$

13. $m + 0.199$ for $m = 49.02$

4-4 4-9 Solve and check.

14. $f + 17.6 = -12.9$

15. $g - 6.43 = 29.62$

16. $1.2p = -5.76$

17. $\frac{w}{3.8} = 4.2$

4-6 Estimate the product by rounding.

18. 4.38×6.1

19. 19.6×9.8

20. 11.02×0.98

Applications

4-5 **21.** Lisa ran a 500-meter race. How many kilometers is the race?

4-11 **22.** There are seven cities in a loop. Every set of three cities is connected by a communications triangle. How many triangles are there all together for these seven cities?

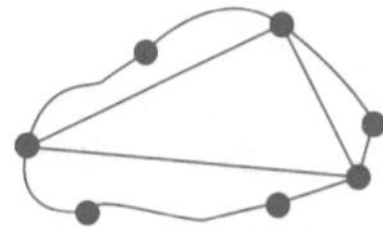

4-8 **23.** Solve by writing an equation. Sophie had 24.7 meters of fencing. She bought a 50 meter roll of fencing. How much fencing does she have now?

5 Number Theory

This vintage automobile was built in 1939. Is 1,939 prime or composite?

5-1 Factors and Multiples

Objective To write multiples and factors of a number.

Explore

Here is a rectangle made of 16 squares. Find as many other rectangles made of 16 squares as you can and draw them on a sheet of graph paper.

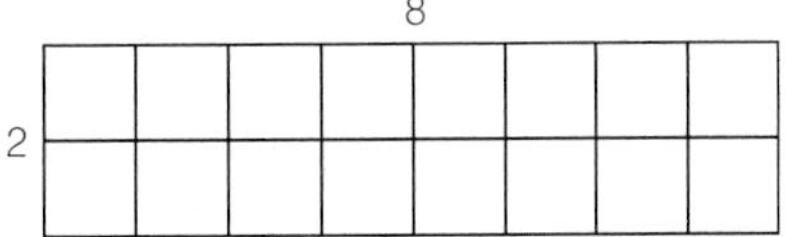

List the numbers that are lengths or widths of these rectangles.

Find all rectangles made of 24 squares and of 17 squares.

Understand the Ideas

You can find several different pairs of numbers whose product is 16. When two or more whole numbers are multiplied to form a product, each number is called a **factor** of the product.

Factors of 16   The **product** of 2 times 8

$$2 \times 8 = 16$$

You can write equations like this to show that 1, 2, 4, 8, and 16 are factors of 16.

You can divide to find out if one number is a factor of a second. Just divide the second number by the first. If the quotient is a whole number with a remainder of 0, then the divisor and the quotient are each factors of the dividend.

$$\begin{array}{r} 2 \\ 8\overline{)16} \\ -\underline{16} \\ 0 \end{array}$$

Example 1

Can 153 floor tiles be put in full rows of 9 with none left over? Decide by answering the question "Is 9 a factor of 153?".

Solution $153 \div 9 = 17$

9 is a factor of 153.

Since $153 \div 9 = 17$, with a remainder of 0, then $17 \times 9 = 153$, and 9 and 17 are factors of 153.

Try This

a. Is 13 a factor of 106?

b. Is 7 a factor of 84?

c. Determine if 96 floor tiles can be put in full rows of 8 with none left over by answering "Is 8 a factor of 96?".

To find all the factors of a whole number, divide the number by each whole number, beginning with 1. Stop dividing when the factors repeat.

Example 2

Find the factors of 12.

Solution The factors of 12 are 1, 2, 3, 4, 6, and 12.

12 ÷ 1 = 12, so **1** and **12** are factors of 12.
12 ÷ 2 = 6, so **2** and **6** are factors of 12.
12 ÷ 3 = 4, so **3** and **4** are factors of 12.
12 ÷ 4 = 3 produces no new factors. The factors 3 and 4 repeat. Stop.

Try This **d.** Find all the factors of 18. **e.** Find all the factors of 32.

You can use a calculator with a memory to find the factors of a given whole number quickly. First enter the number and push M+ to record it in the calculator's memory. Then try each divisor 2, 3, 4, 5, . . . in order, as shown below.

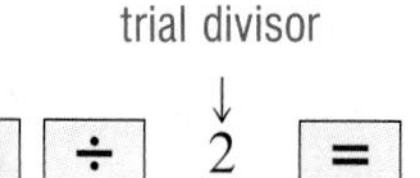

When the answer is a whole number, the trial divisor and the whole number are factors of the number in the memory.

Example 3

Use a calculator to find all the factors of 72.

Solution

72 ÷ 1 = 72 72 ÷ 2 = 36 72 ÷ 3 = 24
72 ÷ 4 = 18 72 ÷ 6 = 12 72 ÷ 8 = 9

Enter 72 into the calculator's memory, 72 M+.

The factors of 72 are 1, 2, 3, 4, 6, 8, 9, 12, 18, 24, 36, and 72.

Try This **f.** Use a calculator to find all the factors of 96.

The product of two whole number factors is a **multiple** of each of the whole numbers. The multiples of a number can be found by multiplying the number by 0, 1, 2, 3, 4, and so on.

$$0 \times 2 = \boldsymbol{0}, \quad 1 \times 2 = \boldsymbol{2}, \quad 2 \times 2 = \boldsymbol{4}, \quad 3 \times 2 = \boldsymbol{6}, \ldots$$

0, 2, 4, 6, . . . are multiples of **2.** All whole numbers that are multiples of 2 are called **even numbers.** All whole numbers that are not multiples of 2 are called **odd numbers.**

Example 4

Write the first five nonzero multiples of 6.

Solution 6, 12, 18, 24, 30

Try This

g. Write the first three nonzero multiples of 7.

h. Write the first five nonzero multiples of 9.

Class Exercises

Is the statement true or false?

1. 25 is a multiple of 5. **2.** 24 is a factor of 7. **3.** 4 is a multiple of 16.

4. 28 is a multiple of 4. **5.** 5 is a factor of 25. **6.** 8 is a factor of 20.

Discuss the Ideas

Decide whether these statements are sometimes, always, or never true.

7. A non-zero whole number has an unlimited number of multiples.

8. A non-zero whole number has at least two factors.

9. For non-zero numbers, if a is a multiple of b, then b is a factor of a.

Exercises

Practice and Apply

Is the first number a factor of the second?

1. 4, 20 **2.** 5, 32 **3.** 4, 96 **4.** 5, 75 **5.** 9, 576

Find all the factors of the given number.

6. 16 **7.** 20 **8.** 28 **9.** 84 **10.** 40 **11.** 60

Use a calculator to find the factors of each number.

12. 78 **13.** 90 **14.** 105 **15.** 120 **16.** 256 **17.** 630

Give the first four nonzero multiples of each number mentally.

18. 3 **19.** 5 **20.** 7 **21.** 11 **22.** 20 **23.** 100

Use a calculator to give 5 nonzero multiples of each number.

24. 68 **25.** 137 **26.** 346 **27.** 599 **28.** 875 **29.** 1056

30. Give the last 6 odd numbers less than 100 and the first 6 even numbers greater than 100.

31. Determine if 114 cars can be parked in full rows of 7 with none left over by deciding if 7 is a factor of 114.

32. Determine if 552 tennis balls can be packed in full cans of 3 with none left over by deciding if 3 is a factor of 552.

33. Teri wanted to paste 18 stamps on a collector's book page. In what different ways can she put stamps in a row to have all full rows and none left over? Decide by finding all the factors of 18.

Extend and Apply

34. Solve the equations. Use the results to list all the factors of 72.

    a. $1m = 72$ b. $2n = 72$ c. $3p = 72$

    d. $4q = 72$ e. $6r = 72$ f. $8s = 72$

35. Solve the equation $18b = 1{,}638$. Then give two 2-digit factors of 1,638.

36. Find a number that has only two factors.

37. Find four numbers that have only three factors. Describe these numbers.

38. If n is any whole number, which expressions represent only even numbers?

    a. $2n$ b. $3n$ c. $4n$ d. $2n + 1$ e. $2n - 1$ f. $2n + 2$ g. $n + 2$

39. Describe five ways in which twenty-four cars can be parked in rows in a parking lot, with the same number in each row.

40. **Find the Missing Data** Tell what data is needed to solve this problem. Then make up data and solve the problem.

    A city planner was planning the construction of a new parking lot with spaces to park 135 automobiles. She intended to choose the number of rows and then determine the number of spaces to include in each row. How many spaces should she include in each row?

41. **Write to Learn** Suppose you were asked to "introduce the number 18" to an audience! Write a short paragraph telling as many things as possible that you could say about 18. Use as many of the terms defined in this section as you can.

Use Mathematical Reasoning

42. Complete these generalizations about even (E) and odd (O) numbers.

    a. E + E = ___ b. O + O = ___ c. E + O = ___

    d. E × E = ___ e. O × O = ___ f. E × O = ___

43. The number 6 is called a perfect number because the sum of its factors other than itself is 6. Show that 28 is a perfect number.

44. Find 3 numbers that are both a multiple of 6 and a multiple of 8.

Mixed Review

Solve and check. **45.** $-9x = 59.4$ **46.** $m \div 3.7 = 3.92$

Evaluate for $h = -9.45, p = 4.5$. **47.** $(h \div p) + 2$ **48.** $2p - h + 1.75$

Write as an algebraic expression. **49.** two more than twice m

5-2 Divisibility

Objective To use divisibility rules.

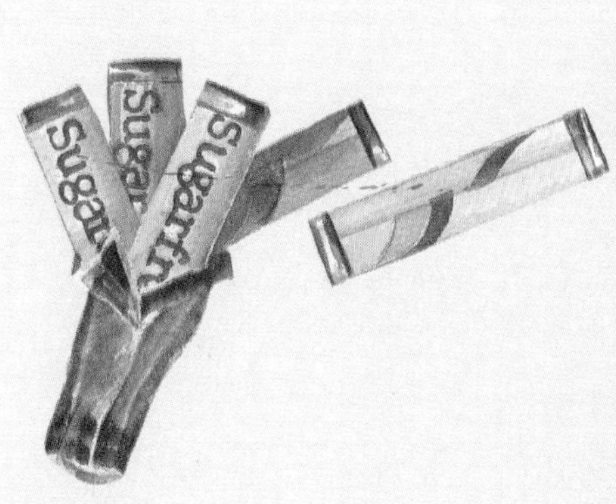

Application

A chewing gum factory packages 5 sticks of gum into a small pack and 2 small packs into a large pack. The packaging supervisor wants to know if 53,760 sticks of gum will make a whole number of full large packs of gum.

Understand the Ideas

A whole number is **divisible** by another whole number if, when it is divided by that number, the result is a whole number quotient with a remainder of zero. For example, **21** is divisible by ***3*** because **21** ÷ ***3*** gives the quotient 7 with the remainder 0. A whole number is divisible by each of its factors.

Every number has 1 as a factor. The divisibility rules below are shortcuts for determining whether a whole number has 2, 3, or 5 as a factor.

Rule Divisibility by 2, 3, and 5

- A number is **divisible by 2** if its ones digit is even (0, 2, 4, 6, or 8).
- A number is **divisible by 3** if the sum of its digits is divisible by 3.
- A number is **divisible by 5** if its ones digit is 0 or 5.

Example 1

In the **application,** 53,760 sticks of gum are ready to be packaged. Answer these questions to see if they will make a whole number of full large packs.

a. Is 53,760 divisible by 5? **b.** Is 53,760 divisible by 2?

Solution **a.** 53,760 is divisible by 5 The ones digit is 0 or 5, so it is divisible by 5.
b. 53,760 is divisible by 2 The ones digit is even (2), so it is divisible by 2.

Since 53,760 is divisible by both five and two, 53,760 sticks of gum will make a whole number of full large packs.

Try This Is the number divisible by 2? Is it divisible by 5?

a. 5,874 **b.** 27,965 **c.** 369 **d.** 8,000 **e.** 9,270 **f.** 5,558 **g.** 87,256

h. Can 275,865 sticks of gum be put into a whole number of full small packs of 5?

i. Can 55,173 small packs of gum be put into a whole number of large packs of 2?

Example 2

Is 837 divisible by 3?

Solution 837 is divisible by 3. 8 + 3 + 7 = 18. Since the sum of the digits is divisible by three, 837 is divisible by 3.

Try This Which numbers are divisible by 3?

j. 81 **k.** 243 **l.** 953 **m.** 9,613

Class Exercises

Tell if the number is **odd** or **even.** Then find the sum of its digits.

1. 456 **2.** 970 **3.** 895 **4.** 438 **5.** 763

Discuss the Ideas

Are these statements true? Test using 504, 156, 608, and other numbers. Explain.

6. A number divisible by 4 and by 2 is always divisible by 8.

7. A number divisible by 8 is always divisible by 4 and by 2.

Exercises

Practice and Apply

State whether the number is divisible by 2.

1. 45 **2.** 74 **3.** 98 **4.** 289 **5.** 170

State whether the number is divisible by 5.

6. 58 **7.** 75 **8.** 60 **9.** 125 **10.** 702

State whether the number is divisible by 3.

11. 98 **12.** 173 **13.** 2,706 **14.** 2,897 **15.** 97,497

16. Can the 250 children in a park recreation program each have a partner? Can they be divided into teams of 5 with no extras?

17. Determine if 5,762 batteries can be put into packages of 3 with none left over by deciding if 5,762 is divisible by 3.

Extend and Apply

A whole number is divisible by 6 if it is divisible by 2 and by 3. State whether each number is divisible by 6.

18. 468 **19.** 2,678 **20.** 42,672 **21.** 54,987

A whole number is divisible by 9 if the sum of its digits is divisible by 9. State whether each number is divisible by 9.

22. 81 **23.** 342 **24.** 5,670 **25.** 8,769

A whole number is divisible by 4 if its last 2 digits are divisible by 4. State whether each number is divisible by 4.

26. 532 **27.** 9,366 **28.** 24,847 **29.** 57,936

30. Write a rule for divisibility by 10.

31. Fill in the missing hundreds and ones digits in 3,▒4▒ so that the number will be:

a. divisible by 2. **b.** divisible by 3. **c.** divisible by 5.

Use Mathematical Reasoning

32. Find the smallest number that is divisible by each of the numbers 1–9.

33. A number is divisible by 1, 5, and 7. It is an even number less than 100. Find the number. Find three other divisors of the number.

Mixed Review

Write <, >, or = for each □. **34.** 1.01 □ 10.1 **35.** -6.25 □ -7.19

36. -0.01 □ 0.001 **37.** 0.14 □ 0.14 **38.** 4.031 □ 4.013

Evaluate. **39.** $k - 61.73$, for $k = 16.937$ **40.** $m - 10.62$, for $m = 10.637$

41. $(17 - r) + 26.1$, for $r = 16.937$ **42.** $\frac{11.776}{x}$, for $x = 5.12$

Mental Math

A way of deciding mentally whether a number is divisible by 3 is to "cast out multiples of 3" before adding the digits. Study the following mental steps for deciding whether the number 356,937 is divisible by 3.

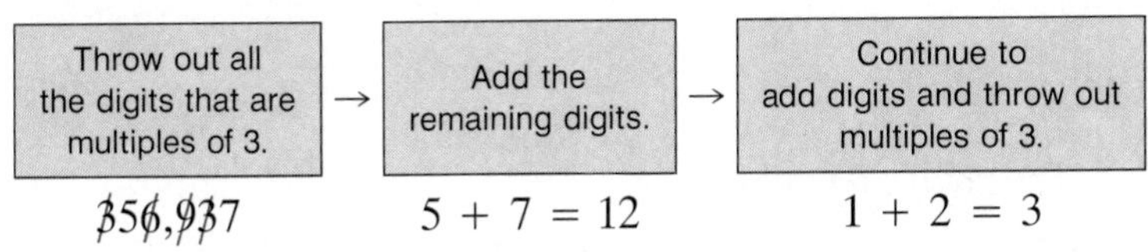

If all the digits in the original number are thrown out, or if the final digit is thrown out, the number is divisible by 3.

Cast out multiples of 3 to decide whether each number is divisible by 3.

1. 919,536 **2.** 273,649 **3.** 6,589,335 **4.** 74,239,436

5-3 Problem Solving: Writing Equations

Writing Equations to Solve Problems

Objective To solve word problems by writing and solving equations.

When solving problems, keep the following questions in mind.

- Can you use a variable to represent an unknown number?
- Can you represent other conditions in terms of the variable?
- What is equal?
- Can you write and solve an equation?

Example

Find the solution by writing and solving an equation. Gloria had \$51, which was just enough to pay for school yearbooks for herself and two friends. How much did a yearbook cost?

Solution Let c = cost of a yearbook. — You want to find the cost of a single yearbook. Choose a variable to represent this.

$$3c = 51$$

\$51 equals 3 times the cost of a yearbook.

$$\frac{3c}{3} = \frac{51}{3}$$

$$c = 17$$

Write and solve an equation.

Check $3(17) \stackrel{?}{=} 51$

$$51 = 51 \checkmark$$

The equation solution checks.

Each yearbook costs \$17. — Estimate: Three \$20 yearbooks would cost \$60. The answer is reasonable.

Try This Find the solution by writing and solving an equation.

a. Todd divided the price of a stereo by 6 to find the amount of one of 6 equal payments. The payment was \$84. What was the total price?

Class Exercises

Discuss the Ideas

Answer **a.** through **e.** for each problem.

a. What are you trying to find?
b. What are the important data?
c. What will the variable represent?
d. What is equal in the problem?
e. What is the equation?

1. The sum of a number and 3 is -5. What is the number?

2. In 17 years, Kenny will be 50. How old is he now?

Exercises

Practice and Apply

Choose the equation or equations that can be used to solve each problem.

1. Therese bought 3 softball bats for \$75.45. How much was each bat?

   a. $\frac{75.45}{b} = 3$ **b.** $3b = 75.45$ **c.** $\frac{b}{3} = 75.45$

2. A conductor earns \$48 more per concert than the cellist. If the conductor earns \$128 for a concert, how much does the cellist earn?

   a. $c - 48 = 128$ **b.** $c + 48 = 128$ **c.** $128 - c = 48$

Solve by writing an equation. Check your answer.

3. Tim picked up a pizza for himself and three friends. Later, when they divided the cost of the pizza equally, each of them paid \$2.41. What was the total cost of the pizza?
4. The even number 146 is twice an odd number. What is the odd number?
5. Sixteen years ago, Sylvia was 26 years old. How old is Sylvia now?
6. A class sold a total of 453 tickets to a play. This was three times the number they had sold on a certain day. How many did they sell on that day?

Extend and Apply

7. To make a 20-percent profit on an item, a store manager must sell the item for 1.2 times the amount he paid. On a compact-disc player that sells for \$354, the manager makes a 20-percent profit. Did the manager pay more or less than \$300 for it?
8. Mrs. Luzinski bought 12 video cassettes in packages of 4. She multiplied the cost of 1 cassette to find a total cost of \$84. How much did each cassette cost?
9. An egg farm shipped out 8,064 eggs on Friday. The eggs were packed in boxes of 1 dozen. How many boxes were used? The boxes were packed in crates that held a dozen boxes. How many crates were used?

Use Mathematical Reasoning

10. Write a word problem that could be solved using the equation $3x = 78$.
11. Write a word problem that could be solved using the equation $x - 26 = 19$.

Mixed Review

Evaluate for $n = 9$. **12.** $n - 11$ **13.** $-n - 11$ **14.** $n + 11$
15. $-n + 11$ **16.** $n - n$ **17.** $2n$ **18.** $\frac{n}{-3}$ **19.** $6 - 2n$

Solve and check. **20.** $-3r = 8.22$ **21.** $\frac{t}{1.6} = 32.2$
22. $m - 19.26 = 0.004$ **23.** $\frac{a}{-9.2} = -6.15$ **24.** $-6.1 = \frac{x}{7.5}$

5-4 Prime and Composite Numbers

Objective To decide whether a number is prime or composite.

Application

Scientists send signals of prime number sequences into space in hopes of communicating with intelligent life on other planets.

Understand the Ideas

The number 7 has exactly two factors, 1 and 7. Any whole number that has exactly two factors, 1 and itself, is called a **prime number.**

Number	Factors	Type
1	1	neither
2	1, 2	prime
3	1, 3	prime
4	1, 2, 4	composite
5	1, 5	prime
6	1, 2, 3, 6	composite
7	1, 7	prime
8	1, 2, 4, 8	composite

Any whole number greater than 1 that has more than two factors is called a **composite number.** The number 1 has only one factor, so it is neither prime nor composite. The table at the right shows whether each number from 1 to 8 is prime, composite, or neither. The first four prime numbers are 2, 3, 5, and 7.

To decide whether a number is prime or composite, find its factors.

Example 1

In the **application,** a signal for the number 11 has been sent. What is the next prime number signal that should follow 11?

Solution The next number, 12, is composite, not prime. 12 has more than 2 factors.

The next number, 13, is prime and should be signaled. 13 has exactly 2 factors, 1 and 13.

Try This **a.** Give the next three prime numbers after 13 that should be signaled into space.

Class Exercises

Discuss the Ideas

Here are some statements made by students. How can you prove that they are incorrect?

1. All prime numbers are odd.

2. All odd numbers are prime.

Exercises

Practice and Apply

State whether the given number is prime or composite. If it is composite, give a factor of the number other than itself and 1.

1. 6	**2.** 7	**3.** 9	**4.** 14
5. 18	**6.** 22	**7.** 61	**8.** 32
9. 40	**10.** 43	**11.** 34	**12.** 45

13. Kaya's teacher said that each number in the sequence of numbers 31, 41, 51, 61, 71 was prime except one. Find the composite number.

Extend and Apply

14. List all prime numbers less than 50.

15. Find the smallest number for n that gives a composite value for

a. $6n + 1$ **b.** $6n - 1$

16. Evaluate the formula $P = (n \cdot n) - n + 11$ for $n =$ each of the whole numbers 1 through 11. For which value of n is P not prime?

Use Mathematical Reasoning

17. Consecutive primes, such as 3 and 5, that have a difference of 2 are called **twin primes.** Find three more pairs of twin primes.

18. Continue this pattern until you arrive at a number that is not a prime. 11, 13, 17, 23, . . .

19. A mathematician named Goldbach claimed that every even number greater than 2 is the sum of two prime numbers. No one has proven this true, but no one has proven it false! Show that it is true for the even numbers 4 through 30.

Mixed Review

Solve and check. **20.** $12.3 = r + 6.72$ **21.** $n \div 0.35 = 1.75$

22. $2.4c = 4.08$ **23.** $t + 0.8 = 1.1$ **24.** $-0.09y = -45$

5-5 Powers and Exponents

Objectives To write, interpret, and multiply numbers using exponential notation.

Understand the Ideas

A product in which the factors are identical is called a **power** of that factor. $32 = 2 \cdot 2 \cdot 2 \cdot 2 \cdot 2$, so 32 is the fifth power of 2. **Exponents** are used to write powers in short form. The exponent indicates the number of times the **base** is used as a factor.

$$2 \cdot 2 \cdot 2 \cdot 2 \cdot 2 = 2^5$$

2^5 ← **Exponent**; 2 ↖ **Base**

We read this as "two to the fifth power."

Other examples in which exponents are used to show powers are given below.

$\mathbf{4^2}$ is 4 to the **second power** (or 4 squared) and means $4 \cdot 4$, or 16.

$\mathbf{10^3}$ is 10 to the **third power** (or 10 cubed) and means $10 \cdot 10 \cdot 10$, or 1000.

$\mathbf{3^4}$ is 3 to the **fourth power** and means $3 \cdot 3 \cdot 3 \cdot 3$, or 81.

$\boldsymbol{a^6}$ is a to the **sixth power** and means $a \cdot a \cdot a \cdot a \cdot a \cdot a$.

A number raised to the first power is that number. For example, $10^1 = 10$.

To show the factors of a number expressed using exponents, you write the number in **expanded form**, also called factored form.

Example 1

A wildlife report stated that there are over 10^6 distinct types of animals in existence today. Write 10^6 in expanded form and simplify if possible.

Solution

$$10^6 = 10 \cdot 10 \cdot 10 \cdot 10 \cdot 10 \cdot 10$$
$$= 1,000,000$$

The exponent, 6, indicates that 10 is a factor 6 times.

Try This Write in expanded form and simplify if possible.

a. 3^4 **b.** $(-2)^4$ **c.** a^3

d. An African elephant can weigh over 10^4 pounds. Write 10^4 in expanded form and simplify.

A calculator with a y^x key can be used to simplify a number written with exponents.

Example 2

Use a calculator to simplify. 8^3

Solution

8 [y^x] 3 [=] 512

Try This Use a calculator to simplify.

e. 4^3 **f.** 2^5 **g.** 12^2

Example 3

Write using exponents. $7 \cdot 7 \cdot 7 \cdot 7$

Solution 7^4 The base, 7, is a factor 4 times.

Try This Write using exponents.

h. $10 \cdot 10 \cdot 10$ **i.** $-2(-2)$ **j.** *bbbb*

To find the product of numbers expressed using exponents, you can simply add exponents to find the total number of factors in the product.

$$2^4 \cdot 2^3 = \underbrace{(2 \cdot 2 \cdot 2 \cdot 2)}_{4 \text{ factors}} \cdot \underbrace{(2 \cdot 2 \cdot 2)}_{+\ 3 \text{ factors}} = \underbrace{2^7}_{=\ 7 \text{ factors}}$$

This leads to a rule for *multiplying* numbers with like bases.

Rule **Multiplying Powers with Like Bases**

To multiply two or more powers with like bases, first add the exponents. Use this sum as the exponent together with the original base to express the product.

For any number a, and whole numbers m and n, $a^m \cdot a^n = a^{m+n}$

Example 4

Multiply. Give the answer in exponent form. $3^2 \cdot 3^4$

Solution $3^2 \cdot 3^4 = 3^6$ To multiply powers with like bases, add the exponents. $2 + 4 = 6$

Try This Multiply. Give the answer in exponent form.

k. $(-5)^2 \cdot (-5)^4$ **l.** $10^2 \cdot 10^5$ **m.** $x^2 \cdot x^3$

The rule above works only when two powers with the *same bases* are *multiplied*. It does not apply when multiplying powers with unlike bases or when *adding* powers with like bases. The following example demonstrates how to add powers with like bases.

Example 5

Simplify. $3^2 + 3^4$

Solution $3^2 + 3^4 = 9 + 81$ Find $3^2 = 3(3) = 9$, and find $3^4 = 3(3)(3)(3) = 81$.

$= 90$ Add.

Try This Simplify. **n.** $10^2 + 10^3$ **o.** $(-5)^2 + (-5)^4$

Class Exercises

Name the base and exponent, then read the expression.

1. 10^4 **2.** 9^5 **3.** 3^{17} **4.** 5^7

Discuss the Ideas

5. A student simplified $3^2 \cdot 4^2$ to 7^2. How do you know it is incorrect? What might the student have been thinking to make the error?

Exercises

Practice and Apply

Write in expanded form. Simplify if possible.

1. 10^7 **2.** 5^4 **3.** 7^3 **4.** 12^5 **5.** 9^3

6. $(-10)^5$ **7.** 8^2 **8.** $(-6)^3$ **9.** n^4 **10.** b^5

Write using exponents.

11. $5 \cdot 5 \cdot 5 \cdot 5$ **12.** $(-3)(-3)(-3)(-3)(-3)$ **13.** $10 \cdot 10 \cdot 10 \cdot 10$

14. $2 \cdot 2 \cdot 2 \cdot 2 \cdot 2$ **15.** $(9)(9)(9)(9)$ **16.** $yyyyyy$

Multiply. Give answers in exponent form.

17. $3^2 \cdot 3^4$ **18.** $2^4 \cdot 2^6$ **19.** $10^7 \cdot 10^3$ **20.** $(-5)^1 \cdot (-5)^3$

Simplify.

21. $2^3 + 2^2$ **22.** $(-3)^2 \cdot (-3)^3$ **23.** $5^1 \cdot 5^2$ **24.** $4^2 + 4^3$

25. There are about 5^8 distinct types of plants known to exist. Give this number in expanded form and use a calculator to simplify.

26. A cubic centimeter of silver has a mass of about 10^1 grams. There are 10^3 cubic centimeters in a cubic decimeter. Find the mass of a cubic decimeter of silver by simplifying $10^1 \cdot 10^3$.

Extend and Apply

Write using exponents.

27. 100 **28.** 1,000 **29.** 10,000 **30.** 100,000

Evaluate the expression.

31. $y^5 \cdot y^3$ for $y = 4$

32. $10^a \cdot 10^b$ for $a = 2, b = 3$

33. $5^x \cdot 5^y$ for $x = 4, y = 3$

34. $10^a + 10^b$ for $a = 2, b = 3$

35. $10^a + b$ for $a = 2, b = 23$

36. $4^p \cdot 4^q \cdot 4^r$ for $p = 3, q = 5, r = 2$

Complete the equations in 37. Then answer the questions in 38–39.

37. $(-2)^1 = ?$ $\quad (-2)^2 = ?$ $\quad (-2)^3 = ?$ $\quad (-2)^4 = ?$

38. When a negative integer is raised to an odd power, is the result a positive or a negative integer?

39. When a negative integer is raised to an even power, is the result a positive or a negative integer?

Use Mathematical Reasoning

40. Jesse suggested to his parents the following plan for his monthly allowance. He would get 1 penny on the first day, 2 pennies on the second day, 4 pennies on the third day, 8 pennies on the fourth day, and so on. If Jesse's parents agree to the plan, how much should he get on the 30th day?

41. A *googol* and a *googolplex* are defined as follows.

10^{100} = one googol $\qquad 10^{\text{googol}}$ = one googolplex

a. One googol is one followed by how many zeros?

b. One googolplex is 1 followed by how many zeros?

Mixed Review

Evaluate for $a = 2.5, b = 3, c = 3.25$. **42.** abc **43.** $a - c$

44. $3a - 2b + c$ **45.** $bc - a$ **46.** $bc \div (-a)$ **47.** $2a - b$

Solve. **48.** $10.4 + x = 8.7$ **49.** $9.8(x) = 22.54$ **50.** $396.49 - x = 177.5$

Estimation

To gain a feeling for certain large number amounts, it helps to compare them to powers of ten. Choose the power of ten, 10^4, 10^5, 10^6, 10^7, 10^8, or 10^9, that you would estimate is closest to each of the following amounts. Use an atlas or other reference book to check your estimates.

1. the population of the city in which you live, or the nearest large city
2. the population of the United States
3. the population of the world
4. the population of the largest city in the world

5-6 Prime Factorization

Objective To write the prime factorization of a number.

Understand the Ideas

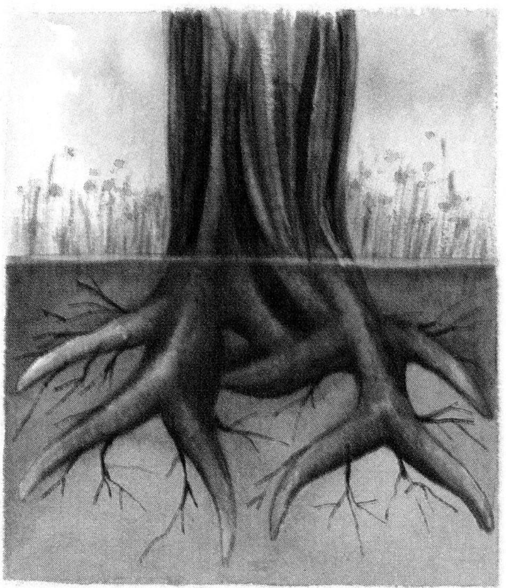

A factor tree shows a number as a product of prime factors. This factor tree shows that $24 = 2 \cdot 2 \cdot 2 \cdot 3$, or $2^3 \cdot 3$.

24

6 · 4

2 · 3 · 2 · 2

Prime factorization of 24

This expression of 24 as a product of prime factors is called the **prime factorization** of 24. We say that 24 has been **factored completely.** A factor tree for 24 that begins with $8 \cdot 3$ will have the same prime factors appearing in the bottom row, but perhaps in a different order. This suggests the following theorem.

Unique Factorization Theorem

Every composite number can be expressed as the product of prime numbers in only one way, except for the order of the factors.

Example 1

Make a factor tree to find the prime factorization of 60.

Solution

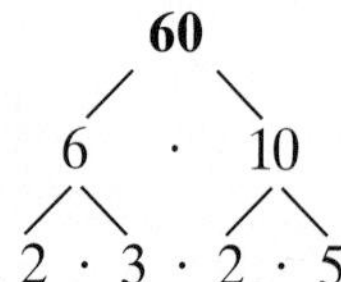

For the first row, look for any two numbers with product 60.

The prime factorization of 60 is $2 \cdot 2 \cdot 3 \cdot 5$.

Try This Make a factor tree to find the prime factorization of each number.

a. 40 **b.** 54

Example 2

Write the prime factorization of 84, using exponents.

Solution $84 = 2 \cdot 42 = 2 \cdot 6 \cdot 7$
$= 2 \cdot 2 \cdot 3 \cdot 7 = 2^2 \cdot 3 \cdot 7$

First find any 2 factors. Then continue to find factors until all are prime.

Try This Write the prime factorization of each, using exponents.

c. 28 **d.** 72

You can use repeated division to find the prime factorization of a number.

Example 3

Use repeated division to find the prime factorization of 60.

Solution

```
2|60
  2|30
    3|15
      5|5
        1
```

Beginning with 2, check whether each prime is a factor of the number. If it is, divide the number by the prime. Continue until you arrive at a quotient of 1.

$60 = 2 \cdot 2 \cdot 3 \cdot 5$ The product of the divisors is the prime factorization of the number.

Try This Use repeated division to find the prime factorization of each.

e. 42 **f.** 315

Class Exercises

Give each number as the product of two factors.

1. 6 **2.** 8 **3.** 15 **4.** 14 **5.** 26

Discuss the Ideas

6. How many different factor trees can you find for the number 12? What do these factor trees have in common?

Exercises

Practice and Apply

Copy and complete each factor tree to find the prime factorization.

1. 36 **2.** 30 **3.** 210

Make a factor tree to find the prime factorization of each number.

4. 32 **5.** 48 **6.** 63 **7.** 140 **8.** 150

Use exponents to show the prime factorization of each number.

9. 12 **10.** 42 **11.** 45 **12.** 225 **13.** 585

Use repeated division to find the prime factorization of each number.

14. 297 **15.** 108 **16.** 216 **17.** 625 **18.** 9,282

19. Jenny and Katie each chose a number between 100 and 200. The winner of the round was the one whose number had the most different primes in its prime factorization. Jenny chose 156. Katie chose 184. Who won the round?

Extend and Apply

Solve the equation to complete the prime factorization.

20. $546 = 2 \cdot 3 \cdot 7 \cdot n$ **21.** $385 = n \cdot 7 \cdot 11$ **22.** $285 = 3 \cdot 5 \cdot n$

Solve the equation to find the number whose prime factorization is given.

23. $3^2 \cdot 5^3 = n$ **24.** $2^2 \cdot 3^4 \cdot 7 = x$ **25.** $t = 2^4 \cdot 5^2 \cdot 7^3$

Use a calculator for Exercises 26 and 27.

26. Evaluate the expression $n \cdot 7 \cdot 11 \cdot 13$ for the following values of n: $n = 263$, $n = 389$, $n = 59$. Do you see a shortcut for evaluating such an expression? Use the shortcut to evaluate the expression for $n = 974$.

27. Rima's teacher asked her to replace a with her age in the expression $a \cdot 3 \cdot 37 \cdot 91$, and then evaluate the expression. If Rima is 14 years old, what is the value of the expression? Evaluate the expression for $a = 23$, $a = 47$, $a = 75$, $a =$ your age. What do you discover?

Use Mathematical Reasoning

28. Jeffrey's teacher told him that her age was a 2-digit number that was equal to twice the product of its digits. How old was Jeffrey's teacher?

29. Find the smallest number that has six different primes in its prime factorization.

30. Look for a pattern in the prime factorization of each number in the sequence. Give the next two numbers. 2, 6, 30, 210, ___ , ___ .

Mixed Review

Use the variable n to write an equation for each statement.

31. 9 times the sum of 12 and a number gives 135.

32. 266 is 56 more than the product of a number and 15.

Solve and check. **33.** $36n = -558$ **34.** $c - 19.65 = -17.3$

5-7 Greatest Common Factor

Objective To find the greatest common factor of numbers.

Application

A ski school has 32 students enrolled for the morning session and 40 students enrolled for the afternoon session. The instructor wants to divide the students into same-sized groups, making each group as large as possible.

Understand the Ideas

The **Greatest Common Factor (GCF)** of two whole numbers is the greatest whole number that is a factor of *both* the numbers.

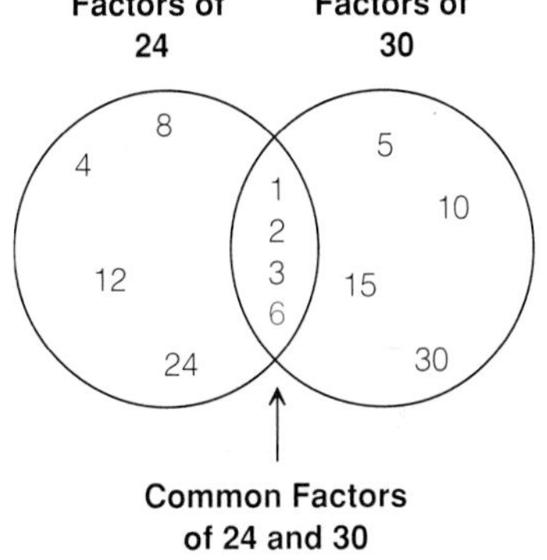

Factors of 24 1, 2, 3, 4, 6, 8, 12, 24

Factors of 30 1, 2, 3, 5, 6, 10, 15, 30

Common Factors of 24 and 30 1, 2, 3, 6

Greatest Common Factor of 24 and 30 6

In the example above, the factors of both numbers were listed to find the GCF. A method often used for finding the GCF of two whole numbers is to list the factors of the smaller number only, then look for the largest of these factors that is also a factor of the larger number.

Example 1

List the factors of 32 and 40 to find the number of students the instructor should place in each group in the **application.**

Solution Factors of 32: 32, 16, 8, 4, 2, 1 — Neither 32 nor 16 is a factor of 40.

8 is the GCF of 32 and 40. — 8 is the largest factor of both 32 and 40.

The instructor should place 8 students in each group.

Try This List factors of the smaller number to find the GCF of each pair. **a.** 18, 27 **b.** 20, 12

c. Determine the size of the group in the application if 20 students are enrolled for the morning session and 45 students are enrolled for the afternoon session.

Another way of finding the GCF is to use the prime factorization of the numbers. This method is useful in work with algebraic expressions. Factors that occur in the prime factorizations of both numbers are included as factors in the GCF.

Example 2

Use prime factorization to find the GCF of 36 and 60.

Solution $36 = \mathbf{2} \times \mathbf{2} \times \mathbf{3} \times 3$ Write the prime factorizations of 36 and 60.

$60 = \mathbf{2} \times \mathbf{2} \times \mathbf{3} \times 5$

GCF of 36 and 60 $= 2 \times 2 \times 3 = 12$ The GCF is the product of all the common prime factors.

Try This Use prime factorization to find the GCF. **d.** 12, 16 **e.** 24, 30

More than 2,000 years ago, Greek mathematicians discovered an unusual method, called the Euclidean Algorithm, for finding the GCF of two numbers. This method is used at the right to find the GCF of 84 and 308. It is also described in the flow chart below.

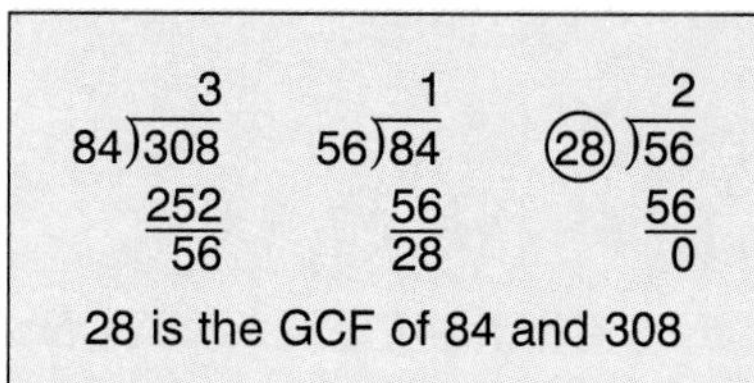

Euclidean Algorithm Flow Chart

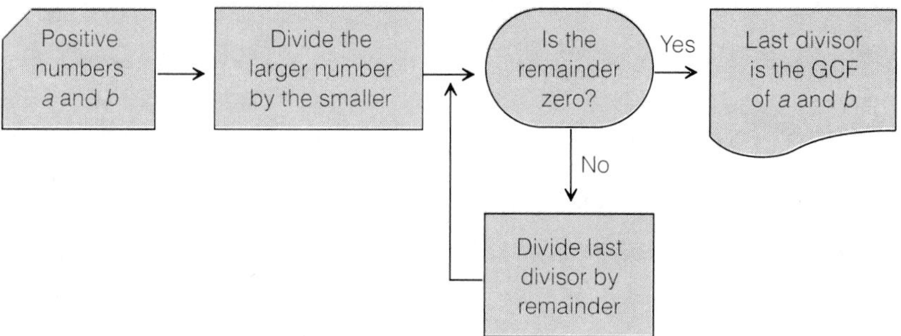

You can use the Euclidean Algorithm and a calculator with an INT÷ key, which divides by integers and shows remainders, to find the GCF.

Example 3

Use a calculator and the Euclidean Algorithm to find the GCF of 2,940 and 1,260.

Solution 2940 INT÷ 1260 = 2 420 The quotient is 2, remainder 420.

1260 INT÷ 420 = 3 0 Divide 1260 by the previous remainder.

The GCF of 2940 and 1260 is 420.

Try This Use a calculator and the Euclidean Algorithm to find the GCF of these pairs of numbers.

f. 135, 351 **g.** 80, 368 **h.** 475, 1501 **i.** 2599, 2825

Class Exercises

Give the GCF of the two numbers. The set of factors of each number is given.

1. 12: {1, 2, 3, 4, 6, 12}
20: {1, 2, 4, 5, 10, 20}

2. 18:{1, 2, 3, 6, 9, 18}
24:{1, 2, 3, 4, 6, 8, 12, 24}

3. 12: {1, 2, 3, 4, 6, 12}
16: {1, 2, 4, 8, 16}

4. 20:{1, 2, 4, 5, 10, 20}
28: {1, 2, 4, 7, 14, 28}

Discuss the Ideas

5. Which method for finding the GCF of a number do you think is easiest? Why?

Exercises

Practice and Apply

List factors of the smaller number to find the GCF of each pair.

1. 8, 27 **2.** 18, 30 **3.** 16, 24 **4.** 21, 28
5. 12, 36 **6.** 18, 27 **7.** 48, 64 **8.** 36, 54
9. 24, 40 **10.** 30, 45 **11.** 10, 21 **12.** 16, 40

Use prime factorization to find the GCF of each pair.

13. 45, 60 **14.** 28, 42 **15.** 48, 72 **16.** 26, 51
17. 63, 84 **18.** 90, 189 **19.** 56, 90 **20.** 84, 108
21. 144, 216 **22.** 136, 162 **23.** 130, 182 **24.** 154, 192

Use a calculator and the Euclidean Algorithm to find the GCF of these pairs of numbers.

25. 69, 184 **26.** 70, 525 **27.** 259, 888 **28.** 1232, 7560

Solve by finding the GCF of the numbers. Check your solutions.

29. A tennis instructor wanted to schedule classes for 28 students on Monday and 42 students on Tuesday, with the same number in each class. What is the largest class size possible?

30. Aretha bought 24 special stamps and Mabel bought 36. The stamps came in small envelopes, with the same number in each envelope. What is the largest number of stamps that could be in each envelope?

Extend and Apply

Use prime factorization to find the GCF of each set of numbers.

31. 12, 18, 24 **32.** 28, 42, 90 **33.** 30, 36, 48

34. 16, 28, 40 **35.** 32, 56, 72 **36.** 30, 45, 60

37. Two numbers whose GCF is 1 are said to be **relatively prime.** Are these number pairs relatively prime?

a. 9, 10 **b.** 20, 27 **c.** 165, 182

Use Mathematical Reasoning

38. The number n is between 60 and 70. The GCF of n and 27 is 9. Find n.

39. A rectangular meeting room in a hotel is 66 feet by 78 feet. The room is to be covered with square pieces of carpet that are all the same size. If the square carpet pieces cannot be cut, what is the largest square piece that can be used?

Mixed Review

Simplify. **40.** $t(6 - 4)$ **41.** $6m + 9m$ **42.** $n \div (-n)$ **43.** $6(2c)$

Evaluate for $n = 6$. **44.** $2(4n)$ **45.** $3n + 2n$ **46.** $n(0)$

Solve and check. **47.** $2x + 3x = 45$ **48.** $-1.5c = 30$

Connections Numbers to Algebra

Prime factorization is used to find the GCF of two algebraic expressions in the same way it is used to find the GCF of two whole numbers.

Numbers	Algebra
■ Find the GCF of 108 and 120. $108 = 2 \cdot 2 \cdot 3 \cdot 3 \cdot 3$ $120 = 2 \cdot 2 \cdot 2 \cdot 3 \cdot 5$ Since 2 is a common factor twice and 3 is a common factor once, the GCF is $2^2 \cdot 3$, or 12.	■ Find the GCF of x^2y^3 and x^3yz. $x^2y^3 = x \cdot x \cdot y \cdot y \cdot y$ $x^3yz = x \cdot x \cdot x \cdot y \cdot z$ Since x is a common factor twice and y is a common factor once, the GCF is x^2y.

Find the GCF of each pair of expressions.

1. xy^3 and x^3y **2.** $x^2y^5z^2$ and x^3y^4

3. $12x^3y^2$ and $18xy^3$ **4.** xy^2z^3 and x^2y^3z

5. $16x^2z^3$ and $24x^3z^2$ **6.** $27ab^3$ and $45a^2b$

5-8 Problem Solving: Applications

Driving a Car

Objective To solve word problems involving braking and stopping distances.

Most states require that anyone applying for a driver's license take a written examination. Questions about reaction, braking, and stopping distances are often included in such an exam. The information in the graph below, taken from a driving manual, is important in road safety.

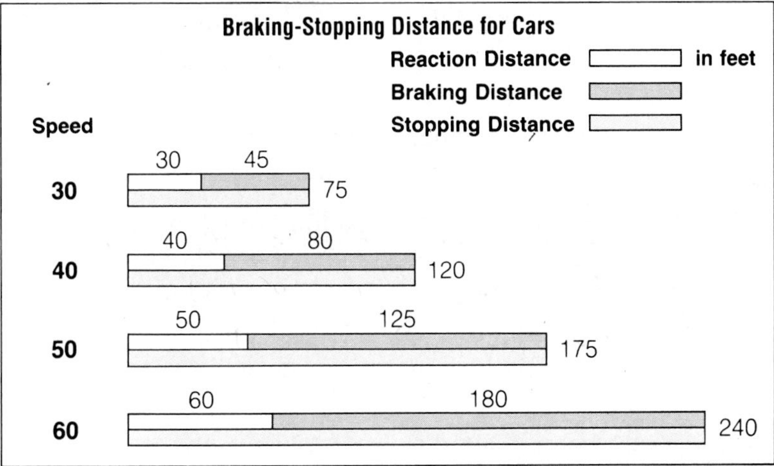

In the graph, the stopping distance is the sum of the reaction distance and the braking distance. The *reaction distance* is the number of feet the car travels *after* the driver decides to stop and *before* he or she applies the brakes.

Problems

Use the graph above to solve problems 1–5.

1. If a car is traveling at a speed of 40 mi/h and the driver sees an animal in the road, the reaction distance before the brakes are applied is the same number of feet as the speed. After the driver applies the brakes, how far will the car go before it stops?
2. What is the reaction distance when a car is traveling 60 mi/h? What are the braking and stopping distances?
3. How much farther is the stopping distance at 60 mi/h than at 50 mi/h?
4. How much farther is the braking distance at 50 mi/h than at 30 mi/h?

5. Estimate the amount by which the stopping distance increases when a car's speed doubles from 30 to 60 mi/h. Is the increase about two, three, four, or five times the original speed?

Use the following formulas as needed to solve problems 6–12.

The ***Reaction Distance,*** **R,** in feet has been determined to be about the same as the speed the car is traveling in miles per hour.

The ***Braking Distance,*** **B,** is the distance in feet traveled after the brakes are applied:

$$\mathbf{B = 0.05R^2}$$

The ***Stopping Distance,*** **S,** is the Reaction Distance plus the Braking Distance:

$$\mathbf{S = R + 0.05R^2}$$

6. Find the braking and stopping distances for the speed of 70 mi/h.
7. Find the braking and stopping distances for the speed of 55 mi/h.
8. Some state highways have a maximum speed limit of 65 mi/h. How does the stopping distance at this speed compare with that at 55 mi/h?
9. If a driver of a car traveling 45 mi/h sees a truck stopped in the road ahead and immediately applies the brakes, how far will the car travel before coming to a stop?
10. A driver education instructor wanted to place 72 sophomores and 120 juniors in driver education classes so that each class would be the same size and would be as large as possible, but the grades would be kept separate. How many students will be in each class, and how many classes will be needed?
11. A highway planner wants to place rest stops at equal distances along an interstate highway connecting three cities. The distance from the first to the second city is 475 miles. The distance from the second to the third city is 285 miles. There is to be a rest stop in each of the cities, and the distance between the rest stops is to be as great as possible. How far apart will the rest stops be?
12. **Data Search** Find three different speed limits posted on streets in your community and calculate the stopping distance for each speed.

What's Your Decision?

How many feet of space should you keep between your car and the car in front of you for every 10 mi/h of speed? Use the data from the graph on page 173 to help you decide. Give reasons for your decision.

5-9 Least Common Multiple

Objective To find the least common multiple of numbers.

Application

Two cars started around the race track at the same time. One car crosses the starting line every 9 minutes and the other car crosses every 12 minutes. A test engineer wants to know how many minutes will pass before both cars cross the starting line together.

Understand the Ideas

The **Least Common Multiple (LCM)** of two whole numbers is the smallest *nonzero* whole number that is a multiple of *both* of the whole numbers.

Multiples of 6 0, 6, 12, 18, 24, . . .

Multiples of 8 0, 8, 16, 24, 32, . . .

Common Multiples of 6 and 8 0, 24, 48, 72, . . .

Least Common Multiple of 6 and 8 24

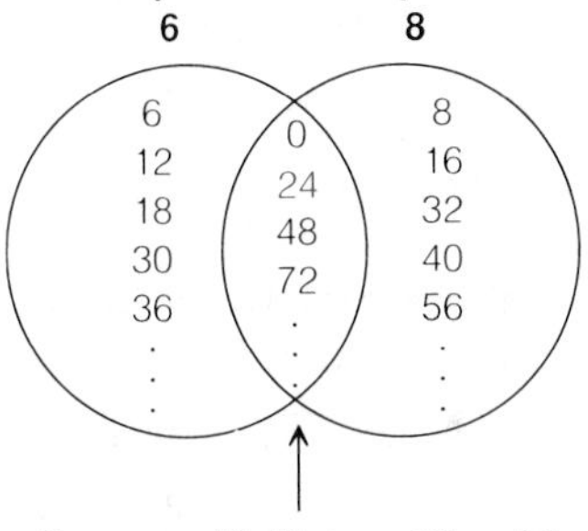

In the example above, multiples of both numbers were listed to find the LCM. A method often used to find the LCM of two numbers is to list multiples of the larger number, then look for the smallest of these that is also a multiple of the smaller number.

Example 1

Find the LCM of 9 and 12 to find how many minutes will pass before both cars cross the starting line together in the **application.** List multiples of the larger number.

Solution 12, 24, 36 — Start a list of the nonzero multiples of the greater number, 12.

The LCM of 9 and 12 is 36 — Find the lowest number in the list that is also a multiple of the lesser number, 9.

Both cars will cross the starting line together in 36 minutes.

Try This List multiples of the greater number to find the LCM of each pair. **a.** 6, 9 **b.** 8, 12

You can use the prime factorizations of two numbers to find the LCM of the numbers. The factors in the LCM are only those factors needed so that the prime factorization of each number occurs in the LCM.

Example 2

Use prime factorizations to find the LCM of 42 and 60.

Solution $42 = 2 \times 3 \times 7$

$60 = 2 \times 2 \times 3 \times 5$

$\text{LCM}(42, 60) = 2 \times 3 \times 7 \times 2 \times 5$

$= 420$

Write the prime factorization of the lesser number. Then include factors from the greater number as needed to include the prime factorization of the greater number in the LCM.

Try This Use prime factorization to find the LCM of each pair.

c. 12, 15 **d.** 24, 30

Class Exercises

Give 5 nonzero multiples of each number

1. 4 **2.** 6 **3.** 9 **4.** 11 **5.** 12 **6.** 15

Discuss the Ideas

7. When the LCM of two numbers equals the product of the numbers, are the numbers always prime? Try to find a pair of numbers, each less than 10, that proves this is false.

Exercises

Practice and Apply

List the multiples of the larger number to find the LCM of each pair.

1. 4, 6 **2.** 6, 21 **3.** 3, 4 **4.** 4, 18 **5.** 5, 9

Use prime factorization to find the LCM of each pair.

6. 20, 25 **7.** 18, 30 **8.** 30, 70 **9.** 60, 18 **10.** 28, 40

11. 27, 36 **12.** 42, 70 **13.** 20, 24 **14.** 63, 90 **15.** 60, 80

16. What is the shortest section of a stable that can be divided into either a whole number of 10 ft. wide horse stalls or into a whole number of 12 ft. wide horse stalls? Solve by finding the LCM of the numbers.

Extend and Apply

Find the LCM of the three numbers given.

17. 4, 6, 15 **18.** 9, 12, 15 **19.** 30, 42, 48 **20.** 28, 40, 56

Using a calculator, list multiples and find the LCM of the numbers given.

21. 108, 135 **22.** 84, 126 **23.** 60, 126, 210

24. What is the shortest length of ribbon that can be cut either into a whole number of 24-cm pieces or into a whole number of 30-cm pieces?

25. Extra Data Tell what data is not needed to solve this problem. Then solve the problem.

A clock alarm was set to go off every 12 hours. A watch alarm was set to go off every 8 hours. The alarms were to sound for 30 seconds. After how many hours will the two alarms go off at the same time?

Use Mathematical Reasoning

26. Carlos said, "You can always find the LCM of two numbers by dividing the product of the numbers by their GCF. You can also find the GCF of two numbers by dividing the product of the numbers by their LCM." Test his idea with these pairs of numbers:

a. 6, 8 **b.** 10, 15 **c.** 12, 18

Is Carlos' generalization true for these three cases?

Mixed Review

Write using exponents. **27.** $x \cdot x \cdot x \cdot x$ **28.** $(-2)(-2)(-2)$

Solve and check. **29.** $-12.5n = 50$ **30.** $t - 16.45 = 2.37$ **31.** $1.4 = \frac{k}{9}$

Connections Numbers to Algebra

Prime Factorization is used to find the LCM of two algebraic expressions in the same way it is used to find the LCM of two whole numbers.

Numbers	Algebra
■ Find the LCM of 30 and 84. $30 = 2 \cdot 3 \cdot 5$ $84 = 2 \cdot 2 \cdot 3 \cdot 7$ The LCM of 30 and 84 is $2 \cdot 2 \cdot 3 \cdot 5 \cdot 7$, or 420.	■ Find the LCM of $2x^2$ and $6xy$. $2x^2 = 2 \cdot x \cdot x$ $6xy = 2 \cdot 3 \cdot x \cdot y$ The LCM of $2x^2$ and $6xy$ is $2 \cdot 3 \cdot x \cdot x \cdot y$, or $6x^2y$.

Find the LCM of each pair of expressions.

1. a^2b and ab^2 **2.** $4x^2y^2$ and $6xy^3$

3. $3mn^2$ and $6m^2$ **4.** $6ab^2$ and $9a^2c$

5-10 Introducing Functions

Objective To describe the relationship between two variables in words and in a graph.

Application

When you rent a VCR, you might pay a fixed charge of $15 for insurance plus an additional $8 for each day you use the machine.

Understand the Ideas

In your work with variables so far, you have seen many real-world situations where one quantity varies according to another quantity. In the application above, when you know the number of days the VCR is rented, there is only one possible value for the total rental cost. Relationships like this are called **functions**.

Example

Study the **application** given above. Then answer the questions below.
(1) Name two variables represented by this situation.
(2) Describe the function that relates the two variables.
(3) Tell which graph might represent the function. Tell why.

A.

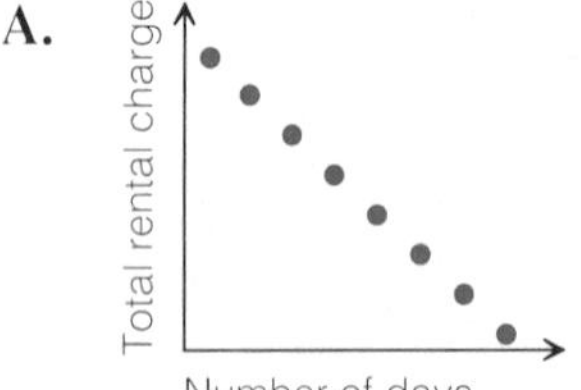

B.

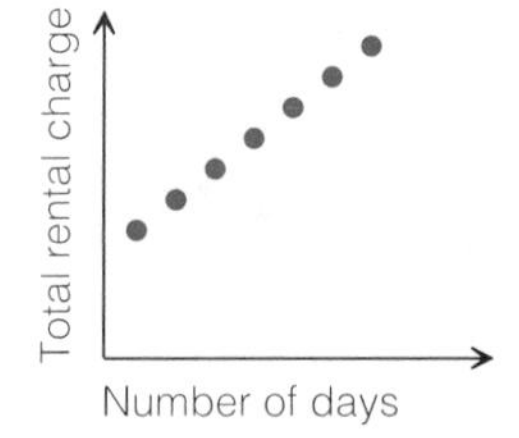

C.

Solution

(1) number of days and total rental charge
(2) The total rental charge is a function of the number of days.
(3) Graph B. It shows that the total charge increases as the number of days increases.

Try This Study the function situation. Then answer the questions.

a. Situation: Water is being pumped from a large swimming pool at a rate of 100 gallons per hour. The number of gallons of water remaining in the pool is measured by a gauge.

(1) Name two variables represented by this situation.

(2) Describe the function that relates the two variables.

(3) Tell which graph might represent the function. Tell why.

A. Number of gallons in the pool / Number of hours

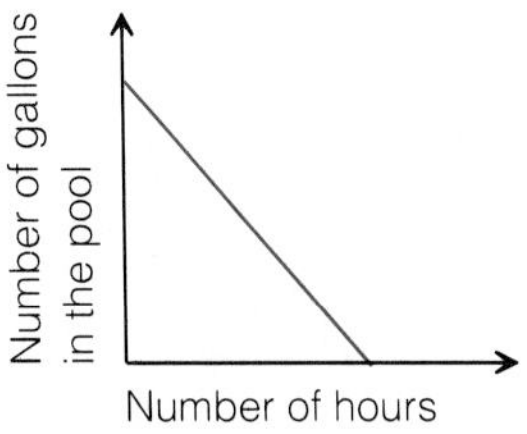

B. Number of gallons in the pool / Number of hours

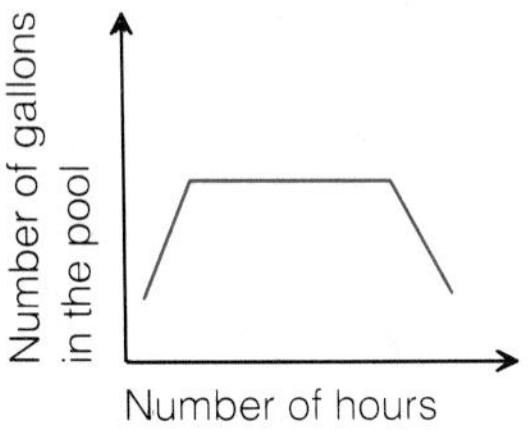

C. Number of gallons in the pool / Number of hours

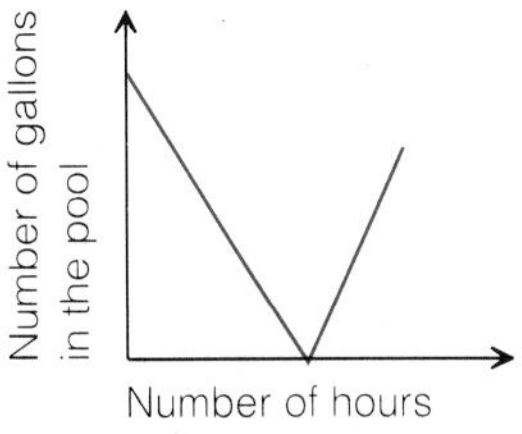

Class Exercises

Discuss the Ideas

Find other variables that have a functional relationship with the given variable.

1. number of hours of studying and ______ .

2. number of hours traveling in a car and ______ .

Exercises

Practice and Apply

Study the function situation. Then answer the questions.

(A) Name two variables represented by this situation.

(B) Describe the function that relates the two variables.

(C) Tell which graph might represent the function. Tell why.

1. Situation: A science class recorded the outside temperature in degrees Celsius every 3 hours for 24 hours.

A. Degrees Celsius / Time of day

B. Degrees Celsius / Time of day

C. Degrees Celsius / Time of day

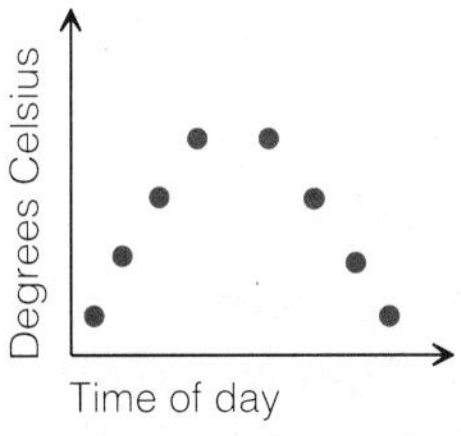

2. Situation: A school keeps records each year of students' heights from kindergarten through eighth grade.

A. Height / Grade level

B. Height / Grade level

C. Height / Grade level

3. Situation: A restaurant owner kept a record of the number of customers in her restaurant each hour from 10 a.m. to 3 p.m.

A. Number of people / Time of Day

B. Number of people / Time of Day

C. Number of people / Time of Day

4. Situation: A computer records the amount of fuel left as a rocket is launched and travels through orbit.

A. Fuel remaining / Time

B. Fuel remaining / Time

C. Fuel remaining / Time

Extend and Apply

Draw a sketch of a graph which could represent the functional relationship.

5. The speed of a ball rolling down a hill is a function of the time it has been rolling.
6. The cost of a 30-second television commercial is a function of the time it is to be telecast.
7. The time between the lightning and the thunder is a function of the distance from you that the lightning strikes.

Use Mathematical Reasoning

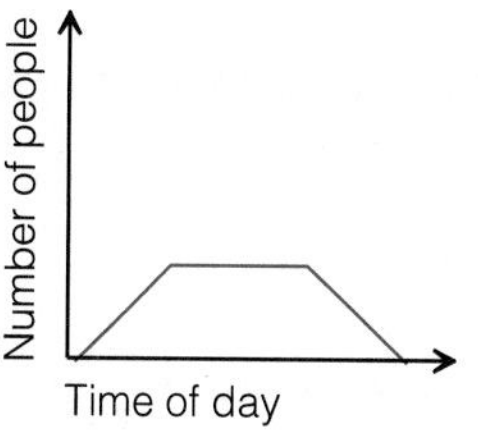

8. Describe in writing a real-world functional relationship that could be represented by the graph at the right.

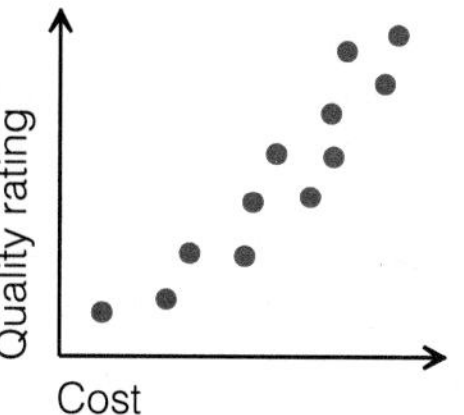

9. Analyze the graph at the right. What generalization can you make about the relationship between the cost of the skateboard and the quality of the skateboard?

Mixed Review

Evaluate.

10. $-6 + 40$	**11.** $-319 - (-67)$	**12.** $-126 + (-12)$
13. $104 + (-35)$	**14.** $48 - (-52)$	**15.** $-16 - 12$
16. $-41 + 93$	**17.** $1.904 + 0.685$	**18.** 1.335×2.5
19. $\frac{33.063}{103}$	**20.** $14.11 - 16.8$	**21.** -4.28×1.6
22. $21.6 - 14.03$	**23.** $1.673 + 0.499$	**24.** $\frac{2.25}{-4.5}$

25. Let m be the amount of money Miles had before he went shopping. Miles spent $4.50 while shopping. Write an expression for the amount Miles had left after shopping.

Computer Activity

This program finds the LCM of two numbers.

```
10 PRINT "TO FIND THE LCM"
20 PRINT "OF A AND B WHERE A>B"
30 PRINT "TYPE IN NUMBERS FOR A AND B"
40 INPUT A,B
50 FOR X=1 TO B
60 LET N=A*X
70 IF N/B=INT(N/B) THEN 90
80 NEXT X
90 PRINT "LCM(";A;",";B;")=";N
100 END
```

1. Run the program to find the LCM of 84 and 126.
2. Use the generalization suggested in Exercise 26 on page 177 to make additions to the program so that it will also find the GCF of the two numbers.

5-11 Problem Solving: Strategies

Make an Organized List

Objective To solve nonroutine problems, using the strategy Make an Organized List and other strategies learned so far.

A strategy called **Make an Organized List** is helpful for solving problems that involve finding all possible ways to accomplish something. Making an organized list helps determine when all possible ways have been found. Consider the problem below.

Sample Problem A computer club's members use two letters followed by three numbers to form identification codes. They use the letters C and I and the numbers 2, 3, and 4. They allow repetition of the letters, but not of the numbers. How many members can there be before they must change their method of making identification codes?

To solve this problem, you might make an organized list to show all the different identification codes that could be formed. There are four possible letter combinations, CI, IC, II, and CC. You can use these to list all possibilities systematically.

CI-234	IC-234	II-234	CC-234	Notice that the numbers starting with 2 are
CI-243	IC-243	II-243	CC-243	listed first,
CI-324	IC-324	II-324	CC-324	then the numbers starting with 3,
CI-342	IC-342	II-342	CC-342	
CI-423	IC-423	II-423	CC-423	and finally, the numbers starting with 4.
CI-432	IC-432	II-432	CC-432	

Twenty-four different identification numbers can be made from the letters C and I and the numbers 2, 3, and 4. After 24 members join the club, the system for forming ID numbers will have to be expanded.

Problem-Solving Strategies

Choose the Operations	Make a Table	**Make an Organized List**
Guess, Check, Revise	Look for a Pattern	Use Logical Reasoning
Draw a Diagram	Write an Equation	Work Backward
	Simplify the Problem	

Problems

Solve, using one or more of the Problem-Solving strategies.

1. How many different arrangements of 3 letters can be made from the letters in the word MATH if no repetition of letters is allowed? How many of these are actual words?
2. A baseball coach listed the possible batting orders for his first four batters, Allen, Burge, Cotton, and Denby. His only requirement was that Cotton could not bat immediately after Denby. How many different batting order choices did the coach have?
3. When Tim puts his coins in groups of 2, 3, or 4, he always has one coin left over. He can put the coins in groups of 5 with none left over. What is the lowest number of coins Tim can have?
4. Jeral's chess club has 9 members. They are planning to have a holiday tournament in which every member plays every other member just once. How many games would be played?
5. A school with 900 students has exactly 900 lockers. The first student is to enter the school and open all the lockers. The second student will then follow the first and close every even-numbered locker. The third student will follow and reverse every third locker by closing open lockers and opening closed lockers. The fourth student will reverse every fourth locker, and so on until all 900 students have walked past and reversed lockers. Which lockers will remain open?

Group Decision Making

6. Work in a group. Discuss and decide.

Situation: You are a business person who travels from Chicago to New York City twice a week. As a frequent flyer you receive 2 free round-trip tickets to anywhere in the continental United States when you have flown 30,000 miles. You want to find out how many round trips to New York you need to make to fly 30,000 miles and how much you will have paid in airfare.

Guidelines for Planning

- **Formulate Problems** you will need to solve.
- Discuss **Assumptions** you will make and **Data** you will need.

a. What decision or decisions do you need to make in this situation?
b. Formulate problems you need to solve to make the decision(s).
c. List any assumptions you need to make to arrive at a decision.
d. What data, if any, do you need to collect to make a decision?
e. Write a paragraph summarizing what your group did, what decisions you made, and why.

Extend Key Ideas

More About Prime Numbers

Euclid, who lived about 300 B.C., proved that there is an infinite number of prime numbers. Today, mathematicians still study the properties of prime numbers, and continue to find larger and larger primes. By studying prime numbers, you can find interesting patterns and relationships.

The First 99 Prime Numbers

	0	1	2	3	4	5	6	7	8	9
0		2	3	5	7	11	13	17	19	23
1	29	31	37	41	43	47	53	59	61	67
2	71	73	79	83	89	97	101	103	107	109
3	113	127	131	137	139	149	151	157	163	167
4	173	179	181	191	193	197	199	211	223	227
5	229	233	239	241	251	257	263	269	271	277
6	281	283	293	307	311	313	317	331	337	347
7	349	353	359	367	373	379	383	389	397	401
8	409	419	421	431	433	439	443	449	457	461
9	463	467	479	487	491	499	503	509	521	523

To use the table, notice that the 56th prime, for example, is found in the row labeled "5" and in the column labeled "6." It is 263.

1. What is the 23rd prime? the 50th prime? the 89th prime?
2. Where are these in the sequence of primes? 59, 113, 227, 379, 521
3. Count the primes between 0 and 100, 100 and 200, 200 and 300, 300 and 400, and 400 and 500. Do you think the primes occur less frequently as the whole numbers get larger?
4. Consecutive primes with a difference of 2, such as 3 and 5, are called twin primes. How many pairs of twin primes are there in the table?
5. How many groups of three consecutive odd numbers are there in the first 99 primes?
6. Look at the ones digit of the 2- and 3-digit primes. What do you discover?
7. Prime numbers 17 and 71 are "reversal primes." What other reversal primes can you find?

Chapter 5 Review/Test

Understanding

True or false? (Exercises 1–5)

5-1 **1.** Every number has at least two factors, the number itself and 1.

5-1 **2.** The product of two numbers is a multiple of each of the numbers.

5-2 **3.** A number is divisible by 3 if the product of its digits is divisible by 3.

5-4 **4.** All odd numbers are prime.

5-5 **5.** In 4^2 the base tells how many times the exponent is used as a factor.

5-7 5-9 **6.** The __?__ (least, greatest) common __?__ (factor, multiple) of two numbers is often greater than either of the numbers.

5-10 **7.** Does the temperature increase or decrease as it gets later in the day?

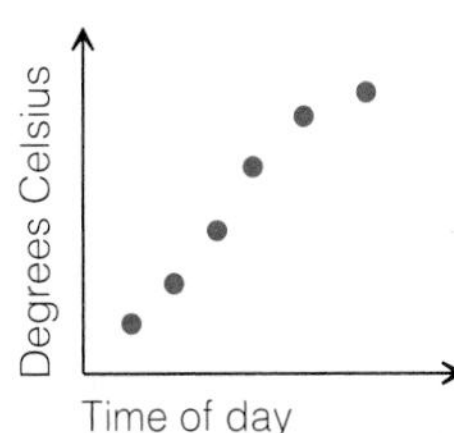

Skills

5-1 **8.** Find all the factors of 28.

5-2 **9.** Tell whether 2,505 is divisible by 2, by 3, and by 5.

5-4 **10.** Is 23 prime or composite?

5-5 Write in expanded form. Simplify if possible.

11. 7^4 **12.** $(-2)^5$ **13.** r^7

5-5 Write each of these products using exponents.

14. $10 \cdot 10$ **15.** $b \cdot b \cdot b \cdot b \cdot b \cdot b$ **16.** $-4(-4)(-4)$

5-5 **17.** Find $(-2)^5 \cdot (-2)^3$. Give the answer in exponent form.

5-5 **18.** Simplify $2^4 + 2^3$.

5-6 **19.** Use exponents to show the prime factorization of **a)** 48. **b)** 105.

5-7 5-9 Find the GCF or LCM.

20. GCF 16, 20 **21.** GCF 42, 60 **22.** LCM 6, 15 **23.** LCM 18, 30

Applications

5-3 5-8 Find the solution by writing and solving an equation.

24. Sandy has \$130 more in her savings account than she has in her checking account. If she has \$571 in her savings account, how much does she have in her checking account?

25. Use the formula $D = r \cdot t$ to find the time (t) it took for Brad to go a distance (D) of 125 miles at a rate (r) of 50 mi/h?

6 Rational Numbers: Addition and Subtraction

In the local skating competition, each person does a $2\frac{1}{2}$ minute routine. Arthur has been skating for $1\frac{3}{4}$ minutes. How much longer will his routine last?

6-1 Fractions and Equivalent Fractions

Objectives To write equivalent fractions and determine whether fractions are equivalent; to reduce fractions to lowest terms.

Application

The city of San Francisco had 25 days of sunshine in a month with 30 days. Lydia is revising a travel guidebook, so she wants to know what fraction of the month was sunny. (See Example 1.)

Understand the Ideas

The symbol $\frac{a}{b}$, where a and b are whole numbers and $b \neq 0$, is called a **fraction.** The number above the bar is the **numerator** and the number below the bar is the **denominator.** A fraction can describe part of a region or a set. Fractions that show the same amount are called **equivalent fractions.**

A school newspaper reserves a fraction of each page for regular copy and the rest for ads. The fraction of the page at the right shaded green is for regular copy. The fractions $\frac{3}{4}$ and $\frac{6}{8}$ name the same part of the region.

Golf balls are usually sold in boxes of a dozen balls. The fraction of the balls in the box below that are orange can be named in two ways. The fractions $\frac{1}{4}$ and $\frac{3}{12}$ name the same part of the set.

Notice that $\frac{3}{4} = \frac{3 \cdot 2}{4 \cdot 2} = \frac{6}{8}$ and $\frac{6}{8} = \frac{6 \div 2}{8 \div 2} = \frac{3}{4}$.

Property of Equivalent Fractions

Multiplying or dividing both the numerator and denominator of a fraction by the same nonzero integer results in an equivalent fraction.

For all numbers ***a*, *b***, and ***c***, ($b \neq 0, c \neq 0$)

$\frac{a}{b} = \frac{a \cdot c}{b \cdot c}$ and $\frac{a}{b} = \frac{a \div c}{b \div c}$

Example 1

In the **application** at the beginning of the lesson, the fraction of the month that was sunny is $\frac{25}{30}$. Write an equivalent fraction by finding the value for y in $\frac{25}{30} = \frac{y}{6}$.

Solution $\frac{25}{30} = \frac{5}{6}$ Since $30 \div 6 = 5$, divide the numerator by 5.

$\frac{5}{6}$ of the days were sunny.

Try This Write an equivalent fraction by finding the value of the variable.

a. $\frac{3}{5} = \frac{x}{60}$ **b.** $\frac{7}{15} = \frac{y}{75}$

c. The fraction $\frac{18}{30}$ tells the fraction of sunny days in Chicago for a month. Find an equivalent fraction by finding the value of c in $\frac{18}{30} = \frac{c}{5}$.

If two fractions are equivalent, their **cross products** are equal. And if the cross products are equal, the fractions are equivalent.

$5 \cdot 36 = 180$ $12 \cdot 15 = 180$

$\frac{5}{12} = \frac{15}{36}$

Example 2

Check cross products to decide whether $\frac{15}{25}$ and $\frac{5}{8}$ are equivalent.

Solution

$\frac{15}{25} \stackrel{?}{=} \frac{5}{8}$

$15 \cdot 8 \stackrel{?}{=} 25 \cdot 5$ Find the cross products.

$120 \neq 125$

$\frac{15}{25} \neq \frac{5}{8}$

Try This Check cross products to decide whether each pair of fractions is equivalent.

d. $\frac{3}{5}, \frac{12}{20}$ **e.** $\frac{7}{12}, \frac{28}{48}$

A fraction is in **lowest terms** when the only common factor of the numerator and denominator is 1. One way to reduce a fraction to lowest terms is to divide the numerator and denominator by the greatest common factor. Another is to factor the numerator and denominator into prime factors and divide common factors.

Example 3

Reduce to lowest terms. $\frac{24}{36}$

Solution

Method 1

$\frac{24}{36} = \frac{24 \div 12}{36 \div 12} = \frac{2}{3}$ The GCF of 24 and 36 is 12. Divide both the numerator and the denominator by 12.

Method 2

$\frac{24}{36} = \frac{2 \cdot 2 \cdot 2 \cdot 3}{2 \cdot 2 \cdot 3 \cdot 3}$ Factor 24 and 36 into prime factors.

$= \frac{\not{2} \cdot \not{2} \cdot 2 \cdot \not{3}}{\not{2} \cdot \not{2} \cdot 3 \cdot \not{3}} = \frac{2}{3}$ Divide common factors.

Try This Reduce to lowest terms. **f.** $\frac{18}{36}$ **g.** $\frac{70}{105}$

Class Exercises

Give two equivalent fractions for each figure.

1. **2.** **3.**

Discuss the Ideas

4. Do the numerator and the denominator of a fraction in lowest terms have to be prime numbers? Explain.

Exercises

Practice and Apply

Write an equivalent fraction by finding the value of the variable.

1. $\frac{7}{15} = \frac{x}{30}$ **2.** $\frac{1}{2} = \frac{y}{36}$ **3.** $\frac{18}{30} = \frac{t}{5}$ **4.** $\frac{4}{9} = \frac{d}{27}$

5. $\frac{16}{64} = \frac{g}{4}$ **6.** $\frac{2}{3} = \frac{x}{54}$ **7.** $\frac{5}{6} = \frac{m}{60}$ **8.** $\frac{56}{80} = \frac{n}{10}$

9. $\frac{13}{15} = \frac{x}{75}$ **10.** $\frac{5}{18} = \frac{y}{90}$ **11.** $\frac{49}{140} = \frac{a}{20}$ **12.** $\frac{156}{240} = \frac{b}{60}$

13. $\frac{7}{12} = \frac{k}{60}$ **14.** $\frac{8}{9} = \frac{h}{108}$ **15.** $\frac{72}{150} = \frac{x}{25}$ **16.** $\frac{25}{60} = \frac{y}{240}$

Check cross products to decide which pairs of fractions are equivalent.

17. $\frac{2}{3}, \frac{4}{9}$ **18.** $\frac{3}{5}, \frac{9}{15}$ **19.** $\frac{4}{7}, \frac{8}{14}$ **20.** $\frac{4}{10}, \frac{6}{15}$

21. $\frac{4}{14}, \frac{6}{21}$ **22.** $\frac{5}{7}, \frac{35}{49}$ **23.** $\frac{12}{54}, \frac{2}{9}$ **24.** $\frac{7}{12}, \frac{3}{4}$

Reduce each fraction to lowest terms.

25. $\frac{40}{52}$ **26.** $\frac{24}{60}$ **27.** $\frac{48}{84}$ **28.** $\frac{66}{102}$ **29.** $\frac{68}{76}$

30. $\frac{108}{156}$ **31.** $\frac{36}{54}$ **32.** $\frac{78}{112}$ **33.** $\frac{52}{56}$ **34.** $\frac{105}{126}$

35. A new compact disc player holds 5 discs. Each disc has 10 songs. A maximum of 32 songs can be programmed at any one time. Find an equivalent fraction by finding the value for t in $\frac{32}{50} = \frac{t}{25}$ to find what fraction of the total number of songs can be programmed.

36. A summer parks and recreation program has space for 60 campers. On the first day of enrollment 32 campers enrolled. Reduce $\frac{32}{60}$ to lowest terms to find what fraction of space is filled.

37. Last Saturday, 120 people took their driver's test. Ninety passed the exam and received their licenses. Reduce $\frac{90}{120}$ to lowest terms to find what fraction of those taking the exam passed.

Extend and Apply

Give two pairs of values for x and y that will make equivalent fractions.

38. $\frac{3}{8}, \frac{x}{y}$ **39.** $\frac{7}{12}, \frac{x}{y}$ **40.** $\frac{20}{32}, \frac{x}{y}$ **41.** $\frac{18}{36}, \frac{x}{y}$

Check cross products to decide which pairs of fractions are equivalent.

42. $\frac{12}{25}, \frac{60}{125}$ **43.** $\frac{7}{9}, \frac{63}{88}$ **44.** $\frac{9}{13}, \frac{45}{72}$ **45.** $\frac{6}{15}, \frac{42}{105}$

46. A new car regularly costing \$12,000 is marked down to \$8,000. What fraction of the total cost is the amount of reduction? Give the answer in lowest terms.

47. At King High School, $\frac{3}{4}$ of the ninth graders say they plan to continue their education after high school. How many of the 240 ninth graders plan to continue their education?

48. Determine Reasonable Answers At Edgewater High School, 150 seniors had their pictures taken for the yearbook. Of these students, 32 wore glasses.

Without computing, determine whether the newspaper headline at the right seems reasonable. If it is not, tell why.

The Eyes Have It!

A count of students in the new yearbook found that 3/5 of the students wear glasses!!

Use Mathematical Reasoning

49. Is the generalization $\frac{a}{b} = \frac{a + c}{b + c}$ true or false?

50. Find all the ways in which the numbers 2, 4, 8, and 16 can be placed in the squares at right to complete a true statement.

51. Find all the ways in which any four of the numbers 2, 3, 4, 5, 6, 7, 8, 9, and 10 can be placed in the squares to make a true statement.

$$\frac{\square}{\square} = \frac{\square}{\square}$$

Mixed Review

Simplify. **52.** $9c - 16c$ **53.** $4m + 2m - m$ **54.** $7x + 5 + 4x$

55. $4(3r) - 10 + 2r$ **56.** $6(y + 4y) + 3y$ **57.** $t + t + t$

58. $p^2 \cdot p^2 \cdot p^4$ **59.** $a \cdot a \cdot a$ **60.** $3^5 \cdot 3^{11}$

Find the greatest common factor (GCF). **61.** 25, 80 **62.** 12, 21

Solve and check. **63.** $14.7 = 9.35 - c$ **64.** $1.5n = -6$

Evaluate for $y = 1.6$. **65.** $y^2 + 4$ **66.** $y^2(y + 2)$

Connections Numbers to Algebra

You can reduce fractional expressions in algebra in the same way you reduce fractions in arithmetic.

Numbers	Algebra
$\frac{6}{15} = \frac{2 \cdot \cancel{3}}{5 \cdot \cancel{3}} = \frac{2}{5}$	$\frac{2an}{5bn} = \frac{2 \cdot a \cdot \cancel{n}}{5 \cdot b \cdot \cancel{n}} = \frac{2a}{5b}$
$\frac{15}{21} = \frac{\cancel{3} \cdot 5}{7 \cdot \cancel{3}} = \frac{5}{7}$	$\frac{6x}{15xy} = \frac{2 \cdot \cancel{3} \cdot \cancel{x}}{\cancel{3} \cdot 5 \cdot \cancel{x} \cdot y} = \frac{2}{5y}$
$\frac{30}{70} = \frac{\cancel{2} \cdot 3 \cdot \cancel{5}}{\cancel{2} \cdot \cancel{5} \cdot 7} = \frac{3}{7}$	$\frac{4mn}{9n} = \frac{2 \cdot 2 \cdot m \cdot \cancel{n}}{3 \cdot 3 \cdot \cancel{n}} = \frac{4m}{9}$

Reduce to lowest terms. The variables *a*, *b*, and *c* represent distinct whole numbers, not including 0.

1. $\frac{2a}{3a}$ **2.** $\frac{5ab}{25a}$ **3.** $\frac{21a}{24b}$

4. $\frac{15ab}{48b}$ **5.** $\frac{abc}{2bc}$ **6.** $\frac{46ab}{48bc}$

7. $\frac{96a}{24bc}$ **8.** $\frac{18c}{12ac}$ **9.** $\frac{15a}{35a}$

10. $\frac{51ab}{102bc}$ **11.** $\frac{24c}{70ac}$ **12.** $\frac{17a^2}{34ab}$

6-2 Improper Fractions and Mixed Numbers

Objectives To write improper fractions as integers or mixed numbers; to write mixed numbers as improper fractions

Application

While training for a 1 mile speed skating race, Eric skated 9 quarter-mile laps around the track. He wanted to record this distance in his training log as a mixed number.

Understand the Ideas

A fraction is a **proper fraction** if its numerator is less than its denominator. If its numerator is greater than or equal to its denominator, it is an **improper fraction.** For example, $\frac{4}{5}$ is a proper fraction, but $\frac{5}{4}$ is an improper fraction. When an improper fraction is written as an integer and a fraction, it is called a mixed numeral or **mixed number.** As shown below, the improper fraction $\frac{5}{4}$ is the same as the mixed number $1\frac{1}{4}$.

$\frac{5}{4} = 1\frac{1}{4}$

To change an improper fraction to a mixed number, use the fact that a fraction $\frac{a}{b}$ can be interpreted as $a \div b$.

Example 1

Write $\frac{9}{4}$ as an integer or a mixed number to find the distance Eric recorded in his training log in the **application.**

Solution

$$\begin{array}{r} 2 \\ 4\overline{)9} \\ \underline{8} \\ 1 \end{array}$$

$\frac{9}{4}$ means $9 \div 4$.

$\frac{9}{4} = 2\frac{1}{4}$ Write the quotient as the integer. Write the remainder over the divisor as the proper fraction.

Eric recorded $2\frac{1}{4}$ miles in his training log.

Try This Write each as an integer or a mixed number.

a. $\frac{11}{3}$ **b.** $\frac{24}{4}$ **c.** $\frac{36}{7}$

Example 2

Write as an improper fraction in lowest terms. $3\frac{1}{7}$

Solution

$3\frac{1}{7}$

$3 \cdot 7 + 1 = 22$ There are $3 \cdot 7$ or 21 sevenths in the 3 whole units.

$3\frac{1}{7} = \frac{22}{7}$ 21 sevenths plus 1 seventh equal 22 sevenths.

Try This Write each as an improper fraction in lowest terms.

d. $4\frac{3}{4}$ **e.** $5\frac{1}{3}$ **f.** $7\frac{3}{10}$

Class Exercises

Give an improper fraction and a mixed number for each.

1.

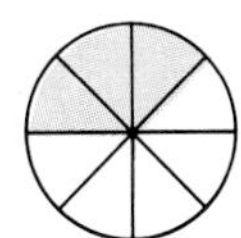

2.

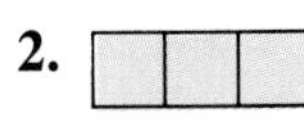
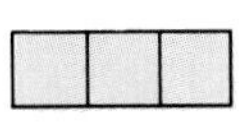
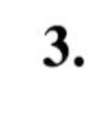

3.

Discuss the Ideas

4. Is the fraction $\frac{6}{6}$ a proper fraction or an improper fraction? Explain.

Exercises

Practice and Apply

Write each as an integer or a mixed number.

1. $\frac{25}{6}$ **2.** $\frac{41}{7}$ **3.** $\frac{51}{3}$ **4.** $\frac{17}{11}$

5. $\frac{91}{11}$ **6.** $\frac{238}{10}$ **7.** $\frac{121}{11}$ **8.** $\frac{215}{15}$

9. $\frac{290}{25}$ **10.** $\frac{75}{12}$ **11.** $\frac{35}{10}$ **12.** $\frac{440}{100}$

Write each as an improper fraction in lowest terms.

13. $3\frac{7}{8}$ **14.** $4\frac{2}{3}$ **15.** $2\frac{9}{16}$ **16.** $3\frac{6}{15}$

17. $5\frac{7}{9}$ **18.** $7\frac{9}{30}$ **19.** $8\frac{2}{3}$ **20.** $9\frac{7}{11}$

21. The chef used $5\frac{1}{2}$ gallons of milk for last week's pancake breakfast. Write this amount as an improper fraction in lowest terms.

22. Darlene put $\frac{35}{2}$ cases of fruit juice in the storeroom. Write this amount as an integer or a mixed number.

Extend and Apply

Evaluate each expression. Write as a mixed number.

23. $\frac{a}{b}$ for $a = 23$ and $b = 5$

24. $\frac{u}{v}$ for $u = 27$ and $v = 11$

25. $\frac{x}{y}$ for $x = 73$ and $y = 17$

26. $\frac{n}{m}$ for $n = 41$ and $m = 12$

27. $\frac{2x}{y}$ for $x = 33$ and $y = 5$

28. $\frac{3a}{2b}$ for $a = 13$ and $b = 7$

29. How many $\frac{1}{4}$ lb hamburgers can be made from $5\frac{1}{4}$ lb of ground beef?

Use Mathematical Reasoning

30. Find how many ways the numbers 1, 2, 3, 4, and 7 can be placed in the boxes to make a true statement. Numbers may be repeated more than once. The fraction part of the mixed number should be less than 1.

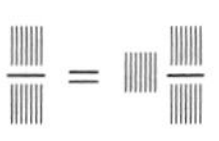

31. Write a generalization for changing any mixed number $a\frac{b}{c}$ to an improper fraction.

Mixed Review

Give the prime factorization of each. **32.** 30 **33.** 27

Evaluate for $a = 1.5$, $b = 2.75$, $c = 3$. **34.** abc **35.** $a(c + b)$

Tell whether the number is prime or composite. **36.** 53 **37.** 15

Write and solve an equation. **38.** A number divided by 5 gives 8.

Computer Activity

This computer program will reduce the fraction $\frac{A}{B}$ to lowest terms.

```
5 PRINT "TYPE IN THE NUMERATOR AND THE DENOMINATOR
OF YOUR FRACTION SEPARATED BY A COMMA."
10 INPUT N,D
20 T=ABS(N):B=ABS(D)
30 X=INT(T/B):R=T-X*B
40 IF R=0 THEN GOTO 60
50 T=B:B=R: GOTO 30
60 PRINT "THE REDUCED FRACTION IS ";N/B;"/";D/B
70 END
```

Run the program for each fraction.

1. $\frac{2{,}945}{32{,}395}$ **2.** $\frac{12{,}369}{11{,}994{,}447}$ **3.** $\frac{1{,}351{,}350}{11{,}781}$

6-3 Rational Numbers

Objectives To write the opposite of a rational number; to graph rational numbers on a number line.

Understand the Ideas

A number that can be expressed in the fractional form $\frac{a}{b}$, where a and b are integers and $b \neq 0$, is called a **rational number.** Each rational number corresponds to *one* set of equivalent fractions and names *one* point on the number line. For example, in the set $\left\{\frac{2}{3}, \frac{4}{6}, \frac{6}{9}, \frac{8}{12}, \ldots\right\}$ each fraction names the same rational number.

The number line below shows points for some rational numbers expressed as fractions or mixed numbers.

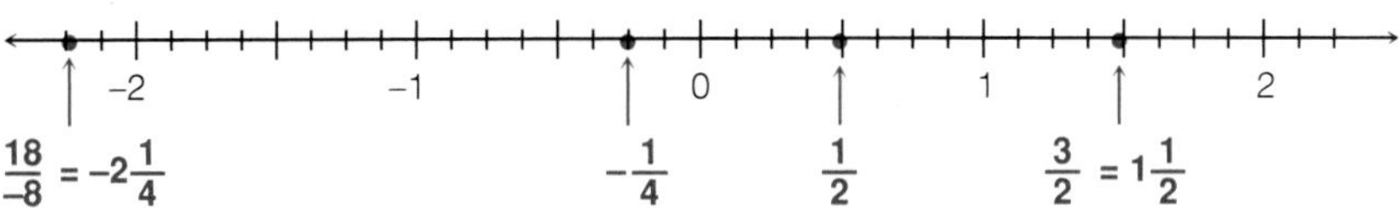

Whole numbers, integers, and certain decimals are rational numbers because they can be expressed as fractions. For example:

$$4 = \frac{4}{1} \qquad -5 = \frac{-5}{1} \qquad 0.3 = \frac{3}{10}$$

The opposite of a negative rational number is a positive rational number. The opposite of a positive rational number is a negative rational number. There are three ways to show a negative rational number.

Example 1

Write the opposite of $\frac{3}{5}$ in three different ways.

Solution

$-\frac{3}{5}, \frac{-3}{5}, \frac{3}{-5}$ The negative sign can precede the entire fraction, precede the numerator, or precede the denominator.

Try This Write the opposite of each in three different ways.

a. $\frac{5}{6}$ **b.** $\frac{7}{3}$ **c.** $\frac{11}{12}$

Example 2

Graph the following rational numbers.

$-\frac{1}{4}, \frac{3}{4}, -\frac{6}{4}, \frac{6}{4}$

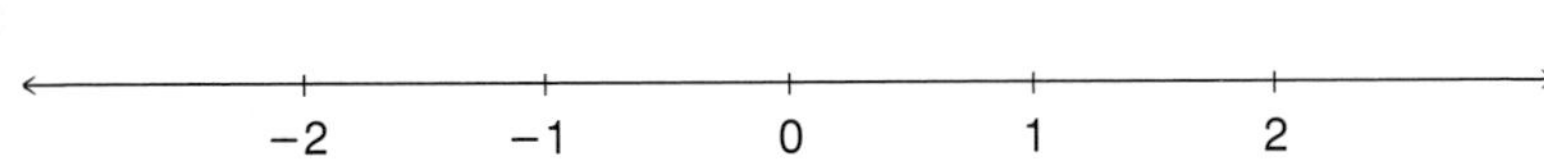

Solution

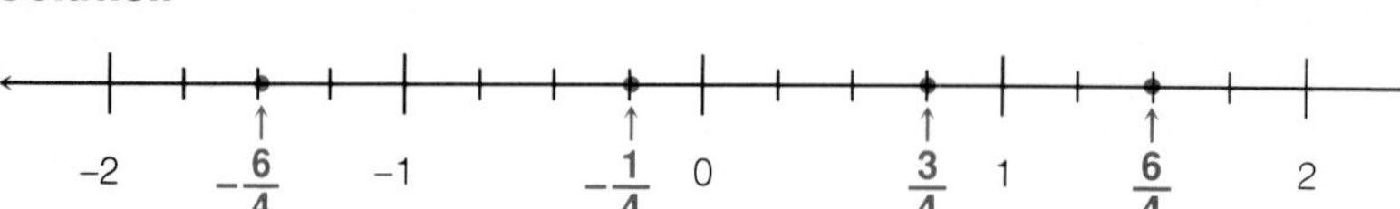

Divide the number line into fourths between integers.

Try This Graph the following rational numbers.

d. $-\frac{3}{8}, -2, \frac{5}{8}, \frac{1}{8}, \frac{9}{8}$

Class Exercises

Give the rational number for each point.

1. 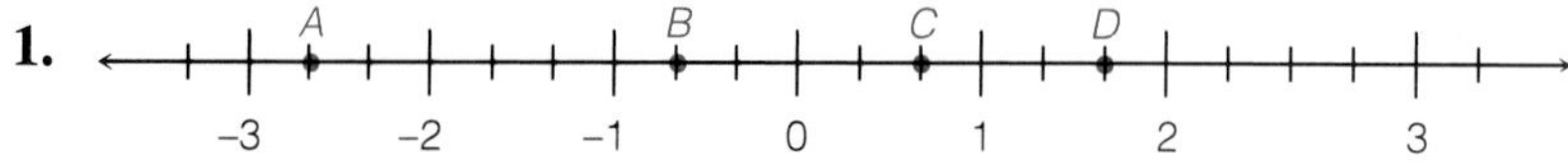

2.
A B C D
-1 0 1

Discuss the Ideas

3. Do the words *negative* and *minus* have the same meaning? Explain.

Exercises

Practice and Apply

Write the opposite of each in three different ways.

1. $\frac{3}{8}$ **2.** $\frac{2}{9}$ **3.** $\frac{11}{16}$ **4.** $\frac{5}{6}$

5. $\frac{5}{2}$ **6.** $\frac{4}{9}$ **7.** $\frac{3}{2}$ **8.** $\frac{1}{10}$

Graph the rational numbers.

9. $1\frac{2}{3}, \frac{1}{3}, \frac{2}{3}, 1\frac{1}{3}$

10. $1\frac{2}{5}, \frac{2}{5}, \frac{3}{5}, 2$

11. $\frac{1}{6}, -\frac{4}{6}, -\frac{5}{6}, \frac{5}{6}$

12. $-\frac{1}{4}, -1\frac{3}{4}, \frac{4}{4}, -1$

13. $3\frac{1}{2}, 2, \frac{1}{2}, 1\frac{1}{2}, \frac{5}{2}$

14. $\frac{2}{7}, 1\frac{1}{7}, \frac{4}{7}, \frac{12}{7}$

15. $-\frac{2}{4}, \frac{3}{4}, -\frac{5}{4}, -2, \frac{1}{4}$

16. $1\frac{1}{3}, -\frac{5}{3}, -2, \frac{2}{3}, \frac{8}{3}$

17. Is the rational number $-\frac{5}{8}$ to the left or to the right of $-\frac{3}{8}$ on the number line?

18. Is the rational number $\frac{4}{5}$ to the left or to the right of $\frac{10}{5}$ on the number line?

Extend and Apply

Write the opposite of each expression.

19. $\frac{3}{x}$ **20.** $-\frac{2}{y}$ **21.** $-\frac{h}{2}$ **22.** $\frac{t}{7}$

23. $-\frac{6}{n}$ **24.** $\frac{y}{10}$ **25.** $-\frac{12}{m}$ **26.** $-\frac{x}{100}$

Evaluate each expression for the values given.

27. $\frac{x + y}{x}, x = 5, y = -2$

28. $\frac{a + b}{c + d}, a = 4, b = 6, c = -5, d = 12$

29. $\frac{2a + 1}{b}, a = 7, b = 2$ **30.** $\frac{5x - 2}{3y}, x = -2, y = 4$

The expression $\frac{W}{W + L}$ gives the fraction of wins for a baseball team. W is the number of wins and L is the number of losses. Evaluate this expression for each school in the PAC-10 Southern Division.

College Standings (through May 1)

PAC-10 SOUTHERN DIVISION

	School	Wins	Losses
31.	Stanford	43	9
32.	Arizona St.	42	13
33.	USC	34	17
34.	UCLA	32	19
35.	Arizona	22	31
36.	California	16	37

Use Mathematical Reasoning

Find the pattern and complete each sequence.

37. $\frac{1}{3}, -\frac{1}{5}, \frac{1}{7}, -\frac{1}{9}, \frac{1}{11}, \_\_, \_\_, \_\_$

38. $-\frac{1}{4}, -\frac{1}{2}, -\frac{3}{4}, -1, -1\frac{1}{4}, \_\_, \_\_, \_\_$

Mixed Review

Simplify. **39.** $(3m + 2n) + (m + 6n)$ **40.** $7(m + 2) + (m + 3)$

Solve and check. **41.** $2a = -7.562$ **42.** $r + 2.695 = -8.305$

Estimation

You can think about a number line to estimate what integer is closest to a given fraction or mixed number.

Estimate.

1. $5\frac{3}{8}$ **2.** $-1\frac{7}{8}$ **3.** $-\frac{1}{3}$ **4.** $1\frac{1}{5}$ **5.** $-4\frac{1}{4}$ **6.** $-4\frac{5}{6}$

6-4 Rational Numbers and Repeating Decimals

Objective To change a rational number to a decimal.

Understand the Ideas

For any rational number in the form $\frac{a}{b}$, when you divide a by b you will get a decimal that either terminates or repeats. You can write $\frac{3}{8}$ as the **terminating decimal** 0.375, because when you divide 3 by 8 the division process ends with a remainder of 0, or terminates. A **repeating decimal** is a decimal with a set of digits that repeats endlessly. For example, you can write $\frac{15}{33}$ as a repeating decimal.

$$\frac{15}{33} = 0.454545\ldots$$
$$= 0.\overline{45}$$

The bar indicates the set of digits that repeats.

A rational number can be expressed as either a terminating or repeating decimal. A decimal that is neither terminating nor repeating, such as 3.121121112 . . . , names an **irrational number.**

Example

Use a calculator to write $\frac{3}{11}$ as a decimal. Use a bar for a repeating decimal.

Solution 3 [÷] 11 [=] 0.2727273

or

3 [/] 11 [F⟷D]  The [F⟷D] key changes a fraction to a decimal.

Many calculators will round a repeating decimal to the last decimal place displayed on the calculator. So,

$$\frac{3}{11} = 0.272727\ldots$$
$$= 0.\overline{27}$$

Try This Use a calculator to write each as a decimal. Use a bar for a repeating decimal.

a. $\frac{2}{9}$ **b.** $\frac{1}{6}$

Class Exercises

State whether each decimal is terminating, repeating, or irrational. For a repeating decimal, identify the digits that repeat.

1. 0.171717 . . . **2.** 0.236 **3.** 3.12121212 . . .

4. 3.123456 . . . **5.** 0.34555 **6.** 2.010010001 . . .

Discuss the Ideas

7. Rosa said that the digits 0 and 3 repeat in the number 0.030030003.., so it is a rational number. Norma said that it is an irrational number. Who is correct? Explain.

Exercises

Practice and Apply

Use a calculator to write each as a decimal. Use a bar for a repeating decimal.

1. $\frac{23}{40}$
2. $\frac{11}{3}$
3. $\frac{9}{24}$
4. $\frac{6}{11}$
5. $\frac{16}{25}$
6. $\frac{48}{11}$
7. $\frac{88}{33}$
8. $\frac{72}{99}$
9. $\frac{65}{18}$
10. $\frac{44}{54}$
11. One share of RoBN stock sells for $12\frac{3}{8}$ dollars. Write this amount as a decimal.
12. Dwayne's desk is $34\frac{5}{8}$ inches long. Write this length as a decimal.

Extend and Apply

13. Solve for x: $x = 34.\overline{45} - 1.\overline{45}$
14. Solve for x: $x = 23.\overline{8} - 2.3\overline{8}$

Write the fractions as decimals to solve. Give an approximate answer if the decimal repeats.

15. A lecture hall has 250 seats. About $\frac{7}{8}$ of the seats have right-hand desks. How many seats have right-hand desks?
16. A consumer guide suggests that people should save about $\frac{1}{6}$ of their earnings. How much money should a person who earns \$32,500 a year save?

Use Mathematical Reasoning

17. Arrange in order from smallest to largest.
$0.44, 0.4, 0.4\overline{3}, 0.4\overline{29}, 0.45, 0.4\overline{5}$
18. Write a decimal that neither terminates nor repeats.
19. Find the decimal equivalents for $\frac{1}{11}, \frac{2}{11}, \frac{3}{11}$, and $\frac{4}{11}$. Look for a pattern in these decimals to give the decimal equivalents for $\frac{5}{11}, \frac{6}{11}, \frac{7}{11}$, and $\frac{8}{11}$.

Mixed Review

Find the least common multiple (LCM). **20.** 3, 4, 5 **21.** 2, 3, 4

Solve and check. **22.** $a - 3.97 = 2.43$ **23.** $-4c = -16.8$

Find the greatest common factor (GCF). **24.** 8, 16, 34

6-5 Comparing and Ordering Rational Numbers

Objective To compare and order rational numbers.

Explore

Draw pictures or use fraction pieces to show five fractions that are each less than $\frac{1}{2}$. Each should have a different denominator and none of the numerators should be 1.

Understand the Ideas

You can use a number line to compare rational numbers. On the number line below, -2 is to the left of $-1\frac{1}{2}$; $-\frac{5}{8}$ is to the left of $-\frac{1}{8}$; and $1\frac{7}{8}$ is to the right of $1\frac{1}{8}$.

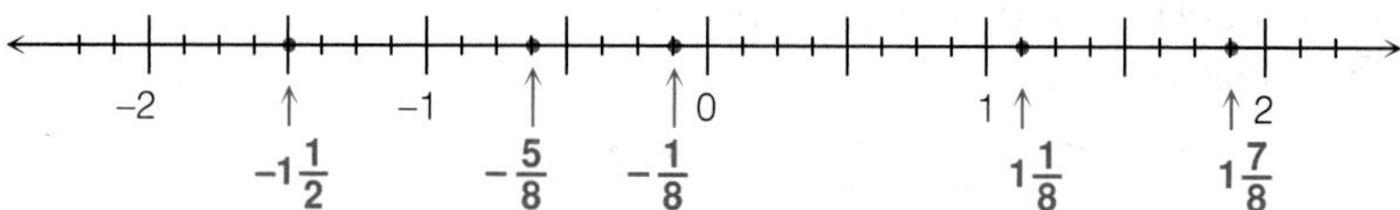

You can show these relationships as:

$$-2 < -1\frac{1}{2} \qquad -\frac{5}{8} < -\frac{1}{8} \qquad 1\frac{7}{8} > 1\frac{1}{8}$$

When two fractions have the same sign, you can compare them by changing them to equivalent fractions with like denominators or to decimals.

Example 1

Write >, <, or = for □. Use equivalent fractions to decide.

$\frac{5}{6} \square \frac{7}{8}$

Solution

$\frac{5}{6} = \frac{20}{24}$ Change $\frac{5}{6}$ and $\frac{7}{8}$ to fractions with like denominators. 24 is the least common multiple of 6 and 8.

$\frac{7}{8} = \frac{21}{24}$

$\frac{5}{6} < \frac{7}{8}$ Since $20 < 21$, $\frac{20}{24} < \frac{21}{24}$, so $\frac{5}{6} < \frac{7}{8}$.

Try This Write <, >, or = for each □.

a. $\frac{3}{5} \square \frac{4}{7}$ **b.** $-\frac{5}{12} \square -\frac{3}{8}$

You can use the fact that $\frac{a}{b}$ means $a \div b$ to change a rational number to a decimal. Since some decimals are repeating or very long, you may choose to round the decimal.

Example 2

Write <, >, or = for □. Use a calculator to write fractions as decimals. Round to the nearest thousandth to decide. $\frac{4}{9} \square \frac{3}{8}$

Solution 4 [÷] 9 [=] 0.4444444 Divide 4 by 9. $\frac{4}{9} = 0.444$

3 [÷] 8 [=] 0.375 Divide 3 by 8. $\frac{3}{8} = 0.375$

$\frac{4}{9} > \frac{3}{8}$ $0.444 > 0.375$, so $\frac{4}{9} > \frac{3}{8}$.

Try This Write <, >, or = for □. Use decimals rounded to the nearest thousandth to decide. **c.** $\frac{5}{8} \square \frac{7}{12}$ **d.** $-\frac{4}{5} \square -\frac{5}{7}$

When two fractions are equivalent, their cross products are equal. You can use this fact to compare positive rational numbers.

Rule Comparing Positive Rational Numbers

To compare two positive rational numbers, compare their cross products. For integers ***a***, ***b***, ***c***, and ***d***,

$\frac{a}{b} < \frac{c}{d}$ if $ad < bc$ and $\frac{a}{b} > \frac{c}{d}$ if $ad > bc$

Example 3

Write <, >, or = for □. Use cross products to decide.
$\frac{5}{9} \square \frac{4}{7}$

Solution $\frac{5}{9} \square \frac{4}{7}$

$5 \cdot 7$ $9 \cdot 4$ First find the cross products. The rational numbers compare as their cross products compare.

$35 < 36$

$\frac{5}{9} < \frac{4}{7}$ $35 < 36$, so $\frac{5}{9} < \frac{4}{7}$.

Try This Write <, >, or = for each □. Use cross products to decide.
e. $\frac{5}{6} \square \frac{4}{7}$ **f.** $\frac{9}{13} \square \frac{8}{15}$

Class Exercises

Tell which rational number is greater.

1. $\frac{5}{7}, \frac{6}{7}$ **2.** $-\frac{4}{18}, -\frac{5}{18}$ **3.** $\frac{5}{9}, \frac{4}{9}$ **4.** $-\frac{15}{12}, -\frac{11}{12}$ **5.** $-\frac{5}{2}, -\frac{1}{2}$

Discuss the Ideas

6. If the numerators are both 1 for two rational numbers, how can you tell by looking at the denominators which fraction is greater?

Exercises

Practice and Apply

Write <, >, or = for each □. Use equivalent fractions to decide.

1. $\frac{2}{5}$ □ $\frac{3}{7}$
2. $-\frac{13}{18}$ □ $-\frac{2}{3}$
3. $\frac{3}{4}$ □ $\frac{5}{8}$
4. $-\frac{3}{8}$ □ $-\frac{5}{17}$
5. $\frac{5}{13}$ □ $\frac{6}{15}$
6. $\frac{35}{31}$ □ $\frac{2}{3}$
7. $\frac{25}{54}$ □ $\frac{4}{9}$
8. $\frac{29}{32}$ □ $\frac{7}{8}$
9. $\frac{27}{24}$ □ $\frac{9}{8}$

Write <, >, or = for each □. Use a calculator to write fractions as decimals. Round to the nearest thousandth to decide.

10. $-\frac{5}{9}$ □ $-\frac{7}{12}$
11. $\frac{4}{5}$ □ $\frac{2}{3}$
12. $\frac{4}{9}$ □ $\frac{3}{7}$
13. $\frac{17}{30}$ □ $\frac{3}{5}$
14. $\frac{3}{5}$ □ $\frac{7}{10}$
15. $-\frac{5}{6}$ □ $-\frac{6}{8}$
16. $\frac{11}{2}$ □ $\frac{13}{5}$
17. $\frac{7}{9}$ □ $\frac{8}{10}$
18. $-\frac{5}{8}$ □ $-\frac{7}{10}$

Write <, >, or = for each □. Use cross products to decide.

19. $\frac{3}{10}$ □ $\frac{1}{3}$
20. $\frac{24}{2}$ □ $\frac{12}{1}$
21. $\frac{13}{12}$ □ $\frac{8}{7}$
22. $\frac{6}{5}$ □ $\frac{15}{12}$
23. $\frac{17}{20}$ □ $\frac{9}{11}$
24. $\frac{9}{24}$ □ $\frac{2}{5}$
25. $\frac{14}{25}$ □ $\frac{16}{30}$
26. $\frac{34}{60}$ □ $\frac{17}{32}$
27. $\frac{9}{13}$ □ $\frac{4}{7}$

28. One share of FTee stock sold for $10\frac{1}{8}$ on Monday and for $10\frac{1}{4}$ on Tuesday. Did the cost of one share of this stock increase or decrease?
29. The interest rate on a computer loan at Freedom Bank is $10\frac{3}{4}$%. A computer loan at Citywide Bank is $10\frac{5}{8}$%. Which bank has the greater interest rate?
30. Melissa needed a wood board $12\frac{3}{8}$ in. long to build a birdhouse. She found a board $12\frac{5}{12}$ in. long in the shed. Could she use the board from the shed?

Extend and Apply

Write in order from least to greatest.

31. $\frac{1}{5}, \frac{1}{3}, \frac{1}{4}$
32. $-\frac{3}{4}, -\frac{7}{8}, -\frac{5}{7}$
33. $\frac{4}{9}, \frac{6}{12}, \frac{2}{3}$
34. $\frac{2}{5}, \frac{7}{15}, \frac{10}{20}$
35. $-\frac{5}{12}, -\frac{6}{15}, -\frac{3}{4}$
36. $\frac{5}{6}, \frac{6}{7}, \frac{3}{8}$

Write <, >, or = for each □. The variable stands for a positive integer.

37. $\frac{x}{5} \square \frac{x}{7}$ **38.** $\frac{y}{24} \square \frac{y}{12}$ **39.** $\frac{j}{8} \square \frac{j}{8}$

40. $\frac{t}{4} \square t$ **41.** $\frac{2d}{6} \square \frac{3d}{6}$ **42.** $\frac{5}{a} \square \frac{3}{a}$

43. $\frac{4}{2x} \square \frac{4}{3x}$ **44.** $\frac{2a}{3b} \square \frac{6a}{9b}$ **45.** $\frac{2x}{8} \square \frac{x}{4}$

46. Write to Learn Write a paragraph describing the three methods you can use to compare two rational numbers, such as $\frac{5}{8}$ and $\frac{7}{12}$.

Use Mathematical Reasoning

47. Write in order from least to greatest. $\frac{5}{6}, \frac{5}{8}, \frac{5}{3}, \frac{5}{2}, \frac{5}{9}, \frac{5}{5}, \frac{5}{12}, \frac{5}{4}$

48. Make an organized list of all rational numbers less than 1 whose numerators and denominators are selected from the numbers 2, 3, 4, 5, 6, 7, 8, 9, and 10.

Mixed Review

Evaluate for $x = 6$. **49.** $x^2 + 19$ **50.** $x(x + 2)$ **51.** $0.5x$

Solve and check. **52.** $-1.35m = -8.37$ **53.** $r - 16.28 = -11.06$

The basic properties for integers also apply to rational numbers. The multiplicative inverse property will be introduced in Chapter 7. The properties below hold for all rational numbers $\frac{a}{b}$, $\frac{c}{d}$, and $\frac{e}{f}$, where $b \neq 0$, $d \neq 0$, and $f \neq 0$.

Basic Property Update

Commutative Properties

$\frac{a}{b} + \frac{c}{d} = \frac{c}{d} + \frac{a}{b}$ $\frac{a}{b} \cdot \frac{c}{d} = \frac{c}{d} \cdot \frac{a}{b}$

Associative Properties

$\left(\frac{a}{b} + \frac{c}{d}\right) + \frac{e}{f} = \frac{a}{b} + \left(\frac{c}{d} + \frac{e}{f}\right)$ $\left(\frac{a}{b} \cdot \frac{c}{d}\right) \cdot \frac{e}{f} = \frac{a}{b} \cdot \left(\frac{c}{d} \cdot \frac{e}{f}\right)$

Identity Properties

$\frac{a}{b} + 0 = 0 + \frac{a}{b} = \frac{a}{b}$ $\frac{a}{b} \cdot 1 = 1 \cdot \frac{a}{b} = \frac{a}{b}$

Additive Inverse Property

$\frac{a}{b} + \left(-\frac{a}{b}\right) = -\frac{a}{b} + \frac{a}{b} = 0$

Distributive Property

$\frac{a}{b}\left(\frac{c}{d} + \frac{e}{f}\right) = \frac{a}{b} \cdot \frac{c}{d} + \frac{a}{b} \cdot \frac{e}{f}$

Mathematical Reasoning

Finding a Counterexample

Objective To find a counterexample for a generalization.

Group Activity Suppose a student in your group made the following generalization: "All of the students in this group have blue eyes." Find a way to prove that this statement is false. Then make up other general statements and figure out how you can prove that they are false.

In everyday or mathematical reasoning, we often make a statement that says that something is always true or is true for every member of a specified set. This kind of statement, called a **generalization,** may be either true or false. Here are some examples of The sentence in parentheses explains how you can prove each one false.

1. All even numbers can be divided evenly by 4.
   (Find an even number that cannot be divided evenly by 4.)
2. A two-place decimal is greater than a one-place decimal.
   (Find a one-place decimal equal to or greater than a two-place decimal.)
3. If a triangle has a right angle, then it has two congruent sides.
   (Produce a right triangle that does not have two congruent sides.)

To show that a generalization is false, you only need to find one example that contradicts the generalization. This example is called a **counterexample.**

A **counterexample** is a single example that shows a generalization to be false.

Apply Mathematical Reasoning

1. Suppose your friend said, "All of my friends have portable televisions." How can you convince your classmate that this is not true?
2. A basketball coach said, "Whenever our opponents score over 80 points, we lose the game." At the next game, his team showed that this generalization was false. Describe what happened at the next game.

Tell whether the generalization is true or false. If it is false, prove it false by giving a counterexample.

3. Subtracting from a number always makes it smaller.
4. Multiplying a number by another number always makes it larger.
5. The product of an odd and an even number is always even.

6-6 Adding and Subtracting with Like Denominators

Objective To add and subtract rational numbers with like denominators.

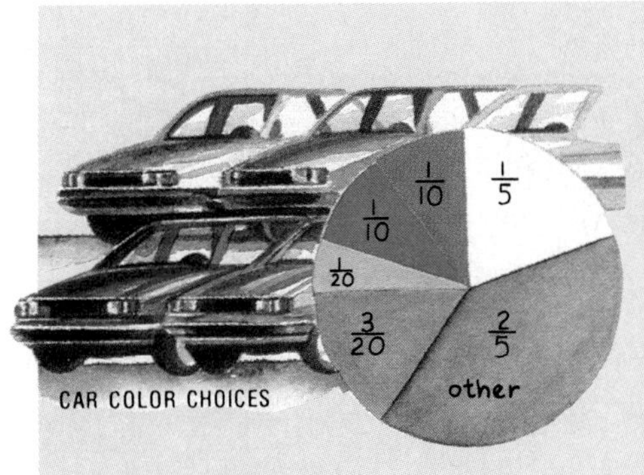

Application

A car dealer wants to know what fraction of their customers picked red or light blue as their favorite car color.

Understand the Ideas

The diagram below shows that $\frac{1}{5} + \frac{3}{5} = \frac{4}{5}$.

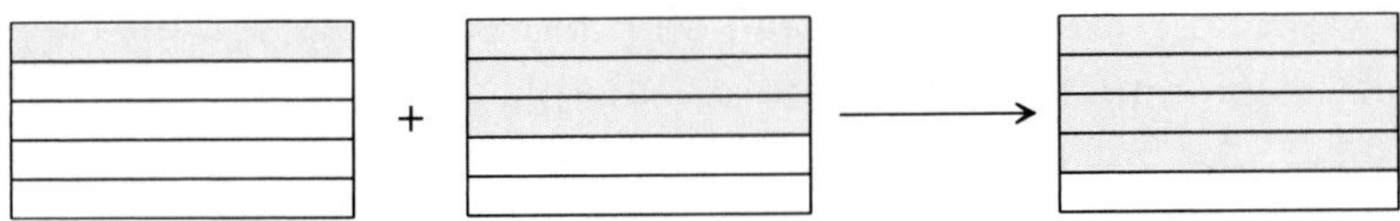

Rule **Adding and Subtracting with Like Denominators**

To add or subtract rational numbers with like denominators, add or subtract the numerators. Write the sum or difference over the common denominator.

For all integers ***a, b,*** and ***c,*** where $c \neq 0$,

$$\frac{a}{c} + \frac{b}{c} = \frac{a+b}{c} \qquad \frac{a}{c} - \frac{b}{c} = \frac{a-b}{c}$$

Example 1

Add $\frac{3}{20} + \frac{1}{20}$ to find what fraction of those surveyed picked red or light blue as their favorite color in the **application.** Reduce to lowest terms.

Solution

$\frac{3}{20} + \frac{1}{20} = \frac{3+1}{20}$ Add the numerators. Write the sum over the common denominator.

$= \frac{4}{20} = \frac{1}{5}$ Reduce to lowest terms.

$\frac{1}{5}$ of those surveyed picked red or light blue as their favorite color.

Try This Add or subtract. Reduce to lowest terms.

a. $\frac{5}{12} + \frac{4}{12}$ b. $-\frac{2}{7} + \frac{4}{7}$ c. $-\frac{7}{18} - \frac{13}{18}$

d. Last year $\frac{7}{12}$ of Apopka businesses listed their telephone number in the Yellow Pages. This year, $\frac{11}{12}$ of the businesses listed their number. By what fraction did the number of listings increase this year?

Example 2

Subtract. Reduce to lowest terms. $\frac{13}{25} - \left(-\frac{7}{25}\right)$

Solution

$\frac{13}{25} - \left(-\frac{7}{25}\right) = \frac{13}{25} + \frac{7}{25}$ Subtracting $-\frac{7}{25}$ is the same as adding $\frac{7}{25}$.

$= \frac{13 + 7}{25}$

$= \frac{20}{25} = \frac{4}{5}$

Try This Subtract. Reduce to lowest terms.

e. $\frac{5}{18} - \left(-\frac{4}{18}\right)$ f. $-\frac{8}{12} - \left(-\frac{5}{12}\right)$

Class Exercises

Name the property (Commutative, Associative, Identity, or Inverse) shown.

1. $\frac{5}{6} + \left(-\frac{5}{6}\right) = 0$
2. $-\frac{3}{4} + \left(-\frac{1}{4}\right) = -\frac{1}{4} + \left(-\frac{3}{4}\right)$
3. $0 + \frac{1}{6} = \frac{1}{6}$
4. $\frac{4}{5} + \left(\frac{2}{5} + \frac{3}{5}\right) = \left(\frac{4}{5} + \frac{2}{5}\right) + \frac{3}{5}$

Discuss the Ideas

5. Do the rules for adding and subtracting integers (pages 82 and 86) apply to adding and subtracting rational numbers? Explain.

Exercises

Practice and Apply

Add or subtract. Reduce to lowest terms.

1. $\frac{3}{8} + \frac{1}{8}$
2. $-\frac{2}{7} + \frac{3}{7}$
3. $\frac{5}{11} - \frac{2}{11}$
4. $-\frac{7}{11} + \frac{9}{11}$
5. $\frac{23}{27} + \frac{13}{27}$
6. $\frac{48}{13} - \frac{22}{13}$
7. $-\frac{14}{15} - \frac{1}{15}$
8. $\frac{24}{15} - \left(-\frac{14}{15}\right)$
9. $-\frac{9}{10} - \left(-\frac{9}{10}\right)$
10. What fraction of the people surveyed in the application chose white or another (other) color as their favorite car color?

11. The Lui family starts a trip with the gas gauge reading $\frac{5}{8}$ full. After 3 hours, the gauge reads $\frac{3}{8}$ full. What fraction of a tank of gas have they used?

Extend and Apply

Evaluate each expression. Reduce to lowest terms.

12. $a - \frac{3}{8}$ when $a = \frac{7}{8}$ **13.** $x + \frac{1}{9}$ when $x = \frac{4}{9}$

14. $s + \frac{27}{2}$ when $s = \frac{11}{2}$ **15.** $y - \frac{9}{14}$ when $y = \frac{13}{14}$

Evaluate. Reduce to lowest terms.

16. $\frac{5}{8} + \left(-\frac{7}{8}\right) - \frac{12}{8}$ **17.** $-\frac{5}{24} - \left(-\frac{13}{24}\right) - \left(-\frac{6}{24}\right)$

Write each expression as a fraction. Example: $\frac{12}{m} - \frac{7}{m} = \frac{12 - 7}{m} = \frac{5}{m}$

18. $\frac{5}{y} - \frac{7}{y}$ **19.** $\frac{6}{z} + \frac{5}{z}$ **20.** $\frac{12}{s} - \frac{7}{s}$

21. $\frac{27}{x} - \frac{15}{x}$ **22.** $\frac{123}{t} + \frac{35}{t}$ **23.** $\frac{67}{u} - \frac{25}{u}$

"Break apart" numbers to find each sum mentally. Example: To find $5\frac{1}{4} + \frac{3}{4}$, think "$\frac{1}{4} + \frac{3}{4}$ is 1, and 5 + 1 is 6."

24. $6\frac{1}{3} + \frac{2}{3}$ **25.** $7\frac{3}{8} + \frac{1}{8}$ **26.** $26\frac{1}{5} + 4\frac{3}{5}$

27. Alicia added $\frac{1}{8}$ cup of water and $\frac{5}{8}$ cup of milk to a bowl. After mixing them together, the recipe said to remove $\frac{2}{8}$ cup of the mixture. How much was left in the bowl?

28. A rancher repaired three sections of fencing. The first section was $\frac{1}{10}$ mile long, the second was $\frac{3}{10}$ mile long, and the third was $\frac{4}{10}$ mile long. What was the total length of the fencing the rancher repaired?

Use Mathematical Reasoning

29. Find all the whole number values of t that make the equation true. $\frac{19}{t} + \frac{5}{t}$ = a whole number

30. Find two rational numbers with a sum of 0 and a difference of $\frac{1}{2}$.

31. Find two rational numbers with a sum of $\frac{1}{2}$ and a difference of 0.

Mixed Review

Solve and check. **32.** $-27a = 334.8$ **33.** $r + 0.414 = 2.396$

Find the greatest common factor (GCF). **34.** 32, 96, 48

Simplify. **35.** $2^4 - 2^1$ **36.** $(-3)^2 + (-3)^3$ **37.** $n^2 \cdot n^7$

6-7 Adding and Subtracting with Unlike Denominators

Objective To add and subtract rational numbers with unlike denominators

Application

Wrestlers keep accurate records of weight gains and losses. If Jim gained $\frac{5}{8}$ pound one week and $\frac{2}{3}$ pound the next week, he could add $\frac{5}{8}$ and $\frac{2}{3}$ to find his total gain for the two weeks.

Understand the Ideas

The models below show that you can add (or subtract) rational numbers with unlike denominators by first changing them to equivalent fractions with like denominators. The like denominator is usually the least common multiple of the denominators, called the **least common denominator.** Add or subtract the numerators and write the sum or difference over the common denominator.

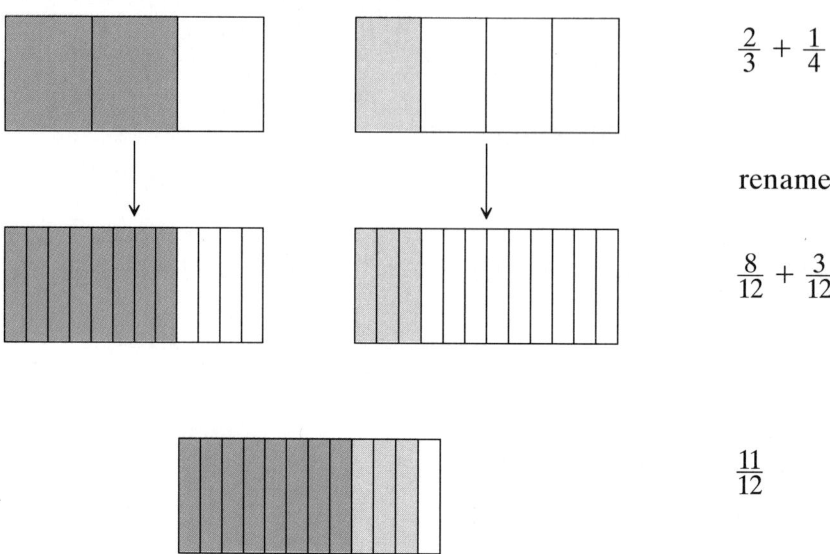

Example 1

Find the total weight gain for the wrestler described in the **application** by adding $\frac{5}{8} + \frac{2}{3}$. Reduce to lowest terms.

Solution

$\frac{5}{8} + \frac{2}{3} = \frac{15}{24} + \frac{16}{24}$ Change each to a fraction with a denominator of 24.

$= \frac{15 + 16}{24}$

$= \frac{31}{24}$

$= 1\frac{7}{24}$

The wrestler gained a total of $1\frac{7}{24}$ pounds.

Try This Add. Reduce to lowest terms.

a. $\frac{4}{5} + \frac{5}{12}$ **b.** $\frac{3}{10} + \frac{6}{15}$

c. In the South Bay youth orchestra, $\frac{2}{5}$ of the string section are first violins and $\frac{1}{3}$ are second violins. What fraction of the string section are violin players?

Example 2

Subtract. Reduce to lowest terms. $-\frac{5}{6} - \frac{1}{2}$

Solution

$-\frac{5}{6} - \frac{1}{2} = -\frac{5}{6} - \frac{3}{6}$ 6 is the least common multiple of 6 and 2.

$= \frac{-5 - 3}{6}$

$= -\frac{8}{6}$

$= -1\frac{2}{6} = -1\frac{1}{3}$ Reduce to lowest terms.

Try This Subtract. Reduce to lowest terms.

d. $\frac{5}{6} - \left(-\frac{1}{8}\right)$ **e.** $-\frac{2}{5} - \frac{3}{6}$

f. For the youth orchestra concert, $\frac{5}{6}$ of the seats were sold, but only $\frac{3}{4}$ of the seats were occupied. What fraction of the seats were sold but not occupied?

Class Exercises

Give the least common denominator for each pair of fractions.

1. $\frac{1}{2}, \frac{3}{4}$ **2.** $\frac{2}{3}, \frac{1}{6}$ **3.** $\frac{1}{5}, \frac{3}{10}$ **4.** $\frac{1}{2}, \frac{2}{3}$ **5.** $\frac{1}{3}, \frac{1}{4}$

6. $\frac{2}{3}, \frac{3}{5}$ **7.** $\frac{1}{4}, \frac{3}{8}$ **8.** $\frac{4}{5}, \frac{7}{25}$ **9.** $\frac{5}{6}, \frac{1}{3}$ **10.** $\frac{1}{2}, \frac{7}{10}$

Discuss the Ideas

11. Find two fractions whose least common denominator is the denominator of one of the fractions. Find two fractions whose least common denominator is not the denominator of either fraction.

Exercises

Practice and Apply

Add or subtract. Reduce to lowest terms.

1. $\frac{1}{2} + \frac{3}{8}$
2. $\frac{2}{3} - \frac{1}{4}$
3. $\frac{1}{6} - \frac{3}{4}$
4. $-\frac{7}{10} - \frac{1}{2}$
5. $\frac{2}{3} - \frac{1}{12}$
6. $\frac{3}{4} + \frac{5}{6}$
7. $-\frac{8}{16} + \frac{3}{4}$
8. $\frac{3}{4} - \frac{1}{5}$
9. $\frac{5}{6} + \frac{7}{10}$
10. $\frac{5}{8} - \left(-\frac{5}{6}\right)$
11. $\frac{5}{18} - \left(-\frac{3}{6}\right)$
12. $-\frac{11}{12} - \left(-\frac{5}{3}\right)$
13. $-\frac{12}{8} - \frac{2}{3}$
14. $-\frac{7}{10} - \left(-\frac{29}{100}\right)$
15. $\frac{14}{8} - \left(-\frac{6}{4}\right)$
16. $\frac{4}{5} - \left(-\frac{3}{8}\right)$
17. $\frac{3}{4} - \frac{4}{7}$
18. $-\frac{1}{8} - \left(-\frac{5}{12}\right)$
19. $-\frac{1}{2} + \frac{1}{5}$
20. $\frac{7}{8} + \left(-\frac{5}{6}\right)$
21. $-\frac{7}{12} - \left(-\frac{4}{9}\right)$
22. A sandwich at Gabriel's Deli is made of $\frac{1}{4}$ lb of meat and $\frac{3}{8}$ lb of bread and toppings. How much does a Gabriel's sandwich weigh?
23. A wrestler lost $\frac{1}{2}$ lb during the morning and another $\frac{3}{4}$ lb during the afternoon. How much weight in all did the wrestler lose that day?
24. The total length of a bicycle race course will be $\frac{7}{8}$ mile, and $\frac{2}{3}$ mile is completed so far. What part of the course is not yet completed?
25. A tailor used $\frac{5}{6}$ yd of material to make a vest and $\frac{4}{9}$ yd of the same material to make a matching scarf. How much material did the tailor use all together?

Extend and Apply

Evaluate. Reduce to lowest terms.

26. $-\frac{4}{9} + \frac{2}{3} - \frac{4}{9}$
27. $-\frac{5}{6} - \frac{3}{4} + \frac{1}{2}$
28. $-\frac{2}{3} + \frac{7}{9} + \frac{1}{2}$
29. $-\frac{4}{6} - \left(-\frac{7}{12}\right) - \frac{3}{8}$
30. The high jump record used to be 5 ft $1\frac{1}{4}$ in. Today the record was broken by $\frac{1}{2}$ in. What is the new high jump record?
31. A recipe called for $\frac{1}{2}$ cup cheddar cheese, $\frac{1}{4}$ cup mozzarella cheese, and $\frac{2}{3}$ cup monterey jack cheese. How much cheese is in the recipe?

32–34. Use the data in the circle graph at the right.

32. What number of bedrooms is most common?

33. How much greater is the fraction for 3 bedroom homes than the fraction for 2 bedroom homes?

34. What fraction of the total number of homes have exactly 1 or 2 bedrooms?

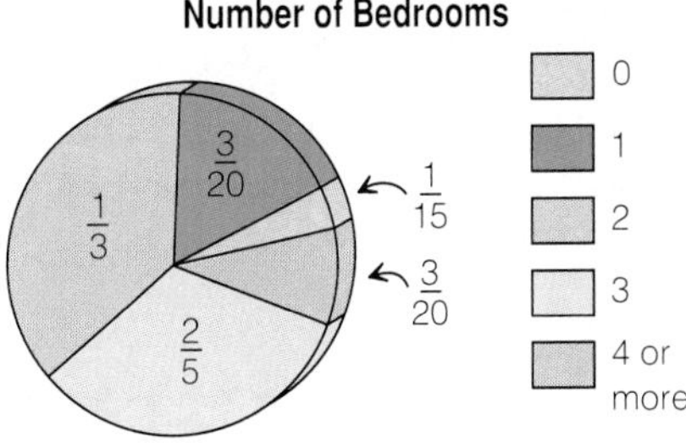

Use Mathematical Reasoning

35. Place the digits 2, 3, 4, and 5 in the boxes to make the equation true.

$$-\frac{\square}{\square} + \frac{\square}{\square} = \frac{7}{20}$$

36. Complete the following proof by supplying the missing reasons.

$\frac{a}{b} + \frac{c}{d} = \frac{a \cdot d}{b \cdot d} + \frac{c \cdot b}{d \cdot b}$	Property of Equivalent Fractions
$= \frac{a \cdot d}{b \cdot d} + \frac{c \cdot b}{b \cdot d}$	Why?
$= a \cdot d \cdot \frac{1}{b \cdot d} + (c \cdot b) \cdot \frac{1}{b \cdot d}$	$\frac{a}{b} = a \cdot \frac{1}{b}$
$= (a \cdot d + c \cdot b) \cdot \frac{1}{b \cdot d}$	Why?
$= \frac{a \cdot d + c \cdot b}{b \cdot d}$	Why?

Mixed Review

Find all the factors of each number. **37.** 25 **38.** 21

Give the absolute value and opposite of each. **39.** -7 **40.** 19

Estimate, then find the value of the variable. **41.** $M = 6.5(68 \div 17)$

Solve and check. **42.** $19.8 = -4c$ **43.** $-11.62 + n = -49.33$

Estimation

You can substitute compatible numbers to estimate the sum or difference of rational numbers by changing them to approximate fractions with like denominators. For example, to estimate the sum $\frac{1}{4} + \frac{7}{8}$, think: $\frac{7}{8}$ is about $\frac{3}{4}$, so $\frac{1}{4} + \frac{7}{8}$ is about $\frac{1}{4} + \frac{3}{4}$, or 1.

Estimate each sum or difference.

1. $\frac{7}{8} + \frac{12}{13}$ **2.** $\frac{3}{7} + \frac{5}{8}$ **3.** $\frac{11}{12} - \frac{3}{4}$

4. $\frac{14}{15} + \frac{1}{2}$ **5.** $\frac{8}{9} - \frac{7}{8}$ **6.** $\frac{99}{100} - \frac{5}{8}$

6-8 Adding and Subtracting with Mixed Numbers

Objective To add and subtract mixed numbers.

Explore

Suppose you have $3\frac{1}{3}$ pies left from a school sale, and a friend orders $1\frac{1}{2}$ pies. Use paper pies, like the ones at the right, to show how many pies will be left. Write a paragraph that describes what you did to find the answer.

Understand the Ideas

The rules for adding and subtracting rational numbers with like and unlike denominators apply to mixed numbers.

Example 1

A builder estimated that $4\frac{1}{2}$ cubic yards of concrete were needed for a job. Only $2\frac{2}{3}$ cubic yards were used. How much less was the amount used than the estimate?

Solution

$$\begin{array}{rcrcr} 4\frac{1}{2} & = & 4\frac{3}{6} & = & 3\frac{9}{6} \\ -2\frac{2}{3} & = & 2\frac{4}{6} & = & 2\frac{4}{6} \\ \hline & & & & 1\frac{5}{6} \end{array}$$

Find equivalent fractions with like denominators and rename $4\frac{3}{6}$ as $3\frac{9}{6}$. Subtract the fractions, and then subtract the whole numbers.

The builder used $1\frac{5}{6}$ cubic yards of concrete less than estimated.

Try This Add or subtract. Reduce to lowest terms if necessary.

a. $\begin{array}{r} 3\frac{1}{4} \\ -1\frac{1}{2} \\ \hline \end{array}$ **b.** $\begin{array}{r} 3\frac{4}{5} \\ +5\frac{5}{8} \\ \hline \end{array}$ **c.** $\begin{array}{r} 4\frac{3}{5} \\ +2\frac{3}{5} \\ \hline \end{array}$

d. Jared worked $5\frac{3}{4}$ hr on Friday and $6\frac{1}{2}$ hr on Saturday. How many hours did he work all together for these two days?

Sometimes it helps to change mixed numbers to improper fractions before adding or subtracting.

Example 2

Add and reduce to lowest terms. $-2\frac{2}{3} + 1\frac{1}{6}$

Solution $-2\frac{2}{3} + 1\frac{1}{6} = -\frac{8}{3} + \frac{7}{6}$ Write each mixed number as an improper fraction.

$= -\frac{16}{6} + \frac{7}{6}$ 6 is the least common denominator.

$= \frac{-16 + 7}{6}$

$= -\frac{9}{6} = -1\frac{3}{6} = -1\frac{1}{2}$

Try This Add or subtract. Reduce to lowest terms.

e. $1\frac{1}{2} + \frac{3}{4}$ **f.** $-3\frac{1}{3} - \left(-4\frac{2}{5}\right)$ **g.** $2\frac{3}{8} + 1\frac{7}{8}$

Class Exercises

Change each mixed number to an improper fraction mentally.

1. $1\frac{3}{5}$ **2.** $-4\frac{1}{2}$ **3.** $-5\frac{3}{4}$ **4.** 4 **5.** $6\frac{2}{3}$

6. $-3\frac{1}{10}$ **7.** $1\frac{7}{12}$ **8.** $2\frac{5}{6}$ **9.** $-3\frac{1}{9}$ **10.** $-7\frac{5}{8}$

Discuss the Ideas

11. Give a mixed number addition problem that would be most easily solved using the mixed number form rather than the improper fraction form. Explain your answer.

Exercises

Practice and Apply

Add or subtract. Reduce to lowest terms.

1. $1\frac{2}{3} - \frac{3}{5}$ **2.** $2\frac{2}{5} + 1\frac{1}{5}$ **3.** $2\frac{3}{7} + \frac{1}{3}$

4. $3\frac{1}{6} - \frac{2}{3}$ **5.** $3\frac{3}{5} + \frac{5}{12}$ **6.** $3\frac{7}{8} + 2\frac{1}{3}$

7. $3\frac{3}{8} + 2\frac{5}{8}$ **8.** $5\frac{5}{12} - 3\frac{2}{3}$ **9.** $5\frac{3}{4} + 6\frac{1}{3}$

10. $-3\frac{5}{6} - 2\frac{1}{8}$ **11.** $-4\frac{3}{10} + 7\frac{3}{4}$ **12.** $-1\frac{2}{9} - 1\frac{5}{12}$

13. $-4 - 2\frac{4}{7}$

14. $-4\frac{5}{6} + 7$

15. $-1\frac{5}{12} - 4\frac{5}{16}$

16. $2\frac{3}{4} - 1\frac{7}{8}$

17. $-6\frac{1}{4} + 4\frac{1}{2}$

18. $5\frac{3}{8} + 2\frac{3}{4}$

19. Mario needs a $2\frac{5}{8}$ ft long board to finish building a dog house. He found a $3\frac{1}{2}$ ft long board in the shed. How much of the board does he need to cut off to make it $2\frac{5}{8}$ ft long?

20. Donnell has a square picture frame that measures $18\frac{5}{8}$ in. × $18\frac{5}{8}$ in. How much will he have to cut off of a poster that is
a) $19\frac{1}{4}$ in. wide and
b) $20\frac{1}{2}$ in. long?

21. Two dirt bike tracks were built in a single stadium. One was a mile and an eighth long and the other was three quarters of a mile. How much shorter was the second track?

22. A school's record for a race was 4 minutes $23\frac{1}{2}$ seconds. A runner ran this race in 4 minutes $35\frac{3}{10}$ seconds. By how many seconds did the runner miss tying the record?

Extend and Apply

For Exercises 23–28, estimate, using rounding to the nearest whole number or a **front-end** technique. For example, to find $7\frac{3}{4} + 2\frac{1}{3}$, think: $7\frac{3}{4}$ is closest to 8, $2\frac{1}{3}$ is closest to 2. Estimate: 10. Or think: 7 + 2 is 9, $\frac{3}{4} + \frac{1}{3}$ is about 1. Estimate: 10.

23. $3\frac{4}{5} - 1\frac{1}{3}$

24. $12\frac{5}{8} - \left(-3\frac{2}{5}\right)$

25. $-7\frac{1}{2} + 3\frac{1}{4}$

26. $\frac{1}{5} - 4\frac{7}{12} + 6\frac{4}{9}$

27. $-5\frac{5}{6} - \left(-\frac{7}{9}\right) + 12$

28. $6\frac{2}{3} - 25 - \left(-12\frac{9}{10}\right)$

Estimate each sum using **clustering**. For example, to find $3\frac{3}{4} + 4\frac{1}{5} + 3\frac{7}{8}$, think "all the numbers cluster around 4, and $3 \cdot 4 = 12$."

29. $4\frac{5}{6} + 5\frac{3}{8} + 4\frac{9}{10}$

30. $6\frac{3}{4} + 7\frac{1}{6} + 6\frac{7}{8}$

31. $12\frac{1}{5} + 11\frac{7}{8} + 11\frac{9}{10}$

32. Trisha earns overtime pay if she works more than 40 hours a week. Did Trisha work overtime for the week shown on her time card?

33. A local law prohibits students from working more than $12\frac{1}{2}$ hours on any one day. On which day could Trisha have worked the most number of additional hours? How many hours?

Time Card

Trisha

Day	Hours
Monday	7 1/4 hr.
Tuesday	8 hr.
Wednesday	7 1/2 hr.
Thursday	9 1/2 hr.
Friday	7 1/2 hr.

34. A carpenter cut $5\frac{1}{2}$ inches off one end of a 6-foot-long piece of wood and $3\frac{3}{5}$ inches off the other end. How long was the wood after these two pieces were cut off?

35. **Write Your Own Problem** Write two word problems using the information from Trisha's time card. One problem should be able to be solved using addition and the other should use subtraction.

Use Mathematical Reasoning

36. Write the rational numbers $\frac{1}{2}$, 1, $1\frac{1}{2}$, 2, $2\frac{1}{2}$, and 3 in the circles so that the sum along each side of the triangle is $4\frac{1}{2}$.

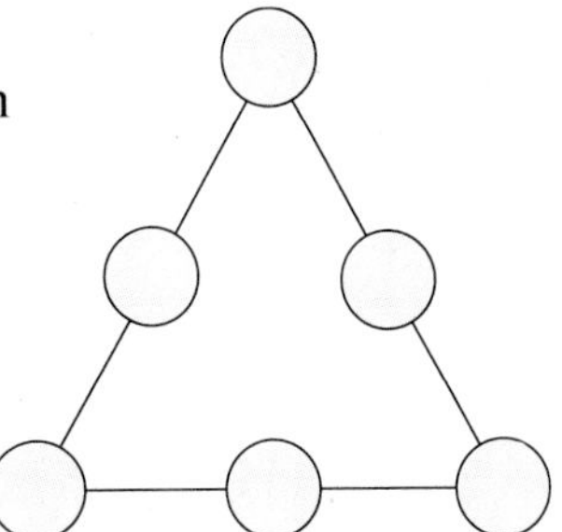

Mixed Review

Find the least common multiple (LCM).

37. 6, 8, 10, 12

Evaluate for $y = -3$.

38. $y(y - 4)$

39. $y^2 + 3y$

40. $9 - 6y$

Mental Math

You can look for compatible numbers to add or subtract rational numbers mentally. For example, in the equation $2\frac{1}{4} + 3\frac{2}{3} + 4\frac{3}{4}$ you can first add $2\frac{1}{4}$ and $4\frac{3}{4}$ to get 7 and then add 7 and $3\frac{2}{3}$ to get $10\frac{2}{3}$.

Look for compatible numbers to add or subtract mentally.

1. $-5\frac{2}{5} + 7 - 1\frac{3}{5}$
2. $6\frac{2}{3} + 4\frac{1}{2} - 2\frac{2}{3}$
3. $3\frac{4}{9} + 4\frac{5}{6} + 1\frac{5}{9}$
4. $10\frac{5}{8} - 2\frac{3}{8} - 3$
5. $-4\frac{4}{5} + 5\frac{5}{12} - \frac{1}{5}$
6. $-5\frac{6}{7} - 7\frac{1}{3} - 2\frac{1}{7}$

6-9 Problem Solving: Applications

The Stock Market

Objective To solve problems involving stock prices.

When you buy **shares** of **stock** from a corporation, you become a part owner of the corporation, and are called a shareholder or a stockholder. A stock's price is given as a fractional part of a dollar. For example, $19\frac{5}{8}$ means 19 and $\frac{5}{8}$ dollars, or $19.625.

Below is a typical newspaper stock report. The company names are given as abbreviations under the word "stock."

Today's Stock Report

(1) High	(1) Low	Stock	(2) High	(2) Low	(3) Last	(4) Chg.
19 3/4	9 1/2	AWARD	16 1/4	14	15 5/8	+2 1/4
28	10 7/8	ConnEt	16 1/8	13	14 1/8	−1 5/8
62 1/4	47	NATS	59 7/8	56 1/2	57 3/4	+1 7/8
45 1/2	22	PODCo	33 1/2	29 7/8	31	−3/4
21 1/4	14 7/8	RICH	19 3/4	18 3/8	19 5/8	+1/2

(1) High/Low—The highest and lowest selling prices of each share for the year
(2) High/Low—The highest and lowest selling prices of each share for this day
(3) Last—The price of the last share sold this day. Also called "closing price."
(4) Chg. (Change)—The difference between today's closing price and yesterday's closing price

Sample Problem 1 Find the price of the last RICH Corporation share sold yesterday.

Solution $19\frac{5}{8} - \frac{1}{2} = 19\frac{1}{8}$ The change (Chg.) was an increase (+) of $\frac{1}{2}$. To find yesterday's last price, subtract $\frac{1}{2}$ from today's last price.

Sample Problem 2 How much less was the closing price for one share of NATS than the high price for the day?

Solution $59\frac{7}{8} - 57\frac{3}{4}$ The closing price is the same as the last price.

$= 59\frac{7}{8} - 57\frac{6}{8} = 2\frac{1}{8}$

The closing price was $2\frac{1}{8}$ points lower than the high price.

Problems

Solve.

1. PODCo shares went down today compared to yesterday. What was the last price for a share yesterday?
2. AWARD shares went up today compared to yesterday. What was the last price for a share yesterday?
3. What was the closing price of ConnEt shares yesterday?
4. What is the difference between the yearly high and low of PODCo shares?
5. What is the difference between yesterday's closing price and today's high price for AWARD shares?
6. Which stock had the greatest difference between the yearly high and low prices?

Below are the daily closing prices for one share of RICH. Use this table for Exercises 7–8.

Day	M	T	W	T	F
Closing Price	$15\frac{1}{8}$	$15\frac{3}{4}$	$16\frac{3}{8}$	$15\frac{1}{2}$	$15\frac{1}{4}$

7. Did the value of a share increase or decrease for the entire week? By how much?
8. Between which two days did the price change the most? By how much?
9. How much would it cost to buy 100 shares of RICH stock at today's high price?
10. About how much would it cost to buy 1500 shares of ConnEt stock at today's high price?
11. Suppose you owned one share in each of the companies listed on page 216. Did the total value of your stock increase or decrease today? By how much?
12. **Data Search** Choose any five stocks from a newspaper report. Find the closing price of each stock for the day previous to the day of the report.

What's Your Decision?

Suppose you have $2,000 to invest in stocks. You want to buy at least 20 shares of each stock and you want at least 3 different stocks. Use estimation to decide which of the stocks in the table on page 216 and how many shares of each you would choose for your investment.

6-10 Solving Equations: Using Addition and Subtraction

Objective To solve equations involving addition and subtraction of rational numbers.

Application

A course was being built at the coliseum for the annual dirt bike race. At last report, $\frac{4}{5}$ mile of the course had been built, leaving only $\frac{3}{10}$ mile to finish. What is the total length of the race course?

Understand the Ideas

Many real-world problems can be translated to an equation involving addition or subtraction of rational numbers. The steps you learned for solving equations involving whole numbers, decimals, and integers apply to equations involving all rational numbers.

- Decide which operation (addition or subtraction) has been applied to the variable.
- Use the inverse operation or use the Additive Inverse Property, adding or subtracting the same number on both sides of the equation.

Example 1

Find the total length of the dirt bike course in the application above by solving and checking $x - \frac{4}{5} = \frac{3}{10}$.

Solution

$$x - \frac{4}{5} = \frac{3}{10}$$

$$x - \frac{4}{5} + \frac{4}{5} = \frac{3}{10} + \frac{4}{5} \qquad \text{Addition Property of Equality}$$

$$x = \frac{3}{10} + \frac{4}{5}$$

$$= \frac{3}{10} + \frac{8}{10}$$

$$x = \frac{11}{10} = 1\frac{1}{10}$$

The total length of the course is $1\frac{1}{10}$ mile.

Check $\frac{11}{10} - \frac{4}{5} \stackrel{?}{=} \frac{3}{10}$ Replace x with $\frac{11}{10}$ in $x - \frac{4}{5} = \frac{3}{10}$.

$\frac{11}{10} - \frac{8}{10} \stackrel{?}{=} \frac{3}{10}$

$\frac{3}{10} = \frac{3}{10}$ ✓ The solution is $1\frac{1}{10}$.

Try This Solve and check.

a. $x + \frac{7}{12} = \frac{1}{4}$ **b.** $y - \frac{5}{6} = -\frac{3}{4}$

c. $-\frac{1}{4} = t - \frac{7}{8}$ **d.** $-\frac{4}{5} + m = \frac{2}{3}$

e. The total length of a race track is $\frac{7}{8}$ mile. So far, $\frac{1}{3}$ mile of the course has been inspected. Solve the equation $x + \frac{1}{3} = \frac{7}{8}$ to find the length of the course that has not been inspected yet.

Example 2

Solve and check. $\frac{5}{6} + a = \frac{4}{9}$

Solution

$$\frac{5}{6} + a = \frac{4}{9}$$

$$\frac{5}{6} - \frac{5}{6} + a = \frac{4}{9} - \frac{5}{6}$$ Subtract $\frac{5}{6}$ from both sides.

$$a = \frac{4}{9} - \frac{5}{6}$$

$$= \frac{8}{18} - \frac{15}{18}$$

$$a = -\frac{7}{18}$$

Check $\frac{5}{6} + \left(-\frac{7}{18}\right) \stackrel{?}{=} \frac{4}{9}$ Replace a with $-\frac{7}{18}$ in $\frac{5}{6} + a = \frac{4}{9}$.

$\frac{15}{18} + \left(-\frac{7}{18}\right) \stackrel{?}{=} \frac{8}{18}$

$\frac{8}{18} = \frac{8}{18}$ ✓ The solution is $-\frac{7}{18}$.

Try This Solve and check. **f.** $f + \frac{5}{12} = -\frac{3}{8}$ **g.** $\frac{5}{9} = y - \left(-\frac{4}{5}\right)$

h. The race track at Florida's Daytona Speedway is $\frac{5}{2}$ mi long. At Sebring, Florida, there is a race track that is $\frac{26}{5}$ mi long. Solve the equation $\frac{26}{5} - d = \frac{5}{2}$ to find out how much longer the race track is at Sebring.

Class Exercises

To solve, would you add or subtract in the first step?

1. $n - \frac{6}{8} = -\frac{2}{3}$ **2.** $y - \frac{5}{2} = -\frac{1}{2}$ **3.** $\frac{3}{4} + b = -\frac{3}{5}$

4. $x - \frac{5}{6} = \frac{7}{12}$ **5.** $-\frac{2}{3} + a = -6$ **6.** $p + \frac{3}{4} = \frac{8}{9}$

7. $t - \frac{7}{10} = -\frac{4}{5}$ **8.** $m - \frac{3}{10} = -\frac{6}{8}$ **9.** $\frac{1}{5} + x = -\frac{3}{8}$

Discuss the Ideas

10. How do you decide whether you add or subtract in the first step when solving an equation like those above? Can you find a way to always add in the first step?

Exercises

Practice and Apply

Solve and check.

1. $x - \frac{2}{3} = \frac{4}{9}$
2. $t - \frac{4}{3} = -\frac{5}{7}$
3. $m - \frac{3}{5} = -\frac{5}{6}$
4. $-\frac{6}{18} + x = \frac{4}{3}$
5. $p - \frac{2}{5} = -\frac{5}{6}$
6. $y - \frac{5}{3} = \frac{5}{12}$
7. $a - \frac{3}{4} = -\frac{5}{8}$
8. $y - \frac{1}{2} = -\frac{7}{10}$
9. $-\frac{3}{20} + b = -\frac{2}{5}$
10. $x - \frac{7}{8} = -\frac{5}{12}$
11. $p - \frac{14}{25} = -\frac{3}{2}$
12. $z - \frac{10}{30} = \frac{2}{5}$
13. $d - \frac{3}{5} = -\frac{1}{10}$
14. $n - \frac{3}{10} = -\frac{2}{50}$
15. $k - \frac{6}{15} = -\frac{12}{9}$
16. $x + \frac{4}{7} = -\frac{2}{5}$
17. $\frac{1}{5} + y = -\frac{1}{8}$
18. $-\frac{6}{24} = \frac{2}{3} + h$
19. $h + \frac{5}{6} = \frac{7}{8}$
20. $\frac{7}{16} + x = -\frac{3}{8}$
21. $\frac{6}{5} = \frac{2}{3} + x$
22. $\frac{9}{16} + y = -\frac{13}{15}$
23. $\frac{3}{7} = h + \frac{4}{5}$
24. $y + \frac{12}{25} = \frac{3}{10}$

Solve.

25. A full box of cereal weighs $\frac{3}{4}$ lb. The empty box weighs $\frac{1}{8}$ lb. Solve the equation $c + \frac{1}{8} = \frac{3}{4}$ to find the weight of the cereal alone.
26. Seven-eighths of the students in ninth grade went on a field trip to the observatory. Half of the ninth graders had been to the observatory before. Solve the equation $s + \frac{1}{2} = \frac{7}{8}$ to find the fraction of ninth grade students going to the observatory for the first time.
27. After breakfast, Ines had $\frac{7}{9}$ of her daily calories left to eat. By dinnertime, she only had $\frac{2}{5}$ of her daily calories remaining to eat. Solve the equation $c + \frac{2}{5} = \frac{7}{9}$ to find how many of her daily calories she ate at lunch.

Extend and Apply

Solve and check.

28. $x + \left(\frac{5}{8} - \frac{5}{6}\right) = \frac{15}{24}$

29. $\left(-\frac{6}{18} - \frac{3}{4}\right) + y = \frac{2}{9}$

30. $-\frac{4}{15} = \left(-\frac{1}{5} + \frac{1}{2}\right) + h$

31. $\left[-\frac{2}{3} - \left(-\frac{5}{6}\right)\right] + k = -\frac{5}{12}$

32. $\left(\frac{4}{7} - \frac{1}{5}\right) + x = \frac{11}{5}$

33. $-\frac{13}{24} = \left(-\frac{5}{12} + \frac{3}{8}\right) + d$

34. At sports camp registration $\frac{9}{10}$ of the students signed up for soccer, tennis, or cycling (one sport per camper). One third of the students signed up for soccer and $\frac{1}{5}$ signed up for cycling. Solve the equation $t + \left(\frac{1}{3} + \frac{1}{5}\right) = \frac{9}{10}$ to find the fraction of the students that signed up for tennis.

35. Write two different equations with the solution $\frac{3}{5}$.
36. Write an equation for which the solution $-\frac{7}{12}$ is found by subtracting.
37. Write an equation for which the solution $\frac{11}{16}$ is found by adding.

Use Mathematical Reasoning

38. Find 3 rational numbers, each with a numerator of 1, whose sum is $\frac{13}{16}$.
39. Chris's wardrobe is made up of 6 different pairs of trousers, half as many shirts as pairs of trousers, and 2 sweaters, one green and one gray. How many different combinations of trousers, shirt and sweater does Chris have with these items?

Mixed Review

Solve and check. **40.** $-36c = 66.6$ **41.** $r \div 16 = -0.575$

Find all the factors of the number. **42.** 19 **43.** 9 **44.** 12

Write using exponents. **45.** $(-4)(-4)(-4)(-4)$ **46.** $t \cdot t \cdot t$

Mental Math

You can use compensation to find certain differences of rational numbers mentally. For example, to find $5 - 3\frac{7}{8}$, think "$5 - 4$ is 1. $\frac{1}{8}$ too much has been subtracted, so it must be added back on. $1 + \frac{1}{8}$ is $1\frac{1}{8}$."

Use compensation to subtract mentally.

1. $8 - 4\frac{3}{4}$
2. $9 - 6\frac{4}{5}$
3. $12 - 4\frac{2}{3}$
4. $7\frac{1}{10} - 3\frac{9}{10}$
5. $8\frac{1}{3} - 2\frac{2}{3}$
6. $5\frac{1}{4} - 2\frac{3}{4}$

6-11 Problem Solving: Writing Equations

Deciding What the Variable Represents

Objective To practice solving word problems by writing and solving equations.

You can use the Problem-Solving Checklist on page 138 to help you solve problems. When your plan involves writing and solving an equation, keep these questions in mind.

- Can you use a variable to represent an unknown number?
- Can you represent other conditions in terms of the variable?
- What is equal?
- Can you write and solve an equation?

Example

Jared and his mother are building a remote-controlled model airplane. The hobby shop has a steel support rod $\frac{11}{16}$ in. long. This rod is $\frac{3}{8}$ in. longer than what they need for their plane. What length rod do they need for their plane?

Solution Let x = length of the needed rod

$x + \frac{3}{8}$ = length of available rod — Let the variable stand for the length of the needed rod.

$\frac{11}{16}$ = length of available rod — The length of the available rod is $\frac{3}{8}$ inch longer or $x + \frac{3}{8}$.

$$x + \frac{3}{8} = \frac{11}{16}$$

$$x + \frac{3}{8} + \left(-\frac{3}{8}\right) = \frac{11}{16} + \left(-\frac{3}{8}\right)$$

The two expressions for the length of the rod must be equal.

$$x = \frac{5}{16}$$

They need a rod $\frac{5}{16}$ in. long for their plane.

Check $\frac{5}{16} + \frac{3}{8} \stackrel{?}{=} \frac{11}{16}$

$\frac{5}{16} + \frac{6}{16} \stackrel{?}{=} \frac{11}{16}$

$\frac{11}{16} = \frac{11}{16}$ ✓ $\frac{5}{16}$ is less than $\frac{11}{16}$. The answer seems reasonable.

Try This Solve by writing an equation.

a. Mr. Lee bought 3 yards of string. After tying up his tomato plants, he had $1\frac{3}{8}$ yards of string left over. How much string did he use?

Discuss the Ideas

Answer **a.** through **e.** for each problem.

a. What are you trying to find?
b. What are the important data?
c. What will the variable represent?
d. What is equal in the problem?
e. What is the equation?

Problem-Solving Checklist

- Understand the **Situation**
- Find the Needed **Data**
- **Plan** the Solution
- **Estimate** the Answer
- **Solve** the Problem
- **Check** the Answer

1. The total cost, including tax, for a model airplane is $12.50. The cost of the plane alone is $11.70. How much is the tax? Let t = the amount of tax.

2. Lyle put $\frac{1}{3}$ cup of milk in a bowl. When he read the recipe, he discovered he should have put $\frac{3}{4}$ cup in. How much more did he need?

Exercises

Practice and Apply

Choose the equation or equations that can be used to solve each problem.

1. John ran $1\frac{1}{4}$ more miles this week than he ran last week. If he ran $3\frac{1}{2}$ miles last week, how many miles did he run this week?

a. $3\frac{1}{2} - 1\frac{1}{4} = r$ **b.** $r + 3\frac{1}{2} = 1\frac{1}{4}$ **c.** $r - 1\frac{1}{4} = 3\frac{1}{2}$

2. Ulanda has worked $32\frac{3}{4}$ hr this week. She is scheduled to work a total of 40 hr. How many more hours does she still have to work? Let h = the number of hours she has to work.

a. $32\frac{3}{4} + h = 40$ **b.** $40 - 32\frac{3}{4} = h$ **c.** $h - 32\frac{3}{4} = 40$

Solve by writing an equation. Check.

3. After cutting $\frac{1}{8}$ inch off the end of a copper pipe, a plumber had the exact length needed to connect a water line. The exact length needed was $\frac{3}{4}$ inch. What was the length of the original piece of pipe?

4. The price of a stereo system increased twice in the last month. The second increase was $25, for a total increase of $45.50. What was the first increase?

5. The total length of a roller skating track is $\frac{5}{8}$ mile. The first $\frac{1}{5}$ mile is very hilly and the rest is flat. How much of the course is flat?

6. Kim grew a lot during the first 6 months of last year. During the second 6 months she grew only $\frac{1}{8}$ inch. She grew $5\frac{1}{2}$ inches in all last year. How much did she grow during the first 6 months?

7. Al had 48 tapes in his music collection. His older sister Carrie gave him some more tapes. Now he has a total of 73 tapes. How many tapes did Carrie give to Al?

8. If Todd had bought his bike last year he would have saved \$35. He paid \$225 for his bike this year. How much did the bike cost last year?

Extend and Apply

9. Rick sold 7 tickets to the talent show during the first week of sales and 5 tickets during the second week of sales. Each ticket cost the same. He turned in a total of \$15. What was the cost of each ticket?
10. A wire had to be wrapped in a plastic coating. The wire was $\frac{7}{12}$ inch thick. Two layers of plastic had to be put over the wire so the total thickness of the plastic would equal the thickness of the wire. The first layer of plastic was $\frac{1}{2}$ inch thick. How thick was the second layer?
11. A machinist usually makes a certain part by welding together two metal strips, one $\frac{1}{8}$ inch thick and the other $\frac{1}{3}$ inch thick. She has a metal strip $\frac{1}{4}$ inch thick that she can use to make this part. How thick a strip must she weld on to make the part the correct thickness?
12. Malcolm recorded some of his homework and test grades incorrectly. He recorded 35 points more than he should have for homework and 15 points more for exams. Malcolm thought he had a total of 261 points. How many points did he actually have?
13. Mrs. Carmen bought 2 adult tickets and 1 child's ticket for a play. The tickets cost \$36, including a \$5 service charge. The adult tickets totaled \$24. How much was the child's ticket?

THE FAR SIDE By GARY LARSON

"Well, here we go again . . . Did anyone here *not* eat his or her homework on the way to school?"

Use Mathematical Reasoning

14. Write a word problem that would be solved using the equation $x + \frac{1}{2} = \frac{5}{8}$.
15. Write a word problem that would be solved using the equation $25 - x = 64$.

Mixed Review

Give the prime factorization of each. **16.** 49 **17.** 34 **18.** 90

Evaluate for $n = 4$. **19.** $5(n + 2) + 12$ **20.** $n(6 - n) + 7$

Simplify. **21.** $x \cdot y \cdot x \cdot y$ **22.** $4m + 3m$ **23.** $c + c + c$

Give the least common multiple (LCM). **24.** 3, 6, 7, 4 **25.** 12, 18

6-12 Problem Solving: Strategies

Use Logical Reasoning

Objective To solve nonroutine problems, using Logical Reasoning and other strategies learned so far.

Some problems must be solved by understanding the given relationships among facts and using known facts and relationships to make conclusions. The problem-solving strategy **Use Logical Reasoning** is a name for this process.

Sample Problem Wally, Kim, José, and Rosalie were hired as coaches for basketball, tennis, volleyball, and swimming. Wally's sister was among those hired, and she coaches tennis. Wally does not coach basketball. Kim coaches a water sport. Which sport was each hired to coach?

You can solve this problem by recording the given information in a chart and making conclusions based on it. The charts below show the reasoning you might go through to solve this problem.

	B	T	V	S
W	no	no		
K				
J		no		
R				

Wally's sister coaches tennis so Wally and José do not coach tennis. Wally does not coach basketball.

	B	T	V	S
W	no	no		no
K	no	no	no	yes
J		no		no
R				no

If Kim coaches a water sport, then no one else coaches swimming.

	B	T	V	S
W	no	no	yes	no
K	no	no	no	yes
J	yes	no		no
R		yes		no

Wally must coach volleyball and Rosalie must coach tennis. José has to coach basketball.

Problem-Solving Strategies

Choose the Operations
Guess, Check, Revise
Draw a Diagram
Make a Table
Look for a Pattern
Write an Equation
Simplify the Problem
Make an Organized List
Use Logical Reasoning
Work Backward

Problems

Solve.

1. Ned, Mary, Steve, and Jack live in the towns Millerville, Jefferson, Newville, and Stovertown. None live in a city that has the same first letter as his or her name. Neither Jack nor Ned has ever been to Millerville. Mary has spent all of her life in Stovertown. Which person lives in which town?

2. Ricky and his friends are sitting at a large round table playing a game. Ricky's mother gave them a box of 25 oranges to share. The box was passed around the table, and each person took 1 orange until there were no more oranges left. Ricky took the first orange and the last orange and he may have taken more than the first and last orange. How many people could have been sitting at the table?

3. A large circus tent is set up with 12 poles. The poles are arranged in a circle with a separate rope connecting each pair of poles. How many ropes are needed to connect these 12 poles?

4. The oil well on Mr. Greeley's property produces 19.7 barrels of oil each day. If a barrel contains 42 gallons and oil is worth $33 a barrel, how much money does the oil well yield per year?

5. Walker, Franklin, and King Schools have students in an all-star band. There are 150 band members. Walker school has 300 students and 30 are in the band. Franklin School has 400 students and 60 are in the band. How many students from King School are in the band?

Group Decision Making

6. Work in a group, Discuss and decide.

Situation Your math club is going to sponsor a booth at the school carnival. People will pay 50¢ to guess the number of jelly beans in a jar. The person who guesses closest to the actual number of jelly beans wins a fraction calculator. The second place winner receives the jelly beans. You want to find out how many people must pay to guess the number of jelly beans so that the math club will make a $25 profit.

Guidelines for Planning

- **Formulate Problems** you will need to solve.
- Discuss **Assumptions** you will make and **Data** you will need.

a. What decision or decisions do you need to make in this situation?

b. Formulate problems you need to solve to make the decision(s).

c. List any assumptions you need to make to arrive at a decision.

d. What data, if any, do you need to collect to make a decision?

e. Write a paragraph summarizing what your group did, what decisions you made, and why.

Extend Key Ideas

If and Only If

Checking cross products was introduced as a method for checking whether two fractions are equivalent.

Property of Cross Products

$\frac{a}{b} = \frac{c}{d}$ if and only if $a \cdot d = b \cdot c$; a, b, c, d are integers and $b, d \neq 0$

The phrase *if and only if* is used in mathematics as a shortcut for two conditional statements. Here is how the Property of Cross Products would be stated without using the phrase *if and only if.*

Property of Cross Products

(i) If $\frac{a}{b} = \frac{c}{d}$ then $a \cdot d = b \cdot c$ and
(ii) if $a \cdot d = b \cdot c$, then $\frac{a}{b} = \frac{c}{d}$, a, b, c, d are integers and $b, d \neq 0$

To decide if two fractions are equivalent, we use part (i) of the Property of Cross Products. Does $\frac{3}{4} = \frac{6}{8}$? Yes, because $3 \cdot 8 = 4 \cdot 6$. Now let's look at a numerical case involving part (ii). If $3 \cdot 8 = 4 \cdot 6$, what can we conclude? There are actually several conclusions. If we divide both sides by $4 \cdot 8$, we get,

$$\frac{3 \cdot 8}{4 \cdot 8} = \frac{4 \cdot 6}{4 \cdot 8} \quad \text{or} \quad \frac{3}{4} = \frac{6}{8}.$$

If we divide both sides by $6 \cdot 8$. we get,

$$\frac{3 \cdot 8}{6 \cdot 8} = \frac{4 \cdot 6}{6 \cdot 8} \quad \text{or} \quad \frac{3}{6} = \frac{4}{8}$$

So, for part (ii) of the Property of Cross Products there is more than one pair of equivalent fractions that can be derived.

1. Find all of the pairs of equivalent fractions if $3 \cdot 8 = 4 \cdot 6$.

2. Find all of the pairs of equivalent fractions if $a \cdot d = b \cdot c$ $(a, b, c, d \neq 0)$.

3. Supply the reasons for each step in the proof of part (i) of the Property of Cross Products.

$\frac{a}{b} = \frac{c}{d}$	Assume these are equal
$b \cdot d \cdot \frac{a}{b} = b \cdot d \cdot \frac{c}{d}$	______
$d \cdot a = b \cdot c$	______
$a \cdot d = b \cdot c$	______

Chapter 6 Review/Test

Understanding

True or false?

6-1 **1.** Equivalent fractions name the same amount.

6-2 **2.** If a fraction is an improper fraction, the numerator is < the denominator.

6-3 **3.** In the rational number $\frac{a}{b}$, a and b are integers and a cannot equal 0.

6-3 **4.** If $\frac{a}{b} > \frac{c}{d}$, then $\frac{a}{b}$ is to the right of $\frac{c}{d}$ on the number line.

Skills

6-1 Write an equivalent fraction by finding the value of the variable.

5. $\frac{6}{7} = \frac{v}{77}$ **6.** $\frac{c}{9} = \frac{49}{63}$ **7.** $-\frac{16}{17} = -\frac{t}{102}$

6-1 Reduce each fraction to lowest terms.

8. $\frac{56}{84}$ **9.** $-\frac{12}{90}$ **10.** $\frac{124}{172}$

6-2 Write as a mixed number or as an improper fraction in lowest terms.

11. $\frac{38}{6}$ **12.** $-\frac{53}{3}$ **13.** $-4\frac{3}{11}$ **14.** $9\frac{7}{20}$

6-4 Write each as a decimal. Use a bar for a repeating decimal.

15. $\frac{11}{18}$ **16.** $\frac{9}{20}$ **17.** $\frac{2}{9}$

6-5 Write <, >, or = for each □.

18. $\frac{5}{9}$ □ $\frac{2}{3}$ **19.** $-\frac{1}{3}$ □ $-\frac{4}{7}$ **20.** $\frac{8}{7}$ □ $\frac{13}{11}$ **21.** $-\frac{9}{24}$ □ $-\frac{12}{36}$

6-6 Add or subtract. Reduce to lowest terms.

6-7 6-8 **22.** $\frac{6}{11} + \frac{4}{11}$ **23.** $6\frac{1}{2} + 1\frac{3}{8}$ **24.** $-\frac{15}{24} - \left(-\frac{7}{24}\right)$

25. $\frac{5}{6} + \frac{2}{3}$ **26.** $-\frac{7}{12} - \frac{1}{4}$ **27.** $8\frac{1}{4} - 1\frac{1}{2}$

6-10 Solve and check.

28. $p - 1\frac{1}{5} = 1\frac{4}{15}$ **29.** $z + \frac{3}{4} = -\frac{1}{6}$ **30.** $\frac{5}{14} = a - \left(-\frac{1}{7}\right)$

Applications

6-9 Solve.

6-9 6-11 **31.** Mr. Cole had $8\frac{1}{2}$ pounds of flour. He gave a neighbor $2\frac{3}{4}$ pounds. How much did he have left?

32. Becky and Linnea rode their bikes $5\frac{3}{4}$ miles, stopped for lunch, then rode $2\frac{3}{8}$ miles more. How far did they ride?

33. Mrs. Chung used $2\frac{1}{2}$ gallons of paint on her bedroom and hallway. If her hallway took $\frac{2}{3}$ gallon of paint, how much did her bedroom take?

Cumulative Review

4-1 Write as a decimal.

1. $4(10) + 7(1) + 8\left(\frac{1}{10}\right)$ **2.** $2(100) + 9\left(\frac{1}{100}\right) + 6\left(\frac{1}{10}\right)$

3. $5(1) + 7\left(\frac{1}{100}\right) + 1\left(\frac{1}{10}\right)$ **4.** $3\left(\frac{1}{10}\right) + 7\left(\frac{1}{100}\right) + 9\left(\frac{1}{1000}\right)$

3-1
4-1 Write $<$, $>$, or $=$ for each □.

5. 4.430 □ 4.43 **6.** 4.01 □ 4.1 **7.** −2.73 □ −3.12

8. 6 □ −4 **9.** −2 □ −10 **10.** −5 □ 0

4-2 Round.

11. 83 to the nearest ten **12.** 7,486 to the nearest thousand

13. 291 to the nearest hundred **14.** 24,576 to the nearest ten thousand

4-2 Round to the nearest ten and estimate the value of each variable.

15. $38 + 21 = a$ **16.** $x = 286 - 57$ **17.** $12 + 54 = p$

4-2 Round to the nearest hundred and estimate the value of each variable.

18. $m = 475 + 391$ **19.** $402 - 174 = w$ **20.** $3927 - 301 = f$

4-2 Estimate the value of x by rounding.

21. $51.32 - 38.11 = x$ **22.** $x = 295.2 + 48.8$

23. $x = 67.59 - 16.63$ **24.** $47.92 + 50.05 = x$

4-6 Estimate the product by rounding.

25. 3.73×7.2 **26.** 7.2×6.8 **27.** 1.08×6.9

5-1 Give the first five nonzero multiples of each number.

28. 4 **29.** 7 **30.** 30

5-1 Find all the factors of the given number.

31. 32 **32.** 42 **33.** 60

5-2 State whether the number is divisible by 2.

34. 48 **35.** 30 **36.** 81

5-2 State whether the number is divisible by 3.

37. 38 **38.** 450 **39.** 522

5-2 State whether the number is divisible by 5.

40. 15 **41.** 510 **42.** 301

7 Rational Numbers: Multiplication and Division

Jeanette finished the Merritt Island Triathalon in just over 2 hours. If she finished the bicycle portion of the race in $\frac{1}{3}$ of her total time, about how long was she cycling?

7-1 Multiplying Rational Numbers

Objective To multiply rational numbers expressed as fractions and mixed numbers.

Application

At the county coliseum, $\frac{5}{12}$ of the seats are reserved. Of the seats that are reserved, $\frac{2}{5}$ are for season ticket–holders. What fraction of the seats in the stadium are reserved for season ticket–holders?

Understand the Ideas

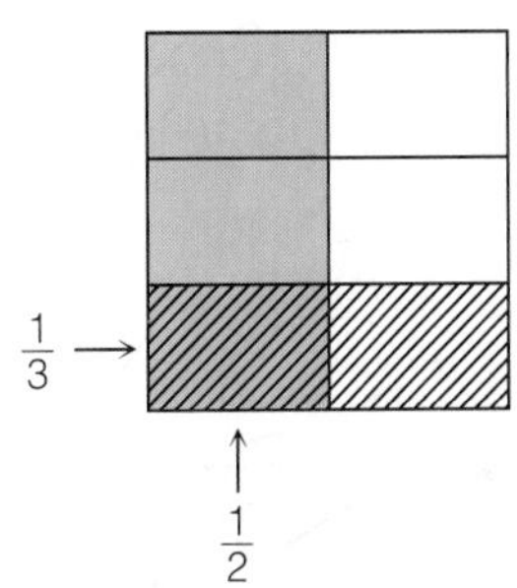

You can divide a unit square into sections to show multiplication of rational numbers. In the square at the right, the blue section represents $\frac{1}{2}$ of the square. The striped section represents $\frac{1}{3}$ of the square. The section where the blue and striped regions overlap represents $\frac{1}{2}$ of $\frac{1}{3}$, or $\frac{1}{6}$ of the square.

This suggests that for all integers a and b, where $(a \neq 0, b \neq 0)$, $\frac{1}{a} \cdot \frac{1}{b} = \frac{1}{ab}$

This rule, together with properties introduced earlier, can be used to explain the steps in multiplying two rational numbers.

$$\frac{2}{3} \cdot \frac{3}{4} = \left(2 \cdot \frac{1}{3}\right)\left(3 \cdot \frac{1}{4}\right) \qquad a \cdot \frac{1}{b} = \frac{a}{b}$$

$$= (2 \cdot 3)\left(\frac{1}{3} \cdot \frac{1}{4}\right) \qquad \text{Commutative and Associative Properties}$$

$$= 6 \cdot \frac{1}{12} \qquad \frac{1}{a} \cdot \frac{1}{b} = \frac{1}{ab}$$

$$= \frac{6}{12} \qquad a \cdot \frac{1}{b} = \frac{a}{b}$$

This suggests the following rule.

Rule **Multiplying Rational Numbers**

To multiply two rational numbers, multiply the numerators and multiply the denominators.

For all rational numbers $\frac{a}{b}$ and $\frac{c}{d}$ $(b \neq 0, d \neq 0)$,
$\frac{a}{b} \cdot \frac{c}{d} = \frac{a \cdot c}{b \cdot d}$

Example 1

Multiply $\frac{2}{5}\left(\frac{5}{12}\right)$ to find what fraction of the total seats are reserved for season–ticket holders in the **application** on the previous page. Reduce to lowest terms.

Solution

$$\frac{2}{5}\left(\frac{5}{12}\right) = \frac{2(5)}{5(12)}$$ Multiply numerators; multiply denominators.

$$= \frac{10}{60}$$

$$= \frac{1}{6}$$

$\frac{1}{6}$ of the seats are reserved for season–ticket holders.

Try This Multiply. Reduce to lowest terms.

a. $-\frac{5}{6}\left(-\frac{3}{8}\right)$ **b.** $\frac{2}{3}\left(\frac{8}{9}\right)$

c. Three fourths of the students at Asheville High School ordered yearbooks. Half of these students had their names engraved on the cover. What fraction of the students at the school ordered a yearbook with their name engraved on the cover?

When multiplying mixed numbers, first change them to improper fractions.

Example 2

Multiply. Reduce to lowest terms. $-1\frac{1}{5}\left(-3\frac{1}{2}\right)$

Solution

$$-1\frac{1}{5}\left(-3\frac{1}{2}\right) = \frac{-6}{5}\left(\frac{-7}{2}\right)$$ Change mixed numbers to improper fractions.

$$= \frac{-6(-7)}{5(2)}$$

$$= \frac{42}{10}$$ When both factors are negative, the product is positive.

$$= 4\frac{2}{10}$$

$$= 4\frac{1}{5}$$

Try This Multiply. Reduce to lowest terms.

d. $2\frac{2}{3}\left(1\frac{1}{5}\right)$ **e.** $3\frac{1}{12}(-2)$

Class Exercises

Give each mixed number as an improper fraction.

1. $3\frac{1}{2}$ **2.** $-4\frac{2}{3}$ **3.** $1\frac{4}{5}$ **4.** $2\frac{1}{8}$

State whether the product is positive or negative. Do not compute.

5. $-\frac{7}{8}\left(\frac{1}{2}\right)$ **6.** $\frac{2}{5}\left(\frac{9}{10}\right)$ **7.** $-\frac{3}{5}\left(-\frac{2}{3}\right)$

8. $4\frac{1}{2}\left(-\frac{3}{4}\right)$ **9.** $-\frac{5}{6}\left(-\frac{7}{9}\right)$ **10.** $\frac{4}{9}\left(\frac{35}{100}\right)$

Discuss the Ideas

Give a multiplication equation for each picture. Each square or rectangle represents one unit.

11. 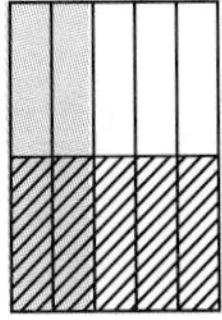

12. 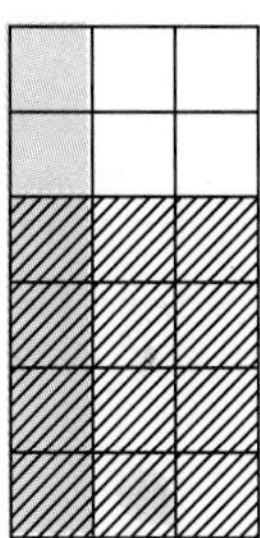

13. 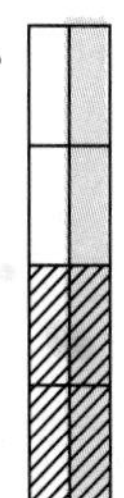

Exercises

Practice and Apply

Multiply. Reduce to lowest terms.

1. $\frac{3}{5}\left(\frac{3}{4}\right)$ **2.** $\frac{3}{5}\left(\frac{5}{7}\right)$ **3.** $\frac{1}{2}\left(\frac{5}{16}\right)$

4. $-\frac{8}{16}\left(\frac{1}{2}\right)$ **5.** $-\frac{4}{3}\left(\frac{5}{8}\right)$ **6.** $-\frac{6}{4}\left(-\frac{3}{5}\right)$

7. $\frac{14}{6}\left(-\frac{3}{10}\right)$ **8.** $\frac{5}{3}\left(\frac{15}{8}\right)$ **9.** $\frac{7}{12}\left(\frac{4}{3}\right)$

10. $-\frac{3}{8}\left(-\frac{2}{3}\right)$ **11.** $-\frac{5}{2}\left(-\frac{5}{10}\right)$ **12.** $\frac{12}{25}\left(\frac{2}{10}\right)$

13. $\frac{4}{12}\left(\frac{15}{24}\right)$ **14.** $\frac{24}{26}\left(-\frac{3}{5}\right)$ **15.** $-\frac{6}{7}\left(-\frac{14}{10}\right)$

16. $-3\frac{1}{10}\left(1\frac{1}{3}\right)$ **17.** $6\frac{1}{2}\left(2\frac{2}{8}\right)$ **18.** $4\frac{1}{4}\left(1\frac{2}{5}\right)$

19. $\frac{6}{2}\left(2\frac{1}{4}\right)$ **20.** $-8\frac{1}{8}\left(-\frac{3}{4}\right)$ **21.** $-4\frac{5}{6}\left(2\frac{2}{3}\right)$

22. $8\frac{7}{9}\left(-5\frac{2}{5}\right)$ **23.** $2\frac{3}{4}\left(8\frac{4}{7}\right)$ **24.** $-1\frac{1}{10}\left(3\frac{2}{10}\right)$

25. $1\frac{3}{4}\left(-\frac{4}{5}\right)$ **26.** $-2\frac{3}{4}\left(-2\frac{1}{4}\right)$ **27.** $5\left(4\frac{2}{5}\right)$

Solve.

28. A cookbook recommends roasting a turkey at a low temperature $\frac{3}{4}$ hour for each pound. How long should you cook a $10\frac{1}{2}$ pound turkey?

29. Each section of a fence is $6\frac{1}{2}$ ft long. How long is this fence if it has 8 sections?

30. A certain steel bar weighs $2\frac{1}{2}$ pounds per foot. What would be the weight of a piece $3\frac{3}{4}$ ft long?

31. Saul is working on his suntan. For the last seven days, he has spent $1\frac{1}{3}$ hours sunbathing each day. How many hours has he spent sunbathing all together?

32. A cross-country plane trip was scheduled to last $5\frac{3}{4}$ h. Because of strong tail winds, the trip took only $\frac{3}{4}$ of the scheduled time. How long did the trip take?

33. A land developer bought $4\frac{1}{2}$ acres of farmland for a shopping center. To please the local residents, $\frac{1}{5}$ of the land was to be left in its natural state. How many acres were to be left in their natural state?

Extend and Apply

Find the value of each expression. Reduce to lowest terms.

34. $\frac{2}{3}b$ for $b = 1\frac{1}{4}$

35. $-\frac{4}{3}a$ for $a = 12$

36. $1\frac{1}{5}y - \frac{3}{10}$ for $y = -1\frac{3}{5}$

37. $\frac{1}{8}x + 2$ for $x = 3\frac{1}{2}$

38. $1\frac{1}{2}h$ for $h = -\frac{5}{6}$

39. $\frac{2}{3}x + \frac{1}{4}$ for $x = -\frac{5}{6}$

Find the value of x. Reduce to lowest terms.

40. $x = \frac{2}{3}\left(\frac{3}{5} + \frac{6}{15}\right)$

41. $x = \left(\frac{1}{2} + \frac{3}{4}\right)\frac{2}{5}$

42. $x = -\frac{18}{24}(9 - 15)$

43. $x = -\frac{4}{5}(-5 + 8)$

44. $x = \frac{4}{5}\left(\frac{4}{5} + \frac{3}{4}\right)$

45. $x = \frac{3}{8}(6 - 7)$

Estimate each product by rounding to the nearest whole number.

46. $3\frac{4}{5}\left(7\frac{1}{8}\right)$

47. $5\frac{1}{6}\left(6\frac{9}{10}\right)$

48. $7\frac{3}{4}\left(4\frac{1}{3}\right)$

49. $8\frac{1}{7}\left(9\frac{7}{8}\right)$

Estimate each product by substituting compatible numbers. For example, to estimate $\frac{1}{3}$ (25), think "$\frac{1}{3}$ of 24 is 8."

50. $\frac{1}{5}(39)$

51. $\frac{1}{4}(27)$

52. $\frac{2}{3}(17)$

53. $\frac{1}{10}(79)$

54. Two large tracts of land are divided into equal-sized lots as shown at the right. A new house will be built on each lot. One third of the houses in each tract will be multi-family units. How many lots will have multi-family houses?

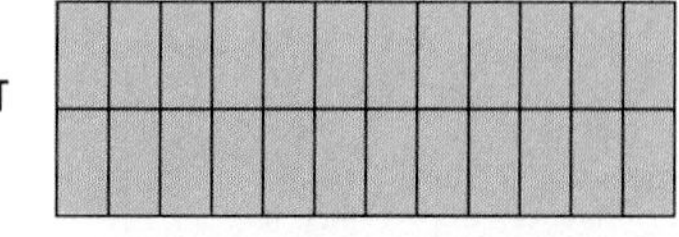

TRACT
2

Use Mathematical Reasoning

55. To find the value of x in the equations below, look for a pattern. Then write two similar equations with the same solution.

$\frac{1}{3}x = 16, \frac{1}{4}x = 12, \frac{1}{6}x = 8$

56. Look for a pattern to find the next two numbers in this sequence.

$\frac{3}{2}, -\frac{3}{5}, \frac{6}{25}, -\frac{12}{125}, \_\_\_, \_\_\_$

57. Marie's age is 4 more than $2\frac{1}{2}$ times her brother's age. If Marie is 24, how old is her brother?

Mixed Review

Simplify. **58.** $(5m + 12) + (4m - 6)$ **59.** $c + t + t + t + c$

Find the greatest common factor (GCF). **60.** 9, 42, 51 **61.** 4, 9

Reduce to lowest terms. **62.** $\frac{16}{100}$ **63.** $-\frac{12}{60}$ **64.** $\frac{27}{51}$

Write each mixed number as an improper fraction.

65. $-6\frac{4}{5}$ **66.** $12\frac{1}{3}$ **67.** $5\frac{7}{16}$ **68.** $-2\frac{7}{8}$

Solve and check. **69.** $19.5x = -1.17$ **70.** $a - 1.06 = -0.98$

71. $n - \frac{1}{2} = \frac{3}{8}$ **72.** $y + \frac{3}{14} = \frac{5}{8}$ **73.** $-\frac{1}{3} = z - \frac{3}{5}$

74. Veronica used $2\frac{1}{4}$ gallons of paint to paint her kitchen and hallway. If she used $\frac{5}{8}$ gallon of paint in the hallway, how much paint did she use in the kitchen?

Mental Math

You can use the Distributive Property and "break apart numbers" to find the products of rational numbers mentally. For example, to find $8 \cdot 3\frac{1}{4}$, think: "8 times 3 plus 8 times $\frac{1}{4}$ equals 24 plus 2, or 26."

Use the Distributive Property to find each product mentally.

1. $12 \cdot 2\frac{1}{3}$ **2.** $-16 \cdot 1\frac{1}{4}$

3. $20 \cdot \left(-2\frac{3}{10}\right)$ **4.** $\frac{1}{2} \cdot 8\frac{1}{3}$

5. $8\frac{1}{2} \cdot 4$ **6.** $-100 \cdot 1\frac{1}{10}$

7. $50 \cdot 2\frac{1}{50}$ **8.** $\frac{1}{4} \cdot 4\frac{1}{2}$

9. $\frac{1}{3} \cdot \left(-27\frac{2}{5}\right)$ **10.** $-\frac{1}{7} \cdot 21\frac{3}{5}$

7-2 Dividing Rational Numbers

Objective To divide rational numbers expressed as fractions and mixed numbers.

Explore

This picture shows that there are six $\frac{1}{3}$s in 2.

Draw pictures or use fraction pieces to answer each question.

- How many $\frac{1}{2}$s are in 2?
- How many $\frac{1}{4}$s are in $\frac{1}{2}$?
- How many $\frac{1}{6}$s are in $\frac{2}{3}$?

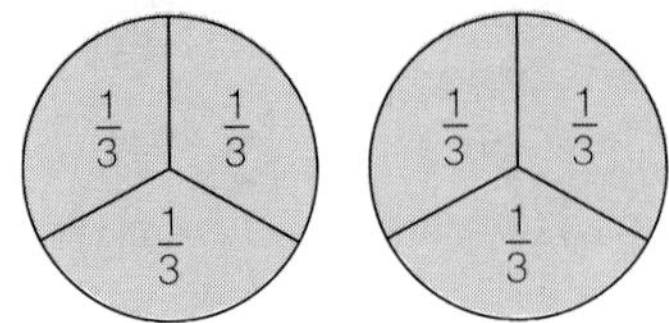

Understand the Ideas

Two numbers are called **multiplicative inverses** or **reciprocals** of each other if their product is 1.

The multiplicative inverse of 3 is $\frac{1}{3}$ since $3 \cdot \frac{1}{3} = 1$.

The multiplicative inverse of $-\frac{3}{4}$ is $-\frac{4}{3}$ since $-\frac{3}{4}\left(-\frac{4}{3}\right) = 1$.

Inverse Property of Multiplication

The product of a rational number and its multiplicative inverse is 1.

For every rational number $\frac{a}{b}$ $(a \neq 0, b \neq 0)$,

$$\frac{a}{b} \cdot \frac{b}{a} = \frac{b}{a} \cdot \frac{a}{b} = 1$$

We can use this property to develop a rule for dividing two rational numbers.

$$\frac{4}{5} \div \frac{2}{3} = \frac{\frac{4}{5}}{\frac{2}{3}} = \frac{\frac{4}{5} \cdot \frac{3}{2}}{\frac{2}{3} \cdot \frac{3}{2}} = \frac{\frac{4}{5} \cdot \frac{3}{2}}{1} = \frac{4}{5} \cdot \frac{3}{2}$$

Rule Dividing Rational Numbers

To divide by a rational number, multiply by its inverse. For rational numbers $\frac{a}{b}$ and $\frac{c}{d}$ $(b \neq 0, c \neq 0, d \neq 0)$,

$$\frac{a}{b} \div \frac{c}{d} = \frac{a}{b} \cdot \frac{d}{c}$$

Example 1

Divide. Reduce to lowest terms. $\frac{1}{4} \div \left(-\frac{2}{6}\right)$

Solution

$\frac{1}{4} \div \left(-\frac{2}{6}\right) = \frac{1}{4}\left(-\frac{6}{2}\right)$ Dividing by $-\frac{2}{6}$ is the same as multiplying by $-\frac{6}{2}$.

$= -\frac{6}{8} = -\frac{3}{4}$

Try This Divide. Reduce to lowest terms. **a.** $-\frac{2}{3} \div \frac{1}{6}$ **b.** $\frac{5}{24} \div 5$

Example 2

Divide. Reduce to lowest terms. $-1\frac{3}{4} \div 2\frac{1}{2}$

Solution

$-1\frac{3}{4} \div 2\frac{1}{2} = -\frac{7}{4} \div \frac{5}{2}$ Change mixed numbers to improper fractions.

$= -\frac{7}{4} \cdot \frac{2}{5}$ Dividing by $\frac{5}{2}$ is the same as multiplying by $\frac{2}{5}$.

$= -\frac{14}{20} = -\frac{7}{10}$

Try This Divide. Reduce to lowest terms. **c.** $8 \div \left(-3\frac{3}{4}\right)$ **d.** $3\frac{1}{8} \div 2\frac{1}{12}$

Class Exercises

Express each as a multiplication problem. Do not solve.

1. $\frac{3}{4} \div \frac{2}{5}$ **2.** $\frac{7}{9} \div \frac{4}{5}$ **3.** $\frac{6}{5} \div \left(-\frac{8}{3}\right)$ **4.** $\frac{5}{8} \div \frac{2}{3}$

Discuss the Ideas

5. Which of the following is a correct interpretation for $3 \div \frac{1}{3}$? Explain.
a. How many 3s are in $\frac{1}{3}$? **b.** How many $\frac{1}{3}$s are in 3?

Exercises

Practice and Apply

Divide. Reduce to lowest terms.

1. $\frac{3}{5} \div \frac{1}{5}$ **2.** $\frac{1}{2} \div \frac{3}{4}$ **3.** $\frac{5}{8} \div \frac{7}{8}$ **4.** $\frac{1}{9} \div \left(-\frac{4}{3}\right)$

5. $-\frac{5}{8} \div \frac{3}{2}$ **6.** $\frac{5}{9} \div \left(-\frac{7}{3}\right)$ **7.** $-\frac{3}{10} \div \frac{8}{5}$ **8.** $\frac{9}{12} \div \frac{5}{6}$

9. $-3\frac{1}{3} \div \left(-\frac{5}{6}\right)$ **10.** $3\frac{1}{3} \div 2\frac{1}{4}$ **11.** $5\frac{2}{3} \div 1\frac{3}{4}$ **12.** $2\frac{1}{4} \div (-6)$

13. Suppose you walk at a rate of $2\frac{1}{2}$ miles per hour. How long would it take to walk to school if the school is $3\frac{1}{2}$ miles from home?

14. A trail marker was placed every $\frac{1}{3}$ mile along an $8\frac{1}{2}$ mile hiking trail through a national park. How many trail markers were needed?

Extend and Apply

Evaluate each expression. Reduce to lowest terms.

15. $\frac{x}{16} - \frac{1}{2}$ for $x = -\frac{3}{8}$

16. $\frac{5}{x} + \frac{3}{4}$ for $x = 1\frac{1}{2}$

17. Christopher wants to engrave his name on an ID bracelet. There are $1\frac{3}{4}$ inches of space on the bracelet. He can choose from three sizes of letters: $\frac{1}{8}$ inch wide, $\frac{1}{4}$ inch wide, or $\frac{1}{2}$ inch wide. Which size or sizes of lettering could he use for his name?

Use Mathematical Reasoning

18. Find two rational numbers with the sum of 1, product of $-\frac{6}{25}$, and quotient of -6.

19. **Communicate** How many ways can four attached postage stamps be connected to each other? Two ways are shown at the right.

   a. Solve this problem.

   b. Write the answer in a complete sentence.

   c. Name the strategy or strategies you used to solve this problem.

Mixed Review

Solve and check. 20. $a \div 1.75 = -16$ 21. $r + 0.9 = -1.3$

Find the least common multiple (LCM). 22. 4, 6, 9, 12

Estimation

You can substitute compatible numbers to estimate quotients involving rational numbers.

Example: Choose the best estimate. $14\frac{1}{8} \div 7$ <2 or >2?
Think: $14\frac{1}{8}$ is about 14 and $14 \div 7 = 2$. Since $14\frac{1}{8} > 14$, the quotient will be greater than 2.

Use compatible numbers to choose the best estimate.

1. $7\frac{2}{9} \cdot 2\frac{1}{3}$ <14 or >14?

2. $\frac{2}{5} \cdot 18$ <18 or >18?

3. $12\frac{1}{3} \div 4$ <3 or >3?

4. $8\frac{3}{4} \div 2\frac{1}{4}$ <4 or >4?

5. $22\frac{1}{3} \div 8$ <3 or >3?

6. $24 \div 2\frac{5}{8}$ <8 or >8?

7-3 Solving Equations: Using Multiplication and Division

Objective To solve equations using the multiplicative inverse.

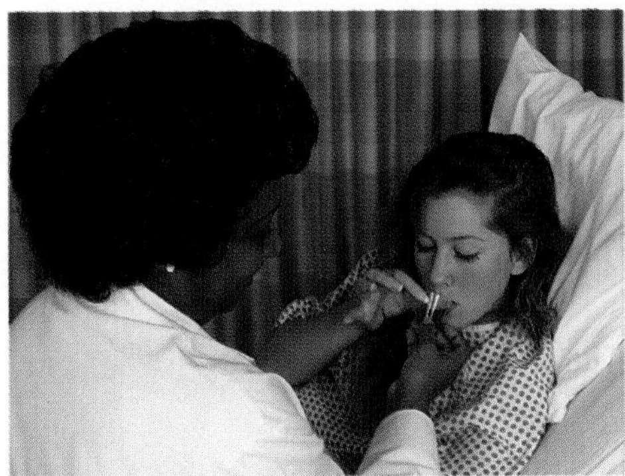

Application

A nurse gave $\frac{3}{4}$ of a normal dose of liquid medicine to a patient. This amount was $\frac{5}{8}$ oz. The patient wanted to know how many ounces were in a full dose so that she could take the medicine herself.

Understand the Ideas

You can solve equations such as $\frac{3}{4}x = \frac{5}{8}$ by dividing both sides by $\frac{3}{4}$. It is simpler, however, to multiply by the reciprocal of $\frac{3}{4}$. When solving these equations, keep in mind the following steps:

- Decide whether multiplication or division has been applied to the variable.
- Use the inverse operation or use the Inverse Property of Multiplication, multiplying or dividing by the same number on both sides.

Example 1

Solve and check the equation $\frac{3}{4}x = \frac{5}{8}$ to find how many ounces are in a full dose of the medicine used in the **application.**

Solution

$$\frac{3}{4}x = \frac{5}{8}$$

$\frac{4}{3} \cdot \left(\frac{3}{4}x\right) = \frac{4}{3} \cdot \frac{5}{8}$ Multiply both sides by the reciprocal of $\frac{3}{4}$ so they remain equal.

$1 \cdot x = \frac{20}{24}$ $\frac{4}{3} \cdot \frac{3}{4} = 1$. Associative Property and Inverse Property

$x = \frac{5}{6}$ Identity Property

There is five-sixths of an ounce in a full dose of medicine.

Check

$\frac{3}{4} \cdot \frac{5}{6} \stackrel{?}{=} \frac{5}{8}$ Replace x with $\frac{5}{6}$.

$\frac{15}{24} \stackrel{?}{=} \frac{5}{8}$

$\frac{5}{8} = \frac{5}{8}$ ✓ The solution is $\frac{5}{6}$.

Try This Solve and check.

a. $\frac{1}{6}f = 4$ b. $-\frac{3}{4}y = 1\frac{1}{2}$ c. $6y = \frac{3}{8}$ d. $7p = \frac{7}{10}$

e. Attendance at last night's basketball game was 624 people. The gymnasium was $\frac{3}{4}$ full. How many people can the gymnasium hold?

Example 2

Solve and check. $-3\frac{1}{2}x = 2\frac{3}{4}$

Solution

$$-3\frac{1}{2}x = 2\frac{3}{4}$$

$$-\frac{7}{2}x = \frac{11}{4} \quad \text{Change mixed numbers to improper fractions}$$

$$-\frac{2}{7}\left(-\frac{7}{2}x\right) = -\frac{2}{7} \cdot \frac{11}{4} \quad \text{Multiply both sides by the reciprocal of } -\frac{7}{2}.$$

$$1 \cdot x = -\frac{22}{28}$$

$$x = -\frac{11}{14}$$

Check

$$-\frac{7}{2}\left(-\frac{11}{14}\right) \stackrel{?}{=} \frac{11}{4} \quad \text{Replace } x \text{ with } -\frac{11}{14} \text{ in } -\frac{7}{2}x = \frac{11}{4}.$$

$$\frac{77}{28} \stackrel{?}{=} \frac{11}{4}$$

$$\frac{11}{4} = \frac{11}{4} \checkmark \quad \text{The solution is } -\frac{11}{14}.$$

Try This Solve and check. f. $4\frac{1}{3}y = 5$ g. $-2\frac{4}{5} = 1\frac{5}{6}h$

Class Exercises

To solve, what operation would you use in the first step?

1. $\frac{1}{6}y = \frac{2}{3}$ 2. $\frac{y}{5} = \frac{1}{2}$ 3. $6b = -\frac{3}{5}$ 4. $\frac{5}{6}x = \frac{7}{12}$

5. $\frac{2}{3}a = -6$ 6. $p - 3\frac{3}{4} = \frac{8}{9}$ 7. $\frac{t}{-7} = \frac{4}{5}$ 8. $m + \frac{3}{10} = \frac{6}{8}$

Discuss the Ideas

9. How do you decide what your first step should be when solving an equation?

Exercises

Practice and Apply

Solve and check.

1. $4x = \frac{3}{4}$ 2. $\frac{t}{4} = \frac{5}{7}$ 3. $\frac{4}{5}m = 5$ 4. $6x = \frac{4}{3}$

5. $\frac{1}{5}y = 1$ 6. $\frac{y}{6} = \frac{5}{12}$ 7. $\frac{2}{3}h = -6$ 8. $-\frac{1}{2}y = \frac{7}{10}$

9. $-\frac{7}{16}x = -\frac{3}{8}$

10. $\frac{9}{16}y = \frac{2}{5}$

11. $\frac{k}{6} = -\frac{12}{9}$

12. $1\frac{2}{3}x = \frac{6}{5}$

13. $-1\frac{3}{8}x = -\frac{3}{4}$

14. $4\frac{3}{5}h = 8$

15. $4\frac{3}{10} = 2\frac{3}{5}g$

16. $1\frac{2}{9} = 18h$

For Exercises 17–20, use the table at the right.

17. Luis received \$3 off the regular price of a sweatshirt. What was the regular price?

18. Marsha received \$5 off the price of running shoes. What was the regular price?

19. Tanya received \$12 off the price of a denim jacket. What was the regular price?

20. Miguel received \$12 off the price of dress shoes. What was the regular price?

21. A new drink container holds $1\frac{1}{4}$ times the amount of the old container. The new container holds 60 oz. How many ounces did the old container hold?

Extend and Apply

Solve and check.

22. $\left(\frac{3}{4} + \frac{5}{8}\right)x = 2$

23. $-\frac{7}{12}(-6y) = 4$

24. $\left(\frac{2}{3}x\right)\frac{1}{2} = 5$

25. $\left(5 - 2\frac{3}{4}\right)x = -2\frac{5}{6}$

26. $\left(\frac{1}{2} + \frac{7}{9} - \frac{1}{2}\right)t = 14$

27. $5\frac{1}{2}r = 0$

For Exercises 28–30, solve mentally by choosing **compatible numbers**. For example, to solve $x = \frac{1}{5}\left(\frac{7}{8}\right)(5)$, think "$\frac{1}{5}(5)$ is 1; $1\left(\frac{7}{8}\right)$ is $\frac{7}{8}$."

28. $x = \frac{1}{6}\left(2\frac{1}{4}\right)(6)$

29. $x = \frac{3}{8}\left(\frac{1}{6}\right)(8)$

30. $x = 9\left(2\frac{1}{5}\right)\left(\frac{1}{3}\right)$

31. Kim started a trip with a full tank of gas. After 4 hours, she had used $\frac{3}{4}$ of the tank. She filled the tank with $12\frac{1}{2}$ gallons of gas. About how many gallons of gas does her tank hold?

32. Jose saw a sign that read, "Ocean City–20 miles." He announced that they were $\frac{9}{10}$ of the way there. How many miles had they traveled?

33. A copy machine enlarges a sheet of paper $1\frac{1}{5}$ times its original size. (Each dimension is $1\frac{1}{5}$ times the original.) What are the original dimensions of a sheet of paper whose enlarged dimensions are $10\frac{1}{5}$ in. by $13\frac{1}{5}$ in.?

34. **Find the Missing Data** Tell what data is needed to solve this problem. Make up needed data and answer the question by writing and solving an equation.

    Boat shoes are on sale for $\frac{1}{4}$ off the regular price. What is the original price of the boat shoes?

Use Mathematical Reasoning

35. Find a number for which the following is true: $\frac{1}{5}$ of the number added to 28 is triple the number.

36. Mentally find two values of y that make this equation true. $\frac{1}{2}y^2 = 8$.

37. Mentally find two values of x that make this equation true. $8x^2 = 2$.

Mixed Review

Simplify. **38.** $(4c + 2) + (4c - 2)$ **39.** $6(x - 3) + 4x + 2$

Solve and check. **40.** $-16.8 = r \div 2$ **41.** $z + 29 = 317$

Today's Stock Report

High	Low	Stock	High	Low	Last	Chg.
17 1/8	12 5/8	BTB	14 7/8	13 3/4	13 3/4	−1/2
25 1/2	10 1/2	Zzt	17 3/8	14 3/8	16 3/4	+1/4

42. What is the difference between the yearly low and today's low for Zzt shares?

43. What was the closing price for BTB shares yesterday?

44. How much would it cost to buy 80 shares of BTB stock at today's high price?

Computer Activity

Usually a computer does not work with fractions in the form $\frac{a}{b}$. You can use a spreadsheet program to fool the computer and make it multiply and divide fractions. Use a spreadsheet program such as Appleworks™ or Lotus. Find out how to enter a formula.

Multiply $\frac{1}{2} \times \frac{3}{4}$. Put each numerator and denominator in separate cells. The numbers in C1 and C2 are the numerator and denominator of the answer.

	A	B	C
1	1	3	Formula for A1 * B1
2	2	4	Formula for A2 * B2

1. Will this work for all problems?

2. What is wrong with the computer's answer?

3. How could you make the computer divide fractions on the spreadsheet?

7-4 Problem Solving: Writing Equations

Deciding What the Variable Represents

Objective To select appropriate variables when writing equations to solve word problems.

You can use the Problem-Solving Checklist on page 138 to help you solve word problems. When your plan involves writing and solving an equation, keep the following questions in mind.

- Can you use a variable to represent an unknown number?
- Can you represent other conditions in terms of the variable?
- What is equal?
- Can you write and solve an equation?

The variable can often represent the number that the question in the problem is asking you to find. Sometimes, however, the variable must be used to represent another unknown in the problem.

Example

A jazz group gave 2 shows in one night. Attendance at the second show was $1\frac{1}{2}$ times the attendance at the first show. If there were 87 people at the second show, what was the total attendance for the two shows?

Solution

Let f = number at the first show.

$1\frac{1}{2}f$ = number at the second show.

Total attendance is the sum of the numbers for both shows. Let the variable stand for the unknown number at the first show. The number at the second show is $1\frac{1}{2}$ times the number at the first show.

$1\frac{1}{2}f = 87$ — The number of people at the second show was 87.

$\frac{3}{2}f = 87$

$\frac{2}{3} \cdot \frac{3}{2}f = \frac{2}{3} \cdot 87$ — Multiply both sides by the reciprocal of $\frac{3}{2}$.

$f = 58$ — There were 58 people at the first show.

$58 + 87 = 145$ — Add the numbers for both shows to answer the question in the problem.

The total attendance was 145.

Try This Find the solution by writing and solving an equation.

a. Twenty-one people came to the first electronics class. This was $\frac{7}{8}$ of the number that signed up. How many people missed the first class?

Class Exercises

Discuss the Ideas

Answer **a.** through **e.** for each problem.

a. What are you trying to find?

b. What are the important data?

c. What will the variable represent?

d. What is equal in the problem?

e. What is the equation?

Problem-Solving Checklist

- Understand the **Situation**
- Find the Needed **Data**
- **Plan** the Solution
- **Estimate** the Answer
- **Solve** the Problem
- **Check** the Answer

1. It takes Bruce $1\frac{1}{2}$ work days to install ceramic tile in an average-size bathroom. How many days would it take him to install tile in 5 bathrooms?

2. A $\frac{2}{3}$-full pitcher of lemonade can fill 6 glasses. How many glasses can be filled from a full pitcher?

3. Paulo brought $\frac{3}{4}$ of his monthly allowance with him to a rock concert. He spent $\frac{2}{3}$ of his money on souvenirs. What part of his allowance did he spend on souvenirs?

Exercises

Practice and Apply

Choose the equation or equations that can be used to solve each problem.

1. In one year, 120 students enrolled at a technical school. This was $\frac{3}{5}$ of the number accepted. How many of those accepted did not enroll?

a. $\frac{3}{5}a = 120$ **b.** $120 = \frac{3}{5} + a$ **c.** $\frac{3}{5} \cdot 120 = a$

2. Floor boards $2\frac{7}{8}$ inches wide are to be used to patch an opening that is $12\frac{1}{2}$ inches wide. How many boards are needed?

a. $\frac{f}{2\frac{7}{8}} = 12\frac{1}{2}$ **b.** $\frac{23}{8}f = \frac{25}{2}$ **c.** $2\frac{7}{8}f = 12\frac{1}{2}$

Find the solution by writing and solving an equation.

3. A cook needed $\frac{1}{3}$ hr cooking time for each pound of turkey. How big was the turkey if it cooked for $5\frac{1}{2}$ hours?

4. The cost of an adult ticket to a show is 2.5 times the cost of a child's ticket. An adult ticket is \$3.75. What would the total ticket cost be for 1 adult and 1 child?

5. A grocery store manager said that $\frac{1}{24}$ of the number of checks received in May were from the same bank. The store received 96 checks from that bank. How many checks did it receive from other banks?

6. To allow for waste and leftovers, a roofer always orders about $\frac{1}{10}$ more shingles than are needed to cover the exact measurements of a roof. The roofer ordered $2\frac{1}{2}$ extra bundles of shingles for a roof. How many bundles were needed for the exact measurements?

Extend and Apply

7. The odometer on Marta's bicycle read 2,375 when she left home. At the end of her trip the odometer read 2,453. Marta bicycled for $6\frac{1}{2}$ hours that day. What was her average speed for the trip?

8. If Tim lost $\frac{1}{2}$ lb on Saturday and another $\frac{1}{4}$ lb on Sunday, he would have been down to the wrestling weight his coach wanted for him. His coach wanted him to weigh $105\frac{1}{2}$ lbs. How much did Tim weigh before Saturday?

9. Fran likes to work 20 hours each week. Last week she worked only $4\frac{1}{2}$ hours on Tuesday, $4\frac{1}{2}$ hours on Thursday, and $2\frac{1}{4}$ hours on Friday. Fran earned \$54. How much would she earn in a 20-hour work week?

Use Mathematical Reasoning

Write a word problem that could be solved using the equation.

10. $\frac{3}{4}x = 8$ **11.** $\left(\frac{1}{2} + \frac{1}{4}\right)x = 10$

Mixed Review

Solve and check. **12.** $x - \frac{3}{8} = \frac{2}{3}$ **13.** $\frac{4}{11} = c + \frac{1}{2}$ **14.** $y + \frac{1}{4} = \frac{11}{16}$

15. $r + 1.03 = -2.67$ **16.** $-9.86m = 226.78$ **17.** $z - 14.4 = 12.73$

Evaluate for $m = \frac{3}{4}$. **18.** $m + \frac{1}{2}$ **19.** $\frac{2}{5} - m$ **20.** $\frac{3}{16} + m$

Add or subtract. Reduce to lowest terms. **21.** $4\frac{3}{5} - 2\frac{1}{2}$ **22.** $8\frac{1}{4} + 1\frac{5}{8}$

23. $\frac{2}{13} + \frac{4}{13}$ **24.** $-\frac{6}{8} + \frac{1}{8}$ **25.** $-\frac{22}{30} - \left(-\frac{4}{30}\right)$

26. Henry and Rhonda hiked $4\frac{3}{8}$ miles, stopped for an hour, and then hiked $5\frac{1}{4}$ miles farther. How far did they hike?

27. Mr. Greyson had $4\frac{1}{2}$ pounds of apples. He used $2\frac{3}{4}$ pounds to make a pie. How many pounds did he have left?

7-5 Problem Solving: Applications

Mathematics and Masonry

Objective To solve applied problems involving multiplication of rational numbers.

A **mason** is a person who builds with stones, bricks and concrete. Much of the work a mason does involves computation with rational numbers.

Problems

Solve. Decide whether to use **pencil and paper, mental math, estimation,** or a **calculator** to find the answer.

1. Figure 1 shows a hollow brick that is used to line the insides of chimneys. What is the overall length of one of these bricks?

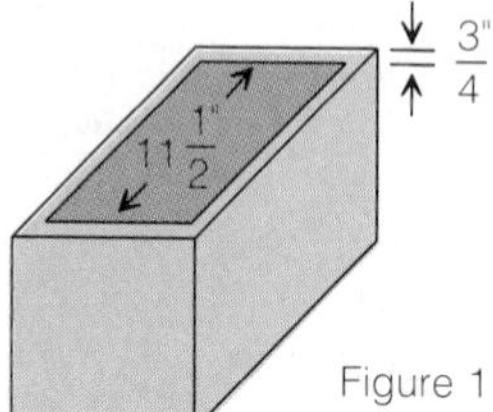

Figure 1

2. The stairway in Figure 2 has five risers. What is the rise of these steps?

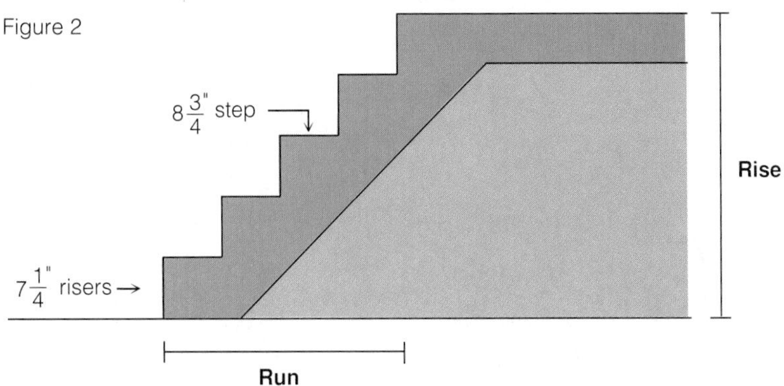

3. The stairway in Figure 2 has 4 steps. What is the run of this stairway?

4. A certain stairway has 14 risers. If each riser is $6\frac{5}{8}$ inches high, what is the rise of this stairway?

5. In Problem 4, each step measures $11\frac{1}{2}$ inches. What is the run of this stairway?

6. A standard-size brick weighs $2\frac{3}{4}$ pounds. How much would 36 of these bricks weigh?

7. Plans for construction of a patio require 888 square feet of brick. The mason figures that with the size of brick and thickness of mortar to be used, about $5\frac{1}{2}$ bricks are needed per square foot. About how many bricks are needed to construct the patio?

8. A mason needs $\frac{5}{8}$ of a cubic yard of mortar to lay 1,000 bricks in a wall. About how many cubic yards of mortar would he need to lay 6,400 bricks?

9. A standard-size brick is $2\frac{1}{2}$ inches thick. What is the height of a wall made of 6 rows of this brick with $\frac{1}{2}$ inch of mortar at its base and $\frac{1}{2}$ inch of mortar between rows?

10. A standard-size brick is $8\frac{1}{4}$ inches long. How long would a wall be if it had 24 bricks side-by-side, with $\frac{3}{8}$ inch of mortar between bricks?

11. **Data Search** Suppose you were going to cover one wall of your classroom with brick. Find the approximate total cost of the brick you would need for the job.

What's Your Decision?

You have 700 standard-size bricks $\left(8\frac{1}{4}'' \text{ by } 2\frac{1}{2}''\right)$ and plan to build a patio, using $\frac{1}{2}''$ of sand between bricks. You hope to use as many of the bricks as possible. What shape and size patio would you design?

7-6 More About Exponents

Objectives To find the quotient of two numbers expressed with exponents; to understand negative exponents.

Understand the Ideas

You have used the rule $a^m \cdot a^n = a^{m+n}$ to multiply powers with the same base.

The following suggests a rule for simplifying expressions in the form $\frac{a^m}{a^n}$.

$$\frac{4^5}{4^2} = \frac{\overset{1}{\cancel{4}} \cdot \overset{1}{\cancel{4}} \cdot 4 \cdot 4 \cdot 4}{\underset{1}{\cancel{4}} \cdot \underset{1}{\cancel{4}}} = 4 \cdot 4 \cdot 4 = 4^3$$

Rule Dividing Powers with Like Bases

To find the quotient of two numbers in exponential form with the same base, subtract the exponent of the denominator from the exponent of the numerator. Write this difference as the exponent of the base.

For all values of a except 0 and for all numbers m and n, $\frac{a^m}{a^n} = a^{m-n}$

Example 1

Simplify. Write the expression with exponents. $\frac{2^5}{2^3}$

Solution

$\frac{2^5}{2^3} = 2^{5-3}$ Since the base is the same, subtract the exponents.

$= 2^2$

Try This Simplify. Write the expression with exponents.

a. $\frac{5^6}{5^3}$ **b.** $\frac{(-3)^7}{(-3)^4}$ **c.** $\frac{10^4}{10}$

You can use the rule above to simplify variable expressions.

Example 2

Simplify. Write the expression with exponents. $\frac{x^6}{x^2}$

Solution

$\frac{x^6}{x^2} = x^{6-2}$ Since the base is the same, subtract the exponents.

$= x^4$

Try This Simplify. Write the expression with exponents.

d. $\frac{y^8}{y^3}$ **e.** $\frac{m^5}{m}$ **f.** $\frac{z^3}{z^2}$

You can use the rule given above to simplify the expression $\frac{5^2}{5^4}$.

$$\frac{5^2}{5^4} = 5^{2-4} = 5^{-2}$$

You could also write the following: $\frac{5^2}{5^4} = \frac{\cancel{5}^1 \cdot \cancel{5}^1}{\cancel{5}_1 \cdot \cancel{5}_1 \cdot 5 \cdot 5} = \frac{1}{5 \cdot 5} = \frac{1}{5^2}$

This shows that $\frac{1}{5^2}$ is the same as 5^{-2}.

In general, you can use a **negative exponent** to write $\boldsymbol{a^{-m} = \frac{1}{a^m}}$

Example 3

Write the expression 3^{-2} without exponents.

Solution

$3^{-2} = \frac{1}{3^2} = \frac{1}{9}$ Since the exponent is negative, rewrite the expression as $\frac{1}{3^2}$, and $3^2 = 9$.

Try This Write each expression without exponents. **g.** 5^{-3} **h.** 4^{-1}

This rule for dividing powers with like bases also shows that any non-zero number to the zero power, $\boldsymbol{a^0}$, is **1.**

Class Exercises

State each using exponents.

1. $3 \cdot 3 \cdot 3 \cdot 3$ **2.** $\frac{1}{2 \cdot 2 \cdot 2 \cdot 2 \cdot 2}$ **3.** $\frac{1}{5 \cdot 5 \cdot 5}$ **4.** $4 \cdot 4 \cdot 2 \cdot 2 \cdot 2$

Discuss the Ideas

5. Explain the meaning of "−2" in each of the following.
a. $3(-2)$ **b.** $3 - 2$ **c.** 3^{-2}

Exercises

Practice and Apply

Simplify. Write the expression with exponents.

1. $\frac{3^4}{3}$ **2.** $\frac{5^4}{5^2}$ **3.** $\frac{(-4)^3}{(-4)}$ **4.** $\frac{2^6}{2^5}$

5. $\frac{10^5}{10}$ **6.** $\frac{(-4)^7}{(-4)^5}$ **7.** $\frac{8^5}{8}$ **8.** $\frac{(-2)^5}{(-2)}$

9. $\frac{t^3}{t}$ **10.** $\frac{r^6}{r^4}$ **11.** $\frac{g^5}{g^4}$ **12.** $\frac{y^4}{y}$

13. $\frac{x^6}{x}$ **14.** $\frac{m^4}{m^2}$ **15.** $\frac{n^6}{n^4}$ **16.** $\frac{s^7}{s^2}$

Write the expression without exponents.

17. 4^{-2} **18.** 3^{-3} **19.** $(-2)^{-4}$ **20.** $(-3)^3$

21. 10^{-4} **22.** $(-2)^2$ **23.** $(-5)^{-2}$ **24.** 2^6

25. A proton has a diameter of about 10^{-12} cm. Write this number using a positive exponent.

26. An *attometer* (*am*) is the smallest unit of linear measurement. One am is 10^{-18} m. Write this number without exponents.

27. A *nanometer* is 0.000000001 m. Write this number with exponents.

Extend and Apply

Simplify. Write the expression with exponents.

28. $3^2 \cdot 3^{-5}$ **29.** $4 \cdot 4^5 \cdot 4^{-3}$ **30.** $x \cdot x^{-3} \cdot x^3$ **31.** $a^{-3} \cdot a^{-4} \cdot a^9$

32. $\frac{4}{4^4}$ **33.** $\frac{3^2 \cdot 3^4}{3^5}$ **34.** $\frac{x^5}{x^2 \cdot x}$ **35.** $\frac{z}{z^2 \cdot z^2}$

36. What does n equal in $3^n = 27$? **37.** What does n equal in $(-4)^n = \frac{1}{-64}$?

38. Compute $4^{-3} \cdot 4^5$. Then compute $4^5 \cdot 4^{-3}$. Is $\boldsymbol{a^n \cdot a^m = a^m \cdot a^n}$ true for all values of a, n, and m? Why? Name a property that explains this.

39. Write $(4x^2)^3$ as an expression with one exponent.

40. Suppose there is a circular virus with a diameter of 10^{-7} m. Another virus is 10 times larger in diameter. Write the diameter of this virus as a power of 10.

Use Mathematical Reasoning

Express each as a whole number without exponents.

41. $\frac{1}{3^{-2}}$ **42.** $\frac{1}{4(4^{-2})}$ **43.** $\frac{2^{-2}}{2^{-4}}$

Mixed Review

Evaluate for $y = -1.2$. **44.** $-1.5y$ **45.** $y + 9.35$ **46.** $6.3 - y$

Solve and check. **47.** $r \div 16 = -3$ **48.** $c + 7 = -1.4$

Connections Numbers to Algebra

You can simplify algebraic expressions as you did numerical expressions.

Numbers	Algebra
$\frac{2^4}{3^3} \cdot \frac{3^2}{2^2} = \frac{\cancel{2} \cdot \cancel{2} \cdot 2 \cdot 2 \cdot \cancel{3} \cdot \cancel{3}}{\cancel{2} \cdot \cancel{2} \cdot \cancel{3} \cdot \cancel{3} \cdot 3} = \frac{2^2}{3}$	$\frac{2x^3}{5y} \cdot \frac{6y^2}{4x^4} = \frac{\cancel{2} \cdot \cancel{x} \cdot \cancel{x} \cdot \cancel{x} \cdot \cancel{2} \cdot 3 \cdot \cancel{y} \cdot y}{5 \cdot \cancel{y} \cdot \cancel{2} \cdot \cancel{2} \cdot \cancel{x} \cdot \cancel{x} \cdot \cancel{x} \cdot x} = \frac{3y}{5x}$

Simplify.

1. $\frac{x^2}{y^4} \cdot \frac{y^6}{x}$ **2.** $\frac{4a^3}{5b^5} \cdot \frac{3b}{6a^2}$ **3.** $\frac{m^4}{n^5} \cdot \frac{6n^7}{5m^5}$ **4.** $xy^2 \cdot x^{-3}y^4$

7-7 Scientific Notation

Objective To convert numbers between scientific notation and standard form.

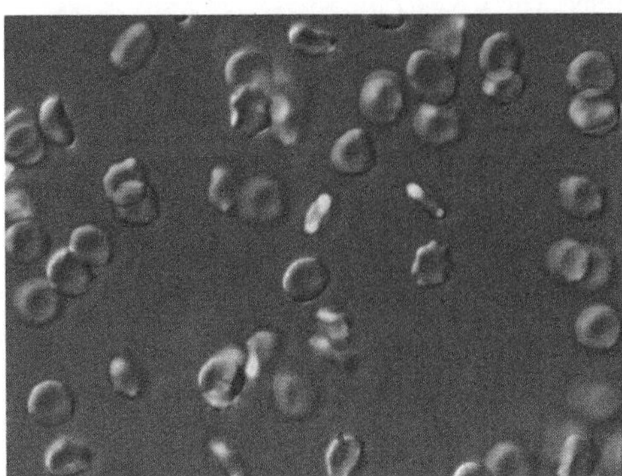

Application

The human body replaces 2.0×10^{11} red blood cells every day. The red blood cell is one of the smallest cells in the human body. It has a diameter of 3×10^{-4} inches. A scientist wants to record this number in standard form.

Understand the Ideas

To simplify work with very large or very small numbers, you can use **scientific notation.** A number written as the product of a power of 10 and a number whose absolute value is greater than or equal to 1 but less than 10 is expressed in scientific notation. The number 3.45×10^3 is in scientific notation. The number 3,450 is expressed in **standard form.**

Example 1

Write 3×10^{-4} in standard form to find the number the scientist in the **application** should record for the diameter of the cell.

Solution

0.0003 Multiplying 3 by 10^{-4} is the same as dividing 3 by 10^4. This moves the decimal point 4 places to the left.

The scientist should record the diameter of the cell as 0.0003 inches.

Try This Write each in standard form.

a. 1.8×10^{-4} **b.** 6.556×10^2 **c.** 4×10^{-2}

Example 2

Write 1,234,000 in scientific notation.

Solution

1.234×10^6 Move the decimal point 6 places to the left. Multiply by 10^6.

Try This Write each in scientific notation.

d. 4567 **e.** 234,000 **f.** 50,000,000

Example 3

Write 0.000345 in scientific notation.

Solution

3.45×10^{-4} Move the decimal point 4 places to the right. Multiply by 10^{-4}.

Try This Write each in scientific notation.

g. 0.0206 **h.** 0.000008 **i.** 0.2004

Class Exercises

Tell where the decimal should be placed to express each number in scientific notation.

1. 32,500 **2.** 35 **3.** 0.005
4. 0.6 **5.** 770 **6.** 82.5
7. 430,000 **8.** 18.6 **9.** 0.000050

Discuss the Ideas

Tell why each of the following is NOT in scientific notation.

10. 12.5×10^4 **11.** 2×4^{-5}

Exercises

Practice and Apply

Write each in standard form.

1. 3.5×10^4 **2.** 6.2×10^{-2} **3.** 4.05×10^5 **4.** 7.0×10^{-5}

Write each in scientific notation.

5. 135 **6.** 23,000 **7.** 345,000 **8.** 8.4
9. 1240 **10.** 650,000 **11.** 4,550,000 **12.** 600
13. 99,000 **14.** 1,000,000 **15.** 0.078 **16.** 0.4
17. 0.000677 **18.** 0.0055 **19.** 0.000001 **20.** 0.05
21. 0.0000405 **22.** 0.000007 **23.** 0.101 **24.** 0.00000003

25. Every 0.4 cubic inch of human blood contains about 5,500,000 red blood cells. Write the number of red blood cells in scientific notation.

26. Some cells in the human body are so small that 200,000 could be placed on the head of a pin. Write this number in scientific notation.

27. A house spider weighs 1.2×10^{-4} kg. Write this number in standard form.

28. A walrus weighs 1.44×10^3 kg. Write this number in standard form.

Extend and Apply

Use the rules for multiplying and dividing exponents to write each product or quotient in scientific notation.

29. $(4.0 \times 10^3)(2.0 \times 10^4)$

30. $(3.2 \times 10^{-2})(5.0 \times 10^{-4})$

31. $\frac{6.0 \times 10^5}{2.0 \times 10^4}$

32. $\frac{5.2 \times 10^5}{1.3 \times 10^3}$

33. Light traveling at about 3.0×10^5 km per second takes about 5.0×10^2 seconds to reach the earth from the sun. Approximately what is the distance, expressed in scientific notation, from the sun to the earth?

34. A certain molecule weighs approximately 4.5×10^{-6} g. There are about 8×10^6 of all of these molecules in a cell. What is the approximate weight of all of these molecules?

Use Mathematical Reasoning

35. Solve for y. $(7 \times 10^2)y = 6.3 \times 10^6$

36. Use each digit 1, 2, 3, and 4 and one negative sign to write a number that is as close to 0.01 as possible. ▯.▯▯ × $10^{▯}$

Mixed Review

Reduce each fraction to lowest terms. **37.** $\frac{27}{135}$ **38.** $\frac{48}{192}$ **39.** $\frac{12}{140}$

Solve and check. **40.** $a - \frac{3}{4} = -\frac{5}{8}$ **41.** $h + \frac{13}{15} = 1\frac{1}{3}$

Simplify. **42.** $z \cdot z \cdot 10 \cdot 4 \cdot z$ **43.** $t + 2t + 3t + 4t$

Calculator Activity

Some calculators allow you to enter numbers in scientific notation. Using a scientific calculator, follow the example below. The EXP key tells the calculator you are entering a power of ten.

Problem in standard notation:
(52,000,000) (230,000,000) = 11,960,000,000,000,000

Problem in scientific notation:
$(5.2 \times 10^7)(2.3 \times 10^8) = 1.196 \times 10^{16}$

5.2 EXP 7 × 2.3 EXP 8 = 1.196 16

Notice that the calculator display shows only 16, rather than 10^{16}, in the product. The answer is written 1.196×10^{16}.

Use a calculator to find each product.

1. $(4.74 \times 10^8)(8.5 \times 10^9)$

2. $(6.33 \times 10^7)(1.9 \times 10^7)$

3. (245,600,000) (700,000)

4. (1,754) (6,570,000,000,000)

5. (1,250,000,000,000) (12,240)

6. (24,400,000,000) (5,500,000,000)

7-8 Problem Solving: Skills

Choosing a Calculation Method

Objective To decide if you need an exact answer or an estimate, and to select an appropriate calculation method.

When solving a word problem, ask yourself the following questions before you pick up your pencil and find an exact answer.

- Do I need an exact answer or an estimate?
- If I need to compute, should I use mental math, paper-and-pencil, or a calculator?

Decide When to Estimate

The situation and the person needing the answer can help you decide whether an exact answer or an estimate is called for.

Sample Problem 1 1,285 pounds of an insecticide mix were to be sprayed on a county park. No more than $\frac{1}{20}$ of the amount sprayed was permitted to be a chemical toxic to animals native to the park. How many pounds of insecticide can be toxic?

- If you were directing this project, you would need to know exactly how much of the insecticide was toxic.
- If you were a newspaper reporter covering the story, an estimate is all that you would need.

Choose a Calculation Method

Once you know you need an exact answer, you need to decide whether the problem can be solved easily using mental math. If mental math is not appropriate, then decide between paper-and-pencil and a calculator.

Sample Problem 2 Erica spent last Saturday working at a car wash to raise money for the homeless. Her group washed 30 trucks at $7.50 each and 45 cars at $5 each. How much money did they earn?

- To solve this mentally, you have to do several operations and remember the results. If a calculator is available, you might consider using it. However, the individual calculations are not too difficult, so they can be done easily using paper and pencil.

Problems

Choose a calculation method and evaluate each expression. Tell which method you used for each.

1. 67×20	**2.** $2{,}356 - 120$	**3.** $\frac{1}{3} + 2\frac{2}{5} + \frac{2}{3}$
4. $875 + 188$	**5.** $300 - 28$	**6.** $1{,}345 \div 15$
7. $35 + 87 + 65$	**8.** $12\frac{1}{6} - 5\frac{3}{8}$	**9.** $\$65.40 \div 8$
10. $6\frac{1}{2} + 18\frac{5}{10}$	**11.** $21{,}538 - 1{,}020$	**12.** $12\frac{3}{10} \div 2$

Indicate whether you need an exact answer or an estimate. Solve the problem and state which calculation method you used.

13. Kim bought a movie ticket for \$3.75, a drink for \$1.25 and popcorn for \$2.25. About how much change should she get from a \$10 bill?

14. Carrie earns \$7.50 each week doing jobs around the house. How many weeks will she have to work to buy a skateboard that costs \$85.99, including tax?

15. Mrs. Wilson had \$15 to spend for groceries. She was keeping a mental record of her purchases while she shopped. Did she stay under \$15?

Item	Exact price
meat	\$3.75
milk	\$1.88
bread	\$0.89
fruit	\$2.25
vegetables	\$4.79

16. The postal workers in a large city find an average of 12 wallets each day in mailboxes throughout the city. About how many do they find in one year?

17. The yearbook staff needed to sell books to at least two-thirds of the students at school to break even. They sold yearbooks to $\frac{3}{4}$ of the student body for a total of 126 books. Did they break even? How many students are there at this school?

18. Dwight worked at a fast-food restaurant 50 hours a week during summer vacation. He earned \$4 an hour for the first 40 hours each week. He was paid one and a half-times the regular rate for each hour over 40 hours. How much did he earn for each 50 hour week?

19. **Communicate** Monthly subscriptions to a daily newspaper cost \$13.95. The Sunday paper costs the same as the total amount for Monday through Saturday's papers. About how much does each weekday paper cost?

   a. Solve.

   b. Write your answer in a complete sentence.

   c. Discuss your answer (exact or estimate) and calculation method with a classmate.

7-9 Problem Solving: Strategies

Work Backward

Objective To solve nonroutine problems using the strategy Work Backward and other strategies learned so far.

Sometimes a word problem describes a sequence of actions involving numbers, gives the result, and asks for the number started with. A problem of this type can be solved by using a strategy called **Work Backward.**

Sample Problem On Monday Jeff opened a savings account for his summer earnings and deposited all of his first week's earnings. On Tuesday, he deposited \$25 into the account. He withdrew \$23 on Wednesday to buy tapes and another \$15 on Thursday for other expenses. On Friday, he withdrew half of what was left in the account to buy some clothing. He then had \$12.50 remaining in the account. How much money did he deposit on Monday?

To solve this problem you can start with the amount of money Jeff had at the end of the week and work backward, using the inverse operations. The lists below show the data given in the story and indicate how to work backward.

Data in the Story	Work Backward
Deposited x	\$38
↓	↑
Deposited (added) \$25	Subtract \$25; \$63 − \$25 = \$38
↓	↑
Withdrew (subtracted) \$23	Add \$23; \$40 + \$23 = \$63
↓	↑
Withdrew (subtracted) \$15	Add \$15; \$25 + \$15 = \$40
↓	↑
Withdrew half (divided by 2)	Multiply by 2; \$12.50 × 2 = \$25
↓	↑
Final amount—\$12.50	\$12.50

Jeff deposited \$38 on Monday.

Problem-Solving Strategies

Choose the Operations	Make a Table	Make an Organized List
Guess, Check, Revise	Look for a Pattern	Use Logical Reasoning
Draw a Diagram	Write an Equation	**Work Backward**
	Simplify the Problem	

Problems

Solve.

1. Ned, Gary, Kris, and Brenda worked at a school car wash on Saturday. One person washed each car. Ned washed twice as many cars as Gary. Gary washed 4 fewer than Kris, who washed 5 more than Brenda. If Brenda washed 8 cars, how many cars did they wash all together?
2. Two jars of chemicals labeled A and B were mixed so that each contained 64 ml at the end. The mixing process involved first pouring from B into A as much liquid as A contained, and finally pouring from A into B as much liquid as B now had. How much liquid was in each jar before they were mixed?
3. Jana spent exactly $1.00 on some snack items at the natural foods store. She bought 11 items on the price list at the right. Which items could she have bought?

Snack Items
Honey Drops 2 for $0.15
Carob Chews 3 for $0.25
Granola Bars $0.10 each

4. Suppose you have two pails, one that holds 4L of water and one that holds 9L. There are no markings on either pail to indicate quantities. How can you measure 6L of water using these two pails?

Group Decision Making

5. Work in a group. Discuss and decide.

Situation You are in charge of purchasing hamburgers, hot dogs, and buns for your class picnic. Each class member has invited a guest from another class. You have to give a report to the principal indicating the cost.

Guidelines for Planning

- **Formulate Problems** you will need to solve.
- Discuss **Assumptions** you will make and **Data** you will need.

a. What decision or decisions do you need to make in this situation?
b. Formulate problems you need to solve to make the decision(s).
c. List any assumptions you need to make to arrive at a decision.
d. What data, if any, do you need to collect to make a decision?
e. Write a paragraph summarizing what your group did, what decisions you made, and why.

Extend Key Ideas

Writing a Repeating Decimal as a Fraction

You can express a terminating decimal as a fraction. For example, $1.235 = \frac{1235}{1000}$.

To write a repeating decimal as a fraction, you can begin by multiplying by 10^n, where n is the number of digits in the repeating decimal part.

Write $0.\overline{36}$ as a fraction.

$$x = 0.\overline{36}$$ Original equation

$$100x = 36.\overline{36}$$ Multiply both sides of the original equation by 10^2 since there are 2 digits in 36.

$$\begin{array}{rl} 100x = & 36.\overline{36} \\ -\quad x = & 0.\overline{36} \\ \hline 99x = & 36 \end{array}$$ Subtract the original equation.

$$x = \frac{36}{99}$$ Solve for x.

$$= \frac{4}{11}$$ Reduce to lowest terms.

The following example involves a single repeating digit.

Write $1.2\overline{3}$ as a fraction.

$$x = 1.233333\ldots$$ Original equation

$$10x = 12.33333\ldots$$ Multiply both sides of the equation by 10, since only 1 digit repeats.

$$\begin{array}{rl} 10x = & 12.33333\ldots \\ -\quad x = & 1.23333\ldots \\ \hline 9x = & 11.1 \end{array}$$ Subtract the original equation.

$$x = \frac{11.1}{9} \cdot \frac{10}{10}$$ Solve for x. Multiply by $\frac{10}{10}$ to remove the decimal from the numerator.

$$x = \frac{111}{90}$$

$$= 1\frac{21}{90} = 1\frac{7}{30}$$

Write each as a fraction. Reduce to lowest terms.

1. $x = 0.\overline{3}$

2. $x = 0.1\overline{6}$

3. $x = 0.41\overline{6}$

4. $x = 0.4\overline{25}$

5. $x = 1.3\overline{8}$

6. $x = 0.5\overline{27}$

7. $x = 1.1\overline{2}$

8. $x = 0.6\overline{18}$

9. $x = 1.\overline{225}$

10. $x = 2.3\overline{23}$

Chapter 7 Review/Test

Understanding

True or false?

7-6 **1.** The expression 4^3 means that 3 is used as a factor 4 times.

7-7 **2.** Numbers greater than or equal to 1 but less than 10 cannot be written using scientific notation.

7-1 **3.** When you multiply two rational numbers, each with an absolute value less than 1, the product will always be less than 1.

7-2 **4.** The product of a rational number and its reciprocal is 0.

7-2 **5.** The reciprocal of a negative rational number is always negative.

Skills

7-1 Multiply or divide. Reduce to lowest terms.
7-2

6. $\left(\frac{5}{12}\right)\left(\frac{3}{8}\right)$ **7.** $\left(\frac{1}{2}\right)\left(-\frac{4}{5}\right)$ **8.** $\left(-1\frac{1}{5}\right)\left(-2\frac{1}{2}\right)$

9. $-\frac{8}{9} \div \left(-\frac{4}{5}\right)$ **10.** $\frac{3}{10} \div \frac{15}{100}$ **11.** $6\frac{3}{7} \div \left(-1\frac{1}{4}\right)$

7-3 Solve and check.

12. $-5y = -\frac{2}{3}$ **13.** $1\frac{1}{2}v = \frac{7}{10}$ **14.** $-6\frac{2}{3} = 3\frac{1}{3}x$

7-6 Simplify. Write each expression with exponents.

15. $\frac{9^8}{9^4}$ **16.** $\frac{(-2)^6}{(-2)^1}$ **17.** $\frac{p^9}{p^5}$

7-7 Write each in decimal form.

18. 1.47×10^6 **19.** 9.0×10^{-3} **20.** 2.11×10^{-5}

7-7 Write each in scientific notation.

21. 0.0079 **22.** 85,000 **23.** 99,000,000

Applications

7-4 Find the solution by writing and solving an equation.
7-5
7-9 **24.** Debbie walked from her house to a bus stop $4\frac{1}{2}$ km away. This was $\frac{1}{3}$ of the total distance to her aunt's house. What was the total distance?

25. A stack of 34 identical books is on the teacher's desk. If the stack is $59\frac{1}{2}$ inches high, how thick is each book?

26. A necklace is made of beads that are $\frac{3}{4}$ inch wide. If there are 30 beads with no space between, how long is the necklace?

27. A mason is building a concrete retaining wall for a swimming pool. The wall will require 117 square feet of brick. About $4\frac{1}{4}$ bricks are needed per square foot. About how many bricks are needed to build the wall?

8 Equations and Inequalities

Chris will not go windsurfing unless the wind speed is less than 30 mi/h. If the wind dies down 7 mi/h, then he will windsurf today. What is the highest speed that the wind might be?

8-1 Solving Equations: Combined Operations

Objective To solve equations involving more than one operation.

Application

A grocer has a full crate of oranges that weighs 40 kg. The crate weighs 8 kg when it is empty. The grocer can solve the equation $0.2n + 8 = 40$ to find the number of 0.2 kg oranges in the crate.

Understand the Ideas

You have learned to solve equations in which one operation has been applied to the variable. To solve equations in which more than one operation has been applied to the variable, you will need to observe the order of operations, then undo them, as shown in the table below.

Equation	Order of Operations Applied to the Variable	To Undo These Operations
$3n + 5 = 44$	First n was multiplied by 3. Then 5 was added.	Subtract 5 from each side. Then divide each side by 3.
$\frac{2}{3}b - 4 = 4$	First b was multiplied by $\frac{2}{3}$. Then 4 was subtracted.	Add 4 to each side. Then multiply each side by the reciprocal of $\frac{2}{3}$, or $\frac{3}{2}$.
$6(x + 2) = 30$	First 2 was added to x. Then this sum was multiplied by 6.	Divide each side by 6. Then subtract 2 from each side.
$\frac{y - 7}{3} = 8$	First 7 was subtracted from y. Then this difference was divided by 3.	Multiply each side by 3. Then add 7 to each side.

This leads to steps for solving equations with combined operations.

Rule Solving Equations with Combined Operations

1. Identify the order in which the operations have been applied to the variable.
2. Undo the operations in reverse order by applying the inverse operations or the inverse properties on both sides of the equation.

Example 1

Solve and check $0.2n + 8 = 40$ to find how many oranges are in the crate in the **application** on the previous page.

Solution

$0.2n + 8 = 40$ First n was multiplied by 0.2. Then 8 was added.

$0.2n + 8 - 8 = 40 - 8$ Since adding 8 was the last operation applied, undo it by subtracting 8 from each side.

$0.2n = 32$

$\frac{0.2n}{0.2} = \frac{32}{0.2}$ Then divide by 0.2 to undo multiplying by 0.2.

$n = 160$

There are 160 oranges in the crate.

Check $0.2(160) + 8 \stackrel{?}{=} 40$ Replace n with 160 in $0.2n + 8 = 40$.

$32 + 8 \stackrel{?}{=} 40$

$40 = 40$ ✓ The solution is 160.

Try This Solve and check.

a. $\frac{3}{4}z + 6 = 18$ **b.** $-y - 5 = 12$ **c.** $6x + 36 = 144$

d. Solve $0.4n + 8 = 40$ to find how many 0.4 kg grapefruit can fit in the same-sized crate as above.

Example 2

Solve and check. $5(x + 7) = 105$

Solution

$5(x + 7) = 105$ First 7 was added to x. Then this sum was multiplied by 5.

$\frac{5(x + 7)}{5} = \frac{105}{5}$ Divide each side by 5.

$x + 7 = 21$

$x + 7 - 7 = 21 - 7$ Subtract 7 from each side.

$x = 14$

Check $5(14 + 7) \stackrel{?}{=} 105$ Replace x with 14 in $5(x + 7) = 105$.

$5(21) \stackrel{?}{=} 105$

$105 = 105$ ✓ The solution is 14.

Try This Solve and check. **e.** $\frac{(x + 8)}{6} = 7$ **f.** $-6(n - 7) = 96$

You can use inverse operations and the calculator to solve certain equations quickly. For example, to solve $3x + 4 = 85$, you might think, "The variable x has been multiplied by 3, then 4 has been added to this product, and the result is 85. Working backward from 85, I'll undo adding 4 by subtracting 4, then undo multiplying by 3 by dividing by 3."

Example 3

Use a calculator to solve. $3x + 4 = 85$

Solution

85 [−] 4 [=] 81 [÷] 3 [=] [27] Use inverse operations.

Try This Use a calculator to solve. **g.** $6x + 16 = 154$ **h.** $\frac{y - 6}{3} = 13$

Class Exercises

To solve, what operation would you use in the first step? the second step?

1. $\frac{x}{2} - 4 = 8$ **2.** $5d + 8 = 18$ **3.** $6(x - 2) = 24$

Discuss the Ideas

4. Juanito looked at the equation $2n + 3 = 13$ and said, "13, 10, 5; $n = 5$." Similarly, what can you say for these equations?

a. $3n - 2 = 16$ **b.** $\frac{n}{2} + 4 = 7$

Exercises

Practice and Apply

Solve and check.

1. $3b - 5 = 16$ **2.** $4r + 16 = -80$ **3.** $9z - 45 = 45$

4. $-x + 46 = 27$ **5.** $68 = 5n + 43$ **6.** $37 = 12p - 23$

7. $\frac{y}{4} - 12 = 8$ **8.** $\frac{c}{8} + 16 = 23$ **9.** $14 = \frac{a}{24} - 13$

10. $0.8a + 3.4 = 7.2$ **11.** $\frac{x + 8}{9} = -6$ **12.** $\frac{p - 7}{12} = -16$

Use inverse operations and a calculator to solve.

13. $4x - 17 = 207$ **14.** $\frac{n}{19} + 26 = 39$ **15.** $\frac{5a}{12} + 13 = 23$

16. Rocky's Rentals charges \$3 to rent a power sander plus \$2 for each day the sander is checked out. Brenda paid \$11 to rent a power sander. Solve the equation $3 + 2d = 11$ to find the number of days she had the sander.

17. Eve bought 3 tickets to a play. She paid \$29 for the tickets, including \$2 tax. Solve the equation $3t + 2 = 29$ to find the price of one ticket.

18. The price of a dozen golf balls has risen \$2 over the last four years. Pamela paid \$36 for 3 dozen golf balls today. Solve the equation $3(c + 2) = 36$ to find the price of a dozen golf balls four years ago.

19. Richard, Lauren, and David were one fish short of having caught 7 fish each. Solve the equation $\frac{f + 1}{3} = 7$ to find the total number of fish they caught.

Extend and Apply

Solve and check.

20. $3 = \frac{6x + 18}{9}$ **21.** $\frac{14n + 8}{3} = 26$ **22.** $\frac{12x - 12}{8} = -9$

Solve. Use the given formula.

23. Fifty meters of mesh are used to fence a 9-meter wide rectangular testing area. How many meters long is the testing area?
Formula: $P = 2l + 2w$ P = perimeter, l = length, and w = width

24. A book on the amount of sleep needed by youths recommends that a person Arturo's age get 10 hours of sleep every night. How old is Arturo?
Formula: $H = 8 + \frac{18 - a}{2}$ H = hours of sleep, a = age in years

25. A physician figured that a person Todd's height should weigh 74 kg. How tall is Todd?
Formula: $W = \frac{4(h - 150)}{5} + 50$ W = weight in kg, h = height in cm

26. Jim used a telephone rate book to calculate that his call cost \$2.32. How many minutes did Jim talk on the phone?
Formula: $C = 52 + 37(m - 1)$
C = cost in cents, m = length of call in minutes

27. Ms. Chan paid \$5.55 for a taxi ride. How far did she travel?
Formula: $F = \$0.75 + \$0.60d$ F = taxicab fare, d = distance in km

28. A chart states that a person Jayne's age should have a maximum heartbeat of 144 beats per minute while exercising. How old is Jayne?
Formula: $B = \frac{4(220 - a)}{5}$ B = beats per minute, a = age in years

Use Mathematical Reasoning

29. A taxi fare included a starting fee of \$1.25 plus \$0.55 for each minute of the trip. The total cost for the trip was \$8.40. How many minutes did the trip take?

30. Complete the generalization for solving each type of equation.

a. If $ax + b = c$, then x = ? **b.** If $ax - b = c$, then x = ?

Mixed Review

Evaluate for $n = \frac{2}{3}$. **31.** $n - 1\frac{1}{2}$ **32.** $\frac{4}{5}n$ **33.** $\frac{3}{5} - n$

Solve and check. **34.** $0.8a = -2.4$ **35.** $1.02 + c = -0.85$

8-2 Problem Solving: Writing Equations

Translating Sentences Involving Combined Operations

Objective To translate verbal statements into equations.

You have learned to translate a verbal statement suggesting a single operation into an equation. To solve some problems you need to choose a variable and translate a verbal statement that suggests a combination of operations, as shown below.

Verbal Statement: Tim's $15 overtime pay is *$3 less* than **twice his regular pay.**

Equation: $15 = 2p - 3$

Example

Write an equation. Carmen's class of 25 students has only three more than twice the number of students in Yoshi's class.

Solution Let s = number of students in Yoshi's class. Choose what the variable represents.

$2s + 3 = 25$ "Twice the number of students" translates to $2s$. "Three more than twice . . ." translates to $2s + 3$.

Try This Write an equation.

a. When Julio's age is doubled and increased by 5, the result is 39.

b. The $65 cost of a pair of shoes is only $4 less than 3 times what shoes cost in 1960.

Class Exercises

Give an equation.

1. 36 more than 6 times a number gives 84.

2. The difference of 3 times the number and -9 is -9.

3. The quotient of 6 times a number and 9 is 45.

4. 12 less than a number divided by 4 gives 13.

Discuss the Ideas

5. Work in groups to make up some verbal statements like those in Class Exercises 1–4. Then write an equation for each statement.

Exercises

Practice and Apply

Write an equation.

1. Emiko's weekly salary, \$200, is \$25 more than twice Jane's salary.
2. Stefan traveled 300 km, which was 35 km less than half as far as he traveled yesterday.
3. The 37 students on the bus are 3 more than twice the number in the van.
4. Earl's class collected 324 cans, which was 4 more than 3 times the number collected last year.
5. The sale price of \$125 for the camera is \$5 less than $\frac{1}{3}$ of the original price.
6. The 468 students enrolled in the school is just 6 less than 22 times the number of students in Adam's class.
7. The 180 mi/h average speed of a race car is 15 more than triple the speed Mr. Blakely likes to drive his car.
8. The 67 students in Gloria's class are 4 more than 3 times the number in Vi's class.
9. Nan earned \$56, which was \$8 more than twice Juanita's earnings.
10. Ben's 94 km bike trip on Tuesday was 17 km more than half the length of his trip on Monday.
11. The \$564 collected for the band trip is \$36 more than $\frac{1}{4}$ the amount needed.
12. The election turnout of 376 was 56 more than $\frac{3}{4}$ of last year's turnout.

Extend and Apply

Write a verbal description of each equation.

13. $2x + 3 = 13$ **14.** $4n - 8 = 7$ **15.** $\frac{1}{4}p + 2 = 9$

Use Mathematical Reasoning

16. Half an hour ago, it was 3 times as long after noon as it was until midnight. What time is it now?
17. **Communicate** If 4 frogs can catch 4 flies in 4 minutes, how many frogs can catch 100 flies in 100 minutes? Explain your solution.

Mixed Review

Solve and check. **18.** $c - 1\frac{2}{3} = \frac{1}{2}$ **19.** $\frac{2}{5}m = 3\frac{3}{4}$

Simplify. **20.** $4(m + 4) - 16$ **21.** $10(t + 30) + 500$

8-3 Problem Solving: Writing Equations

Writing Equations to Solve Problems

Objective To solve word problems by writing and solving equations.

You can use the Problem-Solving Checklist on page 138 to help you solve problems.

Example

Peter bought a 10-speed bike for \$172. He made a down-payment of \$76 and monthly payments of \$24. How many months did it take him to pay for the bike?

Solution

Let m = the number of monthly payments. — Let m represent the unknown number.

$$24m + 76 = 172$$

The total amount paid can be expressed in two equal ways. Write an equation.

$$24m + 76 - 76 = 172 - 76$$
$$24m = 96$$
$$m = 4$$

Check $24(4) + 76 \stackrel{?}{=} 172$ — The equation solution checks.

$172 = 172$ ✓ — Estimate: \$76 plus 4 payments of \$25 would be \$176. The answer is reasonable.

It took Peter 4 months to pay for the bicycle.

Try This Solve by writing an equation.

a. Mr. Meyer's golf score, 83, was only 5 more than twice his age. How old is Mr. Meyer?

Class Exercises

Give an equation.

1. Rachel's present salary, \$25,000, is \$365 more than twice what it was when she began the job. What was her starting salary?
2. Sandy added 16 stamps to her collection and then gave half her stamps to her sister. Then she had 29 stamps. How many stamps did she start with?

Discuss the Ideas

3. Which of the Class Exercises would most easily be solved without writing an equation? What strategy would you use?

Exercises

Practice and Apply

Solve by writing an equation.

1. Three-fourths of the members of a tennis club signed up in advance for a tournament. On the day of the tournament, 9 more entered, making a total of 84. How many members did the tennis club have?
2. Jason earned $6 an hour for a job. He got a bonus of $75, making his total earnings $297. How many hours did he work?
3. Before giving 12 ounces of flour to a friend, Mrs. Higuera had $\frac{3}{4}$ of a sack of flour. The remaining flour weighed 48 ounces. How many ounces did a full bag weigh?
4. The championship basketball team fell three points short of getting double its opponent's score. The team scored 81 points. How many points did its opponent score?

Extend and Apply

5. A tank that was $\frac{3}{4}$ full of liquid fertilizer had 565 gallons pumped out and 832 gallons put in, leaving 2400 gallons in the tank. What would a full tank hold?
6. The temperature dropped by half, decreased by 3°C, and rose 9°C. The thermometer then read 14°C. What was the beginning temperature?
7. **Determine Reasonable Answers** Decide whether the answer given is reasonable. If not, explain why not. Then solve the problem.

   The Ortiz family drove for a while, stopped for lunch, and then drove for 3 more hours. Their average rate of speed was 53 mph. They traveled a total of 371 miles. How long did they drive before lunch? Answer: 7 hours.

Use Mathematical Reasoning

8. Write a word problem that could be solved using the equation.

   a. $3x - 4 = 17$ **b.** $54 - 2x = 20$

Mixed Review

Evaluate for $a = 2.5, b = 1.4$. **9.** $3(a - b)$ **10.** $a(b + 2)$

Solve and check. **11.** $-2.4a = 3$ **12.** $n + 0.6 = -2.4$

8-4 Functions and Function Notation

Objective To express and evaluate functions using $f(x)$ notation.

Application

A cyclist might want to find the total distance traveled when moving at an average speed of 9 mi/h. This distance is a function of the time the cyclist has traveled.

Understand the Ideas

In Chapter 5 you learned that a function is a special relationship between two variables. A function can be thought of as a rule that pairs each member of one set, called the **domain**, with one and only one member of another set, called the **range**. This "Function Machine" illustrates the idea, using numbers as elements.

You should use the letter f to represent a function and $f(x)$ (read "f of x") to represent the value of a function. For the bicycle, if x is the total number of hours the cyclist traveled, then the function would give the total distance traveled, $9x$. We write $f(x) = 9x$.

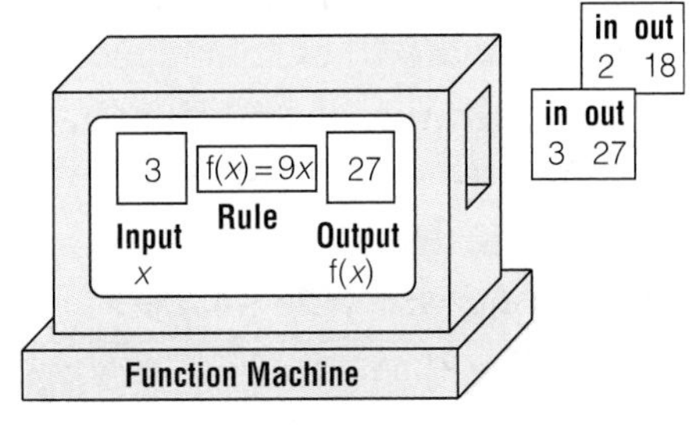

The symbol $f(3)$ represents "the value of the function f when 3 is substituted for the variable x." $f(3) = 9(3) = 27$

The values that can be used for x are the input values of the function. The corresponding values of $f(x)$ are the output values of the function.

Example 1

In the **application**, find out how far you would travel in 4 hours by evaluating the function $f(x) = 9x$ when $x = 4$.

Solution $f(4) = 9(4) = 36$ Substitute 4 for x in $f(x) = 9x$.

You would travel 36 miles in 4 hours.

Try This

a. Evaluate $f(x) = \frac{x}{5} - 3$ for $x = 20, 40, 60,$ and 80.

b. To find how far you have traveled if you average 12 mph for three hours, evaluate $f(x) = 12x$ for $x = 3$.

Example 2

Copy and complete the table. Write the function using function notation.

time (parts of an hour)	0.25	0.5	0.75	1	x
distance traveled (in miles)	2.5	5	7.5		

Solution

time (parts of an hour)	0.25	0.5	0.75	1	x
distance traveled (in miles)	2.5	5	7.5	10	$10x$

Each distance is 10 times greater than the time.

$f(x) = 10x$

Try This

c. Copy and complete the table. Write the function using function notation.

1	2	3	4	5	x
1	4	9			

Class Exercises

Use mental math to evaluate each function for the values given.

1. $f(x) = 10x$ for $x = 2.52$ and 0.87 **2.** $f(x) = \frac{x}{4}$ for $x = 20, 60,$ and 100

Discuss the Ideas

3. Suppose the domain of the following two functions is all whole numbers. How could you describe the range of each function? Explain your reasoning. **a.** $f(x) = 2x$ **b.** $f(x) = 2x + 1$

Exercises

Practice and Apply

Evaluate the function for the values given.

1. $f(x) = 3x - 4$ for $x = 0, 1, 2,$ and 3

2. $f(x) = \frac{x}{3} - 2$ for $x = 3, 6, 9,$ and 12

3. $f(x) = \frac{2x}{5} + 4$ for $x = 5, 10, 15,$ and 20

4. $f(x) = (3x + 4) - 2$ for $x = -2, -1, 0,$ and 2

Copy and complete the table. Write the function using function notation.

5.

1	2	3	4	5	x
6	11	16			

6.

1	2	3	4	5	x
0	2	4			

7. Leo made three phone calls lasting 5, 10, and 13 minutes. Evaluate the function $f(x) = 20x$ when $x = 5$, 10, and 13 to find the cost of each.

8. Yellow Hills Amusement Park charges $10 to enter and $2 for each ride. Evaluate the function $f(r) = 2r + 10$ when $r = 5$, 8, 12 and 20 to find the total costs when r is the number of rides.

9. The fee to rent a limousine is $30 plus $8 per person. Evaluate the function $f(p) = 30 + 8p$ when $p = 2$, 3, 5, and 7 to find the total costs for these numbers of people.

10. To mow a lawn, Ron charges $3 per hour. He charges an extra fee when he uses his own mower and gas. Copy and complete the table. Write the function using function notation.

Hours	1	2	3	4	5	x
Cost	8	11	14			

Extend and Apply

11. At Sam's skateboard rental shop there is a fixed rental charge. There is an additional charge for each hour the board is being used. Look for patterns to copy and complete the table below. Write the function using function notation.

Time (in hours)	1	2	3	4	5	x
Rental cost	$7	$9	$11	$13		

12. The labor charge at a bicycle repair shop is $15 plus $25 for each hour or part of an hour. The total charge is a function of the time, t, and is given by the function $f(t) = 25t + 15$. What is the total charge for $3\frac{1}{2}$ hours of work on a bicycle?

13. **Write to Learn** Write a paragraph to a classmate that explains the meaning of a function. Use examples.

Use Mathematical Reasoning

14. If $f(1) = 9, f(2) = 19, f(3) = 29$, and $f(4) = 39$, then $f(x) = ?$

15. Write your own function using $f(x)$ notation. Make a table of values for x and $f(x)$. Write the domain and range of your function.

Mixed Review

Solve and check. **16.** $y - \frac{5}{12} = -\frac{3}{4}$ **17.** $-\frac{4}{9} = c + 2\frac{1}{3}$ **18.** $6n = \frac{3}{5}$

8-5 Simplifying to Solve Equations: Using the Distributive Property

Objective To simplify equations using the distributive property, then solve them.

Explore

Consider the large rectangle with parts A and B. Write algebraic expressions for the areas of parts A and B. Write an equation that shows two ways of representing the total area of the rectangle.

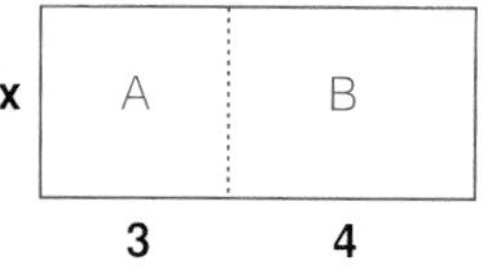

Work with a group to draw rectangles similar to the one above to show that each of the following are true.

a. $3x + 2x = 5x$ **b.** $5x + 4x = 9x$

Understand the Ideas

You have learned to use a reversed form of the Distributive Property to simplify an algebraic expression such as $3x + 4x$ by combining like terms:

$$ba + ca = (b + c)a$$
$$3x + 4x = (3 + 4)x = 7x$$

The Distributive Property of multiplication over subtraction states:

Distributive Property: Multiplication over Subtraction

For all numbers a, b, and c, $a(b - c) = ab - ac$

You can use a reversed form of the Distributive Property of multiplication over subtraction to simplify an algebraic expression:

$$ba - ca = (b - c)a$$
$$7x - 5x = (7 - 5)x = 2x$$

Example 1

Solve and check. $5x + 2x = -161$

Solution $5x + 2x = -161$

$7x = -161$ Because of the Distributive Property, $5x + 2x = (5 + 2)x = 7x$.

$\frac{7x}{7} = -\frac{161}{7}$ Divide each side by 7, or use the Multiplicative Inverse Property and multiply by $\frac{1}{7}$.

$x = -23$

Check $5(-23) + 2(-23) \stackrel{?}{=} -161$ Substitute -23 for x in $5x + 2x = -161$.

$$-115 + -46 \stackrel{?}{=} -161$$
$$-161 = -161 \checkmark$$

Try This Solve and check. **a.** $-6x + 19x = 962$ **b.** $\frac{2}{5}y + \frac{4}{5}y = 36$

Example 2

Solve. $7x - 5x = 86$

Solution $7x - 5x = 86$

$2x = 86$ Because of the Distributive Property, $7x - 5x = (7 - 5)x = 2x$.

$$\frac{2x}{2} = \frac{86}{2}$$

$x = 43$ Substitution will show that 43 checks.

Try This Solve and check. **c.** $-6n - 4n = 65$ **d.** $72 = 13y - 5y$

Class Exercises

Use the Distributive Property to simplify the equation.

1. $4x + 7x = 77$ **2.** $9x + 6x = 30$ **3.** $500 = 75x + 25x$

Discuss the Ideas

4. How could you convince someone that the equation $5n = 20$ is not a simplified version of the equation $8n - (-3)n = 20$? Try to do this in more than one way.

Exercises

Practice and Apply

Solve and check.

1. $5x + 2x = 84$ **2.** $4a + 12a = -48$ **3.** $9c + 8c = 68$

4. $24z - 8z = 64$ **5.** $18r - 9r = -108$ **6.** $-9a - 4a = 78$

7. $65 = 8p + 5p$ **8.** $126 = -14s + 8s$ **9.** $26z + 37z = 315$

10. $\frac{3}{4}y + \frac{1}{2}y = 24$ **11.** $4.6x + 3.4x = 128$ **12.** $\frac{7}{8}n - \frac{3}{4}n = -6$

13. Bronze is an alloy that contains 4 parts copper and 1 part tin. Solve the equation $4x + x = 215$ to find how much tin there is in 215 grams of bronze.

14. Cindy sold the same number of \$2 student tickets and \$3 adult tickets for the science show. Solve the equation $2x + 3x = 145$ to find how many of each kind of ticket she sold if she sold \$145 worth of tickets.

Extend and Apply

Solve and check.

15. $-5x + 7x + 9x = -88$

16. $16n - 9n + 12n = 76$

17. $6.3p + 8.6p - 5.4p = 28.5$

18. $\frac{3}{2}a + \frac{3}{4}a + \frac{3}{8}a = 105$

19. Evaluate both $(b - c)a$ and $ba - ca$ for $a = -3$, $b = 6$, and $c = 9$. Choose new values for a, b, and c and evaluate again. Did the expressions have the same value in both cases?

20. Alicia bought some $6 records and an $18 record-cleaning kit. The total cost was $60. How many records did she buy?

21. Teri bought 8 tickets to the water slide and spent $4 on refreshments. The total cost was $10. What was the cost of each ticket?

Use Mathematical Reasoning

22. Bill wrote: "For all whole numbers a, b, and c, $a(b + c) = a + (bc)$." Check this for $a = 2$, $b = 3$, and $c = 4$, and then for $a = 3$, $b = 5$, and $c = 6$. If you can find one set of values for a, b, and c for which $a(b + c)$ does not equal $a + (bc)$, you will have found a counterexample proving Bill's generalization false! Can you do it?

Mixed Review

Find the greatest common factor (GCF). **23.** 27, 45, 108

Evaluate for $m = 3.2$, $n = -0.8$. **24.** $3n - m$ **25.** $4(m + n)$

Computer Activity

This program will solve equations of the form Ax + B = C. The values for A, B, and C can be positive or negative rational numbers and are entered as decimals.

```
10 PRINT "THIS PROGRAM WILL SOLVE EQUATIONS OF THE
   FORM AX+B=C"
20 INPUT "TYPE IN INTEGER OR DECIMAL VALUES FOR A,
   B, AND C.";A,B,C
30 PRINT "THE EQUATION IS ";A;"X+";B;"=";C
40 PRINT "THE SOLUTION IS X=";(C-B)/A
50 INPUT "DO YOU WANT TO SOLVE ANOTHER ONE?";A$
60 IF LEFT$(A$,1)="Y" THEN GOTO 20
70 END
```

1. Use the program to solve the equation $2x - 1 = 5$.

2. Use the program to solve the equation $\frac{1}{4}n + \left(-\frac{1}{2}\right) = \frac{3}{8}$.

3. Make up some equations and use the program to solve them.

8-6 More Simplifying to Solve Equations

Objective To solve equations requiring simplification of expressions and combined operations.

Understand the Ideas

You learned earlier that terms such as n and $5n$ are called *like terms* because they have the same variable part, n. The terms $-8x$, $0.4x$, and $\frac{2}{3}x$ are also like terms because their variable part, x, is the same. Terms such as $3a$ and $4b$ have different variables and thus are unlike terms. Terms such as $5y$, $5y^2$, and $5xy$ are also unlike terms, since their variable parts are not identical.

To solve some equations you must first simplify expressions by combining all like terms. In the following examples, the Commutative, Associative, and Distributive Properties are used to do this.

Example 1

Solve and check. $9x + 5(x + 7) = -49$

Solution

$9x + 5(x + 7) = -49$ Multiply by 5 first, so you will have like terms to combine.

$9x + 5x + 35 = -49$ Distributive Property: $5(x + 7) = 5x + 5 \cdot 7$

$14x + 35 = -49$ Distributive Property: $5x + 9x = (5 + 9)x = 14x$

$14x + 35 + (\mathbf{-35}) = -49 + (\mathbf{-35})$ Add -35 to each side.

$14x = -84$

$\frac{14x}{\mathbf{14}} = -\frac{84}{\mathbf{14}}$ Divide each side by 14.

$x = -6$

Check $9(-6) + 5(-6 + 7) \stackrel{?}{=} -49$ Replace x with -6 in $9x + 5(x + 7) = -49$.

$-54 + 5(1) \stackrel{?}{=} -49$

$-49 = -49 \checkmark$ The solution is -6.

Try This Solve and check.

a. $2b + 3(b - 7) = 44$ **b.** $4(2y + 9) + 7y = -24$

You can use the Commutative and Associative Properties for addition together to add any three numbers in any order. You can use the Commutative and Associative Properties of multiplication to multiply any three numbers in any order.

Example 2

Solve. $3(5n) + 14 + 6n = 21$

Solution

$$3(5n) + 14 + 6n = 21$$

$$15n + 14 + 6n = 21$$ Associative Property: $3(5n) = (3 \cdot 5)n = 15n$

$$15n + 6n + 14 = 21$$ Commutative and Associative Properties: $15n + 14 + 6n = 15n + 6n + 14$

$$21n + 14 = 21$$ Distributive Property: $15n + 6n = (15 + 6)n = 21n$

$$21n + 14 - \mathbf{14} = 21 - \mathbf{14}$$

$$21n = 7$$

$$\frac{21n}{\mathbf{21}} = \frac{7}{\mathbf{21}}$$

$$n = \frac{1}{3}$$ Substitution will show that $\frac{1}{3}$ checks.

Try This Solve. **c.** $4z + 9 + 3(2z) = 129$ **d.** $-2(7c) - 12 + 5c = 51$

Class Exercises

Simplify.

1. $3(y + 4)$ **2.** $4(p - 8)$ **3.** $5n + 9 + 3n$ **4.** $7 + 8x - 2x$

Discuss the Ideas

5. Without solving the equations below, decide if all have the same solution and explain. Then find and check the solutions.

a. $8n + 3(n + 4) = -21$ **b.** $11n + 12 = -21$ **c.** $11n = -33$

Exercises

Practice and Apply

Solve and check.

1. $5(n + 3) + 5 = -25$

2. $4(x - 3) + 8 = 60$

3. $-8a + 6(a + 7) = 1$

4. $6c + 4(c + 8) = 48$

5. $10z + 5(z - 12) = 0$

6. $7y + 7(y + 3) = -21$

7. $5(4d) + 7 + (-8d) = 88$

8. $-3(7a) + 17 + 6a = 82$

9. A baseball team manager spent \$93 for some \$3 caps and some \$5 helmets. He bought 7 more caps than helmets. Solve the equation $3(x + 7) + 5x = 93$ to find the number of helmets purchased.

10. Odette ordered 10 rolls of film and 4 battery packs from a catalog. A roll of film cost twice as much as a battery pack. She spent \$75, including \$3 for shipping. Solve the equation $10(2x) + 4x + 3 = 75$ to find the cost of a battery pack.

Extend and Apply

Solve and check.

11. $3(x + 4) + 5(x - 2) = 66$

12. $8(p - 3) + 3p + 7p = 138$

13. $-3(4 + x) + 7(-3x) = 72$

14. $-4(3 + z) + 6z - 12 = -36$

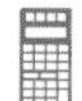

Use a calculator to solve the equations in Exercises 15–16.

15. $678(n + 39) + 457n = 77{,}517$

16. $87(29x) + 43x + 57{,}650 = 1{,}198$

17. If Juana multiplies her age by 6, the result is 156. Mary is 3 times as old as Juana. Write an equation to find Juana's age. Use the solution to find Mary's age.

18. In June, Ben sold 80 cars. This was 8 more than 3 times the number he sold in May. Write an equation to find how many he sold in May.

19. **Finish the Solution** The prices of three Frisbees of increasing quality were consecutive odd integers. The total price for all three was \$33. What was the cost of each of the Frisbees?

Start of a solution: Let n = the price of the first Frisbee.
$n + 2$ = the price of the second Frisbee.

Use Mathematical Reasoning

20. The sum of what three consecutive page numbers in a book is 264?

21. An apartment manager used 339 metal digits to number apartments consecutively, beginning with 1. How many apartments did he number?

Mixed Review

Write each as a decimal. **22.** $\frac{3}{4}$ **23.** $\frac{7}{8}$ **24.** $\frac{3}{5}$ **25.** $\frac{9}{10}$

Give the prime factorization of each. **26.** 15 **27.** 17 **28.** 28

Numbers to Algebra

The number examples below suggest an important generalization in algebra.

Numbers	Algebra
$-(9 - 5) = 5 - 9 = -4$ $-(2 - 7) = 7 - 2 = 5$	For all numbers a and b, $-(a - b) = b - a$

Use the generalization above to simplify.

1. $-(5 - x)$

2. $-(3 - 2n)$

3. $-(7 - 5t)$

4. $-(4 - 3a) + 7$

5. $-(2b - 6) + 9$

6. $-(12a - 4) + a$

8-7 Solving Equations with Variables on Both Sides

Objective To solve equations in which variables appear on both sides.

Application

Connie can solve an equation such as $5h = 12 + 3h$, where h is the number of hours she rents the tool, to decide whether to rent a tool at \$5/hour or at a base price of \$12 plus \$3/hour.

Understand the Ideas

You can solve an equation with like terms on both sides by using the properties of equality to get an equation in which the variable appears on only one side.

Example 1

In the **application**, which rental charge is better? Solve and check $5h = 12 + 3h$ to help you decide.

Solution

$$5h = 12 + 3h$$

$$5h - 3h = 12 + 3h - 3h$$ Subtract $3h$ from each side so that all terms with a variable are on the same side of the equation.

$$2h = 12$$

$$\frac{2h}{2} = \frac{12}{2}$$

$$h = 6$$

The prices are the same if Connie rents for 6 hours. For less than 6 hours, \$5/hour is cheaper. For more than 6 hours, the other price is better.

Check $5(6) \stackrel{?}{=} 12 + 3(6)$ Replace h with 6 in $5h = 12 + 3h$.

$$30 \stackrel{?}{=} 12 + 18$$

$$30 = 30 \checkmark$$ The solution is 6.

Try This Solve and check.

a. $2x + 72 = 4x$ **b.** $24 + y = 9y$

c. Which rental charge is better, \$6/hour or a base price of \$10 plus \$4/hour? Solve the equation $6h = 10 + 4h$ to help you decide.

Example 2

Solve and check. $6x - 2 = 4x + 3$

Solution

$$6x - 2 = 4x + 3$$ First, get the numbers on one side.

$$6x - 2 + 2 = 4x + 3 + 2$$ Add 2 to each side.

$$6x = 4x + 5$$

$$6x - 4x = 4x - 4x + 5$$ Subtract $4x$ from each side so all terms with a variable will be on the same side.

$$2x = 5$$

$$\frac{2x}{2} = \frac{5}{2}$$

$$x = \frac{5}{2}$$ Substitution will show that $\frac{5}{2}$ checks.

Try This Solve and check. **d.** $3y + 4 = 6y + 2$ **e.** $-7a + 8 = 3a - 2$

Class Exercises

What would you do to get the variable alone on one side of the equation?

1. $5x = 14 - 2x$ **2.** $8b = 18 + 2b$ **3.** $7n = 4n + 12$

Discuss the Ideas

4. A student had difficulty solving this equation. What would you say to help? $7n - 2n + 3 = 5n + 3$

Exercises

Practice and Apply

Solve and check.

1. $9x = 26 - 4x$ **2.** $7n = 15 - 8n$ **3.** $12a = 48 - 4a$

4. $13b = 27 + 4b$ **5.** $16c = 42 + 9c$ **6.** $15y = 72 + 7y$

7. $7r = -5r + 144$ **8.** $7z = 3z - 52$ **9.** $180 - 9s = 9s$

10. $9r + 7 = 4r - 8$ **11.** $3s + 7 = -5s - 9$

12. $15z - 9 = -3z + 9$ **13.** $\frac{5}{8}x + 12 = \frac{3}{8}x + 4$

14. $\frac{2}{5}n - 3 = \frac{9}{5}n - 5$ **15.** $\frac{5}{6}a + 4 = \frac{2}{3}a + 6$

16. Tom makes \$5 an hour as a waiter and Jill makes \$3 an hour plus tips as a waitress. They made the same amount of money when Jill earned \$18 in tips and they worked the same number of hours. Solve the equation $5h = 3h + 18$ to find the number of hours they worked.

17. Company A rents a tool for \$3 an hour plus a base price of \$10. Company B rents the same tool for \$5 an hour plus a base price of \$4. Solve $3h + 10 = 5h + 4$ to find the number of hours you would need to use the tool to make the costs equal.

Extend and Apply

Solve and check.

18. $3(x + 4) = -5x - 30$

19. $5(b - 3) = 7b - 14$

20. $6(s + 1) = 4(s + 2)$

21. $4(a - 2) = 2(a + 8)$

22. $\frac{1}{3}(x + 6) = \frac{5}{6}x$

23. $\frac{1}{2}(y - 16) = \frac{3}{4}y$

Write an equation to solve each problem in Exercises 24–26.

24. Mrs. Greer rented a tool for a base charge of \$15 plus \$3 per hour. The total rental cost was \$33. For how long did she rent the tool?

25. Jeff's checking account charges were \$3.00 per month plus \$0.15 per check. Jeff was charged \$7.50 for the month. How many checks did he write?

26. Christina scored 35 points in each round of a game, plus 46 bonus points. Her total score was 256. How many rounds did she play?

Use Mathematical Reasoning

27. If one of the daughters in the Biggs family had been a boy, the number of boys and girls would have been equal. If one of the sons had been a girl, there would have been twice as many girls as boys. How many children were in the family?

28. Each of three large blocks weighs the same. Each of five small blocks weighs the same. Each large block weighs 3 times as much as a small block. All together, the blocks weigh 112 kg. What does a large block weigh?

Mixed Review

Write <, >, or = for each □. **29.** $\frac{5}{9} \square \frac{31}{54}$ **30.** $-\frac{3}{5} \square -\frac{41}{65}$

Solve and check. **31.** $c - 16 = 57$ **32.** $\frac{3}{4}m = 24$ **33.** $r + \frac{1}{2} = -\frac{2}{5}$

Simplify. Write the result with exponents. **34.** $\frac{m^5}{m^2}$ **35.** $\frac{r^3}{r}$

Mental Math

Use a calculator to check whether or not the following equations are true. Then look for a pattern and use it to find the products below mentally.

$29 \cdot 31 = (30 \cdot 30) - (1 \cdot 1)$ $28 \cdot 32 = (30 \cdot 30) - (2 \cdot 2)$

$39 \cdot 41 = (40 \cdot 40) - (1 \cdot 1)$ $38 \cdot 42 = (40 \cdot 40) - (2 \cdot 2)$

$49 \cdot 51 = (50 \cdot 50) - (1 \cdot 1)$ $48 \cdot 52 = (50 \cdot 50) - (2 \cdot 2)$

Find each product mentally.

1. $59 \cdot 61$

2. $69 \cdot 71$

3. $79 \cdot 81$

4. $58 \cdot 62$

5. $68 \cdot 72$

6. $78 \cdot 82$

8-8 Problem Solving: Applications

The Cost of Owning and Operating a Camera

Objective To solve word problems involving costs of camera operation.

It's fun to take pictures, but what does it really cost to own and operate a camera? The chart below gives some useful recent cost estimates that will help you answer this question. You may wish to collect data from your local stores to update the costs.

Cost of Cameras and Film

Camera Costs		Film Costs		Processing Costs	
Fixed Focus, 35 mm	\$ 39	Print Film		Print Film	
Automatic, 35 mm	\$139	24 exp.	\$4.29	24 exp.	\$6.45
Auto Focus SLR, 35 mm	\$429	36 exp.	\$5.37	36 exp.	\$8.45
		Slide Film		Slide Film	
		24 exp.	\$5.39	24 exp.	\$3.95
		36 exp.	\$6.89	36 exp.	\$5.49

Problems

Use the information given above to solve. Decide whether to use pencil and paper, mental math, estimation, or a calculator to find the answer.

1. What would be the cost of buying an SLR 35mm camera, two rolls of print film (24 exp.) and the processing costs for this film?
2. What is the cost per picture for buying and processing 24 exposure print film photos? How much more or less is this than buying and processing 24 exposure slide film photos?
3. Five rolls of print film that were sale priced and an automatic camera cost Jenny Schenkel \$158.35. What was the sale price of a roll of print film?
4. Mr. Spelios planned to take around 400 slide pictures on a vacation trip to Greece and Egypt. About how many rolls of 36 exposure film should he buy and what would be the approximate cost?

5. Margie Caisley was surprised when she looked at her expenses for the year. She had purchased a Fixed Focus camera and had taken 192 prints, in rolls of 24. What was her total cost?

6. Richard Marberry found that 17 rolls of film and an automatic camera cost about the same as 40 rolls of film and a Fixed Focus camera. What kind of film was Richard considering?

7. Sheri Huff bought some rolls of print film at a discount photo store for $2.50 per roll and the same number of rolls of slide film for $3.50 per roll. The total cost of all the film was $36. How many rolls of each type did she buy?

8. Carol Glynn paid $63.20 to have 384 exposures processed. This was an even number of full rolls. What kind of film did she use?

9. At the end of a year, Tim Vasquez calculated his photography expenses. He had purchased an SLR 35mm camera, taken several rolls of 36 exposure slide film, and had the film processed. His total cost was $490.90. How many rolls of film did he use?

10. Leona Ching took some rolls of 36 exposure print film and the same number of rolls of 24 exposure print film on a band trip. Her total cost for buying the film was about $11 more than 7 times the number of rolls of 24 exposure film. How many total rolls of film did Leona take on the trip?

11. **Data Search** Find the total cost at two local stores of buying a camera of your choice and 5 rolls of film. How much, if any, do you save by buying at one store or the other?

What's Your Decision?

You are on a committee to take candid photos of your classmates for a school yearbook. You have decided to take 144 pictures and sort out the ones that are really good. Should you buy rolls with 24 or with 36 exposures? If you can only use 45 of your photos in the yearbook, what estimate of the cost per photo should you give the yearbook budget committee?

8-9 Polynomials

Objective To write and add polynomials.

Explore

You can use algebra tiles to represent algebraic expressions. Light tiles are positive and dark tiles are negative.

- Work together to decide how to model the expressions.

  a. $2x^2 + 3x + 4$
  b. $-3x^2 + (-2x) + 5$
  c. $4x^2 - 3$

  Then lay out some tiles and write the expression they model.

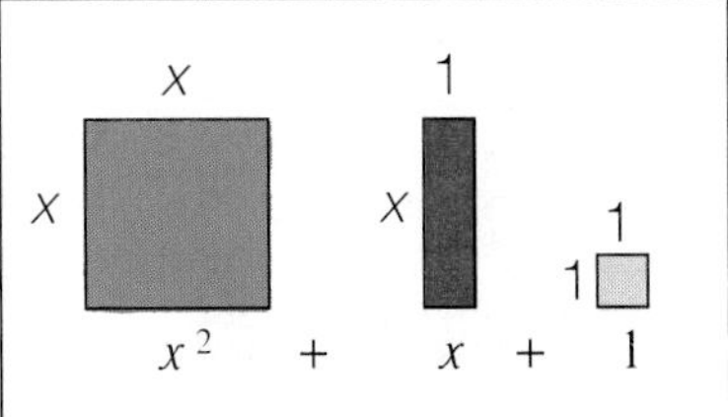

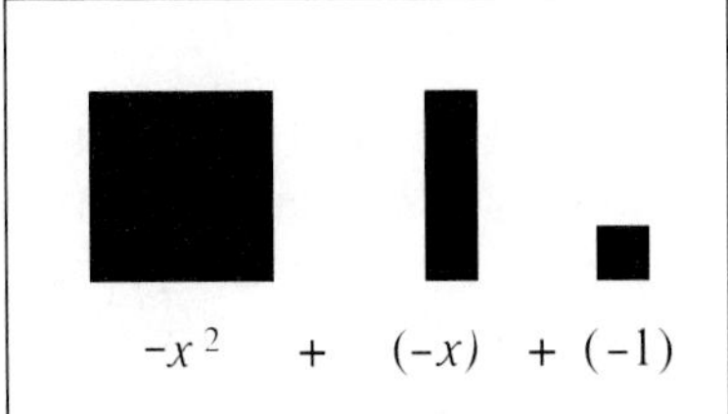

Understand the Ideas

A **monomial** is an expression that is either a numeral, a variable, or a product of numerals and variables with whole number exponents. If the monomial is a numeral, we call it a **constant.** You can use algebra tiles like those in the Explore activity to model monomials.

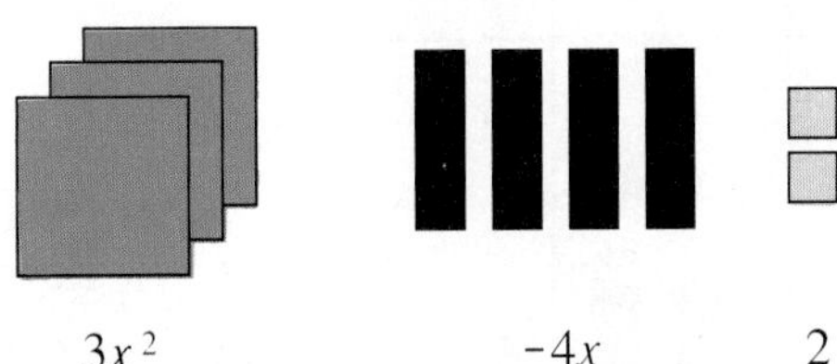

A **polynomial** is a monomial or a sum of monomials. You can use algebra tiles to model polynomials.

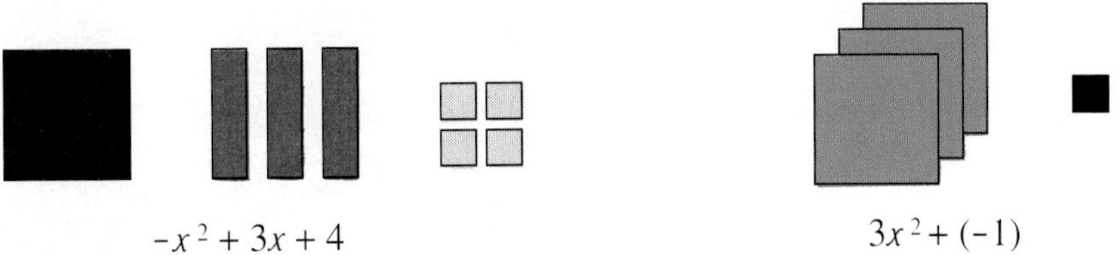

In a polynomial, each monomial is called a **term.** $-x^2 + 3x + 4$ has three terms and $3x^2 + (-1)$ has two terms. A polynomial with exactly two terms is called a **binomial.** A polynomial with exactly three terms is a **trinomial.**

Example 1

Use algebra tiles to model each polynomial. Tell whether the polynomial is a monomial, a binomial, or a trinomial.

a. $3x^2 + x + 1$ **b.** $-4x^2$ **c.** $-2x^2 + (-4)$

Solution

a.

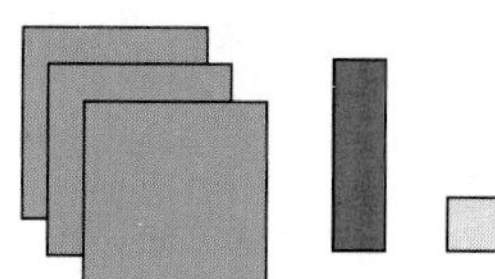

$3x^2 + x + 1$ (trinomial)

b.

$-4x^2$ (monomial)

c.

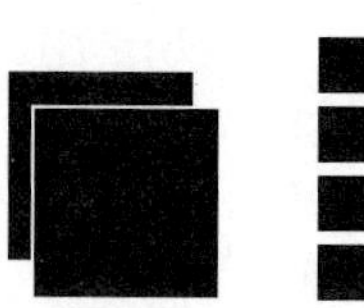

$-2x^2 + (-4)$ (binomial)

Try This Use algebra tiles to model each polynomial. Tell whether the polynomial is a monomial, a binomial, or a trinomial.

a. $4a + 3$ **b.** $-x^2 + x + (-6)$ **c.** $2r^2 + (-5r) + 3$ **d.** $-3p$

To simplify expressions, you sometimes need to add polynomials. You can use algebra tiles to help you do this. Same-sized tiles represent like terms. Same-sized light and dark tiles are opposites and cancel each other. Since polynomials represent real numbers, they follow all of the basic properties and $+(-x) = -x$.

Example 2

Use algebra tiles to add the polynomials $2x^2 - x + 4$ and $x^2 + 3x - 3$.

Solution

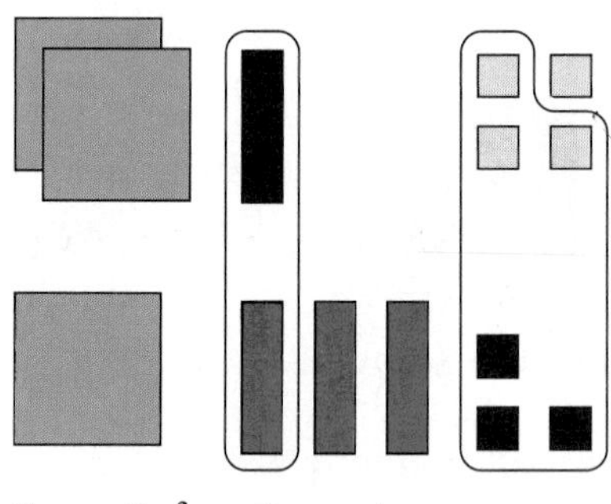

Sum: $3x^2 + 2x + 1$

Show $2x^2 - x + 4$.

Show $x^2 + 3x - 3$.

Combine the tiles.
Cancel same-sized light and dark tiles.
Write the polynomial for the remaining tiles.

Try This Use algebra tiles to add the polynomials.

e. $-4n^2 + 5n - 3$ and $2n^2 - 7n + 8$ **f.** $3x^2 - 7x + 2$ and $-5x^2 + 7x$

Class Exercises

Tell how many terms the polynomial has. Is it a monomial, a binomial, or a trinomial?

1. $5x + 8$ **2.** $-345a^2$ **3.** $7x^2 + (-2x) + 6$ **4.** $-5p^2 + (-4p)$

Discuss the Ideas

5. Use the definitions to help you decide if the statement is *always, sometimes,* or *never* true.
   a. A polynomial is a monomial.
   b. A binomial is a polynomial.

Exercises

Practice and Apply

Use algebra tiles to model each polynomial. Tell whether the polynomial is a monomial, a binomial, or a trinomial.

1. $5x^2$
2. $-2y^2 + 4$
3. $6x^2 + (-4x) + 1$
4. $-3a^2 + 5a$
5. $-x^2 + (-2x) + (-3)$
6. $-3n^2 - 3n$

Use or think about algebra tiles to add the polynomials.

7. $5a^2 + 3a - 6$ and $-3a^2 + 2a + 6$
8. $-2y^2 + 4y - 1$ and $-3y^2 + 5y + 2$

9. $\begin{array}{r} 4d^2 + 2d - 6 \\ \underline{+ -3d^2 - 5d + 1} \end{array}$

10. $\begin{array}{r} -3x^2 - 4x + 1 \\ \underline{+ \;\; 3x^2 + 4x - 3} \end{array}$

11. $\begin{array}{r} 6n^2 + 3n - 4 \\ \underline{+ -3n^2 + 2n + 6} \end{array}$

Extend and Apply

Write a polynomial for each model, then find their sum.

12.    and   

13. Make up a trinomial, a binomial, and a monomial using the variable y.
14. Find the sum of the trinomials $-2x^2 + 5x - 3$, $-3x^2 - 4x + 6$, and $x^2 + 3x - 7$. Record using vertical notation.
15. Make up two trinomials that have the sum $x^2 + x + 1$.

Use Mathematical Reasoning

16. The numerical factors in terms of a polynomial, such as -2, 3, and 1 in $-2x^2 + 3x + 1$, are called **coefficients.** What can you discover about using the coefficients to find the sum of two polynomials? Make up three polynomial addition exercises and use your method to complete them.
17. Is $x^3 + 4x^2$ a polynomial? Explain. If it is, how might you model it?

Mixed Review

Solve and check. **18.** $2(a + 1.7) = 6$ **19.** $1.43 = 0.4y - 0.6y$

20. $16 - 2n = 10$ **21.** $6(m - 4) = 24$ **22.** $19.4 - 0.6c = -16.6$

8-10 Solving Inequalities

Objective To solve inequalities involving one operation.

Explore

What conclusions can you draw about the number of counters in each bag? Use counters and a balance scale to test your conclusions.

$n + 2$ is less than 7

$n + 5$ is greater than 10

Understand the Ideas

An inequality is a statement, such as $n + 2 < 7$, that uses the symbols $>$, $<$, $\leq$ (less than or equal to), or $\geq$ (greater than or equal to) to compare two expressions.

An inequality is like an unbalanced scale. A scale will stay unbalanced in the same way if you add or take away the same amount from both sides. For example, scale A below is unbalanced, left side down. Scale B will remain unbalanced left side down when a block is added to both sides. Scale C will remain unbalanced left side down when two blocks are taken from each side.

The following properties state this idea for inequalities.

Addition and Subtraction Properties of Inequalities

For all numbers a, b, and c,

if $a > b$, then $a + c > b + c$ and $a - c > b - c$

if $a < b$, then $a + c < b + c$ and $a - c < b - c$

The number line below shows the effect of multiplying each side of an inequality by a positive number. $3 < 4$ and $2(3) < 2(4)$

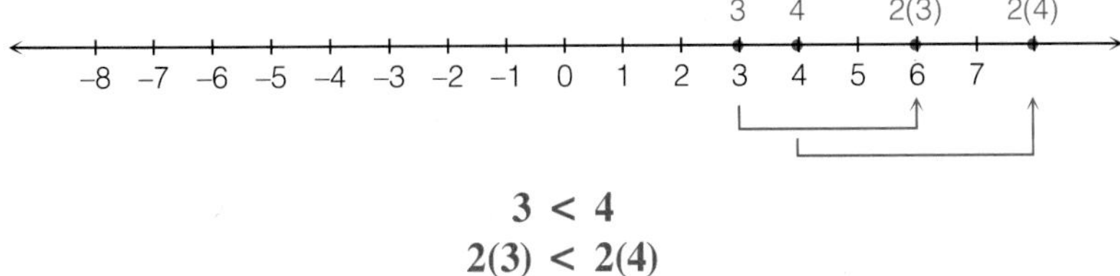

$$3 < 4$$
$$2(3) < 2(4)$$

The number line below shows the effect of multiplying each side of an inequality by a negative number. $3 < 4$, but $-2(3) > -2(4)$

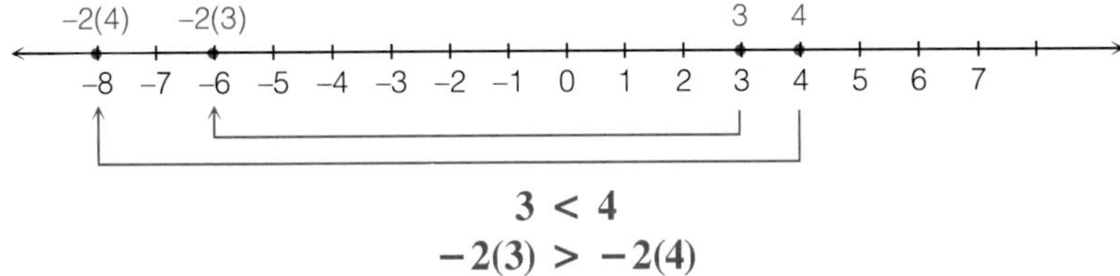

$$3 < 4$$
$$-2(3) > -2(4)$$

The effect of dividing each side of an inequality by a negative number is similar to the effect of multiplying each side of an inequality by a negative number. This is summarized in the display below.

$$3 < 4$$
$$\mathbf{-2} \cdot 3 \ ? \ \mathbf{-2} \cdot 4$$
$$-6 > -8$$

When you multiply or divide each side of an inequality by a **negative** number, the inequality sign is **reversed.**

$$6 < 8$$
$$\frac{6}{\mathbf{-2}} \ ? \ \frac{8}{\mathbf{-2}}$$
$$-3 > -4$$

The following properties are used when solving inequalities by multiplying or dividing.

Multiplication and Division Properties of Inequalities

For all numbers a, b, and c, where c is positive,

if $a > b$, then $a \cdot c > b \cdot c$ and $\frac{a}{c} > \frac{b}{c}$

if $a < b$, then $a \cdot c < b \cdot c$ and $\frac{a}{c} < \frac{b}{c}$

For all numbers a, b, and c, where c is negative,

if $a > b$, then $a \cdot c < b \cdot c$ and $\frac{a}{c} < \frac{b}{c}$

if $a < b$, then $a \cdot c > b \cdot c$ and $\frac{a}{c} > \frac{b}{c}$

To solve an inequality, you can use the above properties to get an inequality with the variable by itself on one side.

Example 1

Solve. $4 + b \geq 7$

Solution

$4 + b \geq 7$ — Undo adding 4 by subtracting 4 from each side of the inequality.

$4 + b - 4 \geq 7 - 4$ — Subtracting from both sides does not change the direction of the inequality sign.

$b \geq 3$

Try This Solve.

a. $n + 4 \leq 5$ **b.** $1 > x - \frac{1}{2}$

Example 2

Solve and check. $-4m > -2$

Solution

$$-4m > -2$$

$$-\frac{1}{4}(-4m) < -\frac{1}{4}(-2)$$ When you multiply both sides by a negative number, you must change the direction of the inequality sign.

$$1 \cdot m < \frac{2}{4}$$

$$m < \frac{1}{2}$$

Check $-4 \cdot \frac{1}{2} \stackrel{?}{=} -2$ — To check the computation, replace the inequality sign in $-4m > -2$ with an equal sign and see whether $m = \frac{1}{2}$ is a solution of the resulting equation.

$-2 = -2 \checkmark$

$-4 \cdot 0 \stackrel{?}{>} -2$ — To check whether the inequality sign is correct, see whether a solution to $m < \frac{1}{2}$, such as 0, is also a solution to $-4m > -2$.

$0 > -2 \checkmark$

Try This Solve.

c. $\frac{3}{4}b > 12$ **d.** $15 < -3p$

Class Exercises

To solve, what operation would you use?

1. $x + 9 > 13$ **2.** $b - 4 < 8$ **3.** $-3n > 12$ **4.** $15 < y + 7$

5. $\frac{c}{4} < 3$ **6.** $18 > z - 2$ **7.** $25 < 5p$ **8.** $4 > \frac{n}{5}$

Discuss the Ideas

9. A student said "You solve inequalities exactly the same way you solve equations." Do you agree? Work together to write a paragraph supporting your conclusion.

Exercises

Practice and Apply

Solve and check.

1. $a - 5 < 1$
2. $2 > b + 2$
3. $c - 1 < 4$
4. $-7z < 35$
5. $\frac{1}{3}p > 7$
6. $25 < 5n$
7. $s - 9 > 0$
8. $-8c > 56$
9. $12 < n + 5$
10. $\frac{3}{8} < n - \frac{5}{6}$
11. $2m \leq \frac{5}{6}$
12. $2\frac{1}{3}b > -6$
13. On vacation, Tim plans to spend less than \$30 a day. If he spends \$18 for lodging, solve $a + 18 < 30$ to describe the amount he can spend per day on other things.
14. Brian wants to install a dishwasher and knows that the circuit can only handle 20 amps. If 8 amps are used by other appliances, solve $d + 8 \leq 20$ to describe the maximum number of amps the dishwasher can use.

Extend and Apply

15. The minimum speed on a highway is 40 mi/h and the maximum speed is 55 mi/h. Write an inequality to describe a car:
    a. breaking the speed limit.
    b. going too slow.

Solve the problems in Exercises 16–19 by writing and solving inequalities.

Example: Five more than an integer is less than 27. Find the largest integer that meets this condition.

Solution: $n + 5 < 27$ $\quad n < 22$ The largest integer satisfying this inequality is 21.

16. Six less than an integer n is greater than 25. Find the least possible value for n.
17. Eight times an integer n is less than 48. Find the greatest possible value for n.
18. Louise said she would sell her house only if the sealed bid were more than \$4,000 above her cost of \$92,000. Bids are in multiples of \$500. What is the smallest bid that Louise would accept?
19. Wanda wanted half of her salary to be more than \$23,000.

Use Mathematical Reasoning

20. Solve the inequality $|x - 3| > 5$ for the replacement set $\{-10, -9, \ldots 10\}$.

Mixed Review

Evaluate for $x = -0.5, y = 0.5$. **21.** $2x^2y$ **22.** $6(x + y)$

23. $1.6x + 3.2y$ **24.** $y(1 - 2x)$ **25.** $x(y - x)$ **26.** $x \div (-y)$

8-11 Solving Inequalities: Combined Operations

Objective To solve inequalities involving more than one operation or requiring simplification.

Application

A person who sells small electronics is paid \$72 daily, plus a \$3 commission on each item she sells. Her goal was to make over \$90 on Monday. The inequality $72 + 3t > 90$ helped her find the number of items she must sell.

Understand the Ideas

You can solve inequalities with combined operations by observing the order in which operations are applied to the variable and undoing the operations in the reverse order. The goal is to get the variable by itself on one side of the inequality.

Example 1

Solve the inequality $72 + 3t > 90$ to find the number of items the salesperson in the **application** must sell to meet her goal.

Solution

$$72 + 3t > 90$$

$$72 + 3t - \mathbf{72} > 90 - \mathbf{72}$$ Subtract 72 from each side. The inequality sign stays the same.

$$3t > 18$$

$$\frac{3t}{\mathbf{3}} > \frac{18}{\mathbf{3}}$$ Divide each side by 3. The inequality sign stays the same.

$$t > 6$$

The salesperson must sell more than 6 items to meet her goal.

Try This Solve. **a.** $\frac{n}{4} - 3 > 2$ **b.** $12 \leq 2a + 3$

c. Suppose the salesperson's commission was \$4 per item and she wanted to earn over \$100 on Tuesday. Solve the inequality $72 + 4t > 100$ to find the number of items she must sell.

To begin to solve an inequality, you often need to simplify an expression by combining like terms or adding a variable expression to each side.

Example 2

Solve. $-6b + 4b \geq 5$

Solution $-6b + 4b \geq 5$

$-2b \geq 5$ Distributive property: $-6b + 4b = -2b$

$\left(-\frac{1}{2}\right)2b \leq \left(-\frac{1}{2}\right)5$ Multiply each side by $-\frac{1}{2}$. Reverse the inequality sign.

$b \leq -\frac{5}{2}$

Try This Solve. **d.** $8r - 5r < -12$ **e.** $5(x + 2) > 25$

To solve an inequality with variables on both sides, you can add or subtract a variable expression from each side to get the variable by itself, as with equations.

Example 3

Solve. $5n - 6 < 3n$

Solution $5n - 6 < 3n$

$5n - 6 + \mathbf{6} < 3n + \mathbf{6}$ Add 6 to each side. The inequality sign stays the same.

$5n < 3n + 6$

$5n - \mathbf{3n} < 3n - \mathbf{3n} + 6$ Subtract $3n$ from each side. The inequality sign stays the same.

$2n < 6$

$\frac{2n}{2} < \frac{6}{2}$ Divide each side by 2. The inequality sign stays the same.

$n < 3$

Try This Solve. **f.** $-2b + 5 > 3b$ **g.** $5 + 6c \leq -8c + 3$

Class Exercises

Is the given number a solution to the inequality?

1. $2z + 3 < 12; 4$ **2.** $\frac{n}{2} - 1 > 20; 50$ **3.** $3(s + 1) < 12; 3$

Discuss the Ideas

4. How can you tell just by looking that $3n - 4 > 3n$ has no solutions?

Exercises

Practice and Apply

Solve.

1. $2a - 1 > 5$ **2.** $3x + 2 < -4$ **3.** $2s + 5 < 3$

4. $-5 + 3c > 31$ **5.** $\frac{n}{3} - 2 < 4$ **6.** $-5 < -3p + 34$

Solve.

7. $4y + 7y > -66$ **8.** $9x + 3x < 96$ **9.** $54 < -7c + 4c$

10. $-2s + 3 < 5s - 4$ **11.** $4c + 7 + 3c < -35$ **12.** $4z - 3 < 10z - 5$

13. $\frac{2}{5}x - 3 > 2$ **14.** $9x - 2 \geq -12x + 1$ **15.** $\frac{3}{8}n - 5 > \frac{7}{8}n$

16. Eric is paid \$74 a day plus a \$5 commission on each stereo he sells. Eric's goal is to earn more than \$100 on Saturday. Solve $74 + 5t > 100$ to find the number of stereos he must sell.

17. It takes Rich 2 hours to mow one lawn and 3 hours to mow another lawn. If he wants to earn more than \$25, solve $2p + 3p > 25$ to describe the amount he needs to charge per hour.

Extend and Apply

Solve and check.

18. $-3x + \frac{1}{2} < \frac{3}{5}$ **19.** $-\frac{x}{2} + \frac{3}{8} > -\frac{1}{8}$ **20.** $-5y - \frac{5}{9} > -2\frac{1}{3}$

21. Write an inequality for "the difference of twice a number and 9 is less than 57."

22. Write an inequality for "12 more than half a number is less than or equal to 30."

23. Write an inequality for "the sum of two thirds of a number and six is less than forty."

24. Five more than twice an integer is less than 51. Write and solve an inequality to find the largest integer that meets this condition.

25. Six less than half an integer is greater than 15. Write and solve an inequality to find the smallest integer that meets this condition.

26. Badminton team A scored five points fewer than half of team B's score. Team B scored fewer than 15 points. What is the greatest score team A could have?

27. Mrs. Taka feels that she should pay no more than \$15,000 plus $2\frac{1}{2}$ times her yearly income for a house. What is the smallest yearly income she could have if she is to buy a \$90,000 house?

Use Mathematical Reasoning

28. A sentence with "and" is true if and only if *both* parts of the sentence are true. Give four solutions to this inequality: $x < 10$ **and** $x > 5$

29. A sentence with "or" is true if and only if *one or the other or both* parts are true. Give four solutions to this inequality: $x < -2$ **or** $x > 2$.

Mixed Review

Find the least common multiple (LCM). **30.** 4, 10, 15 **31.** 9, 15

Simplify. **32.** $p^3 \cdot p^9 \cdot p$ **33.** $m^2 \cdot n^3 \cdot m^4 \cdot n$

Drawing Conclusions from Venn Diagrams

Objective To use a Venn Diagram to decide if a conclusion is correct.

Group Activity Decide how to complete the **Venn Diagram** to show the information below. Then decide whether the conclusion given is correct. In the diagram, the outer circle includes all even numbers and the inner circle includes all numbers divisible by 4.

Venn Diagram

?
Joe's age
All even numbers
All numbers divisible by 4

Information All numbers divisible by 4 are even.
Joe's age is not divisible by 4.

Conclusion Joe's age is not even.

Venn diagrams can be used both in mathematics and in everyday life to help you decide whether your conclusions are correct.

Apply Mathematical Reasoning

Use the Venn Diagram to decide if the conclusion is correct.

1. All voters are over 21.
   Mac is a voter.
   Therefore, Mac is over 21.

2. All squares are rectangles.
   Figure A is not a rectangle.
   Therefore, Figure A is not a square.

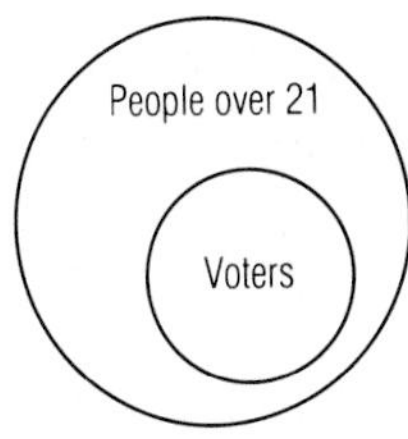

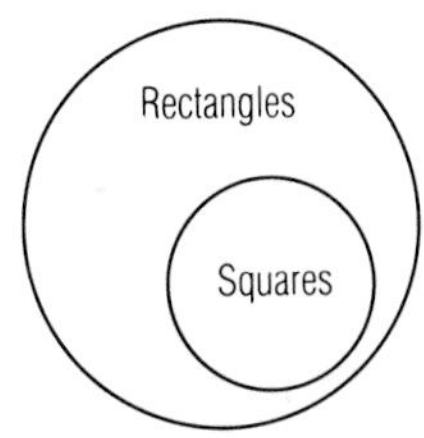

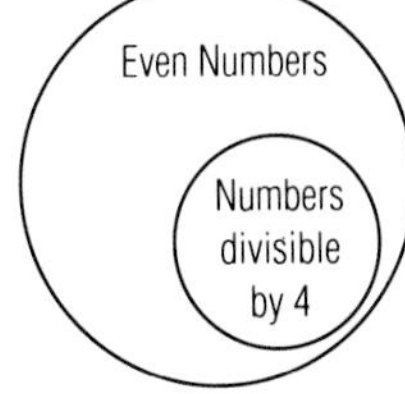

3. All numbers divisible by 4 are even. Jan's age is even. Therefore, Jan's age is divisible by 4.

8-12 **Problem Solving: Strategies**

Using Several Strategies

Objective To solve nonroutine problems using combinations of various strategies.

You have learned that more than one strategy can be used when solving a problem. In fact, using several strategies is often helpful. For example, **Simplify the Problem, Draw a Diagram, Look for a Pattern,** and **Make a Table** are all used to solve the following problem.

Sample Problem How many different squares are there on a patio made of 6 rows of 6 square tiles?

To solve this problem, you might first **simplify** it by starting with fewer squares and **draw** the following pictures.

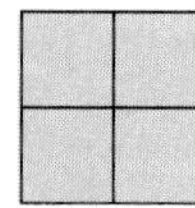

4 1 by 1 squares
1 2 by 2 square

2 by 2

4 + 1 = 5 squares in all

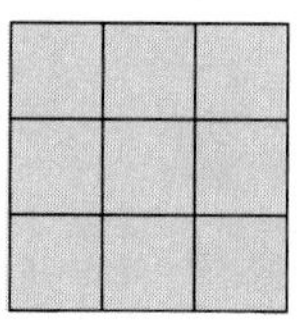

9 1 by 1 squares
4 2 by 2 squares
1 3 by 3 square

3 by 3

9 + 4 + 1 = 14 squares in all

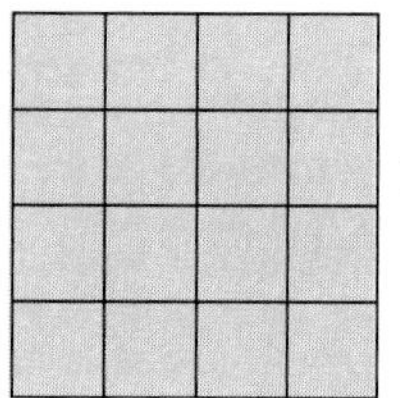

16 1 by 1 squares
9 2 by 2 squares
4 3 by 3 squares
1 4 by 4 square

4 by 4

16 + 9 + 4 + 1 squares in all

Then you could organize the information in a **table** and look for a **pattern.** The total number of squares can be found by squaring the side length and adding this to all the square numbers less than it.

Length of Side	Total Number of Squares
1	1
2	5 = **4** + 1
3	14 = **9** + 4 + 1
4	30 = **16** + 9 + 4 + 1

The total number of different squares on the 6-by-6 square patio is

36 + 25 + 16 + 9 + 4 + 1 = 91.

Problem-Solving Strategies

Choose the Operations	Make a Table	Make an Organized List
Guess, Check, Revise	Look for a Pattern	Use Logical Reasoning
Draw a Diagram	Write an Equation	Work Backward
	Simplify the Problem	

Problems

Solve.

1. How many different sizes of squares are there on an ordinary checkerboard of 64 squares?
2. What is the largest amount of money you could have in quarters, dimes, nickels, or pennies without being able to make change for $1?
3. Two people on motorcycles leave state parks that are 600 miles apart and travel toward each other. One cycle averages 55 mi/h. The other averages 45 mi/h. They both start at 11 a.m. When should they expect to meet?
4. You have 5 sections of chain and each section has 3 links. The cost to have a link cut is 10¢. The cost to have a link welded is 20¢. How can you join the sections into one continuous chain for less than $1?
5. A biologist started with 1 microbe in a special liquid. During each hour, the microbe population became 3 times as large as it was the previous hour. How many microbes were there when the biologist stopped the experiment after 6 hours?

Group Decision Making

6. Work in a group. Discuss and decide.

Situation: Your video club is selling tickets to a film festival to help pay for a new television set. You plan to rent videos to show from 9:00 a.m. until 6:00 p.m. with a 10 minute intermission between films. You want to provide free popcorn for those who attend. You need to decide how much to charge for tickets.

Guidelines for Planning

■ **Formulate Problems** you will need to solve.
■ Discuss **Assumptions** you will make and **Data** you will need.

a. What decision or decisions do you need to make in this situation?
b. Formulate problems you need to solve to make the decision(s).
c. List any assumptions you need to make to arrive at a decision.
d. What data, if any, do you need to collect to make a decision?
e. Write a paragraph summarizing what your group did, what decisions you made, and why.

Extend Key Ideas

Multiplying Polynomials

You can use algebra tiles to multiply polynomials. Here are some examples.

Multiply a Monomial by a Monomial

- Lay out x tiles to show the length and width of a rectangle.
- Decide how many x^2 tiles it takes to fill the rectangle.

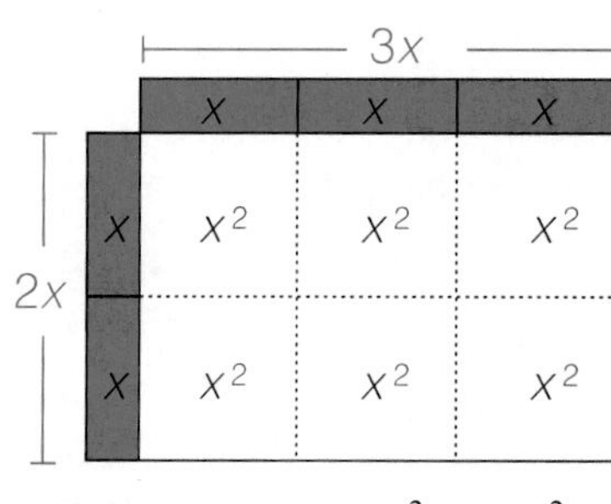

$(2x)(3x) = (2 \cdot 3)x^2 = 6x^2$

Multiply a Binomial by a Monomial

- Lay out x and unit tiles to show the length and width of a rectangle.
- Decide how many x^2 and x tiles it takes to fill the rectangle.

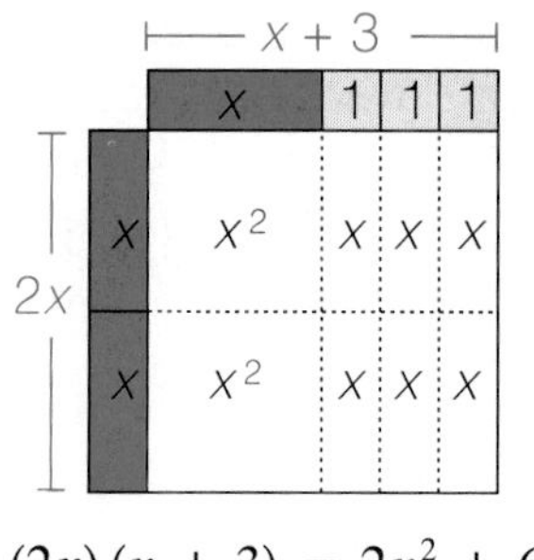

$(2x)(x + 3) = 2x^2 + 6x$

Explorations

Use algebra tiles to model and find each of these products.

1. $3(4x)$	**2.** $(3x)(5x)$
3. $(4x)(7x)$	**4.** $(2x)(4x)$
5. $(5x)(6x)$	**6.** $(2)(5x)$
7. $2x(2x + 1)$	**8.** $x(3x + 2)$
9. $3x(x + 5)$	**10.** $(x + 3)3x$
11. $(x + 2)2x$	**12.** $(2x + 3)x$

Extend the ideas shown above for multiplying by a monomial to multiply the following binomial pairs.

13. $(x + 3)(x + 1)$	**14.** $(x + 4)(x + 2)$
15. $(x + 2)(x + 2)$	**16.** $(x + 5)(x + 1)$
17. $(x + 3)(2x + 2)$	**18.** $(3x + 2)(2x + 4)$

Chapter 8 Review/Test

Understanding

8-1 **1.** In $2n + 5 = 11$, n was multiplied by 2 and 5 was added to produce 11. What operations undo these operations?

8-4 **2.** If $f(x) = 2x - 1$, what is $f(3)$?

8-5 **3.** Which property, Commutative, Associative, or Distributive, helps explain why $3x + 4x = 7x$?

8-1 **4.** Describe what the first step would be when solving the equation $5h = 3h + 24$.

8-10 **5.** When you multiply each side of an inequality by a negative number, how must you adjust the inequality?

Skills

8-1 Solve and check.

6. $5t - 1 = 14$ **7.** $\frac{(a + 5)}{7} = 4$ **8.** $3(m - 5) = -27$

8-2 Write an equation.

9. The \$38 cost of a sweater is \$2 more than 3 times the cost of a tie.

10. Brant's age, 37, is 3 less than twice Ricky's age.

8-5 Solve and check.
8-6
8-7 **11.** $18c + 3c = 84$ **12.** $7c - 8 + 3(2c) = 31$

13. $20x - 13x = -56$ **14.** $3(m + 4) + 6m = 66$

15. $5(x - 8) - 2x = -16$ **16.** $7x - 2 = 5x + 16$

17. $35 + 6n = 5n$ **18.** $20r + 7 = 14r + 22$

Solve and check.

8-10 **19.** $4 > f - 6$ **20.** $8b - 5b > 9$ **21.** $\frac{n}{-3 - 4} > 2$
8-11

Applications

Find the solution by writing and solving an equation.

8-2 **22.** Mike's height is 5 inches less than twice his little sister's height. Mike is
8-3 71 inches tall. What is his little sister's height?
8-12

23. Cheryl averaged 28 points per game this year. This is 4 more than $\frac{3}{4}$ of last year's average. How many points per game did she average last year?

24. Suzy is paid \$5 per hour for washing cars. Her total earnings one Saturday came to \$39. This included \$4 in tips. How many hours did she work that day?

9 Graphs of Equations and Inequalities

The Gunbarrel ski trail at Heavenly Valley has a vertical drop of 1,700 feet and covers a horizontal distance of 1,360 feet. Find the slope of this ski trail.

9-1 Graphing on the Coordinate Plane

Objective To graph an ordered pair on the coordinate plane.

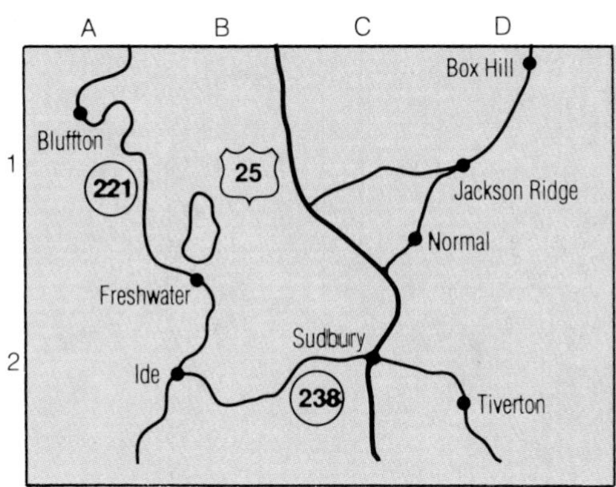

Application

Information is often communicated visually using maps and graphs, particularly in geography and business. When reading graphs and maps, locations are often identified by using an ordered pair of numbers or letters. How can you describe the location of Tiverton?

Understand the Ideas

In a **rectangular coordinate system**, two perpendicular number lines, called **axes**, intersect at a point called the **origin**. The horizontal axis is called the **x-axis** and the vertical axis is called the **y-axis**. These two axes allow each point to be named by an **ordered pair** of numbers called the **coordinates** of the point.

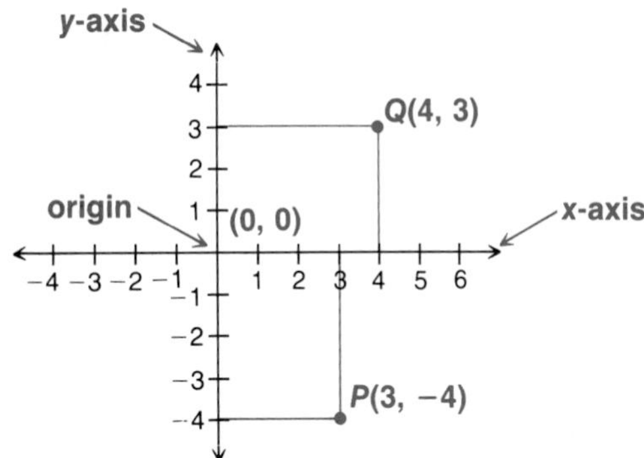

The coordinates of the origin are $(0, 0)$. The coordinates of point P are $(3, -4)$ and the coordinates of point Q are $(4, 3)$. The **x-coordinate** of point P is 3 and the **y-coordinate** of point P is -4.

Example 1

In the **application**, what coordinates best describe the location of the town of Tiverton?

Solution $(D, 2)$

Try This **a.** What coordinates best describe the town of Box Hill?

Example 2

Give the coordinates of points A, B, and C.

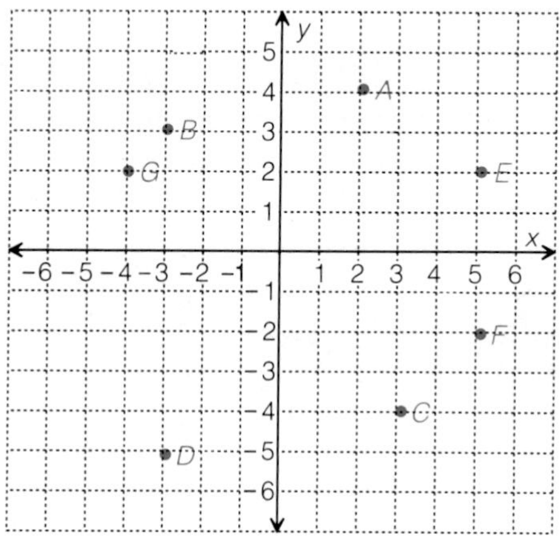

Solution

$A(2, 4)$

$B(-3, 3)$

$C(3, -4)$

Try This **b.** Give the coordinates of points D, E, F, and G.

Example 3

Graph points $A(2, 3)$, $B(-3, 5)$, and $C(4, -1)$.

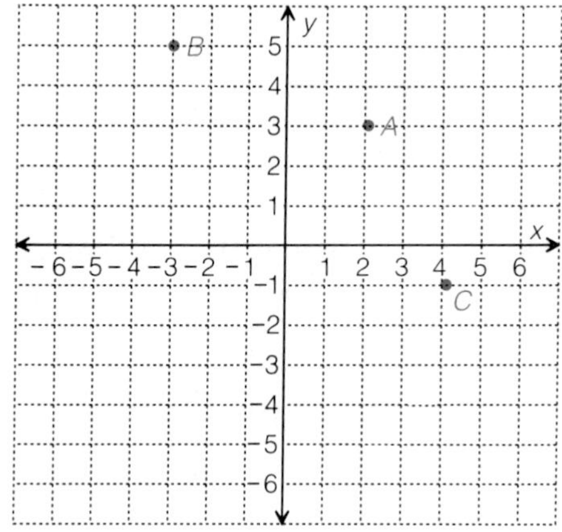

Solution

To graph point A at $(2, 3)$, begin at the origin and move 2 units to the right and 3 units up.

To graph point B at $(-3, 5)$, begin at the origin and move 3 units to the left and 5 units up.

To graph point C at $(4, -1)$, begin at the origin and move 4 units to the right and 1 unit down.

Try This **c.** Graph points $D(-2, -3)$, $E(0, 4)$, and $F(3, 5)$.

Class Exercises

State the x-coordinate and the y-coordinate for each point.

1. $(3, -4)$ **2.** $(-5, 4)$ **3.** $(-1, 4)$

4. $(2, -3)$ **5.** $(-12, -7)$ **6.** $(-3, 0)$

Describe the moves from the origin you would make to graph these points.

7. $(-2, 5)$ **8.** $(3, 5)$ **9.** $(4, -2)$

10. $(1, -1)$ **11.** $(7, -6)$ **12.** $(0, 4)$

Discuss the Ideas

13. Can you make a generalization about all points that have an x-coordinate of 0? a y-coordinate of 0?

Exercises

Practice and Apply

Use the map in the application to describe the location of each city.

1. Sudbury **2.** Bluffton

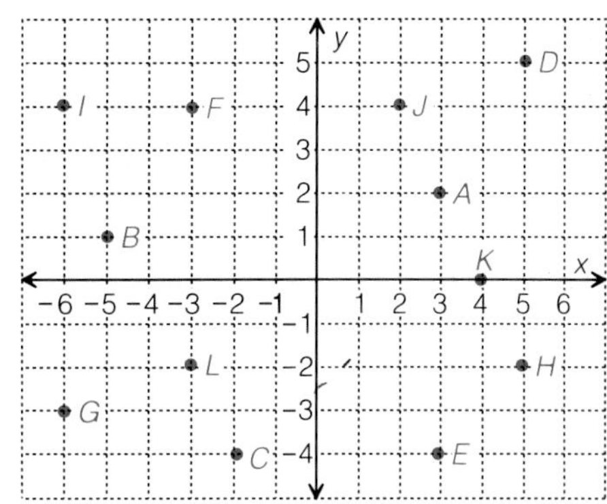

Give the coordinates of each point.

3. A **4.** B

5. C **6.** D

7. E **8.** F

9. G **10.** H

11. I **12.** J

13. K **14.** L

Graph each point.

15. $A(3, 5)$ **16.** $B(-2, 7)$ **17.** $C(4, -3)$ **18.** $D(4, -4)$

19. $E(-2, -3)$ **20.** $F(-5, 1)$ **21.** $G(6, 3)$ **22.** $H(1, -5)$

23. $I(-4, -4)$ **24.** $J(2, 3)$ **25.** $K(0, 4)$ **26.** $L(-3, 0)$

Extend and Apply

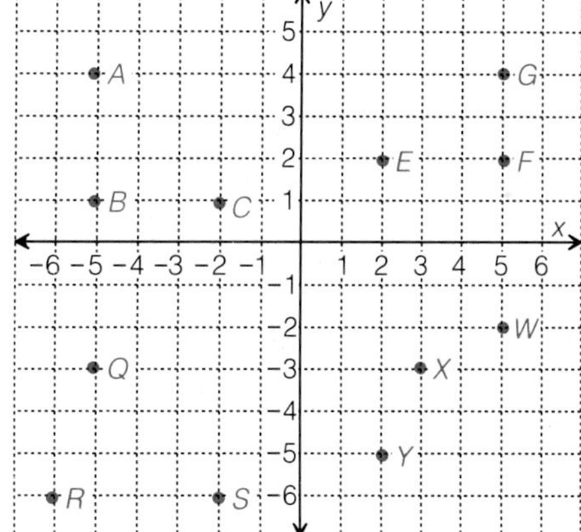

Name the coordinates for each point.

27. the point D that makes $ABCD$ a square

28. the point H that makes $EFGH$ a rectangle

29. the point T that makes $QRST$ a parallelogram

30. the point Z that makes $WXYZ$ a rhombus

On a single pair of axes draw a continuous line from point A to points B, C, D, E, and F for each of Exercises 31–39. What do you discover?

31. $A(-6, 9)$; $B(-5.5, 11)$; $C(-5, 10)$; $D(-4.5, 11)$; $E(-4, 9)$

32. $A(-3, 9)$; $B(-2, 11)$; $C(-1, 9)$; $D(-1.5, 10)$; $E(-2.5, 10)$

33. $A(1, 11)$; $B(3, 11)$; $C(2, 11)$; $D(2, 9)$

34. $A(4, 11)$; $B(4, 9)$; $C(4, 10)$; $D(6, 10)$; $E(6, 11)$; $F(6, 9)$

35. $A(-1.5, 7)$; $B(-0.5, 7)$; $C(-1, 7)$; $D(-1, 5)$; $E(-1.5, 5)$; $F(-0.5, 5)$

36. $A(3, 7)$; $B(1, 7)$; $C(1, 6)$; $D(3, 6)$; $E(3, 5)$; $F(1, 5)$

37. $A(-2, 3)$; $B(-4, 3)$; $C(-4, 1)$; $D(-4, 2)$; $E(-3, 2)$

38. $A(-1, 3)$; $B(-1, 1)$; $C(1, 1)$; $D(1, 3)$

39. $A(2, 1)$; $B(2, 3)$; $C(4, 1)$; $D(4, 3)$

Use Mathematical Reasoning

40. Graph the pairs of points $(2, 1)$ and $(1, 2)$; $(-2, 3)$ and $(3, -2)$; $(3, -4)$ and $(-4, 3)$; $(2, 4)$ and $(4, 2)$; $(3, 5)$ and $(5, 3)$; $(-4, -2)$ and $(-2, -4)$. From the pattern formed, make a generalization about the way the graphs of (a, b) and (b, a) are related.

41. Find an ordered pair (x, y) that is a solution to $|x - 2| + |y - 3| = 0$.

42. Communicate The floorplan of a tunnel maze is shown. Use the coordinate system and write a paragraph that gives directions for getting through the maze.

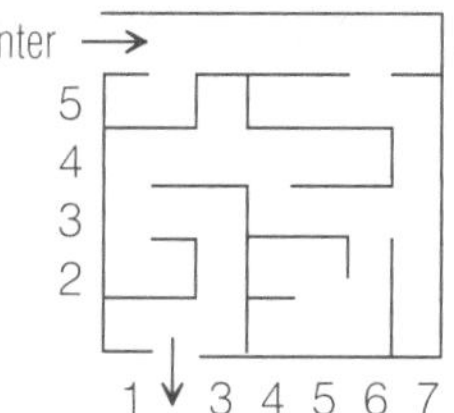

Mixed Review

Fill in the missing numbers in the tables.

43.

1	2	3	4	x
-3	-6	-9	?	?

44.

-2	-4	-6	-8	?	x
3	1	-1	-3	?	?

Evaluate for $x = -3.5$ and $y = 2.1$. **45.** $2x + y$ **46.** $-xy$

Connections Numbers to Algebra

A point $M(x, y)$ on a line segment is the **midpoint** of the segment if it is the same distance from both endpoints. You can find the coordinates of the midpoint if you know the coordinates of the two endpoints. We demonstrate the method for specific points $A(1, 3)$ and B(5, 5), and for the general points $X(a, b)$ and $Y(c, d)$

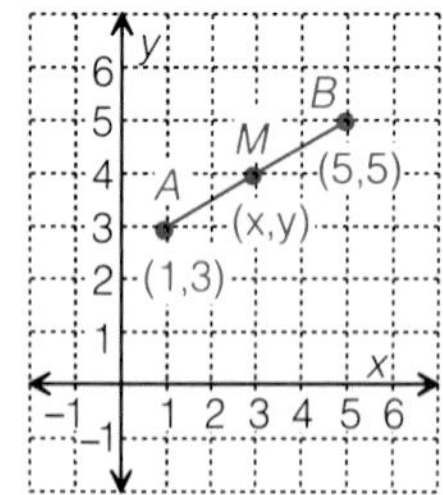

$$x = \frac{1 + 5}{2} = \frac{6}{2} = 3 \qquad y = \frac{3 + 5}{2} = \frac{8}{2} = 4$$

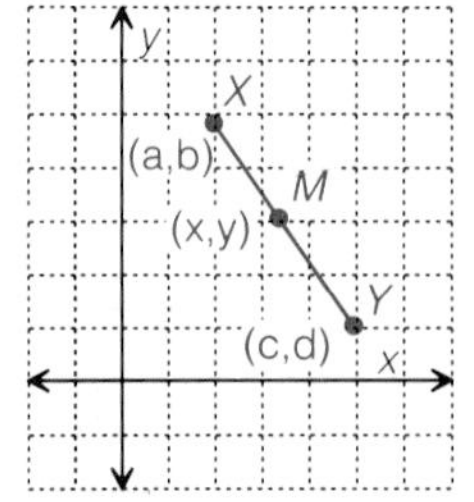

$$x = \frac{a + c}{2} \qquad y = \frac{b + d}{2}$$

Find the midpoints of the segments with endpoints A and B.

1. $A(2, 5)$ $B(8, 3)$ **2.** $A(-2, 4)$ $B(3, 6)$ **3.** $A(-1, -4)$ $B(5, 8)$

9-2 Graphing Linear Equations

Objective To find and graph the solutions of a linear equation.

Explore

Use a graphing calculator or a computer to graph these functions.

a) $y = 2x + 1$

b) $y = -x + 2$

c) $y = \frac{1}{3}x - 2$

Which graphs are straight lines?

Understand the Ideas

The graph of each of the equations $y = 2x + 4$, $2x + y = 5$, and $3x - 4y = 17$ is a line. Any equation that can be written in the form $y = ax + b$, where a and b are numbers and x and y are variables, is called a **linear equation.** An ordered pair is a solution for a linear equation if the equation is true when the coordinates of the ordered pair are substituted for x and y.

Example 1

Which of the ordered pairs (2,7) and (−1,2) is a solution for the linear equation $y = 3x + 1$?

Solution

$$y = 3x + 1$$
$$7 \stackrel{?}{=} 3(2) + 1$$
$$7 \stackrel{?}{=} 6 + 1$$
$$7 = 7$$

To determine whether (2,7) is a solution, substitute 2 for x and 7 for y.

(2,7) is a solution.

$$y = 3x + 1$$
$$2 \stackrel{?}{=} 3(-1) + 1$$
$$2 \stackrel{?}{=} -3 + 1$$
$$2 \neq -2$$

To determine whether (−1,2) is a solution, substitute −1 for x and 2 for y.

(−1,2) is not a solution.

Try This **a.** Which of the ordered pairs (2, −3) and (−2, −2) is a solution to the linear equation $y = 4x - 11$?

A linear equation has an infinite number of solutions. To find solutions for the equation $y = 2x + 1$, substitute a number for x and solve for y.

Substitute 1 for x.	Substitute 2 for x.	Substitute 3 for x.
$y = 2\boldsymbol{x} + 1$	$y = 2\boldsymbol{x} + 1$	$y = 2\boldsymbol{x} + 1$
$y = 2(\mathbf{1}) + 1$	$y = 2(\mathbf{2}) + 1$	$y = 2(\mathbf{3}) + 1$
$y = 3$	$y = \mathbf{5}$	$y = 7$
$(\mathbf{1}, 3)$ is a solution.	$(\mathbf{2}, \mathbf{5})$ is a solution.	$(\mathbf{3}, 7)$ is a solution.

You can use a table to show a set of solutions for a linear equation. Your set of values for x should include at least one negative number, one positive number, and zero.

Example 2

Make a table of solutions for $y = 2x + 3$ when $x = -2, -1, 0, 1$, and 2.

Solution $y = 2x + 3$

x	y
−2	−1
−1	1
0	3
1	5
2	7

Substitute each value of x into the equation and solve for the corresponding value of y. Enter this value of y into the table beside the value of x.

Try This **b.** Make a table of solutions for $y = 2x - 3$ when $x = -3, -2, -1, 0$, and 1.

When the ordered pairs found in a solution table are graphed, the points fall on a straight line. By drawing the line through these points, you *graph the linear equation.* The line represents *all* solutions to the equation.

Example 3

Make a table of solutions for $y = x + 1$. Graph the equation.

Solution $y = x + 1$

x	y
−2	−1
−1	0
0	1
1	2
2	3

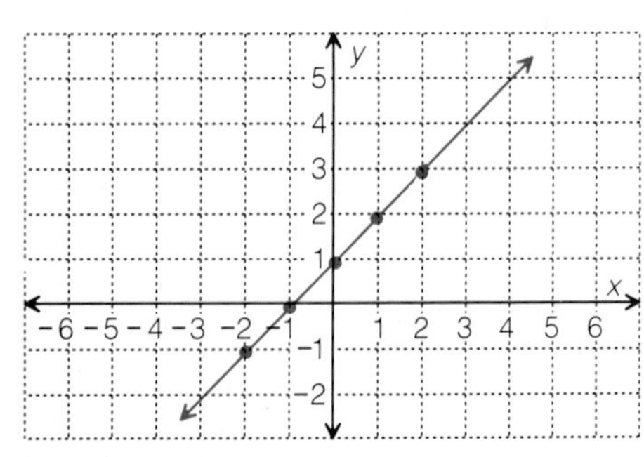

Try This **c.** Make a table of solutions for $y = 2x - 1$. Graph the equation.

When a linear equation like $y = 2x - 1$ is written using function notation, $f(x) = 2x - 1$, we call it a **linear function.** To graph a linear function, make a table of values for x and $f(x)$. Then graph the function on a coordinate system with the horizontal axis labeled x and the vertical axis labeled $f(x)$.

Example 4

Graph the function $f(x) = -x + 2$.

Solution

$f(x) = -x + 2$

x	$f(x)$
-2	4
0	2
2	0
4	-2

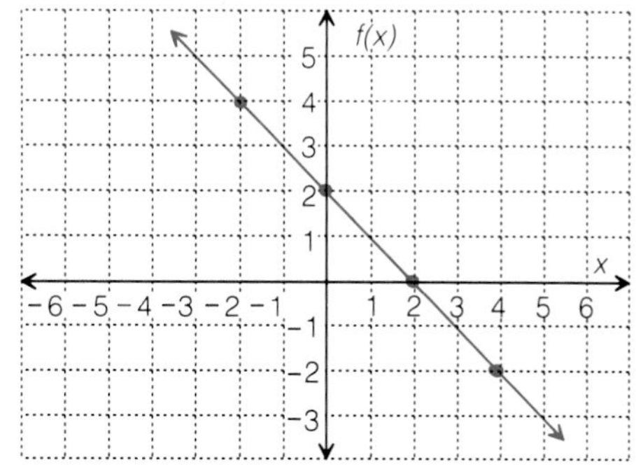

Try This **d.** Graph the function $f(x) = \frac{1}{2}x + 1$.

Class Exercises

These equations are written in the form $y = ax + b$. Give the values of a and b for each equation.

1. $y = 3x + 5$ **2.** $y = 2x - 4$ **3.** $y = -x + 17$ **4.** $y = -x$

Discuss the Ideas

5. Discuss why you should include positive numbers, negative numbers and zero when making a table of solutions for a linear equation.

Exercises

Practice and Apply

Which of the ordered pairs is a solution for the equation?

1. $(2, 3)$ or $(3, 9)$ for $2x + y = 7$
2. $(1, 5)$ or $(2, 6)$ for $3x - y = 0$
3. $(-3, 4)$ or $(3, -4)$ for $3x + 2y = -1$
4. $(5, 7)$ or $(7, 8)$ for $x - 2y = -9$

For each equation, make a table of solutions for $x = -2, -1, 0, 1, 2, 3,$ and 4.

5. $y = 2x - 1$
6. $y = 3x + 2$
7. $-2x + 5 = y$
8. $y = -x + 3$
9. $y = 4x - 7$
10. $y = -2x + 3$

Make a table of solutions and graph each linear equation.

11. $y = x + 1$
12. $y = 2x - 3$
13. $y = -x + 2$
14. $y = 3x - 4$
15. $y = x + 3$
16. $y = -x - 2$

Graph each of these functions.

17. $f(x) = 2x + 1$

18. $f(x) = x - 3$

19. $f(x) = -2x + 1$

20. $f(x) = -x + 3$

Extend and Apply

Rewrite the equation in the form $y = ax + b$. Make a table of solutions and graph the equation.

21. $4x + y = 4$

22. $-2x + y = 6$

23. $2x + y = 8$

24. $y - 2x = 1$

25. $3x = 2y + 4$

26. $3y + 6x = 6$

27. The linear equation F = 50D describes the force, F, applied by a spring if it is displaced D units. Make a table of solutions that describes the force for several displacement lengths.

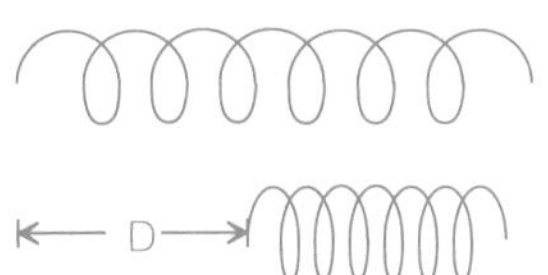

28. Find the Extra Data Tell what data is not needed to explain that the equation $y = 7x + 15$ describes the cost of buying x number of discs.

Tyrone paid \$15 to join a compact disc club. Members pay \$7 for each disc. For every 7 discs purchased, they get 1 free record.

Use a graphing calculator or a computer for Exercise 29.

29. Draw the graphs of $y = 3x - 5$ and $y = 2 - x$. Which graph rises as you move to the right? Which graph falls as you move to the right?

Use Mathematical Reasoning

30. Find an ordered pair that is a solution to both $x + y = 2$ and $x - y = 0$.

31. At what points does the graph of $\frac{x}{2} + \frac{y}{3} = 1$ cross the x- and y-axes?

Mixed Review

Solve and check. **32.** $0.75m + 4 = 13$ **33.** $3t + 11t - 16 = 12$

Give the greatest common factor (GCF). **34.** 18, 27, 30 **35.** 12, 20, 36

Computer Activity

Graph the following equations using a graphing utility. On most computers you must include * for multiplication and ^ for exponents.

a. $y = 5x^2$

b. $y = 4x + 7$

c. $y = x^2 + 5$

d. $y = -\frac{3}{2}x$

e. $y = 4x^3$

f. $y = -2x^2$

1. Which graphs are not lines?

2. How do the nonlinear equations differ from the linear equations?

9-3 Functions and Graphs

Objective To interpret a nonlinear graph.

Application

A traffic engineer records the number of vehicles at a certain intersection throughout the day. The data will be used to help decide whether or not a traffic signal should be installed.

Understand the Ideas

Graphs that show a relationship between two quantities are not always a straight line. One of the two graphs below shows the number of vehicles passing through an intersection as a function of the time of day.

A.

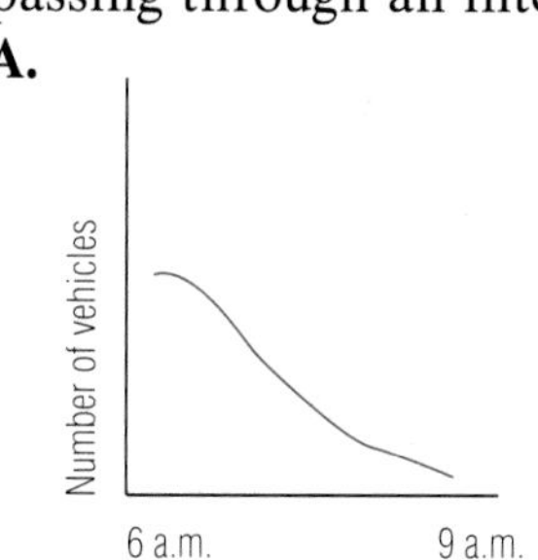

B.

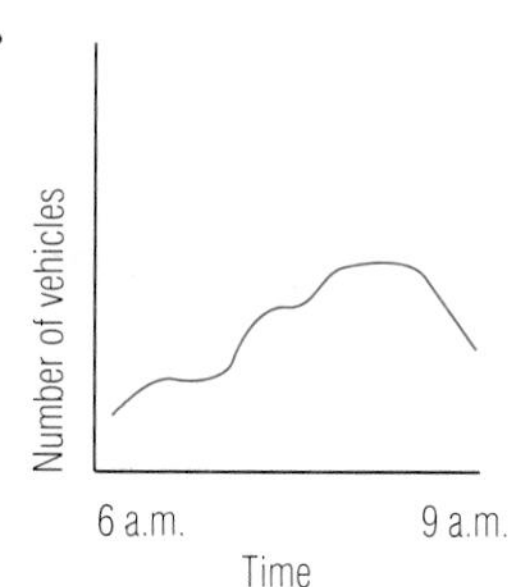

Thinking about the graph of a function helps you understand how the variables are related. The quantities that are being related are shown on the axes of the graph.

Example 1

Which one of the two graphs above is more realistic for the situation described in the **application**?

Solution Graph B is more realistic. Traffic is probably heaviest between 8 a.m. and 9 a.m. as commuters go to work.

Try This

a. Draw a graph that you think would be a reasonable estimate for the number of vehicles at the same intersection between 3 p.m. and 11 p.m.

Example 2

Which graph is more realistic for the situation described below?

Situation Carrie starts her paper route with a full load of papers. She delivers to single homes and to some apartment buildings. It takes her about 2 hours to deliver all of her papers.

A.

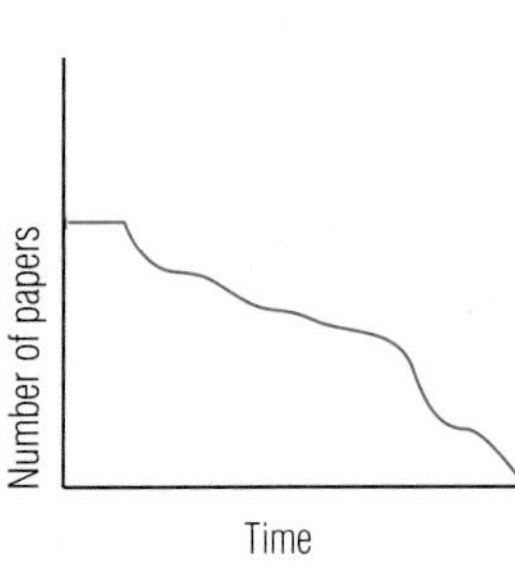

B.

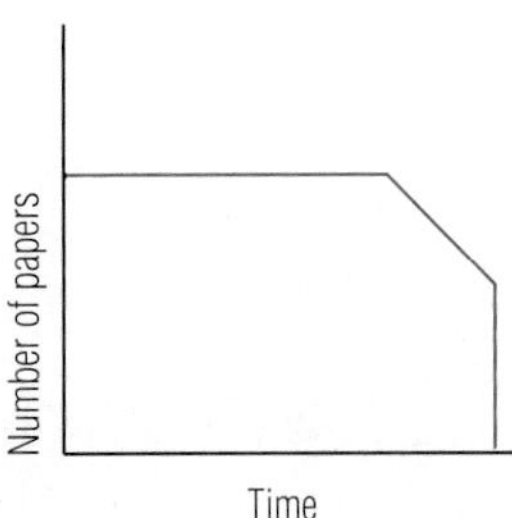

Solution Graph A seems more realistic. She starts with a full load. The changes in the curve show that she delivers to single family homes and to apartments.

Try This **b.** Which graph is more realistic for the given situation?

Situation A toboggan ride usually starts off slowly and picks up speed the farther it travels. On this hill the ride slows part way down and then picks up speed again before coasting to a stop.

A.

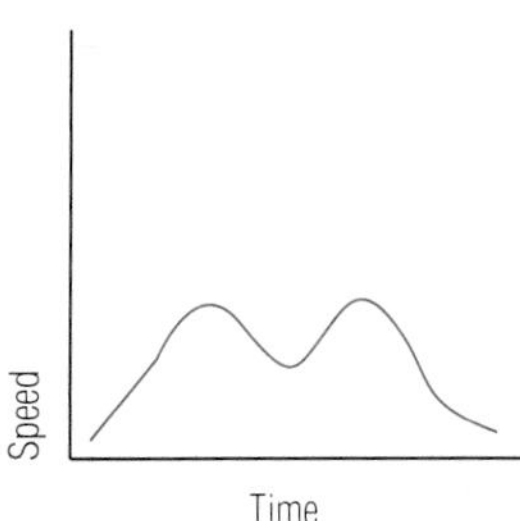

B.

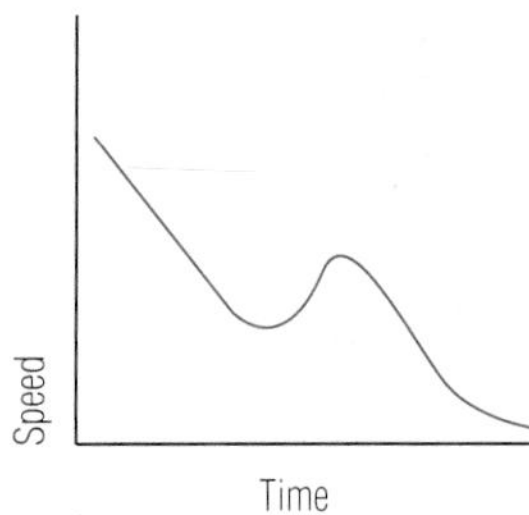

Class Exercises

Discuss the Ideas

Penny rides her bicycle directly to school. Explain how each of these graphs could be realistic for this situation.

1.

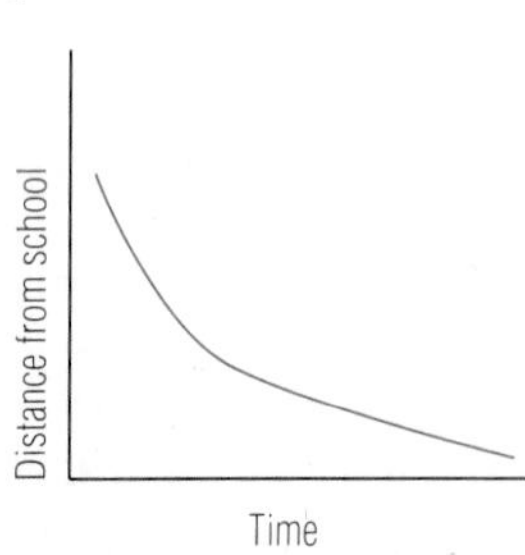

2.

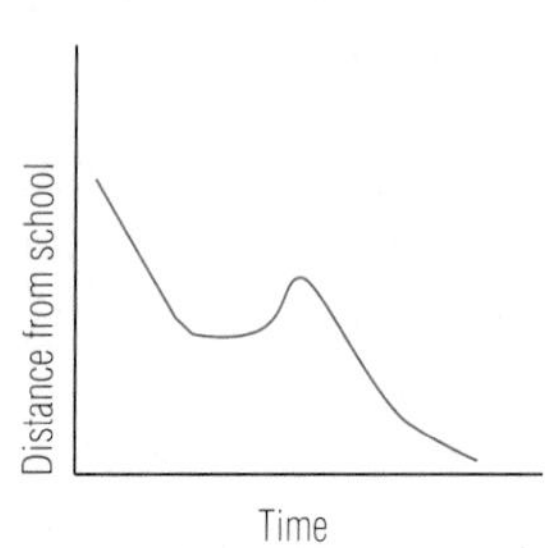

Exercises

Practice and Apply

Choose the graph that could be labeled to best describe each situation in Exercises 1–4.

A.
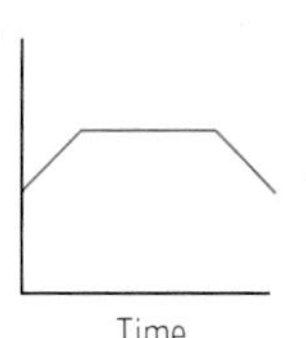

B.
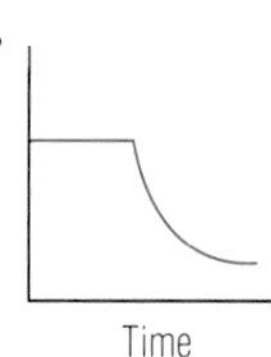

C.
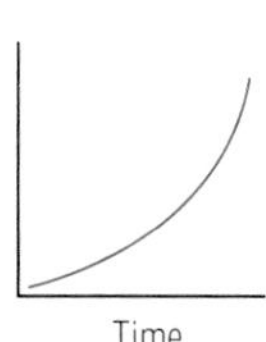

D.
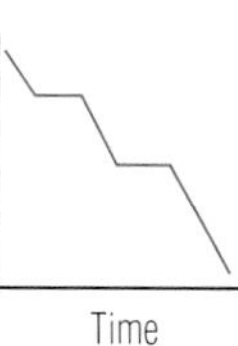

1. A swimming pool was drained during the day. The draining was stopped at night. It took 3 days to drain the pool.

2. Linda's aerobics class starts easy to slowly raise the heart rate. The goal is to keep the heartbeat high for most of the class and then to gradually have it return to near normal.

3. The speed of a baseball is greatest just after it leaves the bat. Then it gradually loses speed until it hits the ground.

4. Runners in the 1500-meter race start at a pace less than their maximum. Near the end of the race they sprint toward the finish line.

Extend and Apply

Write to Learn Describe a situation that could go with each graph.

5.
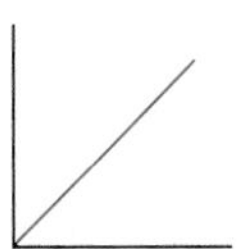

6.
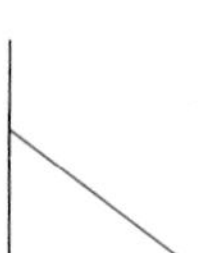

7.
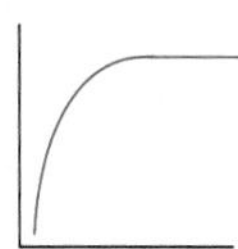

Use Mathematical Reasoning

8. Sketch a graph to show how the temperature might vary according to the time of the day.

9. Suppose you fill the container shown at the right with water at a constant rate. Sketch what the graph might look like.

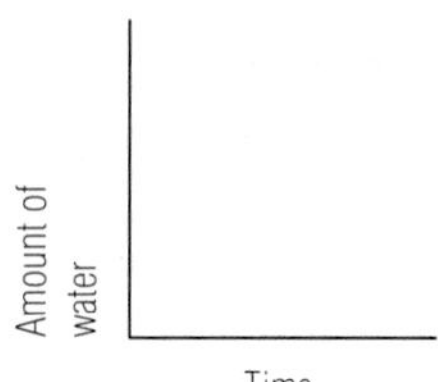

Mixed Review

Add or subtract. Reduce to lowest terms. **10.** $\frac{1}{2} + \frac{3}{8}$ **11.** $\frac{3}{4} - \frac{1}{5}$

Solve and check. **12.** $x - 5 > -10$ **13.** $-7d < 49$ **14.** $4t + 6 < -22$

9-4 Problem Solving: Writing Equations

Translating Problems Involving Two Expressions

Objective To practice writing equations for solving word problems involving two expressions.

Some word problems involve two unknowns. An expression for one of the unknowns can be given in terms of the other. To solve such problems, first decide which unknown the variable will represent, then express the other in terms of the variable.

Example 1

Write an expression for each unknown.
Beverly is 3 years older than Celia. Celia's age? Beverly's age?

Solution

Let c = Celia's age.	Since Beverly's age is given in relation to Celia's, make Celia's age the first unknown.
$c + 3$ = Beverly's age.	Then express Beverly's age in terms of Celia's.

Try This Sue has 3 times as many books as Dawn. Write an expression for each unknown.

a. The number Dawn has? **b.** The number Sue has?

Example 2

Write an equation.
A large bus holds 24 students more than a small bus. The two buses hold 76 students all together.

Solution

Let s = number a small bus holds.	Since the number a large bus holds is given relative to the number a small bus holds, let s represent the number the small bus holds.
$s + 24$ = number a large bus holds.	Then express the number the large bus holds in terms of the number the small bus holds.
$s + (s + 24) = 76$	The two buses together hold 76 students.

Try This Write an equation.

c. Fred collected twice as many shells as Nick. Together they collected 24.

Class Exercises

Let m = the number of math books. Give an algebraic expression for each in terms of m.

1. 7 fewer history books than math books
2. 8 times as many English books as math books
3. $\frac{1}{2}$ as many science books as math books
4. 12 fewer art books than math books

Discuss the Ideas

5. Suppose h was the number of history books in Class Exercise 1. Give an algebraic expression for the number of math books in terms of h. Can more than one algebraic expression be used to represent situations like those above?

Exercises

Practice and Apply

Write an expression for each.

1. Carl had 7 more than Kim. Let k be the number Kim had. How many did Carl have?
2. There are 3 times as many cars as bikes. Let b be the number of bikes. How many cars are there?
3. There are $\frac{1}{2}$ as many boys as there are girls. Let g be the number of girls. How many boys are there?
4. Saturday tickets cost double weekday tickets. Let w be the cost of a weekday ticket. How much does a Saturday ticket cost?
5. Large notebooks cost twice as much as small notebooks. Let s be the cost of a small notebook. What is the cost of a large notebook?
6. A weekday newspaper cost $\frac{1}{4}$ as much as the Sunday paper. Let s be the cost of the Sunday paper. What is the cost of the weekday paper?
7. The price of a certain house today is $4\frac{1}{2}$ times what it sold for in 1965. Let p be the selling price in 1965. What is the selling price today?
8. A 6-pack of a fruit drink cost $\frac{1}{2}$ as much as a case. Let c be the cost of a case. What is the cost of one 6-pack?

Write an equation.

9. There are 8 more boys than girls in the 64-member band this year.
10. One side of a record album lasts 98 seconds longer than the other. The total length of the album is 1,936 seconds.

11. The second math quiz was worth half as many points as the first quiz. Both quizzes together were worth 110 points.

12. A tape cost \$2.10 more than an album. Together they cost \$13.60.

13. John scored 25 more points in his second bowling game than in his first. He had a total of 297 points for the two games.

14. A cassette tape cost \$5 less than a CD. Together they cost \$19.

15. The basketball team scored double the number of points in their Saturday game than they scored in their Friday game. They scored a total of 111 points in these two games.

16. A movie ticket for an adult costs twice as much as a ticket for a senior citizen. The cost of one adult ticket and one senior citizen ticket is \$9.

Extend and Apply

17. A theater has twice as many seats in each row of the middle section as in each row of the two side sections. It has a total of 96 seats per row made up of a middle row and two equal side rows.

    Let s = number of seats in each row of one side section.

    a. What does the expression $2s$ represent?

    b. Write an expression using s that represents the 96 seats.

    c. Write an equation using the information you know.

18. One hundred twenty-two vans were supposed to be shipped by railroad, but 2 vans could not fit on the railroad cars. There were 8 railroad cars, each holding the same number of vans. How many vans were on each car?

    Let v = vans in each railroad car.

    a. What does the expression $8v$ represent?

    b. Write an expression using v that represents the 122 vans.

    c. Write an equation using the information you know.

Use Mathematical Reasoning

Write a word problem that would be solved using the equation.

19. $x + (x + 2) = 18$ **20.** $x + 5x = 36$

Mixed Review

Simplify. **21.** $2a + 3(a - 6) - 4a$ **22.** $-m - 5(2m + 4) - 8m$

Solve and check. **23.** $22 + 9z = 4$ **24.** $2(x + 1) = 0$

25. $3(14 - n) + 7 = 5n + 1$ **26.** $4(c + 3) = 14c - 3$

9-5 Problem Solving: Writing Equations

Solving Problems Involving Two Expressions

Objective To use equations to solve word problems involving two expressions.

You can write and solve an equation to find the answer to a word problem in which one unknown can be expressed in terms of another. Use the Problem-Solving Checklist on page 138 to help you.

Example

A train engine picked up $3\frac{1}{2}$ times as many cars at the second stop as it picked up at its first stop. Then it had a total of 81 cars. How many cars did it pick up at its second stop?

Solution

Let f = number picked up at the first stop.

$3\frac{1}{2}f$ = number picked up at the second stop. The number of cars picked up at the second stop is given relative to the number picked up at the first stop.

$f + 3\frac{1}{2}f = 81$

$4\frac{1}{2}f = 81$

$\frac{9}{2}f = 81$ Multiply both sides by $\frac{2}{9}$ to get f alone.

$f = 18$ The train picked up 18 cars at the first stop.

$3\frac{1}{2} \cdot 18 = 63$ The problem asks for the number picked up at the second stop, so find the value of $3\frac{1}{2}f$ when $f = 18$.

The train picked up 63 cars at its second stop.

Try This Solve.

a. Mrs. Kang has 4 fewer girls than boys in her art club this year. There are 28 students in the art club this year. How many are girls?

Class Exercises

Give an equation.

1. Sid paid \$4 more for jeans than for a shirt. The total cost was \$38. How much was each?
2. The deep end of a swimming pool is $\frac{1}{4}$ the length of the shallow end. The total length of the pool is 90 m. How long is each section?

Discuss the Ideas

3. Vicky used 15 times as much fertilizer as grass seed on her lawn. All together, she used 32 pounds of material. How many pounds of fertilizer did she use?
   a. Give an equation that uses *f*, for fertilizer, as the unknown.
   b. Give an equation that uses *g*, for grass seed, as the unknown.
   c. Do you expect both equations to give you the same answer? Why?

Exercises

Practice and Apply

Solve by writing an equation.

1. An airplane had 65 more occupied seats than empty seats. It had a total of 211 seats. How many seats were occupied?
2. A box of popcorn cost twice as much as a cup of juice. Lyle bought 1 of each and paid $2.25. What was the price of popcorn?
3. A class of 354 graduates has 64 fewer male graduates than female graduates. How many are male and how many are female?
4. Of 410 students graduating, the number planning to get a job is $\frac{1}{4}$ as many as the number planning to go to college. How many students are not planning to go to college?
5. A large bottle of fruit juice contains 4 times as much as the regular size. The total number of ounces in the two sizes is 40. How many ounces are in each size?

Extend and Apply

6. Gilberto bought 2 shirts and a sweater and paid $48. The sweater cost twice as much as each shirt. How much was the sweater? each shirt?
7. Jerry collected twice as many donations as Fred. Tom collected 12 more donations than Fred. Each donation was at least $2. Altogether, the three boys collected 48 donations. How many donations did each boy collect?

Use Mathematical Reasoning

8. Write a word problem that could be solved using the equation
   a. $x + \frac{1}{2}x = 24$ b. $x + 2x + 3x = 126$.

Mixed Review

Find the least common multiple (LCM). **9.** 5, 6, 8 **10.** 3, 6, 7

Evaluate for $n = \frac{2}{3}$. **11.** $\frac{1}{5}n + \frac{1}{2}$ **12.** $n - \frac{2}{7}$ **13.** $\frac{9}{10} - n$

9-6 Direct and Inverse Variation

Objective To recognize direct and inverse variation.

Explore

The equation distance = rate × time or $d = r \cdot t$ relates distance, rate, and time.

a. Complete this table of values using a rate of 25 mi/h. As the amount of time increases, what happens to the distance?

$d = 25 \cdot t$

time (t)	1	2	3	4	5
distance (d)	25	?	?	?	?

b. Complete this table of values using a distance of 100 miles. As the amount of time increases, what happens to the rate of speed?

$100 = r \cdot t$

time (t)	1	2	10	20	100
rate (r)	100	?	?	?	?

c. Graph both tables of values. Which graph is a line? Which is a curve?

Understand the Ideas

In part a. of the Explore, you discovered that as the value of one variable *increases at a constant rate,* the value of the other variable also *increases at a constant rate.* The second variable **varies directly** with the first variable.

Direct Variation

A variable y **varies directly with** x if there is a positive number k such that $y = kx$.

Example 1

Does y vary directly with x? If it does, find the value of k.

x	y
1	3
2	6
3	9
4	12

Solution

$3 = k(1)$ The pair (1, 3) satisfies $y = kx$ if $k = 3$.

$6 = 3(2)$ Check to see whether other pairs satisfy $y = 3x$.

$9 = 3(3)$

$12 = 3(4)$ The pairs (2, 6), (3, 9), and (4, 12) do satisfy $y = 3x$.

y varies directly with x, and $k = 3$.

Try This Does y vary directly with x? If it does, find the value of k.

a.

x	y
1	5
2	10
3	15
4	20
5	25

b.

x	y
1	−2
2	−4
3	−6
4	−8
5	−10

You can use the [Cons] key on a calculator to verify that a table of values represents direct variation. The key sequence [×] 4 [Cons] makes 4 the repeating multiplier.

Example 2

Use the [Cons] key to determine whether y varies directly with x. If it does, find the value of k.

x	y
1	4
2	8
3	12
4	16
5	20

Solution $4 = k(1)$ — The pair (1, 4) satisfies $y = kx$ if $k = 4$.

[×] 4 [Cons] — Set up 4 as your multiplier.

2 [Cons] 8 — Verify each y entry in the table by multiplying each value of x by 4.

3 [Cons] 12

4 [Cons] 16

5 [Cons] 20

y varies directly with x, and $k = 4$.

Try This **c.** Use the [Cons] key to determine whether y varies directly with x. If it does, find the value of k.

x	y
1	3
2	8
3	14
4	18
5	22

In part b. of the Explore, you discovered that as the amount of time increased, the rate of speed decreased. In this situation, as the value of one variable *increases* at a constant rate, the value of the other variable *decreases* and the product of the variables is a constant. The second variable **varies inversely** with the first variable.

Inverse Variation

A variable y **varies inversely with** x if there is a positive number k such that $y = \frac{k}{x}$ or $xy = k$.

You can also use the Cons key on a calculator to verify that a table of values represents inverse variation. Once you have input your multiplier, use the key sequence 1/x Cons to check that values in a table are related by inverse variation.

Example 3

Use the Cons key to determine whether y varies inversely with x. If it does, find the value of k.

x	y
1	24
2	12
3	8
4	6
5	$\frac{24}{5}$

Solution $24 = \frac{k}{1}$ — The pair (1, 24) satisfies $y = \frac{k}{x}$ if $k = 24$.

× 24 Cons — Set up 24 as your multiplier.

2 1/x Cons 12 — Check to see that each pair satisfies $y = \frac{24}{x}$.

3 1/x Cons 8

4 1/x Cons 6

5 1/x Cons $\frac{24}{5}$

y varies inversely with x, and $k = 24$.

Try This Use the Cons key to determine whether y varies inversely with x. If it does, find the value of k.

d.

x	y
1	5
2	4
3	3
4	2
5	1

e.

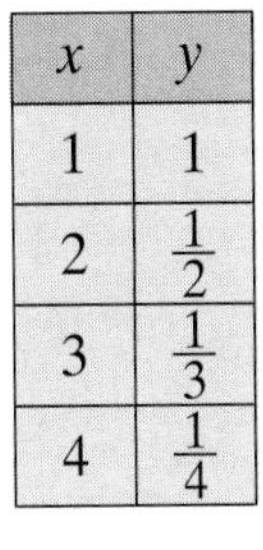

x	y
1	1
2	$\frac{1}{2}$
3	$\frac{1}{3}$
4	$\frac{1}{4}$

Class Exercises

For each question, state whether y varies directly with x, y varies inversely with x, or neither case is true.

1. $y = 2x$ **2.** $xy = 5$ **3.** $xy = 14$

4. $y = 4x$ **5.** $x = \frac{1}{y}$ **6.** $x = \frac{y}{5}$

7. $y = \frac{3}{x}$ **8.** $y = \pi x$ **9.** $x = \frac{2y}{3}$

Discuss the Ideas

10. Would you like your paycheck to vary directly or inversely with the amount of time you spend on the job? Explain your answer.

Exercises

Practice and Apply

Does y vary directly with x? If it does, find the value of k.

1.

x	y
1	1
2	2
3	3
4	4
5	5

2.

x	y
1	2
2	4
3	6
4	8
5	10

3.

x	y
1	2
2	4
3	5
4	6
5	7

4.

x	y
1	−2
2	4
3	−6
4	8
5	−10

Does y vary inversely with x? If it does, find the value of k.

5.

x	y
1	12
2	10
3	8
4	6
5	4

6.

x	y
1	120
2	60
3	40
4	30
5	24

7.

x	y
1	2
2	1
3	$\frac{2}{3}$
4	$\frac{1}{2}$
5	$\frac{2}{5}$

8.

x	y
1	20
2	10
3	5
4	3
5	1

Extend and Apply

9. A truck driver drives 150 miles between rest stops. Does his average speed vary directly or inversely with the time it takes to travel the 150 miles?

10. The tax on Mr. Jones's income is 20%. Does the amount of tax he pays vary directly or inversely with the amount he earns?

Use Mathematical Reasoning

11. Copy and complete the table at right so that y varies

a. directly with x **b.** inversely with x

12. A variable y varies directly with the square of x if $y = kx^2$ when a constant k is a positive number. Complete the table at right so that y varies directly with the square of x.

x	y
1	?
2	?
3	?
4	80

Mixed Review

Compute. **13.** 1.2×25 **14.** $36 + (-25)$ **15.** 3.6×25

Solve and check. **16.** $12.4 = 36m - 5.6$ **17.** $3c - 1.7c = 3.12$

9-7 Slope and Intercepts

Objective To determine the slope, given the equation for a line.

Explore

Place a three-ring binder flat on your desk. Notice how it slants downward as you move from left to right.

- Measure the vertical distance from A to B. This distance will be negative since you are moving in a downward direction.
- Measure the horizontal distance from B to C.

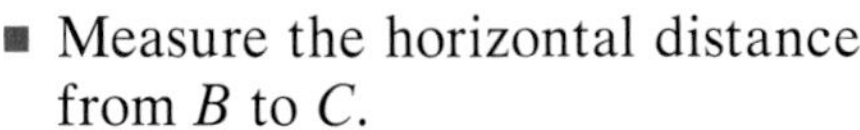

- Calculate the length from A to B divided by the length from B to C. This quotient approximates the slant, or *slope* of the line from A to C.

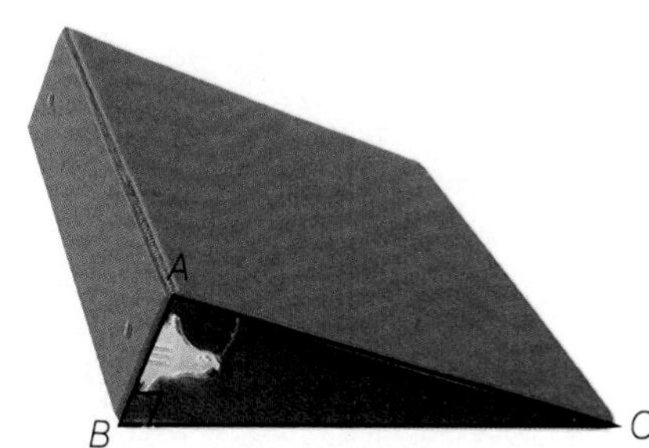

- Compare the approximate slope of your binder to that of your classmates' binders. What conclusions can you make?

Understand the Ideas

The **slope** of a line gives the idea of the steepness of a line. The slope is **the change in y divided by the change in x.** The change in y is called the **rise.** The change in x is called the **run.** To find the slope of a line, choose any two points on the line and calculate the change in the y-coordinate and x-coordinate for these points.

From A to B:

$$\text{slope} = \frac{\text{change in } y}{\text{change in } x} = \frac{2}{4} = \frac{1}{2}$$

From B to C:

$$\text{slope} = \frac{\text{change in } y}{\text{change in } x} = \frac{3}{6} = \frac{1}{2}$$

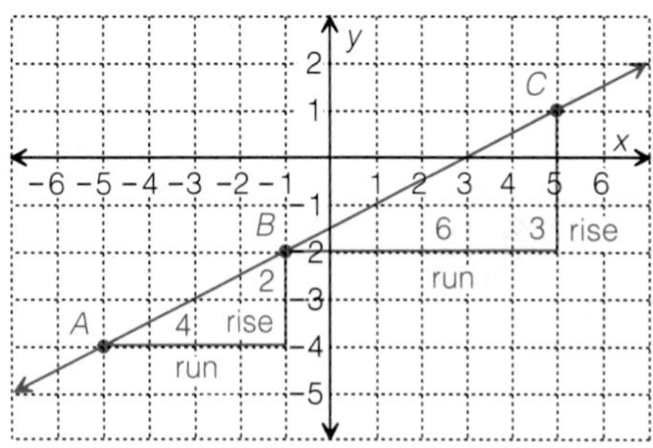

As we move from left to right, if a line slants upward it has a positive slope and if it slants downward it has a negative slope. If the line stays flat, it is a horizontal line with a slope of zero. A vertical line has an undefined slope since there is no change in the x-coordinate.

Example 1

A roof rises 4 feet vertically for every 12 feet of horizontal distance. What is the slope of the roof?

Solution

$$\text{slope} = \frac{\text{rise}}{\text{run}}$$

$$= \frac{4}{12} = \frac{1}{3}$$

The roof has a slope of $\frac{1}{3}$.

Try This **a.** What is the slope of a roof that rises 7 feet vertically for every 12 feet of horizontal distance?

Example 2

Graph the line that contains the points $A(-2, 3)$ and $B(6, -3)$. Find the slope.

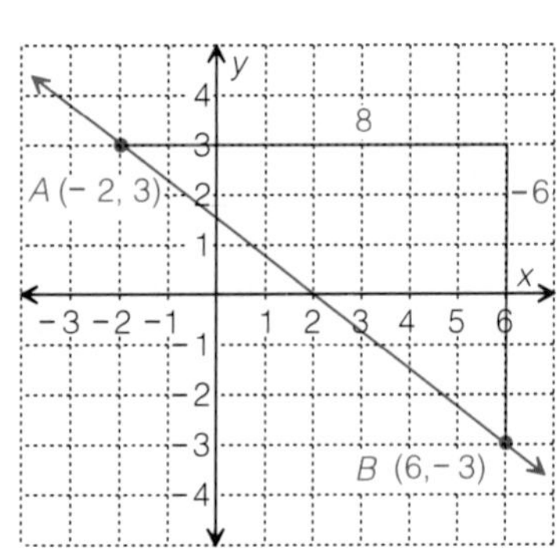

Solution

$$\text{slope} = \frac{\text{change in } y}{\text{change in } x}$$ Subtract the coordinates in the same order.

$$= \frac{-3 - 3}{6 - (-2)} = \frac{-6}{8} = -\frac{3}{4}$$

Try This Graph the line that contains the points given. Find the slope.

b. $A(1, 2)$ and $B(4, 8)$ **c.** $C(-3, 1)$ and $D(5, 3)$

You can find the slope of the line for a linear equation by using any two points that make the equation true.

Example 3

Find the slope of the line $y = 3x - 1$.

Solution

When $x = 1, y = 3(1) - 1 = 2$ Find two points by using any two values of x and calculating the corresponding values of y. $(1, 2)$ is on the graph.

When $x = 2, y = 3(2) - 1 = 5$ $(2, 5)$ is on the graph.

$$\text{slope} = \frac{\text{change in } y}{\text{change in } x}$$

$$= \frac{5 - 2}{2 - 1} = \frac{3}{1} = 3$$ Make sure you begin with the same point in calculating both the change in y and the change in x.

Try This Find the slope of the line.

d. $y = -2x + 1$ **e.** $2x - 3y = 6$

The **x-intercept** is the x-coordinate of the point where the line crosses the x-axis. Since all points on the x-axis have a y-coordinate of 0, you find the x-intercept by letting $y = 0$. The **y-intercept** is the y-coordinate where the line crosses the y-axis. Since all points on the y-axis have an x-coordinate of 0, you find the y-intercept by letting $x = 0$.

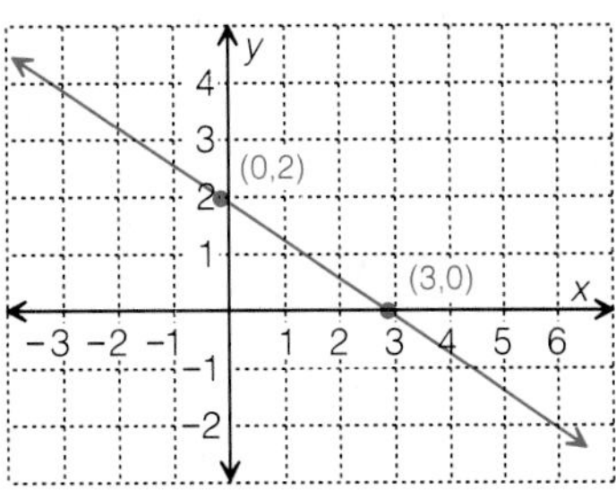

The line is the graph of $2x + 3y = 6$.
The x-intercept is 3.
The y-intercept is 2.

Example 4

Find the x- and y-intercepts for the line $3x + 2y = 12$.

Solution

Let $y = 0$. $3x + 2(0) = 12$ The y-coordinate of the x-intercept is 0. So let $y = 0$ and solve for x.

$3x = 12$

$x = 4$

The x-intercept is 4. The pair $(4, 0)$ satisfies the equation $3x + 2y = 12$.

Let $x = 0$. $3(0) + 2y = 12$ The x-coordinate of the y-intercept is 0. So let $x = 0$ and solve for y.

$2y = 12$

$y = 6$

The y-intercept is 6. The pair $(0, 6)$ satisfies the equation $3x + 2y = 12$.

Try This Find the x- and y-intercepts.

f. $-2x + y = 6$ **g.** $3x - 2y = 10$

Class Exercises

For each line, give the slope, the x-intercept, and the y-intercept.

1.

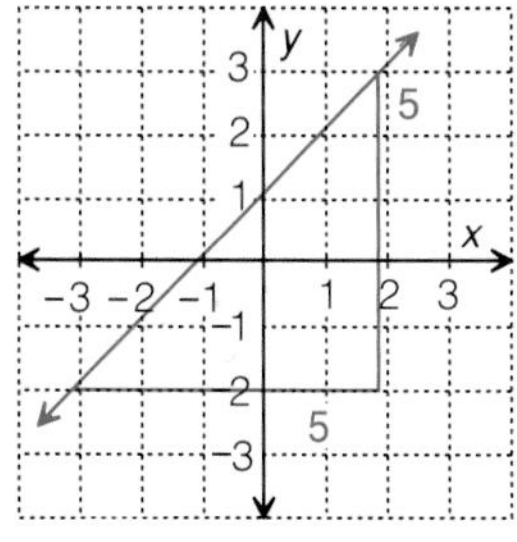

2.

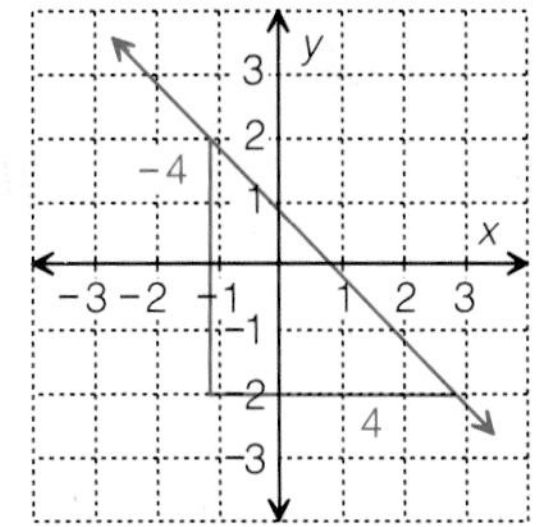

3.

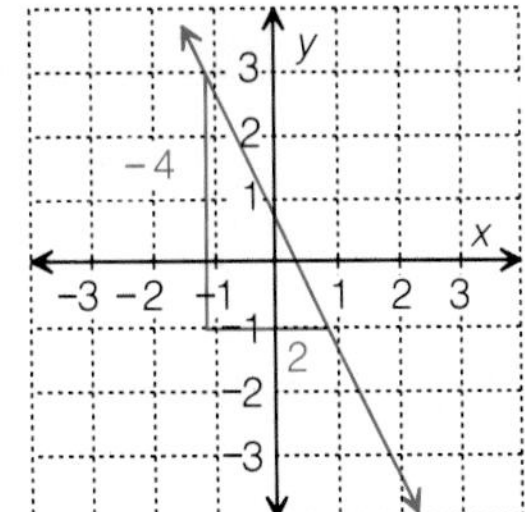

Discuss the Ideas

4. List three things that occur in nature that have slope.

Exercises

Practice and Apply

Find the slope for each situation.

1. A roof rises 6 feet vertically for every 15 feet of horizontal distance.
2. A road rises 50 feet for every 2125 feet of horizontal distance.

Graph the line that contains the given points and find the slope.

3. $A(-2, 8), B(3, -2)$
4. $A(-2, 3), B(4, -6)$
5. $A(8, 4), B(1, 3)$
6. $A(3, 5), B(-2, -3)$
7. $A(-4, -6), B(-1, 3)$
8. $A(3, -5), B(-3, 8)$

Find the slope of each line.

9. $y = 2x - 1$
10. $y = -3x + 7$
11. $2x - y = 5$
12. $3x + 2y = 24$
13. $x + 3y = 6$
14. $2x - 5y = 10$

Find the x- and y-intercepts.

15. $x + y = 5$
16. $2x + y = 4$
17. $x - 3y = 6$
18. $2x - 3y = 24$
19. $4x + 5y = 20$
20. $3x - 4y = 12$

Extend and Apply

Graph the equation. How do the numbers in the equation relate to the slope?

21. $y = 2x - 3$
22. $y = -3x + 5$
23. $y = \frac{1}{2}x + 1$
24. A long grade on a highway through the mountains has a vertical rise of 7 ft for each 100 ft of horizontal distance. How many feet of rise are there in one mile (5,280 ft.) of horizontal change?
25. A ladder is to reach a point 30 feet above the ground. How far from the building should its base be if its slope is 2.5?

Use Mathematical Reasoning

26. Suppose a line through (1, 2) has slope 3. Find values for b, c, and d so that $(2, b)$, $(3, c)$, and $(4, d)$ are points on the line.

Mixed Review

Give the least common multiple (LCM). **27.** 2, 4, 7 **28.** 4, 6, 8

Solve and check. **29.** $3t = 15 - 2t$ **30.** $406 - 5y = 371$

9-8 Problem Solving: Applications

School Newspaper Advertising

Objective To practice solving word problems.

The staff of the school newspaper sells advertising to help pay printing costs. The pages are set up in 3 columns. Each column is 4 inches wide and 14 inches long. A "column inch" is an area 1 column wide by 1 inch long.

Classified Ads	6 lines per column inch	\$ 0.10 per line
Merchant Ads	less than half page half page full page	\$ 0.60 per column inch \$12.00 \$22.00
Ads for School Activities		no charge

Problems

Use the information given above to solve. Decide whether to use **pencil and paper, mental math, estimation,** or a **calculator** to find the answer.

1. How much would 1 column of classified ads earn for the paper?
2. How much would a 2-inch classified ad earn for the paper?
3. How much is earned by 8 inches of classified ads?
4. How much more is earned by a full page of classified ads than by two half-page merchant ads?
5. How much is earned by a merchant ad 3 inches long by 2 columns wide?
6. How much is earned by a merchant ad 4 inches long by 3 columns wide?

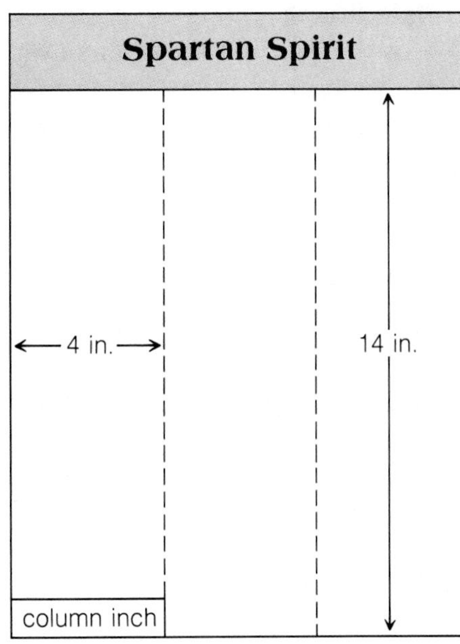

7. How much would the page of ads shown at right earn for the paper?

8. How much more would the page at right earn if the merchant ad 4 inches long by 1 column wide were replaced with a 4-inch classified ad?

9. The typesetter charges the *Spartan Spirit* \$3.00 more to prepare a page of classified ads than it charges to prepare one full-page merchant ad. After paying the extra typesetting cost, how much more has the paper earned from a full page of classified ads than from a full-page merchant ad?

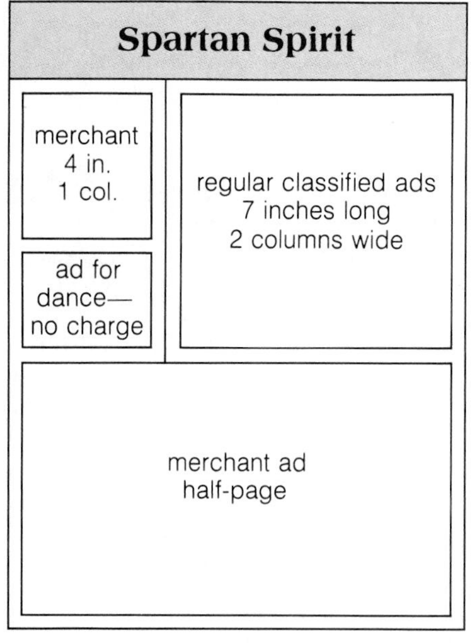

10. The *Spartan Spirit* provides a free ad 4 inches long by 2 columns wide for the school dance on the day of each of 5 home football games. It also provides a half-page ad for the Junior Prom and two half-page ads for the Senior Prom. How much would these ads cost at the merchant advertising rates?

11. The circulation of the *Spartan Spirit* (the number of copies printed and distributed) is 1550. How much per copy does a merchant pay for a full-page ad?

12. **Data Search** Find the cost of a full-page merchant ad in a local newspaper. Find the circulation of the paper. How much per copy does a merchant pay for a full-page ad?

What's Your Decision?

The six-page *Spartan Spirit* is published 17 times per school year. About 50% of the space is devoted to ads that earn money. Printing costs are increasing by \$50 per issue. The following ideas for reducing the budget deficit have been proposed:

a. increase the paid advertising space to 60% per issue

b. raise advertising rates 15%

c. print only 13 issues per year

d. charge each of the 1500 students \$1.50 for a year's subscription.

As the *Spartan Spirit* Managing Editor, which idea would you prefer? Why?

9-9 Graphing Systems of Equations

Objective To find the solution of a system of equations by graphing.

Application

A contractor plans to build a rectangular pool with a perimeter of 50 meters. The length of the pool will be 5 meters longer than the width. Can the pool have dimensions of 15 meters by 10 meters?

Understand the Ideas

When two equations with the same two variables are used to describe a problem, they are called a **system of equations.**

Example 1

Show that the pool in the **application** has dimensions of 15 m × 10 m by checking to see if the ordered pair (15, 10) is a solution to the system.

Solution $2x + 2y = 50$ $\quad\quad$ $x - y = 5$

$2(15) + 2(10) = 50 \checkmark$ $\quad\quad$ $15 - 10 = 5 \checkmark$

The pool has dimensions of 15 m × 10 m.

Try This **a.** Is the ordered pair (1, 2) a solution for the system of equations?

$$y - x = 1$$
$$2y - x = 3$$

To find a solution of a system of equations, find the point of intersection of the graphs of the two equations. You can use a graphing calculator or a computer to graph each line, then decide what point lies on both lines.

Example 2

Graph the equations to solve the system. Check the solution.

$$x + y = 2$$
$$-x + 2y = 1$$

Solution

Graph each equation on the same coordinate system.

Decide what point lies on both lines.

The solution appears to be (1,1).

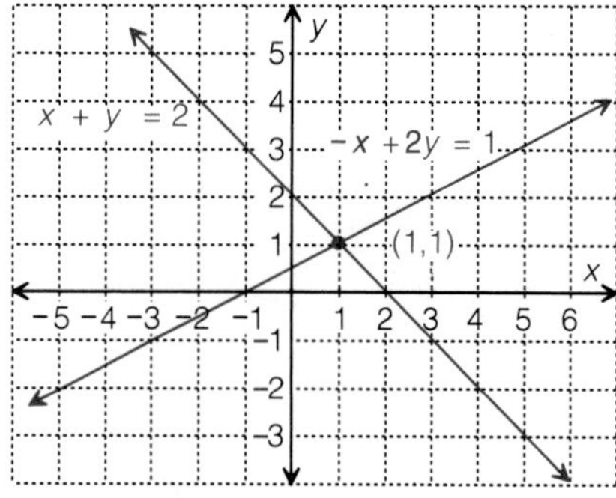

Check

$x + y = 2$ $\qquad$ $-x + 2y = 1$

$1 + 1 = 2$ ✓ $\qquad$ $-1 + 2(1) = 1$ ✓

Check to see that the point you have selected satisfies both equations.

Try This **b.** Graph the equations to solve the system. $\begin{aligned} x - y &= 1 \\ x + y &= 3 \end{aligned}$

Class Exercises

True or false?

1. (1, 3) is a solution of the equation $3x + y = 6$.
2. (1, 3) is a solution of the equation $y - x = 1$.
3. (1, 3) is a solution of the system of equations: $\begin{aligned} 3x + y &= 6 \\ y - x &= 1 \end{aligned}$

Discuss the Ideas

4. If an ordered pair is a solution of one equation of a system, will it sometimes, always, or never be a solution to the other equation of a system? Explain.

Exercises

Practice and Apply

Is the ordered pair given a solution for the system of equations?

1. (1, 2); $\begin{aligned} 2x + y &= 4 \\ 3x - 2y &= -1 \end{aligned}$
2. (3, 1); $\begin{aligned} x + 2y &= 5 \\ 2x - y &= 2 \end{aligned}$
3. (−2, 3); $\begin{aligned} 2x + y &= 1 \\ -x + 2y &= 8 \end{aligned}$
4. (2, −1); $\begin{aligned} -3x + y &= -7 \\ 3x + 5y &= 1 \end{aligned}$
5. A baseball team played 162 games. They won 44 more games than they lost. Is the ordered pair (103, 59) a solution for the system of equations that describes this situation? $\begin{aligned} x + y &= 162 \\ x - y &= 44 \end{aligned}$

6. Four oranges and five apples cost \$2.00. Three oranges and four apples cost \$1.56. Is the ordered pair (0.2, 0.24) a solution for the system of equations that describes this situation? $4x + 5y = 2.00$ $3x + 4y = 1.56$

Graph the equations to find a solution for the system. Check the solution.

7. $x - y = 1$, $x + 2y = 1$
8. $x + y = 2$, $2x - y = 1$
9. $x + y = 0$, $x - y = -2$
10. $2x - y = -1$, $x + y = -2$
11. $x + y = 3$, $x - y = 1$
12. $-2x + y = -4$, $2x + y = 0$

Extend and Apply

A system of equations has **no solutions** if the lines of the system have the same slope, making the lines parallel. A system of equations has an **infinite number of solutions** if the graphs of the two linear equations are the same line. Decide whether each system has no solutions, an infinite number of solutions, or a one-point solution.

13. $3x - 2y = 2$, $4y - 6x = -4$
14. $2x + y = 3$, $2x + y = 5$
15. $3x + 2y = 6$, $4y - 12 = -6x$

Use a graphing calculator or a computer to graph each equation, then decide what point lies on both lines.

16. $y = x + 1$, $y = -2x + 1$
17. $y = x + 3$, $y = -2x + 4$
18. $y = \frac{1}{2}x + 2$, $y = -x + 2$
19. What value of k will make $2x + 3y = k$ and $4x + 6y = k$ have the same set of solutions?
20. Translate to a system of equations and solve. The sum of two numbers is 6 and their difference is 2. Find the two numbers.

Use Mathematical Reasoning

21. Cheap-at-the-Price Rent-a-Car charges \$20 a day and \$0.15 per mile. More-for-Your-Money Rent-a-Car charges \$15 a day and \$0.20 per mile. Which company charges the least for 75 miles in one day? For what mileage is the cost the same?
22. Guess and check to find the value of k that makes (1, 2) a solution of the system. $3x - y = 1$, $-x + ky = 3$

Mixed Review

Solve and check.

23. $12t - 10t = 26$
24. $495 = 27m + 90$
25. $1{,}640 + 32x = 360$
26. $9y + 4.75 = 31.3$
27. $3c - 2.4c = 3$
28. $-3\frac{1}{8}c = \frac{15}{16}$
29. $\frac{m}{4} = -\frac{2}{9}$
30. $4t = -\frac{2}{5}$
31. What is the shortest length of ribbon that can be cut into a whole number of 10-cm pieces or into a whole number of 12-cm pieces?

9-10 Data Collection and Analysis

Scatterplots

Objective To recognize positive and negative correlations in scatterplots.

The data at the right shows the number of calories, grams of protein and grams of carbohydrates for 3 oz. of several kinds of meat and fish. Ordered pairs of data, called **data points,** can be shown on a **scatterplot.**

Meat, Fish	Calories	Protein	Carbohydrate
Bl bluefish	135	22	4
C clams	50	5	3
S shrimp	190	17	9
B beefsteak	330	20	27
T tuna	170	24	7
P pork	340	21	28

Making a Scatterplot

To make a scatterplot that shows how *the amount of protein* is related to *the number of calories* follow these steps.

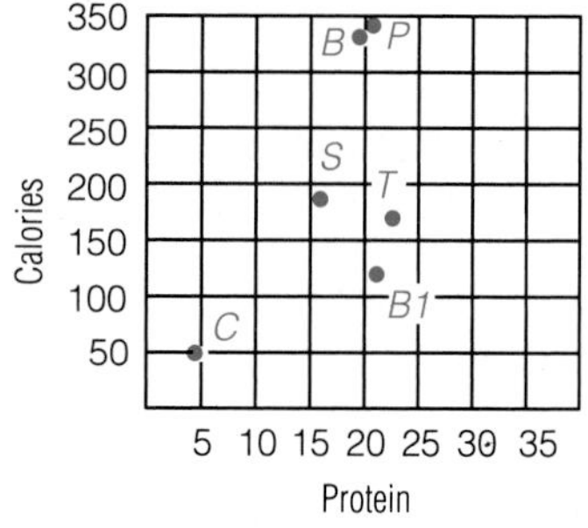

Step 1. Label the horizontal axis with a scale for the number of grams of protein.

Step 2. Label the vertical axis with a scale for the number of calories.

Step 3. For each food item plot the data point on the graph. For example, for clams (C) plot the ordered pair (5, 50).

Project

1. Make a scatterplot that shows how grams of carbohydrate are related to grams of protein.
2. Make a scatterplot that shows how grams of carbohydrate are related to number of calories.

The data at the top of page 329 shows the won-lost record of the National League West on Oct. 2, 1989. It includes the record for home games, games versus right-handed pitchers, and games played on grass. Use this data to complete Exercises 3–5.

3. Make a scatterplot that shows how total wins are related to wins on grass fields.
4. Make a scatterplot that shows how total number of wins are related to wins against right-handed pitchers.
5. Make a scatterplot that shows how total number of wins is related to losses at home.

National League Baseball					
West	**W**	**L**	**Home**	**RH**	**Grass**
San Francisco	92	70	53-28	56-50	73-47
San Diego	89	73	46-35	62-54	66-54
Houston	86	76	47-35	59-55	21-27
Los Angeles	77	83	44-37	46-53	61-57
Cincinnati	75	97	38-43	55-61	22-26
Atlanta	63	97	33-46	40-59	46-71

Interpreting a Scatterplot

With a visual inspection of a scatterplot, you can determine if there is a **positive correlation, a negative correlation,** or **neither.**

Positive Correlation
Both sets of data increase together.

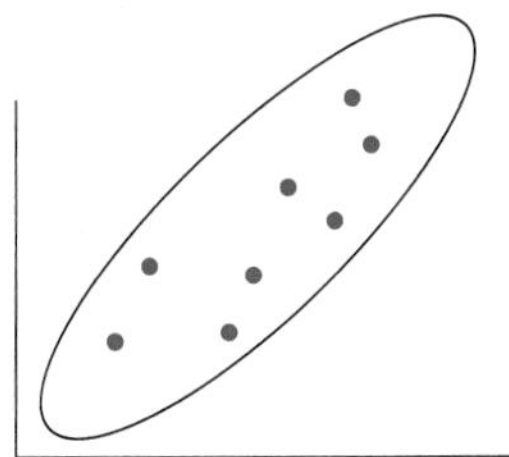

Negative Correlation
One set of data increases as the other decreases.

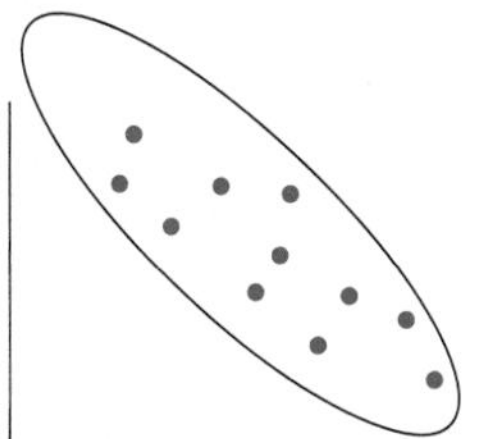

If data points are randomly scattered over the graph, we say there is **no correlation.**

Study the scatterplot relating protein to calories shown on page 328.

6. Does the item with the largest amount of protein also have the largest number of calories?
7. Does the item with the least amount of protein also have the least number of calories?
8. Does this scatterplot show positive or negative correlation?

The next three questions refer to the scatterplots you completed in Exercises 3, 4, and 5.

9. Which scatterplot shows the clearest positive correlation—total wins vs wins on grass, total wins vs wins against right-handers, or total wins vs losses at home?
10. For the same three scatterplots, which one shows negative correlation?
11. Do any of these three graphs show no correlation?

9-11 Graphing on the Number Line

Objective To graph solutions of inequalities on a number line.

Understand the Ideas

The **real numbers** are the numbers represented by the points on the number line. Solutions to inequalities are graphed on the number line.

Recall that a solution of an inequality is any number that makes the inequality true. The graph of an inequality in one variable is a diagram of all its solutions on a number line.

Example 1

Solve $2x - 5 < 1$. Graph the solutions on a number line.

Solution

$2x - 5 < 1$ To solve the inequality, you need to get x by itself on one side.

$2x - 5 + 5 < 1 + 5$ Add 5 to both sides of the inequality.

$\frac{2x}{2} < \frac{6}{2}$ Divide both sides by 2.

$x < 3$ This solution is "all real numbers less than 3." They are shown by shading all points to the left of 3. The open circle means the number 3 is not included.

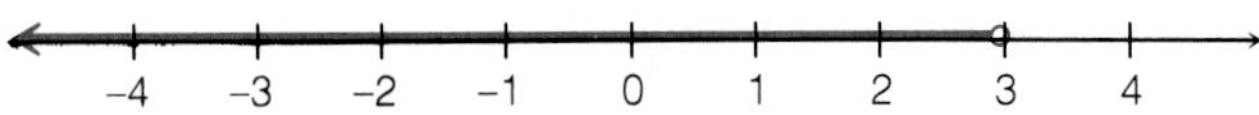

Try This Solve. Graph the solutions on a number line.

a. $3x + 2 > -6$ **b.** $3x + 4 < 7$

Example 2

Solve $-2x + 1 \leq 5$. Graph the solutions on a number line.

Solution

$-2x + 1 \leq 5$

$-2x + 1 - 1 \leq 5 - 1$ Subtract 1 from both sides of the inequality.

$-2x \leq 4$

$\frac{-2x}{-2} \geq \frac{4}{-2}$ Divide both sides by -2. Reverse the inequality sign.

$x \geq -2$ Use a closed circle to indicate that -2 is included.

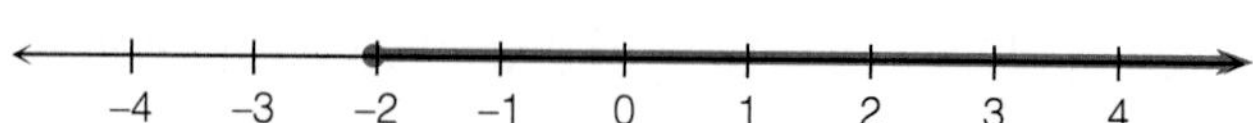

To graph any inequality, follow these steps.

- Solve the inequality.
- Decide whether your solution will include an open or closed circle.
- Shade on a number line all of the points that represent the solution.

Try This Solve. Graph the solutions on a number line.

c. $3x + 7 \leq 13$

d. $-2x + 5 \geq 3$

Class Exercises

Give an inequality for each solution shown.

1. 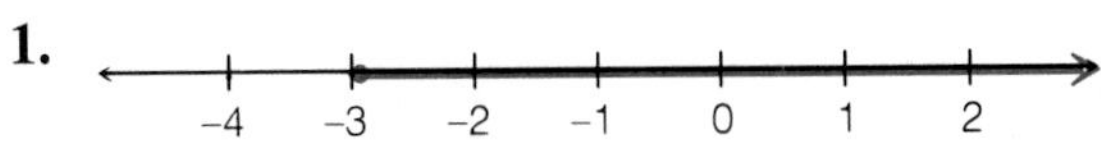

2. 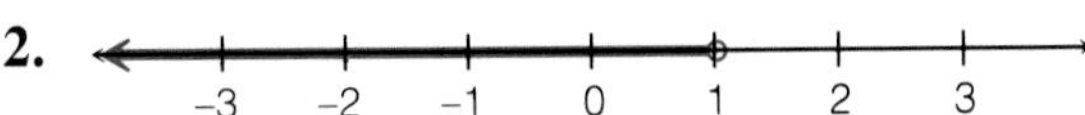

Discuss the Ideas

3. How can you use inequalities to describe the solution shown on this number line?

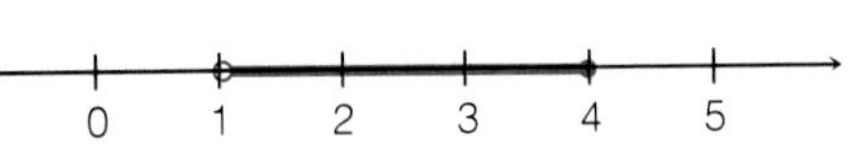

Exercises

Practice and Apply

Solve. Graph the solutions on a number line.

1. $x < 3$
2. $x \geq -1$
3. $4x > 2$
4. $-3x \geq -1$
5. $x + 2 \leq -3$
6. $x - 5 \leq -4$
7. $-x + 5 < 2$
8. $3x + 5 \geq -4$
9. $2x + 3 \leq 5$
10. $x - 2 > -4$
11. $\frac{1}{3}x + 1 < 4$
12. $-3x + 5 < -4$
13. Leo is planning to buy one pair of jeans and two shirts and he plans to spend less than \$50. The jeans cost \$19.50. Solve and graph the inequality $2x + 19.50 < 50$ to see how much he can spend per shirt.

Extend and Apply

Graph the solutions on a number line.

14. $-1 < x \leq 3$
15. $1 \leq x \leq 3$
16. $-2 < x < 3$
17. $-3 \leq x < -1$

Use Mathematical Reasoning

18. Graph on a number line all real numbers that satisfy both $-2 < x \leq 3$ and $1 \leq x < 4$.
19. Determine the graph of the solutions to $|x - 5| < 3$.

Mixed Review

Evaluate for $a = 3, b = -1$. **20.** $2(a - b)$ **21.** $a - 3b$ **22.** $b(ba)$

Solve and check. **23.** $21t - 15t = 4t + 8$ **24.** $7y = 6 + 2y$

9-12 Graphing Inequalities

Objective To graph the solutions of a linear inequality.

The graph of a linear equation such as $y = x + 2$ divides the plane into two regions, one above the line and the other below the line. The line is the **boundary** of the two regions.

Point (1, 4) is a solution to $y > x + 2$, and is a point in the region **above** the line.

Point (1, 3) is a solution to $y = x + 2$, and is a point **on** the line.

Point (1, 2) is a solution to $y < x + 2$, and is a point in the region **below** the line.

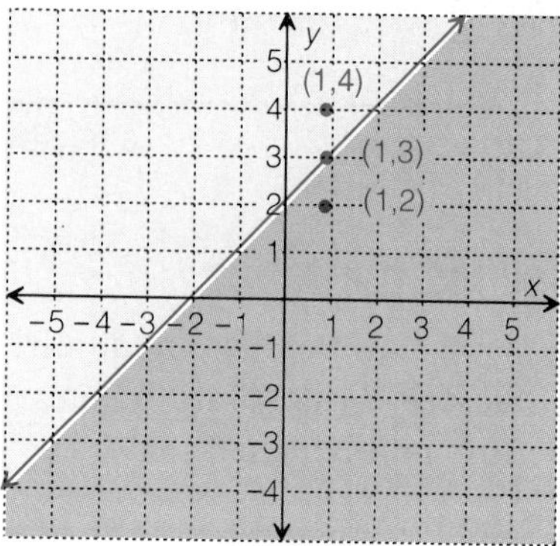

The region above the line is the set of all points that are solutions to the inequality $y > x + 2$. The region below the line is the set of all points that are solutions to the inequality $y < x + 2$. To graph a linear inequality, shade the graph to indicate the region that represents the solutions. If the inequality is $\leq$ or $\geq$, the boundary line is part of the region and is drawn as a solid line. If the inequality is $<$ or $>$, the boundary line is *not* a part of the region, and is drawn as a dashed line.

Example

Graph the inequality $y < x - 1$.

Solution

First, graph the boundary line $y = x - 1$.

The graph is the region below the line $y = x - 1$.

Since the inequality is $<$, draw the boundary line as a dashed line rather than a solid line.

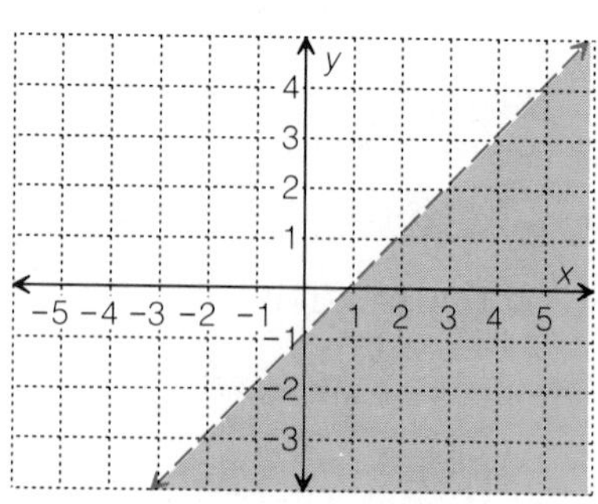

Try This Graph the inequality. **a.** $y > 2x - 1$ **b.** $y \leq \frac{1}{2}x + 1$

Class Exercises

When the inequality is graphed, will the boundary line be drawn as a solid line or a dashed line?

1. $y < 4x - 5$ **2.** $3x + 2 > y$ **3.** $-x \geq 4 + y$

Discuss the Ideas

4. Describe all of the points in the coordinate plane that satisfy the inequality $x \geq 3$.

Exercises

Practice and Apply

Graph the inequality.

1. $y < 3x - 2$
2. $y \geq -x + 2$
3. $y > -2x + 1$
4. $x \geq 1$
5. $y < 5$
6. $y < \frac{1}{2}x + 3$
7. $y < 2x - 5$
8. $x + 4 \geq y$
9. $y < 3 - x$

Extend and Apply

Graph the inequality.

10. $2x + 3y \geq 6$
11. $3(x + 2y) \geq 6$
12. $x < 2y + 1$
13. $3 \leq \frac{6}{x}$
14. $2x + 7 > y - 3x$
15. $4y - 3x < 12$
16. Jim and Sally are a two-person relay team in a bicycle marathon. Jim averages 20 mi/h, and Sally averages 18 mi/h. The team with the current record rode 872 miles. Write an inequality that must be satisfied for Jim and Sally to set a new record if Jim rides x hours and Sally rides y hours.
17. Suppose corn seed cost \$5/lb and wheat seed cost \$7/lb. A farmer has a budget of \$500 for seed. She plants x pounds of corn and y pounds of wheat. Write an inequality that must be satisfied for her to stay within the budget.

Use Mathematical Reasoning

To find the solution for a system of linear inequalities, you graph each inequality and identify the region common to both graphs. Graph each system of linear inequalities.

Example: Graph the system $x \geq 1$
$y \leq 2$

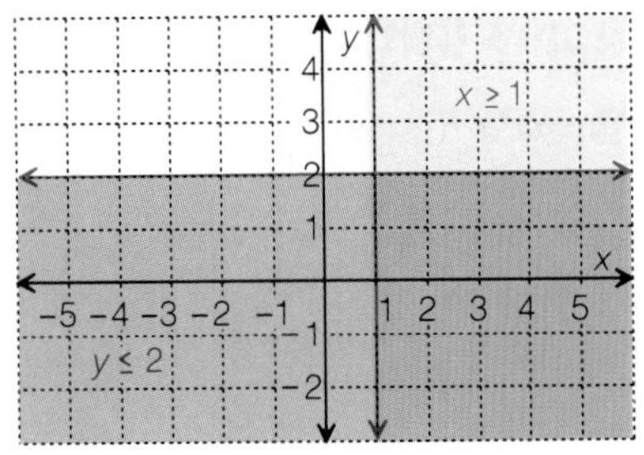

Graph each system of inequalities.

18. $x \leq 3$
    $y \geq -1$
19. $y \leq x + 2$
    $y \leq -x + 1$

Mixed Review

20. Make a table of solutions for $y = -x + 3$.

Solve and check. 21. $13t + 16 = 3$ 22. $4m + 17 - 7m + 5m = 21$

Critical Thinking

Graph Analysis Decisions

Objective: To use critical thinking when analyzing graphs.

Critical thinking is a process of making decisions to help you decide what to believe or do. Try your critical thinking skills in the following activity.

Group Activity A student made the graph below to show the changes in a biker's speed on the race course shown. Work in a group to decide if you believe that the graph is correct. If it isn't, figure out a way to change it so it will be correct. Write a paragraph supporting your decision.

You can use these processes to improve your critical thinking.

- Understand the Situation
  What's it all about? What decision is required?
- Deal with the Data/Evidence/Assumptions
  What is the useful evidence? What assumptions have been made?
- Go Beyond the Data/Evidence/Assumptions
  What other information can you figure out using the data or evidence?
- State and Support your Conclusion/Decision/Solution
  What decision did you make? What are your reasons for this decision?
- Apply the Conclusion/Decision/Solution
  How can you use this decision to help you in another situation?

Apply Critical Thinking

Draw a diagram of a bike race course used to make the graph.

1.

Speed

Location

2.

Speed

Location

3. Draw a graph for a race course that has a hill, a valley, and another hill.

9-13 Problem Solving: Strategies

Multiple Solutions

Objective To solve nonroutine problems, finding more than one way to solve each.

You have learned that many problems can be solved by using a combination of strategies. You might first simplify the problem, then draw a picture, make a table, and finally look for a pattern. For many problems, a solution can be found in several different ways. Two people can use completely different strategies but find the same correct solution. In the following example, a problem is solved two ways.

Sample Problem Ms. Malito saves coupons from a service station to get a gift. The station gives 5-point coupons and 3-point coupons. She has exactly 22 coupons, for a total of 86 points. She has fewer than 15 of each type of coupon. How many of each does she have?

Solution 1

One way to solve this problem is to use the **Guess, Check, Revise** strategy. You could guess a number for each type of coupon so that the sum of the two numbers is 22, and check whether they would total 86 points. If they did not, you would revise your guess and continue the process until you found the right combination. The process might be like this.

Try 14 for 3-point coupons and 8 for 5-point coupons: $14 \cdot 3 = 42$, $8 \cdot 5 = 40$, $42 + 40 = 82$ Too low.

Try 12 for 3-point coupons and 10 for 5-point coupons: $12 \cdot 3 = 36$, $10 \cdot 5 = 50$, $36 + 50 = 86$ Correct!

Solution 2

Another way to solve this problem is to **Make a Table** and look for the correct combination.

3-point coupons	Number	1	2	3	4	5	6	7	8	9	10	11	**12**	13	14
	Points	3	6	9	12	15	18	21	24	27	30	33	**36**	39	42
5-point coupons	Number	1	2	3	4	5	6	7	8	9	**10**	11	12	13	14
	Points	5	10	15	20	25	30	35	40	45	**50**	55	60	65	70

Problem-Solving Strategies

Choose the Operations	Make a Table	Make an Organized List
Guess, Check, Revise	Look for a Pattern	Use Logical Reasoning
Draw a Diagram	Write an Equation	Work Backward
	Simplify the Problem	

Problems

Find two different ways to solve Problem 1. Solve Problems 2–4.

1. Jim Westly has a pine tree farm. Twenty of his trees were killed in a very cold winter. That spring he bought the same number of new trees as had survived last winter. Later, he sold all of his trees to 6 customers, each of whom bought 15 trees. How many trees did he start with?
2. Fred drove 25 km farther than Tammy. If she had driven twice as far as she did, Fred would have driven only 10 km more than Tammy. How far did each drive?
3. Cesar has $50 to buy tickets to a concert. Seats in the front section cost $7 and seats in the back section cost $5. Cesar bought 8 tickets, and spent exactly $50. How many of each kind did he buy?
4. An airline reported that on flights from city A to city B, only 2 out of every 5 seats were filled. Each plane holds 250 passengers and each ticket costs $125. How much more money per flight would the airline make if it had every seat filled with a paying passenger?

Group Decision Making

5. Work in a group. Discuss and decide.

Situation Your class is having a car wash to raise money for a camping trip. Groups of 8 students each will be washing cars from 8:30 a.m. to 3:30 p.m. You have estimated that a group of 8 students can wash 3 cars every 20 minutes. You will need to buy car wash soap and pay a $5 fee for using the water. You want to find out what profit you might make.

Guidelines for Planning

- **Formulate Problems** you will need to solve.
- Discuss **Assumptions** you will make and **Data** you will need.

a. What decision or decisions do you need to make in this situation?
b. Formulate problems you need to solve to make the decision(s).
c. List any assumptions you need to make to arrive at a decision.
d. What data, if any, do you need to collect to make a decision?
e. Write a paragraph summarizing what your group did, what decisions you made, and why.

Extend Key Ideas

Telephone Rate Function

A telephone directory lists various rates for long-distance calls. The table below lists daytime rates for direct-dialed calls at \$0.58 for the first minute and \$0.39 for each additional minute. It shows a relationship between the length of a call in minutes and the cost of the call. The pairs of points in the table are graphed on the right.

time/min	total cost
0.5	\$0.58
1	0.58
1.5	0.97
2	0.97
2.5	1.36
3	1.36
3.5	1.75
4	1.75
4.5	2.14
5	2.14

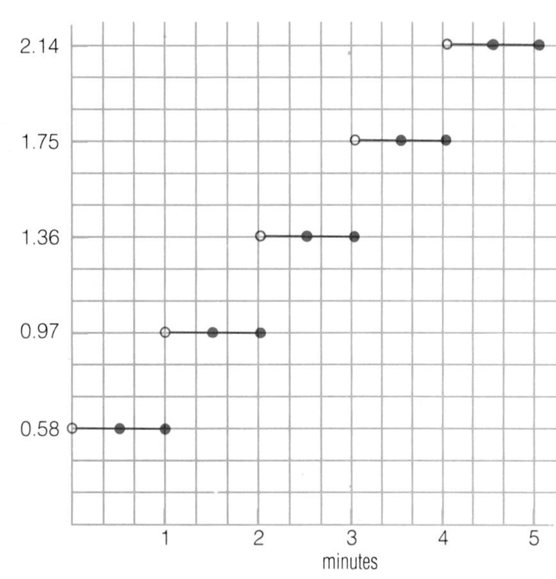

The cost of a call stays the same for any part of a minute. For example, from the beginning of the call to the end of the first minute, the cost is \$0.58. On the graph, this is a horizontal line from 0 to 1. As soon as the call goes over 1 minute in length, the cost jumps to \$0.97, and the line on the graph also jumps. The graph shows a jump at the end of each minute.

1. Between 5 p.m. and 11 p.m., rates are reduced to \$0.34 for the first minute and \$0.24 for each additional minute. Complete a table of values and make a graph showing the relationship between time and cost.
2. On Saturday and Sunday, rates for direct-dialed calls are reduced to \$0.23 for the first minute and \$0.16 for each additional minute. Complete a table of values and make a graph.
3. For calls handled by the operator, a \$1.55 charge is added to the regular charges. Complete a table of values and make a graph for Saturday and Sunday calls handled by the operator. Refer to Exercise 2 for the regular charges.

Chapter 9 Review/Test

Understanding

True or False?

9-2 **1.** Point $(2, 3)$ is on the graph of $y = ax + b$ only if $3 = 2a + b$.

9-6 **2.** Variable y varies directly with x in this table.

x	1	2	3	4	5
y	3	6	10	13	15

9-2 **3.** All the number pairs in this table satisfy the equation $y = 3x + 1$.

9-7 **4.** A line that passes through the points $(1, 5)$ and $(3, 1)$ has a slope of -2.

9-9 **5.** Point $(1, 1)$ is a solution for the system of equations $\begin{aligned} 2x + 3y &= 5 \\ x + ay &= 2 \end{aligned}$ if $a = 1$.

9-11 **6.** The solution to the inequality $y < 2x + 1$ consists of all the points on the line $y = 2x + 1$.

Skill

9-1 **7.** Draw a rectangular coordinate system and graph the points $A(-2, 3)$, $B(2, 5)$, $C(-2, -4)$, and $D(4, 3)$.

9-2 **8.** Which of the ordered pairs $(-3, -6)$ or $(-3, 6)$ is a solution for the linear equation $2x + y = 0$?

9-7 **9.** Find the slope of the line that contains the points $A(-1, 2)$ and $B(2, -4)$.

9-7 **10.** Find the slope of the line $y = 3x + 4$.

9-9 **11.** Graph the equations to solve the system $x + 2y = 1, x - y = -2$.

9-10 **12.** Graph on the number line the solution to $3x - 2 > 1$.

9-11 **13.** Is $(4, -1)$ a solution to the inequality $y < 2 - x$? Graph this inequality.

Applications

9-5 **14.** Bob sold a radio at a garage sale for \$17. This was \$3 more than $\frac{1}{7}$ of its original price. What was the original price of the radio?

9-5 **15.** A house-painting company charges \$180 to paint two rooms, and \$80 for each additional room. How much would it cost to have 5 rooms painted?

9-12 **16.** The band is selling boxes of cookies for \$2 per box and frozen pizzas for \$7 per pizza. The band needs to sell a total of \$1,125 to pay for new flags. Write an inequality that must be satisfied if they are successful in their project.

Cumulative Review

5-5 Write in expanded form. Simplify if possible.

1. 9^5 **2.** $(-6)^4$ **3.** t^3

5-5 Write using exponents.

4. $9 \cdot 9 \cdot 9 \cdot 9$ **5.** $ccccccc$ **6.** $-2(-2)(-2)$

5-5 Multiply. Give the answer in exponent form.

7. $4^3 \cdot 4^2$ **8.** $(-5)^7 \cdot (-5)^3$ **9.** $v^3 \cdot v$

5-5 Evaluate each expression.

10. $3^3 + 3^1$ **11.** $(-4)^2 + (-4)^2$

5-6 Give the prime factorization.

12. 72 **13.** 25 **14.** 110 **15.** 200

5-7 Find the Greatest Common Factor (GCF) of each pair of numbers.

16. 12, 20 **17.** 42, 48 **18.** 45, 120

5-9 Find the Least Common Multiple (LCM) of each pair of numbers.

19. 2, 15 **20.** 8, 12 **21.** 12, 30

6-4 Write each as a decimal. Use a bar for repeating decimals.

22. $\frac{2}{3}$ **23.** $\frac{7}{8}$ **24.** $\frac{5}{11}$

7-6 Simplify. Write the expression with exponents.

25. $\frac{5^8}{5^3}$ **26.** $\frac{(-7)^7}{(-7)^3}$ **27.** $\frac{r^5}{r^8}$

7-6 Write the expression without exponents.

28. 2^{-3} **29.** $(-3)^{-2}$ **30.** $\frac{(-6)^5}{(-6)^7}$

7-7 Write in scientific notation.

31. 414 **32.** 33,000 **33.** 12,000,000

34. 0.05 **35.** 0.0000225 **36.** 0.0089

7-7 Write in decimal form.

37. 2.78×10^4 **38.** 3.0×10^{-5} **39.** 7.08×10^{-3}

9-7 Find the slope of the line.

40. A line that contains the points $A(-2, 2)$ and $B(2, -2)$.

41. $4x + y = -2$

10

Ratio, Proportion, and Percent

When Rochelle and Al rode the Spin-A-Whirl, 7 of the 20 cars were empty. Find the ratio of full cars to empty cars.

10-1 Ratio

Objective To understand ratios and to write a ratio as a fraction in lowest terms.

Application

In the 1933 version of the movie *King Kong,* the big ape was reported to be 50 ft tall! The model used for King Kong was actually 18 in. tall. All objects used for models in this movie had to be of the same ratio.

Understand the Ideas

You have used the symbol $\frac{a}{b}$ to represent a fraction and a rational number. Here you will see another way this symbol is used in mathematics.

A comparison of one number to another is called a **ratio.** If we say the ratio of two numbers is 2 to 1, then the first number is twice as large as the second number. This ratio can be written as

$\frac{2}{1}$ 2:1 or 2 to 1.

A ratio is in **lowest terms** when the only common factor of the numbers being compared is 1.

Example

Write the ratio used for *King Kong,* as given in the **application,** as a fraction in lowest terms.

Solution

We can write the ratio of King Kong's reported height to the actual height. For the comparison to make sense, the numbers must have the same units. 50 ft $\times$ 12 in./ft = 600 in. so we can write $\frac{600}{18}$.

$\frac{600}{18} = \frac{100}{3}$ Divide 600 and 18 by 6, the greatest factor.

The ratio used for all models in *King Kong* was 100 in. to 3 in.

Try This Write each ratio as a fraction in lowest terms.

a. 9:27 **b.** 36 in. to 2 ft **c.** $\frac{35}{28}$

d. The ratio of the length of an airplane to the length of a model of the airplane is 432:12. Write this ratio as a fraction in lowest terms.

There are several types of comparisons that can be expressed as a ratio. In Example 1, you compared different objects using the same units. A ratio can also be a comparison of one part of a set to another part of a set. The ratio of the number of G-rated movies to the number of PG-rated movies for the data at the right is 3 to 5 or $\frac{3}{5}$.

Central Ten Theaters
Waves on the Beach (G)
Bonzo the Flea (G)
Weekend at the Beach (PG)
What's in the Basement? (PG)
Bomber Brat (R)
Fuzzy Comes Home (G)
Fly Away (R)
Kim's Adventure (PG)
Bikers' Parade (PG)
Balloons for Bambi (PG)

A ratio can also be a comparison of one part of a set to the whole set. The ratio of the number of G-rated movies to the total number of movies is 3 to 10 or $\frac{3}{10}$. A fraction compares one part of a set to the whole set. So, a fraction is one type of a ratio.

Class Exercises

Give the ratio. Do not express in lowest terms.

1. cellos to violins
2. double basses to harps
3. harps to total strings
4. violas to cellos
5. flutes to total woodwinds
6. flutes to harps
7. saxophones to all instruments listed

Strings	Woodwinds
34 violins	2 oboes
10 cellos	1 English horn
12 violas	2 flutes
9 double basses	1 piccolo
2 harps	5 bassoons
	6 clarinets
	2 saxophones

Discuss the Ideas

8. Which three of the Class Exercises above are examples of how a ratio can be the same as a fraction? Explain.

Exercises

Practice and Apply

Write each ratio as a fraction in lowest terms.

1. $\frac{24}{16}$	**2.** 8 to 14	**3.** 16:36	**4.** 26:10
5. 9 to 24	**6.** $\frac{3}{33}$	**7.** 12 to 7	**8.** 30:18
9. 36:24	**10.** 7 to 35	**11.** $\frac{16}{10}$	**12.** $\frac{8}{64}$
13. 28:7	**14.** 10 to 90	**15.** 64 to 36	**16.** 48:144
17. 10 to 36	**18.** 24:60	**19.** 18:36	**20.** 60 to 200

Write each ratio using the data at the right.

21. singles to doubles

22. doubles to triples

23. singles, doubles, and triples to homeruns

24. total hits to total at bats

25. A rock band needed 250 hours of studio work to record an album with 45 minutes of music. What is the ratio of minutes of album music to minutes of work needed?

1989 National League Championship Series **Will Clark's Hits**	
Bases	**Number**
singles	7
doubles	3
triples	1
homeruns	2
total times at bat	20

26. A plane that held a total of 225 passengers had 12 passengers in first class and 113 passengers in "coach." What was the ratio of full seats to empty seats?

27. Six buses took 425 students to a state capital. Four adults were on each bus. What was the ratio of adults to students?

Extend and Apply

Write each ratio in two other ways.

28. x to y **29.** y to x **30.** $3a$ to b

31. $(s + t)$ to p **32.** $(m + n)$ to z **33.** $(a + b)$ to $(a - b)$

34. **Communicate** The Empire State Building is 1,250 ft (15,000 in.) high. What was the height of the model used for this building in the movie King Kong?

a. Solve this problem using any method you choose.

b. Compare your solution with a classmate. Do you have the same answer? Did you solve the problem in the same way? If not, which method do you like best?

Use Mathematical Reasoning

35. How many girls are in a class of 32 students if the ratio of girls to boys is 3:5?

36. A builder used 12 parts sand, 15 parts gravel, 6 parts cement, and 3 parts water in a concrete mix. You can write these relationships as 12:15:6:3. Give the ratio in lowest terms.

Mixed Review

Solve and check. **37.** $9y = 3y - 45$ **38.** $2(a + 6) - 4(a + 1) = 4$

39. $z + 45 < 36$ **40.** $18 > -3c$ **41.** $9 < t + 2$

Write each as a decimal. **42.** $3 \div 8$ **43.** $1 \div 20$ **44.** $3 \div 25$

Evaluate. Reduce to lowest terms. **45.** $\left(\frac{3}{4}\right)\left(\frac{2}{3}\right)$ **46.** $\frac{4}{7} + \frac{1}{2}$

10-2 Proportion

Objective To determine whether ratios are equal; to solve proportions.

Application

Fly By Night Airlines tries to keep the ratio of the number of discount-fare seats to total seats at about 2 to 15 for all of their flights. How many discount-fare tickets should be sold for a flight with 240 seats? (See Example 3.)

Understand the Ideas

The ratios $\frac{10}{18}$ and $\frac{15}{27}$ can both be written in lowest terms as $\frac{5}{9}$. You can write the equation $\frac{10}{18} = \frac{15}{27}$.

An equation stating that two ratios are equal is called a **proportion.** Notice that the cross products shown by the arrows below in the proportion $\frac{10}{18} = \frac{15}{27}$ are equal.

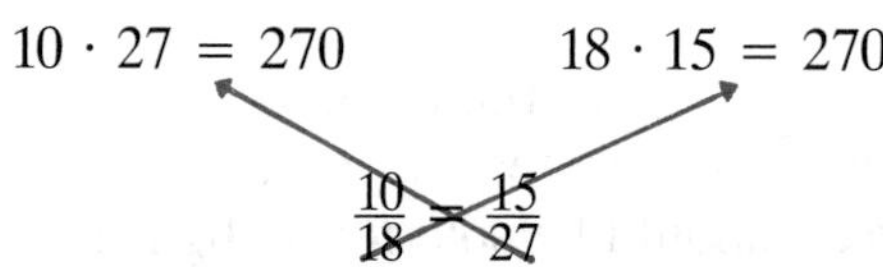

Property of Proportions

Two ratios are equal if and only if the cross products are equal.

$\frac{a}{b} = \frac{c}{d}$ **if and only if** $ad = bc (b \neq 0 \text{ and } d \neq 0)$

Example 1

Write = or ≠ for the □. Use the Property of Proportions. $\frac{28}{21} \square \frac{8}{6}$

Solution

$\frac{28}{21} \square \frac{8}{6}$

$28 \cdot 6 \stackrel{?}{=} 21 \cdot 8$ Find the cross products.

$168 = 168$

$\frac{28}{21} = \frac{8}{6}$ Since the cross products are equal, the ratios are equal.

Try This Write = or ≠ for the □. Use the Property of Proportions.

a. $\frac{8}{12} \square \frac{12}{15}$ **b.** $\frac{8}{3} \square \frac{16}{6}$

When one of the numbers in a proportion is not known, you can use the Property of Proportions to write an equation.

Example 2

Solve and check. $\frac{x}{40} = \frac{3}{5}$

Solution

$$\frac{x}{40} = \frac{3}{5}$$

$$5 \cdot x = 40 \cdot 3 \quad \text{Property of Proportions}$$

$$5x = 120$$

$$\frac{5x}{5} = \frac{120}{5} \quad \text{Divide each side by 5.}$$

$$x = 24$$

Check

$$\frac{24}{40} \stackrel{?}{=} \frac{3}{5} \quad \text{Replace } x \text{ with 24.}$$

$$5 \cdot 24 \stackrel{?}{=} 40 \cdot 3 \quad \text{Property of Proportions}$$

$$120 = 120 \checkmark \quad \text{The solution is 24.}$$

Try This Solve and check. **c.** $\frac{3}{4} = \frac{m}{20}$ **d.** $\frac{2}{7} = \frac{18}{b}$

Example 3

Use a proportion to solve the problem posed in the **application.** Fly By Night Airlines keeps the ratio of discount-fare seats to total seats at 2 to 15. How many discount fare tickets should be sold for a flight with 240 seats?

Solution

$$\frac{2}{15} = \frac{x}{240}$$

To write the proportion, set up each ratio in the same way. Both ratios compare discount seats to total seats.

$$2 \cdot 240 = 15 \cdot x$$

Set up an equation by finding the cross products. Then solve the equation.

$$\frac{2 \cdot 240}{15} = x$$

$$32 = x$$

There should be 32 discount-fare seats sold on a flight with 240 seats.

Try This **e.** Use a proportion to solve. Chemical C is made up of chemicals A and B in the ratio of 17 to 5. To make a batch of chemical C with 102 units of chemical A, how many units of chemical B are needed?

Example 3 could have been solved using a different proportion.

$$\frac{2}{x} = \frac{15}{240}$$

In this case, each ratio compares the number of seats in the general ratio, 2:15, to the number of seats on the plane. Notice that the cross products give the same equation. Whenever you solve an application using proportions, there is more than one way to translate the problem into a proportion.

Class Exercises

State the equation you would solve to find the missing number.

1. $\frac{1}{2} = \frac{x}{18}$
2. $\frac{n}{48} = \frac{3}{4}$
3. $\frac{4}{1} = \frac{24}{t}$
4. $\frac{3}{10} = \frac{y}{40}$

Discuss the Ideas

5. What, if any, are the differences between a ratio and a proportion?

Exercises

Practice and Apply

Write = or ≠ for each □. Use the Property of Proportions.

1. $\frac{4}{5}$ □ $\frac{12}{15}$
2. $\frac{5}{2}$ □ $\frac{35}{14}$
3. $\frac{4}{15}$ □ $\frac{3}{7}$
4. $\frac{8}{6}$ □ $\frac{28}{22}$
5. $\frac{9}{16}$ □ $\frac{3}{4}$
6. $\frac{8}{15}$ □ $\frac{20}{45}$
7. $\frac{3}{2}$ □ $\frac{12}{8}$
8. $\frac{17}{34}$ □ $\frac{1}{2}$
9. $\frac{28}{35}$ □ $\frac{4}{5}$
10. $\frac{4}{7}$ □ $\frac{32}{56}$
11. $\frac{9}{4}$ □ $\frac{63}{28}$
12. $\frac{12}{30}$ □ $\frac{10}{25}$

Solve and check.

13. $\frac{24}{x} = \frac{4}{3}$
14. $\frac{5}{3} = \frac{y}{42}$
15. $\frac{1}{2} = \frac{m}{18}$
16. $\frac{t}{14} = \frac{5}{2}$
17. $\frac{12}{27} = \frac{8}{m}$
18. $\frac{r}{27} = \frac{8}{18}$
19. $\frac{u}{7} = \frac{22}{14}$
20. $\frac{12}{30} = \frac{10}{n}$
21. $\frac{4}{5} = \frac{28}{x}$
22. $\frac{15}{y} = \frac{10}{8}$
23. $\frac{63}{144} = \frac{t}{16}$
24. $\frac{8}{15} = \frac{m}{105}$
25. $\frac{7}{x} = \frac{4}{9}$
26. $\frac{y}{42} = \frac{15}{18}$
27. $\frac{100}{m} = \frac{90}{45}$
28. $\frac{18}{y} = \frac{126}{150}$

Use a proportion to solve Exercises 29–32.

29. Four shovels of sand are used for every 5 shovels of gravel in making concrete. How many shovels of sand are needed for 25 shovels of gravel?
30. Bob's snack mix contains both peanuts and pecans in a ratio of 8 to 5. How many grams of pecans does he need if he uses 520 g of peanuts?
31. The ratio of Ann's weight to Tina's weight is 5:6. Ann weighs 85 pounds. How much does Tina weigh?
32. The ratio of expenses to income in the Johnsons' business is 5 to 8. What are their expenses for a month in which their income is $9,800?

Extend and Apply

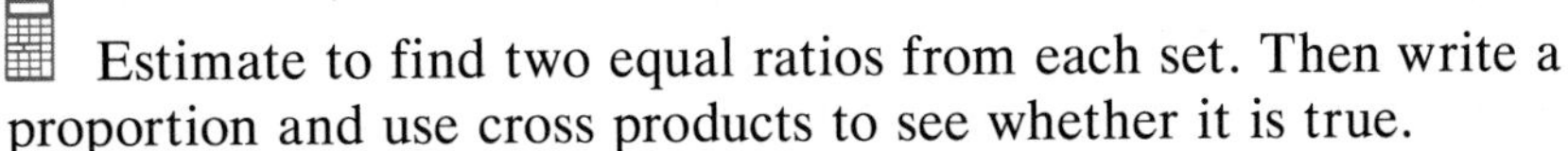

Estimate to find two equal ratios from each set. Then write a proportion and use cross products to see whether it is true.

33. $\frac{5}{12}; \frac{25}{60}; \frac{50}{144}$ **34.** $\frac{24}{125}; \frac{4}{25}; \frac{32}{200}$ **35.** $\frac{6}{15}; \frac{42}{90}; \frac{84}{180}$

36. The ratio of full seats to the total number of seats on Eli's flight is 3 to 7. There are 28 empty seats. How many people are on the plane?

37. The ratio of girls to boys in Maria's school is 3:4. The school has 228 boys. How many students does it have all together?

38. Find two values for x and y so that $\frac{x}{12} = \frac{28}{y}$.

Use Mathematical Reasoning

39. Eric's school system has 9000 pupils and a teacher-pupil ratio of 1:30. How many more or fewer teachers are needed to reduce the teacher-pupil ratio to 1:25?

40. It takes 12 minutes to cut a log into 4 pieces. How long will it take to cut a log into 6 pieces?

Mixed Review

Reduce to lowest terms. **41.** $\frac{70}{98}$ **42.** $\frac{27}{144}$ **43.** $\frac{12}{22}$ **44.** $\frac{40}{64}$

Estimate each product or quotient. **45.** 385×22 **46.** 2.85×16.3

47. $71.2 \div 12.3$ **48.** $83.7 \div 8.5$ **49.** $608 \div 33$ **50.** $124.7 \div 11.1$

Connections Numbers to Algebra

Study the examples to see how proportions involving numbers are related to proportions in algebra.

Numbers	Algebra	
$\frac{8}{5} = \frac{16}{12 - 2}$	$\frac{5}{3} = \frac{10}{x - 1}$	
$8 \cdot (12 - 2) = 5 \cdot 16$	$5 \cdot (x - 1) = 3 \cdot 10$	Property of Proportions
$8 \cdot 12 - 8 \cdot 2 = 5 \cdot 16$	$5x - 5 = 30$	Distributive Property
$96 - 16 = 80$	$5x = 35$	
$80 = 80$	$x = 7$	

Solve each proportion. Check your solution.

1. $\frac{2}{3} = \frac{a + 1}{12}$ **2.** $\frac{n + 1}{9} = \frac{2}{6}$ **3.** $\frac{4}{3} = \frac{32}{x - 1}$ **4.** $\frac{x - 3}{6} = \frac{12}{9}$

10-3 Rate

Objective To simplify rates, and to solve problems involving rates.

Application

Lynette is planning a trip to visit her cousin. She knows that the bus trip is 216 miles long and that it is scheduled to last 4 hours. What is the average rate of speed of the bus?

Understand the Ideas

A **rate** is a ratio that involves two different units. A rate is usually given as a quantity per unit, such as miles per hour (mi/h). You can use division to simplify a rate.

Example 1

Simplify 216 mi/4 h to find the average rate of speed of the bus in the **application.**

Solution $\frac{216 \text{ mi}}{4 \text{ h}} = 54 \text{ mi/h}$ 54 mi/1 h can be written as 54 mi/h.

The bus travels at an average speed of 54 mi/h.

Try This Simplify each rate. **a.** 87 km/10 L **b.** 750 word/2 min

Example 2

Solve. Tyrone types 150 words in two minutes. How many words can he type in 5 minutes?

Solution

$$\frac{x}{5} = \frac{150}{2}$$
$$2x = 150 \cdot 5$$
$$2x = 750$$
$$x = 375$$

He can type 375 words in 5 minutes.

Try This Solve.

c. How much should Fran get for 3 hours of work at $6.25/hour?

Class Exercises

Describe a situation in which each rate might be used.

1. km/L **2.** miles/hour **3.** km/hour

4. revolutions/min **5.** beats/min **6.** words/min

Discuss the Ideas

7. Would you best describe rate as a special type of ratio or a special type of proportion? Explain.

Exercises

Practice and Apply

Simplify each rate.

1. $56/7 h **2.** 75 km/10 L **3.** 1250 words/5 min

4. 78 cm/6 s **5.** 3,750 km/4 h **6.** 35 days/5 weeks

7. $220/40 h **8.** 105 people/35 cars **9.** 143 players/11 teams

Solve.

10. A motorist drove 1200 km on 45 L of gasoline. How many liters are needed to drive 500 km?

11. Apples are on sale at 4 for 60¢. How much will 18 apples cost?

12. What is the rate in beats per minute for a pulse rate of 25 beats per 15 seconds?

Extend and Apply

13. A man bought a crate of apples for $10. The apples cost 90¢/lb and 4 apples equal about 1 pound. About how many apples should the crate contain?

14. How long would it take to lay 8 rows of 18 bricks each at a rate of 4 bricks per minute?

Use Mathematical Reasoning

15. If $\frac{a}{b} = \frac{c}{d}$ then $\frac{a+b}{b} = \frac{c+d}{d}$. Show why this is true.

16. A recipe calls for two ounces of butter to every 5 tablespoons of flour. A cube of butter is 4 oz, and there are 4 cubes per pound. How many tablespoons of flour are needed for $4\frac{1}{2}$ pounds of butter?

Mixed Review

Solve and check. **17.** $4(m + 2) = 14$ **18.** $3.35 = 1 - t$

19. $r + 0.027 = -0.901$ **20.** $(x + 5) \div 6 = 102$ **21.** $3r = -0.24$

10-4 Scale Drawings

Objective To use scale drawings to find actual dimensions; to reduce actual dimensions to a scale.

Understand the Ideas

In the **scale drawing** below, the dimensions of every object in the drawing are reduced by the same ratio or **scale.** The scale for this drawing is 5 cm to 2 m. This means that an object that has a length of 5 cm in the scale drawing has an actual length of 2 m.

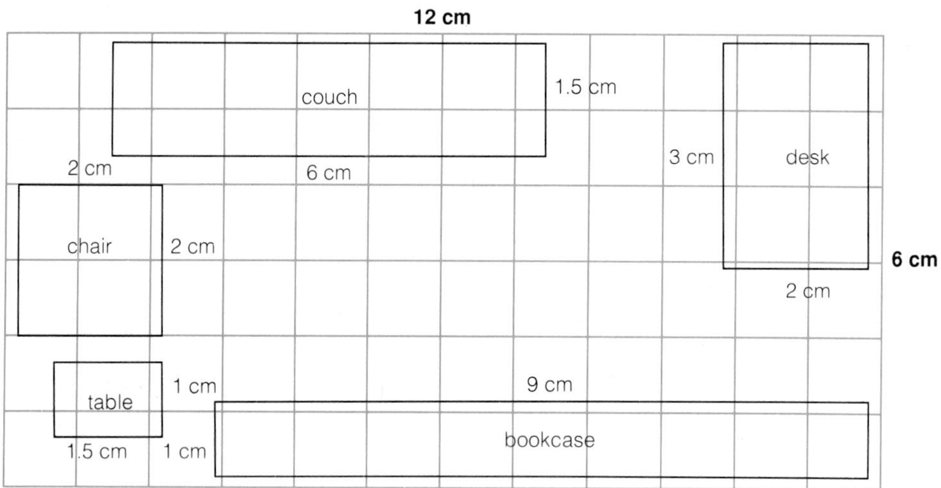

You can use the scale in the drawing to set up a proportion and find the actual dimensions of the objects shown in the picture.

Example 1

Find the actual length of the couch in the scale drawing above.

Solution Let L = actual length of couch.

$\frac{5}{2} = \frac{6}{L} \begin{matrix} \leftarrow \text{cm} \\ \leftarrow \text{m} \end{matrix}$ The scale is 5 cm to 2 m. The length of the couch in the drawing is 6 cm, and the actual length of the couch is unknown.

$5 \cdot L = 2 \cdot 6$

$L = 2.4$

The actual length of the couch is 2.4 m.

Try This

a. Find the actual length of the desk in the drawing above.

b. Find the actual width of the table in the drawing above.

c. Find the actual length of the chair in the drawing above.

You can find the scale dimensions of an object if you know its actual dimensions and the scale.

Example 2

The actual dimensions of a park are 825 m wide by 1350 m long. Find the width of this park on a scale drawing with a scale of 1 cm = 75 m.

Solution

Let W = scale drawing width of the park.

$\frac{W}{825} = \frac{1}{75} \begin{matrix} \leftarrow \text{cm} \\ \leftarrow \text{m} \end{matrix}$ The width of the park in the scale drawing is unknown. The actual width is 825 m.

$75 \cdot W = 1 \cdot 825$

$W = 11$

The width of the park in the scale drawing is 11 cm.

Try This **d.** Find the scale dimension for the length of the park.

Class Exercises

Refer to the scale drawing of the living room on the previous page and give the proportion you would solve to find the actual dimension. The scale for the drawing is 5 cm:2 m.

1. width of chair **2.** width of bookcase **3.** width of couch

Discuss the Ideas

4. When you use a proportion to solve scale drawing problems, can the proportion be set up in more than one way? Use Example 1 to explain.

Exercises

Practice and Apply

Refer to the scale drawing to find the actual straight-line distance between each pair of towns.

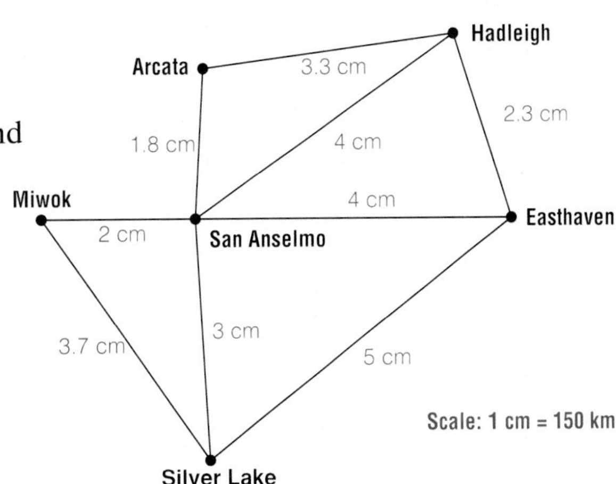

1. San Anselmo to Easthaven
2. Arcata to Hadleigh
3. Easthaven to Miwok
4. Hadleigh to San Anselmo
5. Arcata to Silver Lake
6. Silver Lake to San Anselmo
7. Miwok to Silver Lake

Find the scale dimensions for each if the scale is 5 mm:2 m.

8. Dining Room: 5 m × 4 m

9. Bedroom: 4 m × 5 m

10. Bench: 1.5 m × 1 m

11. Table: 1 m × 3 m

12. Dresser: 2 m × 0.5 m

13. Kitchen table: 1.4 m × 0.66 m

Extend and Apply

The scale for this drawing of a patio is 1 cm:1.25 m. Measure the dimensions of the patio to the nearest millimeter. Then use a proportion to calculate the actual dimensions.

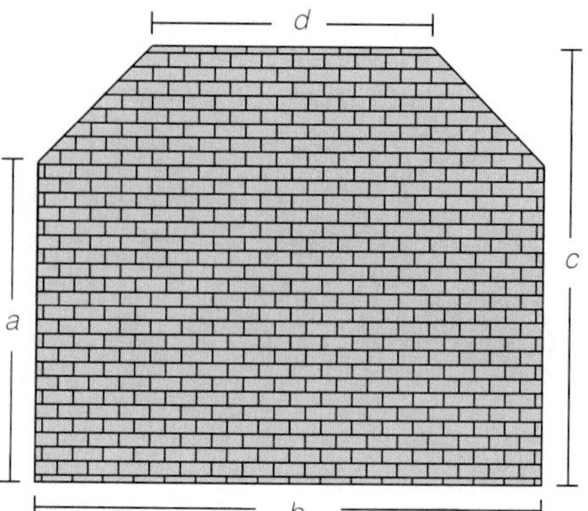

14. dimension a

15. dimension c

16. dimension b

17. dimension d

18. The distance from A to B on the map is 4.2 cm. The distance from B to C is 1.4 cm. B is on a straight road from A to C. The scale on the map is 1 cm:125 km. What is the actual distance from A to C?

19. On a map with scale 2 cm:25 km, what would be the dimensions of a 145 km by 80 km rectangle?

Use Mathematical Reasoning

20. An insect in a picture is $\frac{1}{2}$ inch long and a label says "enlarged 12 times." What is the insect's actual length?

21. Charles wants to make a scale drawing to represent a driveway 64 ft long. His paper is $8\frac{1}{2}$ inches square. Which of the following scales could he use?

a. 1 in. = 1 ft **b.** $\frac{1}{4}$ in. = 1 ft **c.** $\frac{1}{8}$ in. = 1 ft **d.** $\frac{1}{16}$ in. = 1 ft

22. The length of a rectangle is 5 m more than the width. The ratio of the length to the width is 5 to 4. What are the dimensions of the rectangle? (Let x = the width of the rectangle.)

Mixed Review

Simplify. **23.** $14m + 7m$ **24.** $3c + 9 + (-6c) - 12$ **25.** $t + 3t + 8$

Evaluate for $a = \frac{1}{2}, b = \frac{2}{3}, c = \frac{1}{5}$. **26.** $ab + c$ **27.** $a(2c - b)$

Simplify. **28.** $\frac{x^5}{x^4}$ **29.** $\frac{5^4}{5^2}$ **30.** $\frac{x^6}{x^4}$ **31.** $\frac{7^5}{7}$

Write each as an improper fraction. **32.** $9\frac{2}{3}$ **33.** $-6\frac{3}{5}$

10-5 Problem Solving: Applications

Determining the Best Buy

Objective To compare unit prices and determine best buys.

The cost of one unit of an item is called the **unit price.** You can find and compare unit prices to determine the better buy. The item with the lower unit price is usually considered the better buy.

A & B Discount	
100 vitamins	2/$1.99
video cassettes	3/$17.50
earrings	2 pair for $5
hand lotion	6 oz/$4.99
cologne	2 oz/$2.99
shampoo	15 oz/$2.99
glass cleaner	32 oz/$1.19

Bob's Super Saver	
100 vitamins	4/$3.75
video cassettes	2/$11
earrings	4 pair for $11
hand lotion	10 oz/$8.10
cologne	3 oz/$3.59
shampoo	24 oz/$5.28
glass cleaner	24 oz/$0.96

Example

Find the unit prices and determine which price advertised above is the better buy for a video cassette.

Solution

17.50 [÷] 3 [=] 5.8333333 $\approx$ 5.84

11.00 [÷] 2 [=] 5.5

Divide the total price by the number of cassettes to find the unit price. Prices are rounded to the next highest cent.

The price 2 for $11 is better than the price 3 for $17.50.

Problems

Use data from the advertisements on page 353 to find the unit prices and tell which store has the better buy for each.

1. hand lotion **2.** shampoo **3.** cologne

4. glass cleaner **5.** earrings **6.** vitamins

Solve.

7. Jones' store has a price of 3 for $50 on video games. Smith's store is selling 8 video games for $134.50. Which store has the better unit price for video games?

8. Soup is priced at 2 cans for $0.75 at one store. At another store, six cans of the same soup cost $1.98. Find the unit prices to determine the better buy.

9. At A & B Discount, apple juice costs $1.26 for the 1.4 L size. At Bob's Super Saver it costs $1.53 for the 1.8 L size. Which store has the better buy on apple juice?

10. Ground beef is on sale for $1.25/lb. How much could you get for $5?

11. Shampoo at A & B Discount is usually $2.99 for 15 oz. Today, the 10 oz. size is on sale for $2.10. Estimate the cost per ounce. About how much more or less per ounce would the smaller size cost?

12. Squash costs $1.85/kg. Estimate the cost of a squash weighing 0.54 kg.

Use the advertisement below to solve.

13. Mrs. Hamilton bought 2 loaves of wheat bread, 3 loaves of rye bread, 12 muffins, and 15 biscuits on sale. How much did she save off the regular price?

Item	Sale Price	Regular Price
Wheat Bread	2 for $1.25	$0.75 a loaf
Rye Bread	2 for $1.40	$0.90 a loaf
Muffins	6 for $0.75	$0.15 each
Biscuits	6 for $0.54	$0.12 each

14. **Data Search** Choose two grocery stores. Find common brands for: $\frac{1}{2}$ gallon whole milk; 20 lbs dog food; 3 cans frozen orange juice; 2 loaves whole wheat bread; 1 whole chicken. Which store has the better buy for each?

What's Your Decision?

You have $10 to spend on items in the advertisements on page 353. What would you buy and from which store? Justify your decision.

10-6 Percent and Fractions

Objective To write a percent as a fraction in lowest terms; to use a proportion to write a fraction as a percent.

Explore

Using a 10 by 10 grid, find three ways you can shade small squares to make one of your initials. Your figure should be made of whole squares only. For each initial, tell how many of the 100 squares are shaded. Compare to see who has the most and the least shaded squares.

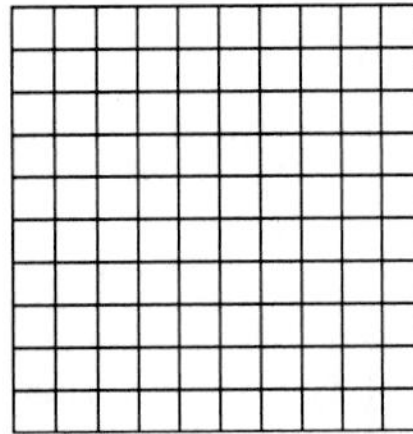

Understand the Ideas

The ratio of a number to 100 is called a **percent.** The word percent means *per one hundred,* and is represented by the symbol **%.** You can write a percent as a fraction.

Example 1

Write 68% as a fraction in lowest terms.

Solution

$68\% = \frac{68}{100} = \frac{17}{25}$ Write the number in front of the % sign over 100.

Try This Write each as a fraction in lowest terms.

a. 55% **b.** 4% **c.** 21%

Example 2

Write $12\frac{1}{2}\%$ as a fraction in lowest terms.

Solution

$12\frac{1}{2}\% = \frac{12\frac{1}{2}}{100}$ Write the number in front of the % sign over 100.

$= 12\frac{1}{2} \div 100$ $\frac{a}{b}$ is the same as $a \div b$.

$= \frac{25}{2} \div 100$

$= \frac{25}{2} \times \frac{1}{100} = \frac{25}{200}$

$= \frac{1}{8}$ $12\frac{1}{2}\% = \frac{1}{8}$

Try This Write each as a fraction in lowest terms.

d. $5\frac{1}{2}\%$ **e.** $2\frac{3}{4}\%$ **f.** $6\frac{2}{3}\%$

You can use a proportion to change a fraction to a percent. This method is recommended when you have a fraction that is easy to change to an equivalent fraction with a denominator of 100.

Example 3

Use a proportion to write $\frac{3}{4}$ as a percent.

Solution

$\frac{3}{4} = \frac{x}{100}$	3 is to 4 as what is to 100? Change $\frac{3}{4}$ to a fraction with a denominator of 100.
$100 \cdot 3 = 4 \cdot x$	Property of Proportions
$300 = 4x$	
$\frac{300}{4} = \frac{4x}{4}$	
$75 = x$	
$\frac{3}{4}$ is equal to 75%	The numerator over 100 is the percent. Write the numerator in front of the % sign.

Try This Use a proportion to write each as a percent.

g. $\frac{24}{25}$ **h.** $\frac{2}{5}$ **i.** $\frac{3}{20}$

Class Exercises

Give each as a percent.

1. $\frac{37}{100}$ **2.** 88:100 **3.** 53 to 100 **4.** 40 out of 100

Discuss the Ideas

5. What do you think is meant by the statement, "There is a 50% chance of rain."?

Exercises

Practice and Apply

Write each as a fraction in lowest terms.

1. 45% **2.** 70% **3.** 5% **4.** 75%

5. 20% **6.** 50% **7.** 10% **8.** 35%

9. 100% **10.** $10\frac{1}{4}\%$ **11.** $5\frac{3}{4}\%$ **12.** $3\frac{1}{3}\%$

13. $9\frac{3}{4}\%$ **14.** 91% **15.** $14\frac{9}{10}\%$ **16.** $1\frac{1}{10}\%$

Use a proportion to write each as a percent.

17. $\frac{3}{5}$ 18. $\frac{1}{2}$ 19. $\frac{1}{4}$ 20. $\frac{4}{40}$

21. $\frac{18}{25}$ 22. $\frac{50}{50}$ 23. $\frac{4}{5}$ 24. $\frac{3}{10}$

25. Six of the 10 copies of *Gulliver's Travels* were checked out of the library. What percent of the copies were checked out?

26. In a survey of 500 mothers, about 300 worked outside the home. What percentage of those surveyed was this?

Extend and Apply

Solve.

27. If the ratio $2x:100$ is equivalent to 68%, what is x?

28. The Better Business Bureau of Greenville had 85 buyer complaints one year. Twenty of these involved automobile businesses. What percentage of the complaints involved automobile businesses?

29. What percentage of the whole numbers from 1 to 100 are prime numbers? What percentage are composite numbers?

Use Mathematical Reasoning

Use estimation to decide which test each student took if the math test had 30 questions and the English test had 50 questions.

30. Wanda had 24 correct and scored 80%.

31. Danny missed 10 and scored 80%.

32. James scored 90%. If he had answered 5 more questions correctly, he would have scored 100%.

Mixed Review

Solve and check. 33. $3m + 13 = 1 + m$ 34. $4(3 - t) = 3(1 - t)$

35. $-32 = 16a$ 36. $6(c + 4.5) = 36.6$ 37. $14k - 21 = 0$

Estimation

Study the percents to which these commonly used fractions correspond.

$\frac{1}{5} = 20\%$ $\frac{1}{4} = 25\%$ $\frac{1}{3} = 33\frac{1}{3}\%$

$\frac{1}{2} = 50\%$ $\frac{2}{3} = 66\frac{2}{3}\%$ $\frac{3}{4} = 75\%$

Substitute compatible numbers to estimate the equivalent percent for each.

1. $\frac{24}{49}$ 2. $\frac{29}{41}$ 3. $\frac{9}{28}$

4. $\frac{5}{16}$ 5. $\frac{13}{18}$ 6. $\frac{5}{24}$

10-7 Percent, Decimals, and Fractions

Objectives To write percents as decimals and decimals as percents; to write fractions as decimals and then as percents.

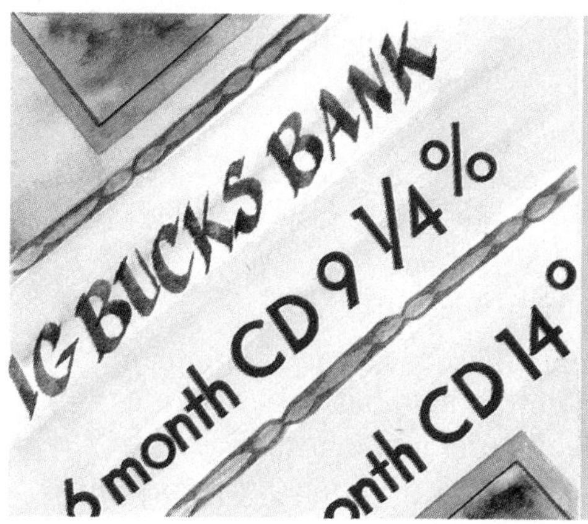

Application

Big Bucks Bank is offering a 6-month certificate of deposit (CD) for $9\frac{1}{4}\%$. Floyd wants to express this percent as a decimal to find out how much interest he'll earn on his CD.

Understand the Ideas

When you solve problems involving percent, you will often work with percents expressed as fractions or as decimals. The following examples show how to change a percent to a decimal and a decimal to a percent.

Example 1

Write $9\frac{1}{4}\%$, the interest rate for the CD in the **application,** as a decimal.

Solution $9\frac{1}{4}\% = 9.25\%$ Rewrite the mixed number as a decimal.

$= \frac{9.25}{100}$ Write as a fraction with a denominator of 100.

$= 0.0925$ Change the fraction to a decimal.

The interest rate for the CD expressed as a decimal is 0.0925.

Try This Write each as a decimal.

a. 5% **b.** $8\frac{1}{4}\%$ **c.** 125%

Example 2

Write 0.35 as a percent.

Solution $0.35 = \frac{35}{100}$ Change the decimal to a fraction.

$= 35\%$

Try This Write each as a percent.

d. 0.60 **e.** 0.085 **f.** 2.14

Here are three illustrations of a percent expressed as a decimal.

Percent		Decimal
68%	$\frac{68}{100}$	0.68
1.8%	$\frac{1.8}{100} \cdot \frac{10}{10} = \frac{18}{1000}$	0.018
127.5%	$\frac{127.5}{100} \cdot \frac{100}{100} = \frac{12750}{10000}$	1.275

This chart suggests shortcuts for changing a percent to a decimal or a decimal to a percent. To change *a percent to a decimal,* move the decimal point in the percent two places to the left and drop the percent symbol. To change a *decimal to a percent,* move the decimal point in the decimal two places to the right and add the percent symbol.

You can change a fraction to a percent by first changing the fraction to a decimal and then changing the decimal to a percent.

Example 3

Change $\frac{7}{8}$ to a percent.

Solution

7 [÷] 8 [=] [0.875]

Divide the numerator by the denominator to change the fraction to a decimal.

0.875 = 87.5%

Move the decimal point in 0.875 two places to the right to change the decimal to a percent.

If you have a fraction calculator, you can follow this key sequence.

7 [/] 8 [F↔D] [0.875]

If you have a calculator with a percent key, you can follow this key sequence.

7 [÷] 8 [%] [=] [87.5]

Notice that the calculator display shows the percent.

Try This Use a calculator to change each fraction to a percent. Round to the nearest tenth of a percent if necessary.

g. $\frac{1}{6}$ **h.** $\frac{3}{8}$ **i.** $\frac{1}{9}$

Class Exercises

Is the equation true or false?

1. $67\% = \frac{67}{100}$
2. $41\% = 41$
3. $0.78 = 7.8\%$
4. $0.07 = 7\%$
5. $\frac{42.5}{100} = 42\frac{1}{2}\%$
6. $3\% = 0.3$
7. $425\% = 0.425$
8. $1\% = 0.01$
9. $105\% = 1.05$

Discuss the Ideas

10. Which fraction, $\frac{1}{20}$ or $\frac{5}{8}$, could be easily changed to a percent using mental math? Explain.

Exercises

Practice and Apply

Write each percent as a decimal.

1. 40%
2. 10%
3. 5%
4. 65%
5. 2%
6. 15%
7. 150%
8. 1%
9. 12%
10. $10\frac{1}{2}\%$
11. 34%
12. $2\frac{1}{4}\%$
13. $\frac{3}{4}\%$
14. $12\frac{3}{4}\%$
15. $5\frac{5}{8}\%$
16. $75\frac{3}{4}\%$

Write each decimal as a percent.

17. 0.62
18. 0.55
19. 0.05
20. 0.75
21. 0.8
22. 1.25
23. 0.001
24. 0.95
25. 0.015
26. 3.05
27. 0.125
28. 0.508
29. 4.38
30. 2.456
31. 0.006
32. 0.06

Use a calculator to change each fraction to a percent. Round to the nearest tenth of a percent if necessary.

33. $\frac{1}{3}$
34. $\frac{5}{8}$
35. $\frac{5}{6}$
36. $\frac{2}{11}$
37. $\frac{3}{16}$

38. The variable interest rate for a home loan at Big Bucks Bank is 8.625% and the fixed interest rate is 10.625%. Express each rate as a decimal.

39. The computer loan interest rate at Big Bucks Bank is 0.1005. Lotsa Money Savings is advertising computer loans at an interest rate of 0.1050. Express each rate as a percent. Which is greater?

40. Big Bucks Bank offers an interest rate of $9\frac{3}{5}\%$ on checking accounts. Lotsa Money Savings offers 9.45% interest on their checking accounts. Express each rate as a decimal. Which is lower?

Extend and Apply

41. Change $x\%$ to a decimal where x is a whole number.

42. Change y to a percent where y is a whole number.

Copy and complete the chart. Round to the nearest tenth of a percent if necessary.

	Fraction	Decimal	Percent
43.		0.68	
44.	$\frac{3}{8}$		
45.			38%
46.	$\frac{4}{15}$		
47.		0.1225	

Solve.

48. A batting average is the number of hits divided by the number of times at bat, expressed as a decimal rounded to the thousandths place. In 1941, Ted Williams got a hit 40.6% of his times at bat. What was William's battting average in 1941?

49. In 1927, Babe Ruth hit 60 home runs to set a major league record that held for 34 years. In that same year, Ruth's batting average was 0.356. What percentage of his times at bat in 1927 did Ruth get a hit?

50. In 1985, Willie McGee had 216 hits in 612 at-bats. What was his batting average?

51. In 1985, Dwight Gooden won 24 games and lost 4. What percentage of these games did he win?

Use Mathematical Reasoning

Use estimation to find a value for x. Then use a calculator to find the exact value for x.

52. $\frac{x}{16} = 75\%$ **53.** $\frac{x}{20} = 55\%$ **54.** $\frac{x}{90} = 34\frac{4}{9}\%$ **55.** $\frac{x}{500} = \frac{3}{5}\%$

Mixed Review

Solve and check. **56.** $19(m + 3) = 76$ **57.** $2(r - 5) = 11r + 8$

58. $-15 = 3(9 + m) - 3$ **59.** $14 < 3r + 2$ **60.** $-4c + 2c > -16$

Evaluate for $a = 3, b = 4$. **61.** $3(a - b)$ **62.** $b(3a + 2b)$ **63.** $a \div (2b)$

64. $-a(5 - b)$ **65.** $b(b - a)$ **66.** $6(-a)(-b)$

10-8 Problem Solving: Writing Equations

Practice Solving Problems

Objective To solve word problems by writing equations in which one unknown is represented in terms of another.

You can use the Problem-Solving Checklist on page 134 to help you solve problems.

Example

Solve by writing an equation. The cost of a small pizza is 75% of the cost of a medium pizza. What is the cost of each size pizza if the total cost for 1 medium and 1 small pizza is \$15.05?

Solution

Let m = cost of medium pizza.

$0.75m$ = cost of small pizza

$$m + 0.75m = 15.05$$

$$1.75m = 15.05$$

$$m = 8.6$$

A medium pizza costs \$8.60.

$$0.75m = (0.75)(8.6) = 6.45$$

A small pizza costs \$6.45.

Since the cost of the small pizza is given relative to the cost of the medium pizza, let m represent the cost of the medium pizza.

Try This Solve by writing an equation.

a. Linda has half as many paper route customers as George. Together they have 102 customers. How many does George have?

Class Exercises

Discuss the Ideas

1. Suppose you let s = the cost of a small pizza in the example. Will you get a different equation? Will you get a different answer?

Exercises

Practice and Apply

Solve by writing an equation.

1. Donna has 3 times as many books as Gloria. Together they have 76 books. How many does Gloria have?

2. Mr. Lee saved $24.00 when he bought a suit on sale at 15% off the regular price. What was the regular price of the suit?
3. A delivery person has 5 more than twice the number of morning customers on his afternoon route. He has 45 customers in the afternoon. How many morning customers does he have?
4. Rick bought 1 record at the regular price and another for 50% of that price. The total price was $12.24. What was the cost of each record?

Extend and Apply

5. Martha bought a pair of jeans on sale. The sale price was 50% of the original price. She paid with a $20 bill and received $4.25 in change. If there was no tax on the jeans, what was the original price?
6. A salesperson said she would take 10% off the price of a sweater. What was the original price of the sweater if the reduced price was $24.30?
7. Pat was given a 15% raise. She works 20 hours per week. Her earnings after the raise were $103.50 per week. How much money did she make per week before her raise?
8. **Determine Reasonable Answers** Decide whether the answer given is reasonable. If not, explain why. Then solve the problem.

   The owner of a lightbulb factory wants no more than 2 defective bulbs for every 100 bulbs made. Out of a batch of 3,500 bulbs, how many defective bulbs would you expect to find? Answer: 100 defective bulbs

Use Mathematical Reasoning

9. Write a word problem that could be solved using the equation
   a. $0.05x = \$16.80$ **b.** $2x + 5 = 25$.

Mixed Review

Evaluate for $a = 2, b = 3, c = 2$. **10.** b^2c^2 **11.** $2ac - 3b$ **12.** $2b - a$

Write without exponents. **13.** 5^3 **14.** 4^{-3} **15.** $\frac{(-6)^4}{(-6)^6}$

Estimation

Use any estimation techniques you have learned to estimate the following rates.

1. 729 km on 25 L of gasoline. How many km per L is this?
2. $4.13 for 5 hours parking. What is the hourly parking rate?
3. $37.20 for 9 hours of work. What is the hourly wage?
4. 500 miles in $3\frac{1}{4}$ hours. How many miles per hour is this rate?

10-9 Percents Greater Than 100 and Less Than 1

Objectives To write fractions and decimals as percents greater than 100 and less than 1; to write such percents as fractions and decimals.

Application

Alma is enlarging a 5″ by 5″ drawing. The enlarged drawing needs to be 6″ by 6″. What percent should she enter into the copying machine to enlarge the drawing?

Understand the Ideas

"The cost of a house has increased 120% since we moved." "Inflation in that country is running at 125%." It is not uncommon to hear statements involving percents greater than 100. This means that there is more than 1 whole unit.

Example 1

Express $\frac{6}{5}$ as a percent to find what percent Alma used to enlarge the photo in the **application** above.

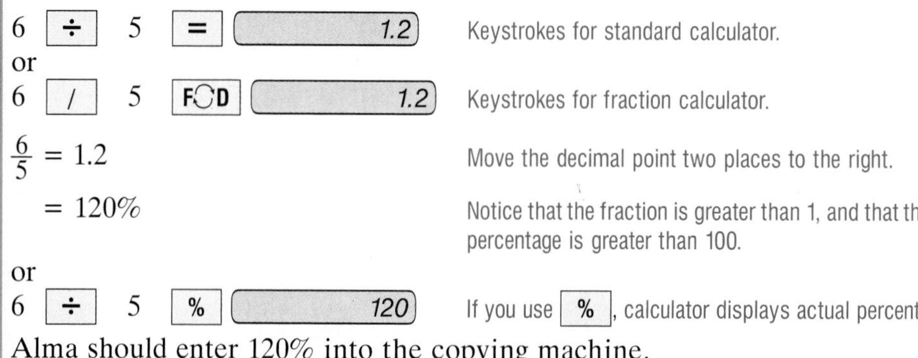

6 [÷] 5 [=] 1.2 — Keystrokes for standard calculator.

or

6 [/] 5 [F◌D] 1.2 — Keystrokes for fraction calculator.

$\frac{6}{5} = 1.2$ — Move the decimal point two places to the right.

$= 120\%$ — Notice that the fraction is greater than 1, and that the percentage is greater than 100.

or

6 [÷] 5 [%] 120 — If you use [%], calculator displays actual percent.

Alma should enter 120% into the copying machine.

Try This Write each fraction as a percent.

a. $\frac{5}{4}$ **b.** $1\frac{3}{20}$

c. A commuter airline flight had 15 reservations for 10 seats. What percent of the seats on the plane were reserved?

You have seen that $\frac{1}{100}$ is the same as 1%. Suppose 1 person out of 200 applicants is hired for a job. The fraction of applicants hired is $\frac{1}{200}$. Since this is less than $\frac{1}{100}$, $\frac{1}{200}$ will be less than 1% when expressed as a percent.

Example 2

Write $\frac{1}{200}$ as a percent in decimal form and in fraction form.

Solution

1 [÷] 200 [=] [0.005]

$\frac{1}{200} = 0.005$ Move the decimal point two places to the right.

$= 0.5\%$

$= \frac{1}{2}\%$ Notice that the fraction $\frac{1}{2}$ is less than 1, and that the percentage is less than 1.

Try This Write each fraction as a percent in decimal form and in fraction form.

d. $\frac{3}{400}$ **e.** $\frac{2}{250}$

f. At Know It All University, 3 of every 2000 applicants were accepted last year. What percent of applicants were accepted?

Example 3

Write 150% as a fraction or mixed number in lowest terms.

Solution

$150\% = 1.50$ Write the percent as a decimal by moving the decimal point two places to the left.

$= 1\frac{1}{2}$

Try This Write each percent as a fraction or mixed number in lowest terms.

g. 225% **h.** 164%

Example 4

Write $\frac{1}{4}\%$ as a fraction or mixed number in lowest terms.

Solution

$\frac{1}{4}\% = 0.25\%$ Write the fractional percent as a decimal percent.

$= 0.0025$ Write the percent as a decimal.

$= \frac{25}{10{,}000}$

$= \frac{1}{400}$

Try This Write each percent as a fraction or mixed number in lowest terms.

i. $\frac{1}{2}\%$ j. $\frac{1}{8}\%$

Class Exercises

Give each ratio as a percent. Which are greater than 100%? Which are less than 1%?

1. $\frac{23}{100}$
2. $\frac{125}{100}$
3. $\frac{2}{3}:100$
4. $\frac{\frac{3}{4}}{100}$
5. $\frac{9}{100}$
6. 200:100
7. $\frac{1}{2}$ to 100
8. $\frac{105}{100}$

Discuss the Ideas

9. Before changing a fraction to a percent, how can you tell by inspection whether the percent will be greater or less than 100%. Give examples to justify your answer.

Exercises

Practice and Apply

Write each fraction as a percent.

1. $\frac{175}{100}$
2. $\frac{3}{2}$
3. $2\frac{1}{4}$
4. $\frac{5}{3}$
5. $3\frac{1}{5}$
6. $\frac{1}{125}$
7. $\frac{8}{1000}$
8. $\frac{1}{160}$
9. $\frac{3}{500}$
10. $\frac{4}{600}$

Write each percent as a fraction, mixed number, or whole number in lowest terms.

11. 175%
12. 500%
13. 250%
14. 1000%
15. $\frac{1}{5}\%$
16. $\frac{3}{4}\%$
17. $\frac{3}{8}\%$
18. $1\frac{1}{4}\%$
19. Fran was expected to sell 12 boxes of fruit to raise money for the homeless. She sold 15 boxes. What percent of what she was expected to sell did she sell?
20. A school has 400 students. Only 2 students are on the student council. What percent of all students are on the student council?

Extend and Apply

21. Bike shop employees set a goal of selling 200 new bikes in a 3-month period. They sold 75 the first month, 130 the second month, and 125 the third month. What percentage of their goal did they reach?
22. A survey of 250 schools showed that 10 schools had more than 30 computers. What percentage of the schools surveyed had more than 30 computers?

23. Does $x\% + y\% = (x + y)\%$? Use number replacements for x and y to show why the two expressions are or are not equivalent.

24. Does $\frac{x\%}{y\%} = \left(\frac{x}{y}\right)\%$? Use number replacements for x and y to show why the two expressions are or are not equivalent.

Use Mathematical Reasoning

25. Within a 10 cm by 10 cm region on a sheet of paper, draw a rectangle with a perimeter of 20 cm and an area that is 16% of the 10 cm by 10 cm region.

26. This large cube is made up of 27 smaller cubes. If the large cube was painted green on all 6 sides, what percentage of the cubes would be painted green on exactly 1 side? 2 sides?

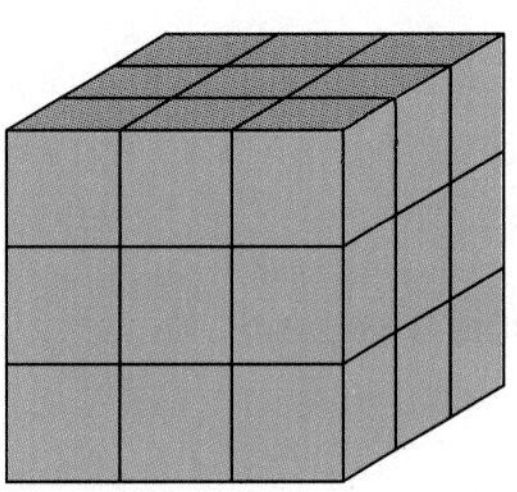

Mixed Review

Find the greatest common factor (GCF). **27.** 8, 64, 92 **28.** 6, 21

Write each as a mixed number. **29.** $\frac{26}{3}$ **30.** $\frac{211}{16}$ **31.** $\frac{67}{8}$

Computer Activity

Use a spreadsheet program to make a chart that calculates percents. Use data for a subject that interests you, such as nutrition, grades, or sports. Your chart should have at least three columns: the first two columns should contain two related numbers and the third column should calculate the percent the first number in the row is of the second number. You could also have a column with labels to identify the data. Find out how percent is handled by the spreadsheet. Use percent to create a formula or format for the third column. Your chart should have at least five rows of data. Sample output is shown:

	A	B	C	D
1	Item	Grams of fat	Total weight	Percent fat
2	Whole milk	8	244	3.28%
3	Oatmeal	2	130	1.54%
4	Cheese pizza	4	60	6.67%
5	Doughnut	5	25	20.00%

10-10 Problem Solving: Strategies

Problems Without Solutions

Objectives To solve nonroutine problems; to recognize problems without solutions.

For some problems, no solution is possible. In the following example, the strategy **Make an Organized List** is used to determine that there is no solution.

Sample Problem Nancy said she lost 72¢ behind the sofa. Although she wasn't sure what coins she had lost, Nancy knew she did not have a half-dollar and she thought she had lost 5 coins. What 5 coins did Nancy lose that totaled 72¢?

You can use an organized list to make sure you have checked all possibilities. Possible coins to consider are quarters, dimes, nickels, and pennies. Since she had 72¢, she must have had 2 pennies. This reduces the problem to finding 3 coins that total 70¢. The organized list below shows that there are no combinations of quarters, dimes, nickels, and pennies that give 72¢ in 5 coins.

Quarters	Dimes	Nickels	Pennies	Total
3	0	0	2	77¢
2	1	0	2	62¢
1	2	0	2	47¢
1	1	1	2	42¢
1	0	2	2	37¢

If she did not have a half-dollar, Nancy could not have lost 5 coins that totaled 72¢.

Problem-Solving Strategies

Choose the Operations	Make a Table	Make an Organized List
Guess, Check, Revise	Look for a Pattern	Use Logical Reasoning
Draw a Diagram	Write an Equation	Work Backward
	Simplify the Problem	

Refer to this chart of Problem-Solving Strategies as you work the problems on page 369.

Problems

Solve. If the problem has no solution, show why.

Sandwiches Prices include tax.	
Hamburger	$1.25
Chicken	$1.65
Pizza	$1.10
Roast Beef	$1.45

1. Ms. Banfield bought 2 different sandwiches from this menu and paid for them with a $5 bill. The clerk said the change was $2.35. Which sandwiches did Ms. Banfield buy?

2. Nicole was in a walkathon for charity. She got 25 people to pledge $0.15 for each kilometer she walked and 45 people to pledge $0.25 for each kilometer she walked. She walked 35 km in the walkathon. How much money did she collect in pledges?

3. Thirty-five people signed up for a 25-km run. The race organizer wants to give each runner a different 4-digit number by using the digits 3, 4, 5, and 6 so that each digit is used once in each number. How many more people could sign up for the race and each be given a different number?

4. Kara found 17 coins in a drawer, each valued at 25¢ or less. She counted a total of $1.15. How many coins of each kind did she find?

5. Will works for the school yearbook. He sets the page numbers for the yearbook by hand. If each digit has to be set separately, and there are 250 pages in the yearbook, how many digits must Will set?

6. Jeremy makes 3-legged stools and 4-legged stools. He has 48 legs for stools. He wants to make 12 stools, some of each kind. Can he do this and use all the legs?

Group Decision Making

7. Work in a group. Discuss and decide.

   Situation You are selling greeting cards for $3.50 per box on 8% commission. In addition, you receive one box of cards free for each 50 you order from the company. You want to know how many boxes of greeting cards you will need to sell in order to buy a new 12-speed bicycle.

   Guidelines for Planning

   - **Formulate Problems** you will need to solve.
   - Discuss **Assumptions** you will make and **Data** you will need.

   a. What decision or decisions do you need to make in this situation?

   b. Formulate at least two problems you need to solve to make the decision(s).

   c. List any assumptions you need to make to arrive at a decision.

   d. What data, if any, do you need to collect to make a decision?

   e. Write a paragraph summarizing what your group did, what decisions you made, and why.

Extend Key Ideas

A Golden Rectangle

Early Greek architects, painters, and sculptors identified what they believed to be the rectangle most pleasing to the human eye. They called it the **Golden Rectangle.** The ratio of the length l to the width w of this rectangle, $\frac{l}{w}$, was called the **Golden Ratio.** The Greeks discovered that the following proportion holds only for a Golden Rectangle:

$$\frac{l}{w} = \frac{l + w}{l}$$

1. Each of the rectangles below is a Golden Rectangle. Measure the length and width of each, to the nearest millimeter. Find the ratio $\frac{l}{w}$ for each. Express each ratio as a decimal, and use them to estimate the Golden Ratio as a decimal.

2. Measure the length and width of each rectangle below to the nearest millimeter and compute the ratio $\frac{l}{w}$ for each. For which rectangle is this ratio closest to the Golden Ratio? Is this rectangle most pleasing to your eye?

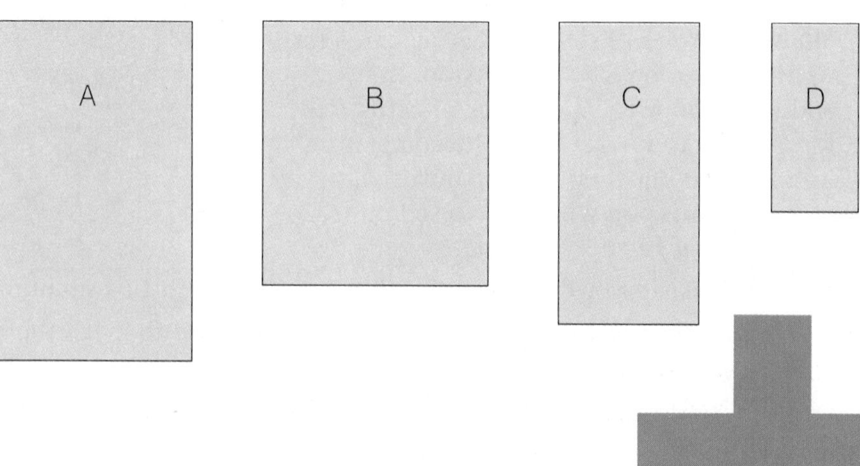

Chapter 10 Review/Test

Understanding

True or false?

10-1 **1.** A ratio can be another name for a fraction.

10-2 **2.** A proportion is a statement that two ratios are equal.

10-9 **3.** Percents greater than 100 cannot be expressed as a decimal.

10-7 **4.** A percent is a special kind of a ratio.

10-3 **5.** A rate compares some quantity to a unit of cost.

Skills

10-1 Write each ratio as a fraction in lowest terms.

6. 8:32 **7.** 12 to 15 **8.** $\frac{72}{27}$

10-2 Solve and check.

9. $\frac{a}{42} = \frac{3}{7}$ **10.** $\frac{5}{6} = \frac{m}{30}$ **11.** $\frac{3}{4} = \frac{15}{c}$

10-3 Simplify the rate.

12. 225 km/3 h **13.** \$500/4 days **14.** 186 beats/3 minutes

10-5 Find the scale dimensions of each. The scale is 1 cm = 0.5 m.

15. Desk: 1.5 m × 1 m **16.** Patio: 3.5 m × 3 m

10-7 Use a proportion to write each as a percent.

17. $\frac{12}{5}$ **18.** $\frac{17}{20}$ **19.** $\frac{3}{8}$

10-7 Write each percent as a fraction or mixed number in lowest terms.
10-9

20. 22% **21.** 1% **22.** $4\frac{1}{2}\%$

23. 325% **24.** $\frac{3}{4}\%$ **25.** $2\frac{1}{2}\%$

10-7 Write as a decimal. **26.** 9% **27.** $12\frac{1}{5}\%$

10-7 Write as a percent. **28.** 0.20 **29.** 0.025

Applications

10-6 **30.** Orange juice costs \$2.69 for the 64-ounce size and \$1.27 for the 32-ounce size. Which size is the better buy?

10-3 **31.** Mr. Bertolini charged \$60 for 4 hours labor. What is his hourly rate?

10-8 **32.** Peter has taken piano lessons for half as many years as Laura has. The sum of the number of years they have both taken lessons is 12. How many years has each taken lessons?

11 Applying Percent

In yesterday's tennis match, Earl approached the net 35 times and he hit 21 winners. What percent of his shots at the net were winners?

11-1 Finding a Percent of a Number

Objective To find a percent of a number.

Explore

Copy each segment. Estimate to mark the indicated point on the number line. The 50% mark is given to help you estimate.

- Mark a point to show 60% of 60.
- Mark a point to show 10% of 80.

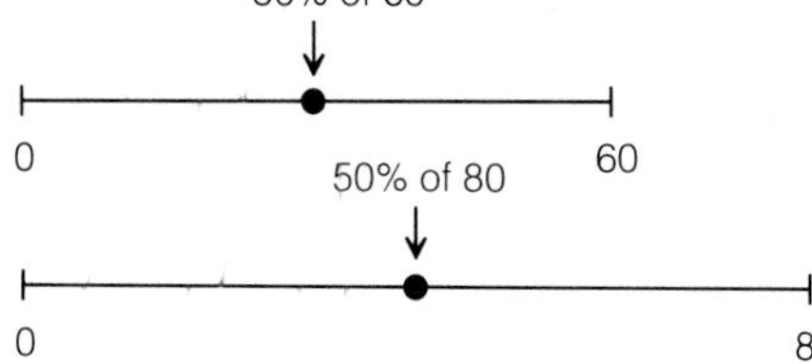

- Mark a point to show 90% of 120.

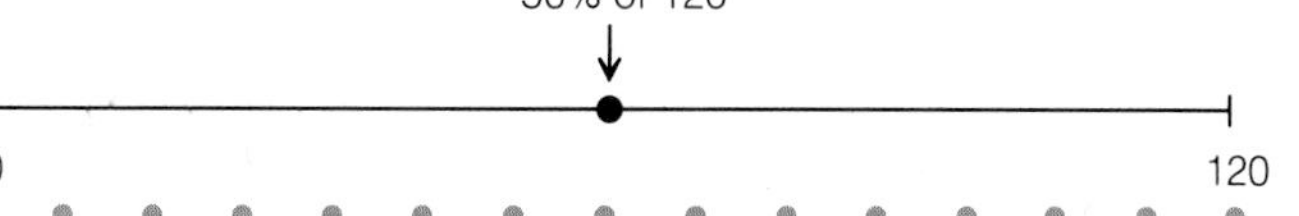

Understand the Ideas

When finding a percent of a number it is helpful to first estimate the answer. You can often use compatible numbers to estimate.

Example 1

Estimate 72% of 210.

Solution

72% of 210 is about 150. Think: 72% of 210 is about 75% of 200. $75\% = \frac{3}{4}$ and $\frac{3}{4} \times 200 = 150$.

Try This

a. 20% of \$505 **b.** 8% of 95 **c.** 78% of 240

You can find a percent of a number by using a proportion or an equation.

Example 2

Estimate 22% of 150. Then use a proportion to find the exact answer.

Solution

Estimate .... 22% of 150 is about 30. 22% of 150 is about 20% of 150 or 30.

$\frac{22}{100} = \frac{n}{150}$ You are looking for a number that has the same ratio to 150 as 22 has to 100.

$100 \cdot n = 22 \cdot 150$ Property of proportions.

$$\frac{100n}{100} = \frac{22 \cdot 150}{100}$$ Divide both sides by 100 to get the variable by itself.

$n = 33$ 33 is close to the estimate so the answer seems reasonable.

22% of 150 is 33.

Try This Estimate the answer. Then use a proportion to find the exact answer.

d. 5% of 120 **e.** 150% of 60 **f.** 12% of 30

When the percent involves a fraction or decimal, you may want to find the percent of the number using an equation.

Example 3

Estimate $12\frac{1}{2}\%$ of 25. Then use an equation to find the exact answer.

Solution

Estimate .... $12\frac{1}{2}\%$ of 25 is about 2.5. $12\frac{1}{2}\%$ of 25 is about 10% of 25 or 2.5.

$0.125 \times 25 = n$ Think: $12\frac{1}{2}\%$ of 25 is what number?

↓ ↓ ↓ ↓ ↓

$3.125 = n$ $0.125 \times 25 = n$

$12\frac{1}{2}\%$ of 25 is 3.125.

Try This Estimate. Then find the exact answer using an equation.

g. 60% of 130 **h.** $4\frac{1}{2}\%$ of 75 **i.** 120% of 85 **j.** 4.8% of $12.50

When you are finding a percent of a number and you need an exact answer, it is helpful to use a calculator with a percent key. Use these keystrokes.

12.5   25 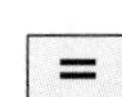 3.125

Example 4

The Armstrongs' dinner bill totals $69.85. They want to leave about 15% of the bill as a tip. How much money might they leave in all for their dinner?

Solution

15% of $69.85 is about $10.50. Think: 15% of $69.85 is about 15% of 70.
10% of $70 is $7.
5% of $70 is half of this or $3.50.
So, 15% of $70 is $10.50.

They should leave about $80.50. $69.85 is about $70.
$70 + $10.50 is $80.50.

Try This

k. Mori took her parents out to dinner. The bill totaled $82.35. About how much should she pay if she wants to leave about 15% of the bill as a tip?

Class Exercises

Give each percent as a decimal and as a fraction in lowest terms.

1. 25% **2.** 50% **3.** 75% **4.** $66\frac{2}{3}\%$ **5.** 1%

Discuss the Ideas

6. Describe the two methods you can use to find a percent of a number.

Exercises

Practice and Apply

Estimate.

1. 25% of 65 **2.** 38% of 50 **3.** 90% of 144 **4.** 12% of 76
5. 140% of 80 **6.** 65% of 25 **7.** 110% of 350 **8.** 7% of 95

Estimate the answer. Then use a proportion to solve.

9. 20% of 60 **10.** 9% of 360 **11.** 15% of 160 **12.** 4% of 60
13. 90% of 50 **14.** 70% of 8 **15.** 3% of 180 **16.** 25% of 18

Estimate the answer. Then use an equation to solve.

17. 40% of 20 **18.** $12\frac{1}{2}\%$ of 56 **19.** $\frac{1}{2}\%$ of 500
20. 35% of 40 **21.** 0.3% of 126 **22.** 2.5% of 3

Estimate the answer. Then use a proportion or an equation to solve.

23. 18% of 54 **24.** 9% of 24.5 **25.** 250% of 20
26. $\frac{1}{4}\%$ of 148 **27.** 4.5% of 60 **28.** 0.5% of 12

29. The Garrett's total bill was $92.45. About how much money should they pay if they want to leave about a 20% tip?

30. A high school had 700 students in its graduating class. Out of this graduating class, 65% of the students went to college. How many students went to college?

31. A salesperson made $45,500 last year. Her expenses were $67\frac{1}{2}\%$ of her income. How much money did she have left after expenses?

Extend and Apply

Evaluate each expression.

32. 34% of n, $n = 85$ **33.** $x\%$ of 150, $x = 5\frac{1}{2}$ **34.** 150% of h, $h = 20$

35. Rubén took 24 shots in last night's basketball game. His shooting percentage was $37\frac{1}{2}\%$. Each basket was worth 2 points. How many points did Rubén score?

Use the graph at the right to answer the following questions.

36. About how many of the men surveyed reported reading 7–9 books per year?
37. About how many of the women surveyed reported reading 1–3 books per year?
38. About how many more women than men reported reading 10 or more books per year?

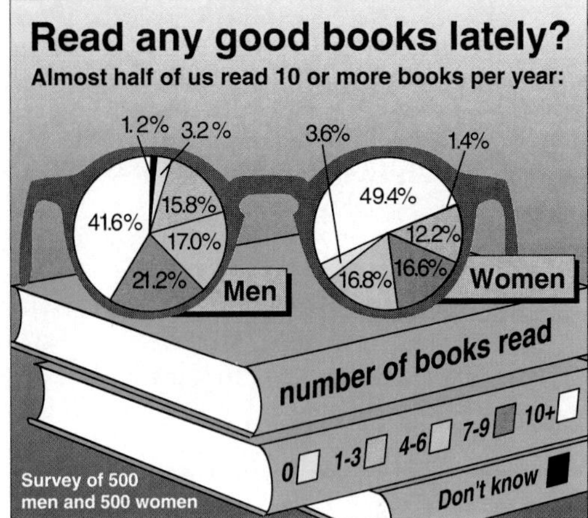

Use Mathematical Reasoning

Estimate the percentage of each square that is shaded.

39. 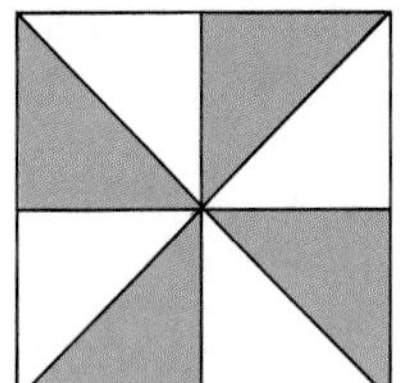

40. 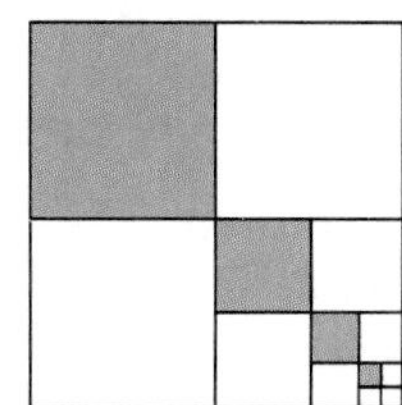

41. 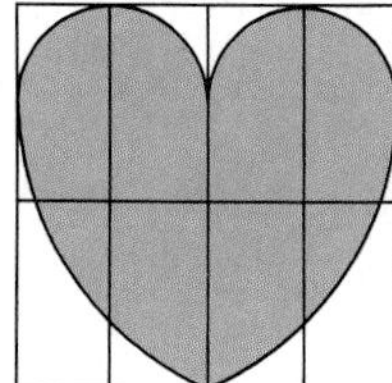

42. Write an equation to show each relationship.
    a. a is 45% of b
    b. 5% of g is m

Mixed Review

Solve and check. 43. $9 + 11c = -13$ 44. $21 - 3c > 0$

45. $9z + 36 = -9$ 46. $4(m + 6) + 7 = 3(5m + 2) - 8$

Mental Math

You can change a percent to a fraction to compute a percent of a number mentally. For example, to find $66\frac{2}{3}\%$ of 12, you can think, "$66\frac{2}{3}\%$ is the same as $\frac{2}{3}$, and $\frac{2}{3}$ of 12 is 8."

Compute mentally.

1. 50% of 90
2. $33\frac{1}{3}\%$ of 30
3. 200% of 35
4. 25% of 48
5. 75% of 20
6. 10% of \$80
7. $66\frac{2}{3}\%$ of 18
8. 150% of 150
9. $12\frac{1}{2}\%$ of \$80

11-2 Finding What Percent One Number is of Another

Objective To find what percent one number is of another.

	CDs	Tapes
Country	20	10
Rock	78	67
Classical	17	19
Jazz	35	24
Total Sold	150	120

Application

A record store manager wants to compare the number of CDs and tapes sold of each type of music before he places his next order. This can be done by finding what percent each number is of the total sold.

Understand the Ideas

Sometimes you may want to find what percent one number is of another. You can use a proportion to help you find the percent.

Example 1

In the application, 24 jazz tapes were sold out of a total of 120 tapes. Use a proportion to find what percent of the tapes sold were jazz tapes.

Solution

$\frac{n}{100} = \frac{24}{120}$ You want to find a number that has the same ratio to 100 as 24 has to 120.

$120 \cdot n = 100 \cdot 24$ Property of Proportions.

$\frac{120n}{120} = \frac{100 \cdot 24}{120}$

$n = 20$

24 is 20% of 120. $\frac{20}{100}$ is the same as 20%.

20% of the tapes sold were jazz tapes.

Try This Use a proportion to solve.

a. 30 is what percent of 150? **b.** What percent of 120 is 40?

c. Use a proportion to find what percent of the tapes sold were country tapes.

Example 2

The chart in the application shows that 78 of the 150 CDs sold were rock music. Write an equation to find what percent of the CDs sold were rock.

Solution $78 = p \cdot 150$ Think: 78 is what percent of 150?

$$\frac{78}{150} = \frac{p \cdot 150}{150}$$ $78 = p \cdot 150$

$0.52 = p$ Change $\frac{78}{150}$ to a decimal by dividing 78 by 150.

78 is 52% of 150. $0.52 = \frac{52}{100}$ or 52%.

52% of the CDs sold were rock music.

Try This Use an equation to solve.

d. 61 is what percent of 120? **e.** What percent of 150 is 50?

f. What percent of the CDs sold were country?

Another way to find what percent one number is of another is to first write a fraction. Then you can use a calculator to change the fraction to a decimal. Finally, you can change the decimal to a percent. For Example 2, you would write $\frac{78}{150} = 0.52 = 52\%$.

Class Exercises

Discuss the Ideas

Tell whether each statement is true or false. If it is false, tell why.

1. 1 out of 10 is 10%.
2. 70 out of 150 is greater than 50%.
3. 60 out of 120 is 50%.
4. 90 out of 75 is greater than 100%.
5. 40 out of 50 is less than 30%.
6. 2 out of 100 is greater than 1%.

Exercises

Practice and Apply

Use a proportion to solve.

1. What percent of 20 is 3?
2. 25 is what percent of 125?
3. 27 out of 45 is what percent?
4. 3 is what percent of 24?

Use an equation to solve.

5. What percent of 40 is 8?
6. 60 out of 150 is what percent?
7. What percent of 24 is 8?
8. 18 out of 108 is what percent?

Use a proportion or an equation to solve.

9. What percent of 50 is 40?
10. 17 is what percent of 68?
11. 25 is what percent of 1,000?
12. 1 is what percent of 200?

13. Of 200 grocery shoppers surveyed, 92 did not have a regular day of the week on which they shopped. What percentage of shoppers did not have a regular shopping day?

14. An English test has a total of 120 points. A score of 70% is passing. Dana got 80 points. Did she pass?

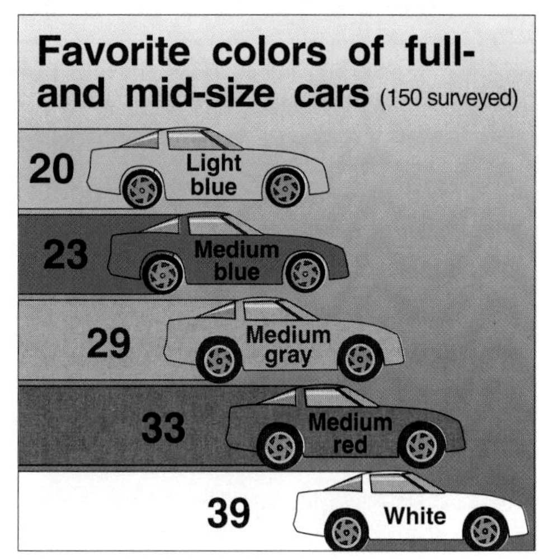

Use data from the graph. Round to the nearest tenth of a percent.

15. What percent of those surveyed prefer white?
16. What percent of those surveyed prefer medium blue?
17. What percent of those surveyed prefer medium red?
18. What percent of those surveyed prefer medium gray?

Extend and Apply

19. Of 150 people who went to a play, 40 thought it was excellent, 60 thought it was average, and 50 thought it was poor. What percent of the people thought the play was better than average?

20. **Write to Learn** Estimate. Then write a paragraph describing how you made your estimate.

    a. 62 is what percent of 245? **b.** 12 is what percent of 96?

Use Mathematical Reasoning

21. Find x and y: x is 50% of y and $x + y = 75$.
22. Find x and y: x is $33\frac{1}{3}\%$ of y and $3x + y = 120$.
23. A solution for the following problem is started for you. Copy and complete the solution. Write a paragraph telling how you finished the solution.

	Kathy	Lynn	Micaelia	Nicki
Art		2nd	4th	
Brent	4th	3rd		
Chuck			3rd	
Darin				2nd

Art, Brent, Chuck, and Darin each went on four dates with four different girls—Kathy, Lynn, Micaelia, and Nicki.

- Second date: Art dated Lynn and Darin dated Nicki.
- Third date: Chuck dated Micaelia and Brent dated Lynn.
- Fourth date: Micaelia dated Art and Kathy dated Brent.

What couples went out together on the first date?

Mixed Review

Write as a decimal. **24.** 25% **25.** 80% **26.** 124% **27.** 19%

Solve and check. **28.** $6(m + 3) = 0$ **29.** $4(9r + 7r) = 256$

11-3 Finding a Number When a Percent of it is Known

Objective To find a number when a percent of it is known.

Application

Packages of computer disks are on sale for 25% off the regular price. This is a savings of \$15 per package. What is the regular price for a package?

Understand the Ideas

You can find a number when a percent of it is known using a proportion or an equation.

Example 1

Find the regular price for a case of computer disks in the **application** using a proportion to solve. 15 is 25% of what number?

Solution

$$\frac{25}{100} = \frac{15}{n}$$

15 has the same ratio with what number as 25 has with 100?

$$25 \cdot n = 100 \cdot 15$$

$$\frac{25n}{25} = \frac{100 \cdot 15}{25}$$

$$n = 60$$

15 is 25% of 60.

The regular price for a case of disks is \$60.

Try This Use a proportion. Round to the nearest tenth if necessary.

a. 25% of what number is 15? **b.** 24 is 12% of what number?

Example 2

Use an equation to solve. 45% of what number is 18?

Solution

$$0.45n = 18$$

Think: 45% of what number is 18?
$0.45 \cdot n = 18$

$$\frac{0.45n}{0.45} = \frac{18}{0.45}$$

$$n = 40$$

45% of 40 is 18.

Try This Use an equation to solve. Round to the nearest tenth if necessary.

c. 22 is 35% of what number? **d.** 4.5% of what number is 9?

Class Exercises

State the equation you would use for each problem.

1. 60 is 75% of what number? **2.** 40% of what number is 90?

3. 30% of what number is 15? **4.** 15 is 150% of what number?

Discuss the Ideas

5. For which problem are you asked to find a number when a percent of it is known? What are you asked to find in the other problem?

a. 45% of 60 is what number? **b.** 60 is 45% of what number?

Exercises

Practice and Apply

Use a proportion to solve. Round to the nearest tenth if necessary.

1. 75% of what number is 24? **2.** 20 is 4% of what number?

3. 40 is 25% of what number? **4.** 15 is 6% of what number?

Use an equation to solve. Round to the nearest tenth if necessary.

5. 60 is 20% of what number? **6.** 75% of what number is 120?

7. 85 is 30% of what number? **8.** 7 is 23% of what number?

Use a proportion or an equation to solve. Round to the nearest tenth if necessary.

9. $4\frac{1}{2}$% of what number is 12? **10.** 25% of what number is $10\frac{1}{2}$?

11. 4 is 1% of what number? **12.** 26 is 50% of what number?

13. 2.25 is $12\frac{1}{2}$% of what number? **14.** 250% of what number is $\frac{3}{4}$?

Solve.

15. The choir at a local high school is the largest in the state. The choir has 192 members. This is 24% of all the students in the school. What is the total number of students in the school?

16. A car race was stopped after 425 miles had been completed. The race was considered official, since 85% of the race had been completed. What was the length of the original race?

17. So far, 135 cubic yards of concrete have been poured for new tennis courts. The job foreman says 75% of the pouring is now completed. What is the total amount of concrete that will be used for this job?

Extend and Apply

Give an estimate for Exercises 18–23. Then find the exact answer using a calculator.

18. 85% of what number is 350?

19. 28.75 is 75% of what number?

20. $12\frac{1}{2}\%$ of what number is 95.5?

21. 775 is $25\frac{1}{4}\%$ of what number?

22. 130 is 85% of what number?

23. 120% of what number is 25.25?

24. There are 120 students involved in athletic programs at Washington School this year. This number is 150% of the students involved last year. How many students were in the athletic programs last year?

25. One day 20% of the students in a school went on a field trip. Only 240 students were left in the school. How many students went on the field trip?

Use data in the chart at the right to answer the following questions.

26. How many paralegals were there in 1991?

27. How many medical assistants were there in 1991?

28. How many physical therapists were there in 1991?

29. How many home health aides were there in 1991?

Fastest Growing Occupations in Woodintown for 1992

Occupation	*Estimated No.*	*Growth Since 1991*
paralegal	75	90%
medical assistant	60	85%
physical therapist	50	70%
home health aide	42	50%

Use Mathematical Reasoning

30. What is 45% of $3x$ if 30% of x is 45?

31. A jar has 100 ml of water in it and is 20% full. How much water will be in the jar when it is 80% full?

32. Look at the 10×10 block shown. Imagine stacking blocks like it and then painting only the outside faces of the stack red. How many blocks would need to be stacked so that $53\frac{1}{3}\%$ of the 1-by-1 blocks had only one face painted red?

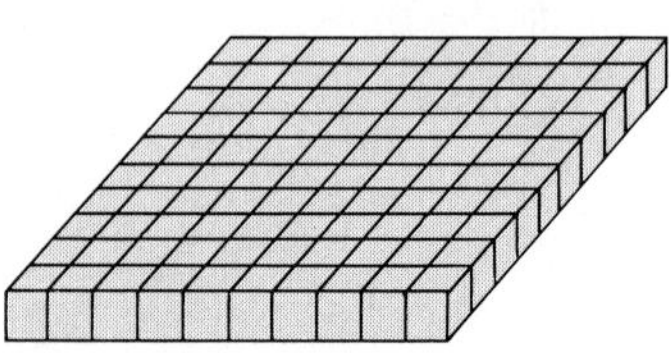

Mixed Review

Write each fraction in lowest terms, then write it as a percent.

33. $\frac{6}{8}$ **34.** $\frac{27}{15}$ **35.** $\frac{60}{12}$ **36.** $\frac{45}{75}$ **37.** $\frac{18}{4}$

Solve and check. **38.** $\frac{3}{4}x + \frac{1}{3} = \frac{5}{6}$ **39.** $\frac{2}{5}r - \frac{3}{4} = \frac{1}{2}$

40. $-\frac{5}{6} = \frac{2}{3}m + \frac{4}{9}$

Critical Thinking

Proportional Thinking Decisions

Objective: To use critical thinking when making decisions.

Critical thinking is a process of making decisions about what to believe or do. Some questions that may help you do this are given on page 334. Drew, Megan, and Jay used their critical thinking skills to explore the following situation.

Sample Problem

Situation: A team of 5 boy scouts went on a 3-day survival trip. Their leader told them they would need 8 pounds of food for every 4 people for 1 day. Would 28 pounds of food be enough for them to take?

Drew's Solution
8 lb for 4 persons for 1 day would be 40 lb for 20 people for 1 day, or 120 lb for 20 people for 3 days. Dividing by 4, this would be 30 lb for 5 people for 3 days. 28 lb would not be enough.

Megan's Solution
5 people would need $1\frac{1}{4}$ times as much as 4 people, so 8 lb for 4 people for 1 day would be $8\left(1\frac{1}{4}\right) = 10$ lb for 5 people for 1 day, or 30 lb for 5 people for 3 days. 28 lbs would not be enough.

Jay's Solution
8 lb for 4 people for 1 day would be 24 lb for 4 people for 3 days. Letting $x =$ the number of pounds for 5 people for 3 days, we solve the proportion $\frac{24}{4} = \frac{x}{5}$. $x = 30$, so 28 lb would not be enough.

Apply Critical Thinking

Work together to make decisions in each of the following situations. Write an explanation of how and why you made your decision.

1. Three friends will divide $75 in the ratio of their ages. Bill is 6 years old, Jill is 9, and Tim is 10. Someone suggests that they instead divide the money into thirds. Do you think Jill and Tim will agree?
2. A camp guide says that every 8 campers need 6 lb of potatoes each day. A group of 12 campers went on a 4-day camping trip. The cook packed 30 lb of potatoes. According to the camp guide, should he take more or fewer?
3. A stereo magazine says that the ratio of the costs of speakers, a receiver, and a compact disc player should be 4:3:2. You have $900 to spend and want a compact disc player that costs $500. Does this price fit the ratio given what you have to spend?

11-4 Problem Solving: Writing Equations

Practice Solving Problems

Objective To solve word problems by writing and solving equations.

Problems

Practice and Apply

Solve by writing an equation.

1. Joanna broke the old high-jump record, set in 1980, by $1\frac{3}{4}$ in. The new record is 6 ft $5\frac{1}{2}$ in. What was the old record?
2. Mr. Bertolini saved $48 on a tape deck by buying it at 30% off the regular price. What was the regular price of the tape deck?
3. Popcorn costs $0.25 more than a cup of juice. What is the price of each if they cost $1.65 together?
4. Teresa bought 3 pairs of hiking shorts. Each pair cost the same amount. The sales tax on the 3 pairs of shorts came to $2.25. The total cost, including tax, was $39.75. What was the cost of each pair of shorts?
5. Lynn got a $4 rebate for buying two hair dryers. Each dryer cost the same amount. The cost for both dryers after the rebate was $21. What was the cost for one dryer before the rebate?

Extend and Apply

6. Patrick worked 6 hours on Monday and 8 hours on Wednesday. He did not work the rest of the week. A total of $13 was taken out of his paycheck that week for taxes and insurance. His "take home" pay was $39.50. What was his hourly wage?
7. An airline has a holiday special. When 2 people travel together, the cost of the second ticket is $\frac{1}{2}$ the price of a full-fare ticket. Jayne paid a total of $210 for 2 tickets. What was the price of a full-fare ticket?

Use Mathematical Reasoning

8. Write a word problem that could be solved using the equation.
   a. $0.5x + 1.25 = 7.5$ **b.** $x + 2x + 3x = 120$

Mixed Review

Use a proportion to find: **9.** 12% of 20 **10.** 15% of 120

Solve and check. **11.** $a + 2.5a = -7$ **12.** $3n < 10 - 2n$

11-5 Applying Percent: Percent of Increase and Decrease

Objective To find percents of increase and decrease.

Application

Beatriz Hernandez earned $500 per week last year. This year she will earn $530 per week. What was the percent of increase of her salary?

Understand the Ideas

To find the percent of increase or decrease:

- First subtract to find the amount of increase or decrease.
- Then find what percent of the original that amount is.

You can use a calculator to find the percent of increase or decrease.

Example 1

Use the data in the **application** to find the percent of increase in Ms. Hernandez's salary.

Solution

Amount of increase:

530 [−] 500 [=] 30

amount of increase = new salary − original salary

Percent of increase:

30 [÷] 500 [%] [=] 6

Find what percent 30 is of 500 to find the percent of increase.

Ms. Hernandez received a 6% increase in salary.

Try This

Find the percent of increase.

a. original amount = 40; new amount = 45

Example 2

Find the percent of decrease. Original amount = 60; new amount = 45

Solution

Amount of decrease:

60 [−] 45 [=] [15] amount of decrease = original amount − new amount

Percent of decrease:

15 [÷] 60 [%] [=] [25] Find what percent 15 is of 60 to find the percent of decrease.

The percent of decrease is 25%.

Try This Find the percent of decrease.

b. original amount = 125; new amount = 65

Class Exercises

State whether the change would be an increase or a decrease.

1. Original price: $65
Sale price: $59

2. Last year's cost: $100
This year's cost: $112

3. Last year's income: $420
This year's income: $375

4. Price 5 years ago: $12
Price today: $17.50

Discuss the Ideas

5. How do you decide which number to find the percent of when trying to find a percent of increase or decrease? Give examples to justify your answer.

Exercises

Practice and Apply

Find the percent of increase. Round to the nearest tenth if necessary.

1. Original amount = $120
New amount = $150

2. Original amount = $300
New amount = $360

3. Original amount = $140
New amount = $168

4. Original amount = $345
New amount = $483

Find the percent of decrease. Round to the nearest tenth if necessary.

5. Original amount = $60
New amount = $15

6. Original amount = $85
New amount = $34

7. Original amount = $190
New amount = $80

8. Original amount = $135
New amount = $120

Find the percent of increase or decrease. Round to the nearest tenth if necessary.

9. Original amount = \$20
New amount = \$30

10. Original amount = \$78
New amount = \$39

11. Original amount = \$80
New amount = \$45

12. Original amount = \$50
New amount = \$75

13. Last year 30 students took a drafting class. This year 35 students are taking the class. What is the percent of increase in enrollment?

14. Kevin weighed 45 kg last month. As a result of his training program, he now weighs 42 kg. By what percent did his weight decrease?

15. A starting teacher's salary at Get Smart School is \$25,500. Next year, the starting salary will be raised to \$28,000. What is the percent of increase in starting salary?

16. Attendance at all of the school dances last year was 825. This year only 600 attended the dances. By what percent did attendance decrease?

Extend and Apply

17. A gold ring cost \$125 five years ago. There was a 420% increase in the price in the last five years. What is the price of that ring today?

18. A computer had 128 KB of internal memory when it was first produced. Now its internal memory has been increased by 300%. What is its amount of internal memory now?

Use Mathematical Reasoning

19. Last month a clothing store manager decreased prices on all stock by 10%. This month she increased all prices by 10%. What would you pay for a coat this month that had cost \$75 before prices were decreased last month?

20. When the original price of an item is increased by a certain percent, the increased price is \$310. When the original price is decreased by the same percent, the decreased price is \$190. What is the original price? What is the percentage of increase or decrease?

Mixed Review

Write each as a decimal. Use a bar for a repeating decimal.

21. $\frac{4}{5}$ **22.** $\frac{6}{11}$ **23.** $\frac{8}{3}$ **24.** $\frac{3}{8}$ **25.** $\frac{5}{16}$

Reduce to lowest terms. **26.** $\frac{16}{64}$ **27.** $\frac{35}{112}$ **28.** $\frac{52}{78}$ **29.** $\frac{9}{114}$

Solve and check. **30.** $26a + 2(a + 3) = 146$ **31.** $14r + 3 = 2r - 21$

32. $42 - 13t = 9 - 2t$ **33.** $6(a - 7) + 2 = 50a + 4$

11-6 Applying Percent: Discount, Sale Price, and Commission

Objective To find percents of discounts, sale prices, and commissions.

Application

When Trevor passed Gulf Coast Boat Works, he saw an advertisement for a boat that was regularly priced at $8,500. The sign said that there was a 15% discount today only. Trevor wanted to figure out the amount of the discount and the sale price of the boat.

Understand the Ideas

When you buy an item on sale, you receive a discount from the original price. The **discount** is the amount subtracted from the **regular price.** The **sale price** of an item is the regular price less the discount. A **commission** is the amount a salesperson receives for making a sale. A commission is usually a percent of the sale price.

Example 1

Find the discount and the sale price for the boat in the application

Solution

Discount = 15% of $8,500

15 [%] [×] 8500 [=] 1275

Find the discount by multiplying the original price by the discount percent.

The discount is $1,275.

Sale price = $8,500 − $1,275

8500 [−] 1275 [=] 7225

Find the sale price by subtracting the amount of the discount from the original price.

The sale price is $7,225.

Try This

a. A new motorcycle that regularly costs $2,250 is on sale for 20% off. How much is the discount and what is the sale price?

Example 2

The sale price of a boat is $7,225. What is the amount of commission for the sale of the boat if the commission is 1.5%? Round to the nearest cent.

Solution

Commission = 1.5% of $7,225.

1.5 [%] [×] 7225 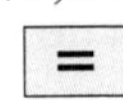 [108.375]

Find the commission by multiplying the sale price by the commission percent.

The commission is $108.38.

Try This

b. Rochelle sold a television for $600. Her commission was 2%. How much commission did she earn for this sale?

Class Exercises

Tell whether each statement is true or false.

1. A discount is an amount subtracted from the original amount.
2. The percent of discount tells the amount of commission.
3. The sale price is less than the regular price.
4. The sale price is the regular price less the discount.

Discuss the Ideas

5. When a sign says 20% off, what percent of the original price is the sale price? Give an example to prove your point.

Exercises

Practice and Apply

Find the discount and sale price for each. Round to the nearest cent if necessary.

1. Regular price = $12
   Discount = 2.75%
2. Regular price = $30
   Discount = 15%
3. Regular price = $260
   Discount = 12.5%
4. Regular price = $9.85
   Discount = 4%
5. Regular price = $689.95
   Discount = 15%
6. Regular price = $249.95
   Discount = 10%
7. Regular price = $4,570
   Discount = 12.5%
8. Regular price = $25,750
   Discount = 6%

Find the commission. Round to the nearest cent if necessary.

9. Sale price = $45
   Commission = 3%
10. Sale price = $125
    Commission = 2%
11. Sale price = $12.95
    Commission = $5\frac{1}{2}\%$
12. Sale price = $58.60
    Commission = $1\frac{3}{4}\%$

13. How much would you save if you bought both the screen house and the tent canopy on sale?

14. What is the percent of the discount, to the nearest tenth, on the tent canopy?

15. What is the percent of discount on a tent with a sale price of \$64.95 and regular cost of \$84.95?

Camping Gear
Screen House REG. \$79.95 Today—18% OFF!!
Tent Canopy REG. \$29.95 Today—Save \$9.00

Extend and Apply

16. Suppose you bought a bicycle at a 10% discount. The sale price you paid was \$100. What was the original price of the bicycle? [Hint: What percent of the original price is \$100?]

17. A stereo system regularly costs \$750. What percent discount would allow you to buy the system with the \$624 you have saved?

Use Mathematical Reasoning

18. A store had a 20% discount on every item. Would a customer be better off if the 15% sales tax were calculated before or after the discount?

Mixed Review

Write each as a fraction in lowest terms. **19.** 35% **20.** 40% **21.** 125%

Evaluate for $a = 6, b = 3$. **22.** $\frac{2}{3}(a + b)$ **23.** $\frac{a}{b}$ **24.** $4(a - b)$

Computer Activity

The program below will compute the discount (D) and the sale price (S) of an item when you input the list price (L) and the percent of discount (P).

```
10  PRINT "FIND THE SALE PRICE."
20  PRINT "ENTER THE LIST PRICE, L, AND"
30  PRINT "THE PERCENT OF DISCOUNT, D, (DECIMAL)."
40  INPUT L,P
50  PRINT "THE LIST PRICE IS $";L
60  PRINT "THE PERCENT OF DISCOUNT IS ";P
70  D=P*L: S=L-D
80  PRINT "THE DISCOUNT IS $";D
90  PRINT "THE SALE PRICE IS $";S
100 END
```

Use this program to find the discount and sale price for each item.

1. List, \$375; discount, 10%
2. List, \$2,250; discount, 30%
3. List, \$9,479; discount, 5%
4. List, \$359; discount, $12\frac{1}{2}\%$

Finding Sales Tax

Objective To solve problems involving sales tax percentages.

In many places you pay a sales tax when you buy an item. The sales tax is a percentage of the selling price of the item. The tables below show tax rates in certain states and cities for a recent year. If you live in a state that has a sales tax and a city that has a sales tax, both taxes are added to the price of an item you buy.

STATE SALES TAXES			
STATE	**% RATE**	**STATE**	**% RATE**
California	6.25	S. Dakota	4
Colorado	3	Texas	6.25
Missouri	4.225	Virginia	4.5
New York	4	Washington	6.5

CITY SALES TAXES			
CITY	**% RATE**	**CITY**	**% RATE**
Anaheim, CA	0.5	New York, NY	4.25
Berkeley, CA	1	Rapid City, SD	2
Boulder, CO	2.86	San Antonio, TX	2
Jefferson City, MO	2	Seattle, WA	0.925

Sample Problem Use the tax rate table to find the total cost, including state sales tax, of a $500 television set bought in Virginia.

Solution

Let T = amount of tax paid

$T = \$500 \times 0.045 = \$22.50$ — Tax = selling price × tax percent.

Let C = total cost of the television set

$C = \$500 + \$22.50 = \$522.50$ — Total cost = selling price + tax.

The total cost of the television set is $522.50.

Problems

Use the tax rate tables to solve. Round to the nearest cent if necessary.

1. Celia bought a car in Texas for $1200. How much state tax did she pay?

2. What would the New York state sales tax be on a $900 video camera?
3. A family in Colorado bought a $12,500 camper. How much was the state sales tax?
4. A man in Anaheim, CA, bought a new suit for $125. How much city sales tax did he pay?
5. In the state of Washington, what would the total cost be for a car priced at $7500?
6. A tape deck was on sale in Seattle, WA, for $379. What is the city tax on this tape deck?
7. Mr. Montes paid $10,000 for a boat. This price was 5% less than the original price. Mr. Montes lived in San Antonio, TX. How much city tax would he pay on the boat?
8. A refrigerator originally priced at $875 was on sale for $696.99 in Berkeley, CA. What was the city tax on this refrigerator?

To find the total state and city tax on an item, add the two percentage rates. An item bought in Berkeley, CA, would have a city tax of 1% plus a state tax rate of 6.25%. The total tax on the item would be 7.25%.

9. Ms. Flores bought a portable television on sale for $175 in San Antonio, TX. What was the total tax she paid on the item?
10. Ms. Harrison bought 4 new tires for a truck. Each tire was priced at $50. She bought the tires in Boulder, CO. What was the approximate total cost for all of the tires, including tax?
11. The Cho family in Seattle, WA, bought 3 coats that cost $125, $65, and $50. What was the total cost for the coats, including tax?
12. Mr. Sanders of Anaheim, CA, was given $1,250 off the price of a $10,450 van. What was the total price he paid for the van, including tax?
13. **Data Search** Find the total cost, including all taxes, of purchasing a $200 stereo in your home town. If there is no state or local sales tax where you live, use the tax rate for a city or state near you.

What's Your Decision?

Suppose you had your choice between three surfboards. Each was on sale. The sales tax in your city is 7%. You have an old board and would consider trading it in. Which board would you buy? What factors other than price might influence your decision?

Windjammer	Whitewater	The Shark
Regular price: $385	Their price: $450	Originally $390
On sale: $\frac{1}{4}$ OFF	Ours: 40% OFF!	Today: $295 less $20 for your old board

11-8

Applying Percent: Simple Interest

Objective To find simple interest amounts.

Understand the Ideas

Interest is a charge for the use of money. When you borrow money, you pay interest for the use of the money. When you place money in a savings account, the bank pays you interest for the use of your money. To find **simple interest,** you multiply the amount of money borrowed or saved by the interest rate and multiply that amount by the time the money is used.

Formula **Simple Interest**

$I = Prt$; I = simple interest
P = principal (amount borrowed or saved)
r = interest rate
t = time

An interest rate is given as a percentage for a unit of time such as 5% per year or $1\frac{1}{2}\%$ per month. When you use the formula for simple interest, the unit of time for the interest rate and the time that the money is earning interest (t) must be the same.

Example 1

Adam borrowed \$300 from his bank for 6 months. The bank charges an interest rate of 1.5% per month. Find the interest charged and the total amount Adam owed the bank.

Solution $I = Prt$ Interest = principal × rate × time

$= 300(0.015)(6)$ P = \$300, r = 1.5% per month, t = 6 months

$= 27$

The amount of interest is \$27.

$A = P + I$ Total amount = principal + interest

$= 300 + 27$

$= 327$

The total amount of money is \$327.

Try This

a. What is the interest earned and the total amount if you deposit \$250 for 3 years at 10% per year?

b. Hannah borrowed \$75 at 5% per month for 6 months. What is the interest and total amount she owed?

Example 2

Melba's bank charges an interest rate of 12% per year for loans. How much interest would she pay and what would be the total amount owed if she pays off a $600 loan in 6 months?

Solution $P = \$600$

$r = 12\%$ per year

$t = 6$ months $= \frac{1}{2}$ year $= 0.5$ year

$I = Prt$

$= 600(0.12)(0.5) = 36$

r and *t* must be for the same unit of time. Change months to years.

The amount of interest is $36.

$A = P + I$

$= 600 + 36 = 636$

The total amount owed is $636.

Try This

c. Lionel's savings account earns 1% interest per month. Suppose he has a balance of $125. How much interest will he earn and what will be the total amount in his account after one year if he makes no deposits or withdrawals?

Class Exercises

Replace each variable to make a true statement.

1. $0.75 = x\%$ **2.** 1 year $= y$ months **3.** 4 months $= d$ years

4. $0.45 = t\%$ **5.** $0.2 = m\%$ **6.** 3 months $= n$ years

Discuss the Ideas

7. When finding simple interest, why must the unit of time for the interest rate and the time that the money is earning interest be the same?

Exercises

Practice and Apply

Find the interest earned and the total amount. Round to the nearest cent.

1. $120 at 1% per month for 3 months

2. $95 at 18% per year for 2 years

3. $695 at $1\frac{1}{4}\%$ per month for 14 months

4. $200 at $1\frac{1}{2}\%$ per month for 6 months

5. $400 at 1% per month for 2 years

6. \$90 at 8% per year for 21 months
7. \$845 at $1\frac{1}{2}$% per month for 3 years
8. \$2,000 at $1\frac{1}{2}$% per year for 3 months

9. Vietta borrowed \$800 from her bank for 6 months. The bank charges a simple interest rate of 1.5% per month. Find the interest charged and the total amount Vietta owed the bank.
10. Chen borrowed \$75 to buy a school jacket. He will pay back the loan at the end of 6 months and he will pay a simple interest rate of 1% per month. How much will Chen end up paying for the jacket?
11. The Santanas got a simple interest loan to pay for a trip to Washington, D.C. They borrowed \$750 at 1.25% interest per month for half a year. How much will they have to pay when the loan is due?

Extend and Apply

12. You have \$500 saved to buy a \$1,200 scooter. Suppose you can borrow the rest at 2% per month simple interest. You want to take out the loan for one year. How much money will you have to earn over the next year to pay for the loan, including the interest?
13. Carmen wants to have \$1,000 in her savings account at the end of the year. Her bank pays a one-year simple interest rate of $6\frac{1}{2}$%. How much money does she need to deposit now to have the \$1,000 at the end of one year?

Complete the credit card payment schedule for a monthly finance charge of 1.5%. Always round the finance charge to the next whole cent.

Example: October \$1,500 − 200 = \$1,300 new amount
\$1300(0.015) = \$19.50 finance charge
\$1300 + 19.50 = \$1319.50 balance

	Month	Balance	Payment	New Amount	Finance Charge	Balance
	Oct.	\$1,500	\$200	\$1,300	\$19.50	\$1,319.50
14.	Nov.	\$1,319.50	\$200	\$1,119.50		\$1,136.30
15.	Dec.	\$1,136.30	\$200			
16.	Jan.	\$950.35	\$200		\$11.26	\$761.61
17.	Feb.		\$200			
18.	Mar.		\$200			
19.	Apr.	\$375.60	\$200			
20.	May	\$178.24		—0—	—0—	—0—
21.	TOTAL					

Write an equation and solve for the missing value. Round to the nearest tenth of a percent, or the nearest cent, if necessary.

22. $I = \$8.44; P = \$75; t = 7\frac{1}{2}$ months

23. $I = \$12.50; r = 1\%$ per month; $t = 1$ year

24. $I = \$27; P = \$450; r = 18\%$ per year

Use Mathematical Reasoning

25. Write the digits 1, 2, 3, 4, or 5 in the boxes to obtain a simple interest amount of approximately $13. Use each digit only once.

$$I = Prt$$
$$13 = (\square\square)(0.\square\square)(\square)$$

26. Lucky Larry found an amazing investment plan. For every $2.50 invested, he had a 360% rate of increase. When he closed his plan, he had a total of $138. How much did he invest?

Mixed Review

Solve and check. **27.** $\frac{6}{5} = \frac{x}{2}$ **28.** $\frac{n}{15} = \frac{64}{80}$ **29.** $\frac{27}{9} = \frac{54}{t}$

Write an expression for each if there are half as many trucks as cars.

30. Number of cars **31.** Number of trucks

Write an expression for each if $\frac{1}{3}$ of the trucks are red.

32. Number of trucks **33.** Number of red trucks

Connections Numbers to Algebra

You can use the skills you learned for solving equations to write a related formula for $I = Prt$.

Numbers	Algebra
Solve $15 = 100(0.05)t$ for t, $\frac{15}{100(0.05)} = t$	Solve $I = Prt$ for t. $\frac{I}{Pr} = t$

Write a related formula.

1. Solve $D = rt$ for t.

2. Solve $V = LWH$ for L.

3. Solve $F = 1.8C + 32$ for C.

4. Solve $p = 2A + B + C$ for A.

5. Solve $P = 2L + 2W$ for W.

6. Solve $A = P + Prt$ for t.

11-9 Problem Solving: Skills

Choosing a Calculation Method

Objectives To decide if you need an exact answer or an estimate, and to select an appropriate calculation method.

When exact answers are needed for problems involving percent, it's usually best to use a calculator. When simple percents are involved, exact answers can often be found using mental math. When you have a problem to solve that involves percent, ask yourself the following questions.

- Do I need an exact answer or an estimate?
- If I need to compute, should I use mental math, paper and pencil, or a calculator?

Sample Problem 1 About how many of the people who responded said they exercise at least once during the week?

- The question calls for an estimate. 74% is about 75%, which is the same as $\frac{3}{4}$. 411 respondents is close to 400. You can estimate using mental math. $\frac{3}{4} \times 400 = 300$. So, about 300 people said they exercise at least once during the week.

Sample Problem 2 A Cyclone convertible costs $12,500. Prices are expected to increase by 5% for the next model year. What will be the new price for this car?

- The question calls for an exact answer. You might use a calculator to find the answer. Next year's price will be 5% more than this year's price. $0.05 \times 12{,}500 = 625$; $12{,}500 + 625 = 13{,}125$. The new price will be $13,125.

Problems

Choose a calculation method and evaluate each expression. Tell which method you used for each.

1. 32% of 168 is what number?
2. 20% of 80 is what number
3. 12 is about what percent of 34?
4. $\frac{1}{2}$% of $5,000 is how much?
5. 70 is what percent of 210?
6. 34 is what percent of 125

Solve. Tell whether each calls for an exact answer or an estimate. Tell which calculation method you used.

7. A recent newspaper article suggests that families have the equivalent of 30% of their yearly income in an emergency fund. About how much should a family earning $48,500 a year have in this emergency fund?
8. Tuition at Quick College is $5,075 this year. They have announced a 7% increase in tuition for next year. What will the new tuition be?
9. A charity hopes to raise $2,000. Copy and complete the table at the right.

Total Contributions	Percent of Goal
$500	___
$825	___
$1,000	___
$1,200	___
$1,650	___
$2,500	___

10. Brenda's parents own a service station. Each month they place 35% of their income into a tax account. They average $4,750 a month in income. How much of this do they put into the tax account?
11. A television network has 24.5% of the viewing households watching its prime-time special on safe driving. The viewing area has $1\frac{1}{2}$ million viewing households. About how many households watched the special?
12. In a recent survey of 350 families, 214 reported that they moved their own furniture the last time they moved. What percent of those surveyed moved their own furniture?
13. A survey of 500 teenagers who wear glasses found that only 120 want to get contact lenses someday. What percent want contacts?
14. Look at the graph on the right. Among those surveyed, how many more people visited family or friends than went to the beach?
15. How many of those responding went either to an historic site or to an amusement park?
16. **Communicate** Suppose the price of consumer goods is increasing by 5% per year. How much more will a $325 bicycle cost three years from now than it costs now?
    a. Solve.
    b. Discuss your solution with a classmate. Evaluate each other's solution.

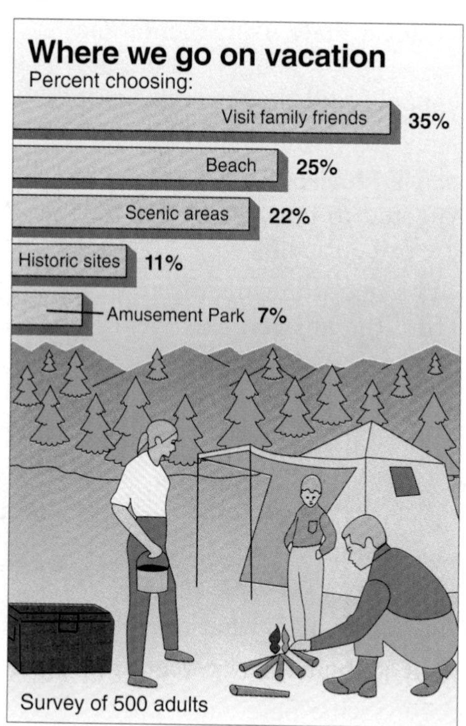

11-10 Applying Percent: Analyzing and Making Circle Graphs

Objective To analyze and make circle graphs.

Explore

Analyze the graph at the right to answer the questions below.

- About how many of those surveyed picked the computer?
- Did more students pick the VCR or the television? About how many more?
- What are some of the "other" advances students might have picked?
- What do you think is the most influential technological advance of the 20th century? Collect data for your class.

Technology marches on

What high school students think are the most influential technological advances of the 20th century:

Other/ no answer 16%
VCR 4%
Television 12%
Computer 68%

survey of 3,319 students

Understand the Ideas

A **circle graph** is useful for picturing a total amount that is divided into parts. Each part of the circle graph is called a **sector.** A circle graph shows the relationships of the parts to each other and to the total.

The circle graph at the right has four sectors. The measure of the angle for each sector is shown. The sum of the angles of the sectors of a circle equals 360°. To make sectors, you need to draw angles. You can use a protractor to draw angles for sectors.

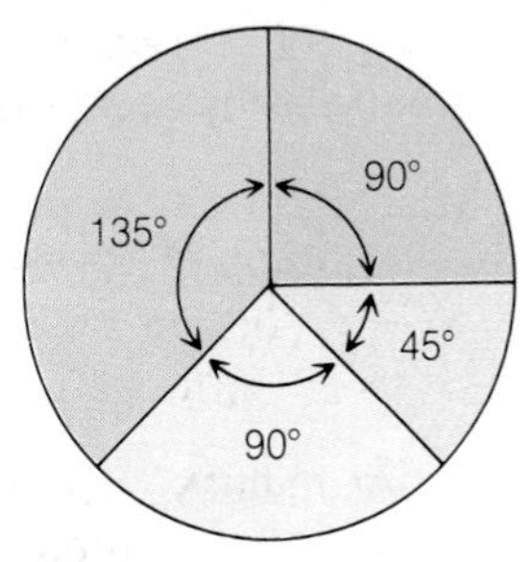

To make a circle graph, follow these steps:

1. Find the total for the data.
2. Express each part as a percent of the total.
3. Find the degrees for each sector.
4. Draw and label the sectors.
5. Title the graph.

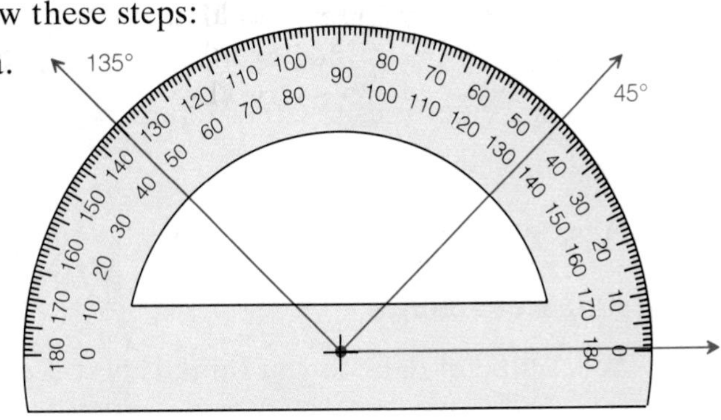

Example

Denise's college expenses for one semester were \$1,500 for tuition, \$2,250 for room and board, and \$1,250 for miscellaneous expenses.

a. Make a circle graph to show the data.

b. Which item was the least of Denise's expenses? Which sector of the graph is the smallest?

c. How might you tell from the graph that the amount for room and board is less than 50% of Denise's expenses?

Solution

a. $1500 + 2250 + 1250 = 5000$ The circle represents the total expenses.

Tuition: $\frac{1500}{5000} = 0.30 = 30\%$ Find what percent of the whole each item represents.

Room/Board: $\frac{2250}{5000} = 0.45 = 45\%$

Miscellaneous: $\frac{1250}{5000} = 0.25 = 25\%$

Tuition: $0.30 \times 360 = 108°$ Every circle is made up of 360°.

Room/Board: $0.45 \times 360 = 162°$ Find what part of the 360° each sector represents.

Miscellaneous: $0.25 \times 360 = 90°$

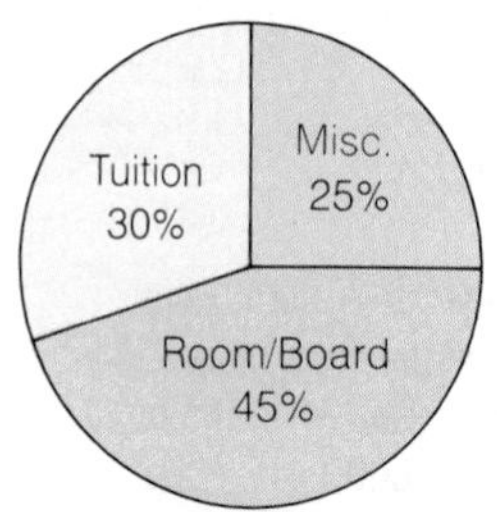

Denise's College Expenses

Use a compass to draw a circle. Use a protractor to draw each angle. Label each sector.

Give the graph a title that clearly indicates what the graph shows.

b. Miscellaneous expenses were the least. The sector called Miscellaneous is the smallest on the graph.

c. The sector for room and board is less than half of the circle.

Try This Plans of seniors at Cooper High School: 4-year college, 100; work, 55; 2-year college, 30; armed services, 10; undecided, 5.

a. Make a circle graph of the data.

b. Were any of the sectors larger than half the circle?

c. Which 2 categories together represent about 20% of the respondents?

Class Exercises

Discuss the Ideas

1. What type of data do you think is best represented by a circle graph?

Exercises

Practice and Apply

Make a circle graph to show the data.

1. Movies in town over the last six months: adventure, 50%; science fiction, 20%; children's, 15%; comedy, 10%; other, 5%.
2. After-school jobs: restaurants and food stands, 45%; stores, 35%; private homes, 10%; other, 10%.
3. Transportation to school: walk, 45%; bus, 30%; bicycle, 17%; car, 8%.
4. Ms. Bradley's expenses for one month: rent, \$425; food, \$350; clothing, \$150; entertainment, \$50; other, \$25.
   a. Make a circle graph to show the data.
   b. Did Ms. Bradley keep her clothing budget below 33% of her expenses?
   c. Ms. Bradley wants to spend no more than 3% of her expenses on entertainment. How much more or less than her budget did she spend on entertainment?

Extend and Apply

5. Make a circle graph to show the data your class collected in the Explore.
6. Make a circle graph to show the monthly electricity use.

	Present Reading (kWh)	Previous Reading (kWh)
Jan–Feb	6781	4993
Mar–Apr	8305	6781
May–Jun	9738	8305
Jul–Aug	0538	9738
Sep–Oct	1163	0538
Nov–Dec	2403	1163

To find the number of kilowatt hours (kWh) used, subtract the previous reading from the present reading (except when the meter passes 9999 and starts at 0000).

Use Mathematical Reasoning

7. Make a circle graph, using the numbers 1–20 and the categories below. Numbers with: 1 or 2 factors, 3 or 4 factors, 5 or 6 factors.

Mixed Review

Write each as a fraction in lowest terms. **8.** 8% **9.** 35% **10.** 48%

Solve and check. **11.** $4t - 19 = -7$ **12.** $11(t + 3) = 18t - 2$

11-11 Problem Solving: Strategies

Problems with More than One Answer

Objectives To solve nonroutine problems; to recognize and provide all answers for problems with more than one answer.

Some problems have more than one answer. You need to check solutions carefully to see whether a problem could have other answers. Consider the following problem.

Sample Problem Some members of the school band were thirsty after a parade. They stood in a circle and passed around a tray with 31 cups of lemonade. Each person in order took one cup until no cups were left. The tuba player took the first and the last cup. He may have had more. How many band members were in the group?

You could use the **Guess, Check, Revise** strategy to find a solution. You might guess that there were 20 members in the group. When you checked this guess, you would see that if the tuba player took the first cup, the cups would be gone before he could take the last cup. Since about half the number of members as cups would work, you might revise the guess to 15. You could **Draw a Picture** and verify that 15 is an answer.

Each of 15 members gets a cup.

Each of 15 members gets another cup.

The tuba player gets the last cup. Total 31 cups.

To be sure your solution is correct, you must check to see whether any other answers are possible. The problem above has several answers. You can **Make a Table** of answers and **Look for a Pattern** to help you describe a solution.

No. of Band Members	2	3	4	5	6	7	8	9	10	···	15	···	30
Is this a solution?	yes	yes	no	yes	yes	no	no	no	yes	no	yes	no	yes

Any number that is a factor of 30 will work. There might have been 2, 3, 5, 6, 10, 15 or 30 band members in the group.

Problem-Solving Strategies

Choose the Operations	Make a Table	Make an Organized List
Guess, Check, Revise	Look for a Pattern	Use Logical Reasoning
Draw a Diagram	Write an Equation	Work Backward
	Simplify the Problem	

Problems

Solve. Check to see whether the problem has more than one answer.

1. In a dart contest, Jennifer hit the dart board shown here with 4 darts. Each dart hit a different number. Her total was 58. Which numbers did she hit?

23 7 19 5 9 13 21 10 27

2. Jun asked Yuki for her telephone number. Yuki described her number as follows: "It contains all the digits 1–7. Each digit is used only once. The 3 numbers in the first part (prefix) are in the order from least to greatest and add up to 14. The numbers in the second part (suffix) are in order from least to greatest and add up to 14. The number does not begin with 1." Using this information, could he figure out her phone number?
3. A cashier often gave change for $1 so people could use the soda machine. Just for fun, he tried to find all the ways to do this, using no more than 4 of any coin and no coin smaller than a nickel or bigger than a quarter. How many ways are there?

Group Decision Making

4. Work in a group. Discuss and decide.

Situation You want to buy a used car and need to know how many weeks you must work at a fast-food restaurant in order to have enough money to buy a car.

Guidelines for Planning

- **Formulate Problems** you will need to solve.
- Discuss **Assumptions** you will make and **Data** you will need.

a. What decision or decisions do you need to make in this situation?
b. Formulate problems you need to solve to make the decision(s).
c. List any assumptions you need to make to arrive at a decision.
d. What data, if any, do you need to collect to make a decision?
e. Write a paragraph summarizing what your group did, what decisions it made, and why.

Extend Key Ideas

Compound Interest

The formula $I = Prt$ can be used to find **compound interest.** When interest is **compounded,** the amount of interest earned is added to the principal. Interest is then earned on the new principal.

Suppose $5,000 is deposited at an interest rate of 10% per year, compounded semiannually. What will the principal be after one year?

First $\frac{1}{2}$ Year

Store 5,000 in memory.	5000 [M+] (5000)	Principal.
Multiply the principal by the interest rate (0.1) and the time (0.5 year) to find the interest.	5000 [×] 0.1 [×] 0.5 [=] (250)	Interest.
Add the interest to the principal amount stored in the memory.	250 [+] [MR] [=] (5250)	New principal.

Second $\frac{1}{2}$ Year

Replace 5,000 with 5,250 in memory.	[ON/AC] 5250 [M+]	
Find the interest for the second half year, using the new principal.	5250 [×] 0.1 [×] 0.5 [=] (262.5)	Interest.
Add the interest to the principal.	262.50 [+] [MR] [=] (5512.5)	Principal at the end of the year.

The amount after the first half year is $5,250. The amount after the full year is $5,512.50.

Use a calculator and the formula $I = Prt$ to solve.

1. Amount deposited: $150. Rate of interest: 5% per year, compounded semiannually. What will the principal be after 2 years?
2. Amount deposited: $3,500. Rate of interest: 6% per year, compounded quarterly. What will the principal be after 2 years?

Chapter 11 Review/Test

Understanding

True or False?

11-2 **1.** To find what percent 5 is of 25, you can divide 5 by 25 and change the decimal to a percent.

11-1 **2.** 120% of a positive number is greater than the number.

11-6 **3.** Discount means the price of an item after the percent of decrease is subtracted.

11-1 **4.** To find a percent of a number the percent must first be written as a decimal or as a fraction.

11-10 **5.** A circle graph is best used to show trends in data over time.

11-5 **6.** When you buy something for "30% off," the price you pay is less than the original price of the item.

Skills

11-1 11-2 11-3 Use a proportion or an equation to solve. Round to the nearest tenth.

7. 25% of 64

8. 12.5% of 40

9. What percent of 25 is 7?

10. 15 out of 150 is what percent?

11. 3 is 5% of what number?

12. 66 is 75% of what number?

Applications

11-3 **13.** Pam teaches karate and 35% of her students are children. If Pam teaches 180 students, how many are children?

11-6 **14.** Lisa was given a 6% discount on a scooter that regularly costs $1,550. What did she pay for the scooter not including tax?

11-6 **15.** Carlos made a 4% commission on a sale of $70. How much commission did he make?

11-8 **16.** How much interest would you make on a $350 investment at 15% per year for 6 years?

11-8 **17.** Ted paid interest of 2% per month for three months on a $700 loan. How much interest did he pay?

11-7 **18.** James bought a fish tank for $58. If the sales tax rate is 6.5%, how much did he pay in total for the fish tank?

11-10 **19.** Make a circle graph to show the data. Greeting cards sold: birthday, 25%; anniversary, 15%; graduation, 10%; special occasion, 30%; other, 20%.

12

Equations in Geometry

Find the circumference of the circle formed by the rotating propellers if the end of each propeller is 50 inches from the center of the nose cone.

12-1 Basic Figures

Objective To recognize and identify basic geometric figures.

Understand the Ideas

Domed structures, towers, bridges, and buildings are designed using geometric figures. The three basic geometric figures are point, line and plane.

	Figure	Name	Symbol
A **point** is the simplest geometric figure. It shows a location.	A •	Point *A*	A
Given any two points, there is only one **line** through the two points.	A B	Line *AB*	$\overleftrightarrow{AB}$
Three points that are not on the same line determine a **plane.**	B • A • • C	Plane *ABC*	ABC

Segments and rays are parts of a line.

	Figure	Name	Symbol
A **segment** *PQ* includes endpoints *P* and *Q* and all points between.	P Q	segment *PQ*	$\overline{PQ}$
A **ray** *AB* extends in one direction from endpoint A.	A B	ray *AB*	$\overrightarrow{AB}$

Example

Name a point, a line, a plane, a segment, and a ray on the figure.

Solution W

$\overleftrightarrow{WX}$

WXZ

$\overline{XW}$

$\overrightarrow{YX}$

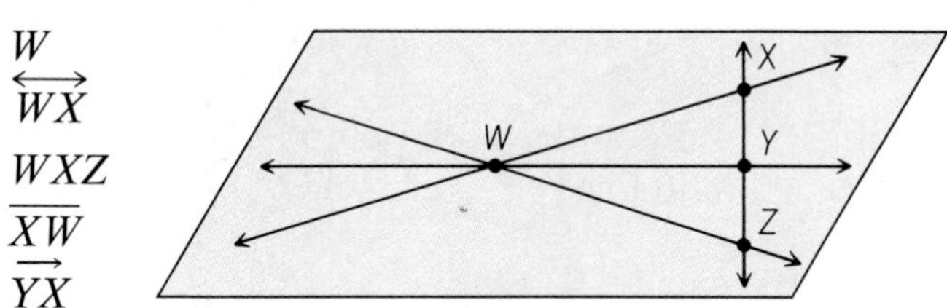

Try This **a.** Name another point, line, segment, and ray on the figure.

Class Exercises

Discuss the Ideas

Discuss whether the object suggests a point, a ray, a segment, or a plane.

1. tip of an ice pick
2. top of a desk
3. a tightly-stretched string
4. a laser beam

Exercises

Practice and Apply

Use the figure at the right for Exercises 1–6.

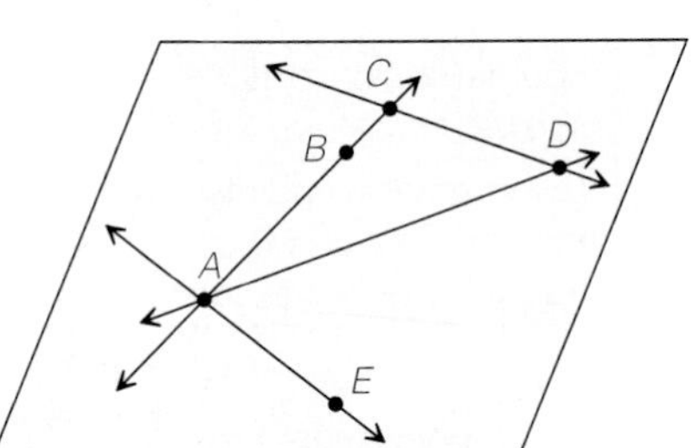

1. Name three points.
2. Name three lines.
3. Name a plane.
4. Name two segments with endpoint C.
5. Name two lines that pass through point C.
6. Name two rays with endpoint B.

Extend and Apply

Use the figure at right for Exercises 7–10.

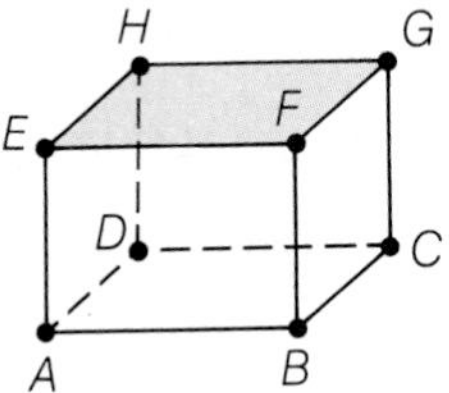

7. Name three segments with endpoint A.
8. Name two planes that include $\overline{EF}$.
9. Name twelve different segments.
10. Name six different planes.

Use Mathematical Reasoning

11. Copy and complete the third and fourth figures below. Then draw the next two figures to find the next three numbers in the pattern.

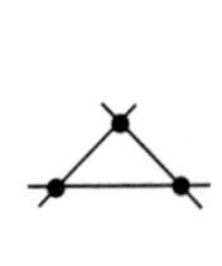

3 points
3 lines

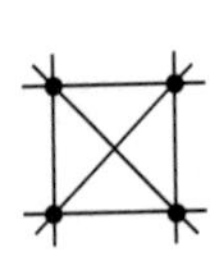

4 points
6 lines

5 points
10 lines

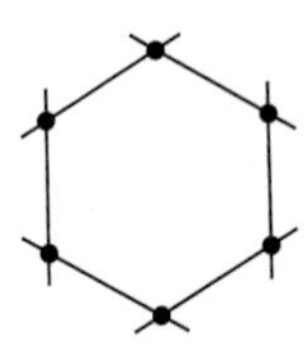

6 points
? lines

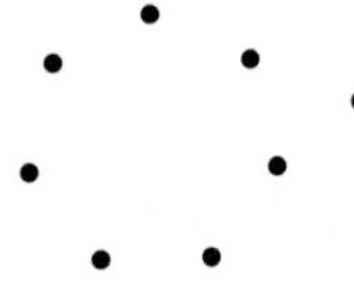

7 points
? lines

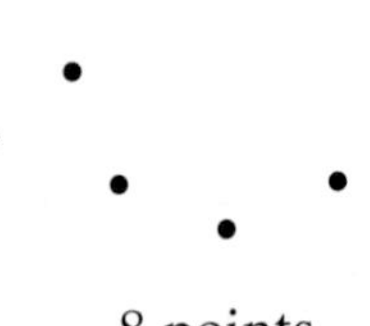

8 points
? lines

Mixed Review

Solve and check. **12.** $2(m - 9) + 5m = 6 + m$ **13.** $29.6 - t = -3.9$

14. $2x < 5$ **15.** $3x - 6 > 15$ **16.** $4x + 2 > 10$ **17.** $-2x + 1 < 3$

12-2 Length and Perimeter

Objective To estimate and measure lengths of segments; to write equations to find perimeters and unknown lengths.

Understand the Ideas

To find the length of a segment, choose a unit of length and count the number of times the unit can be laid end-to-end from one endpoint to another.

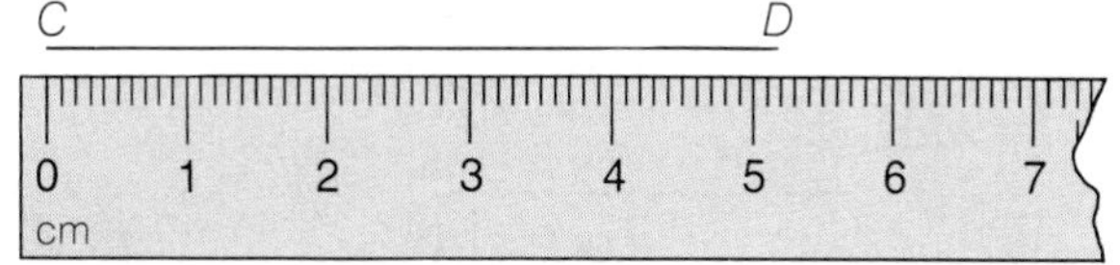

The length of $\overline{CD}$ is equal to 5.2 cm. We write $CD = 5.2$ cm.

Example 1

Estimate the length of $\overline{AB}$ to the nearest centimeter. Use a ruler to check your estimate, and give the length.

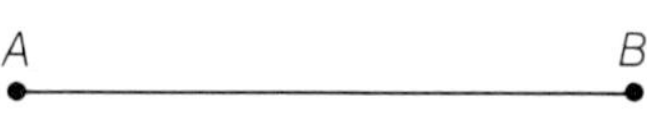

Solution

$AB \approx 4$ cm Mentally picture one centimeter to estimate how many centimeters long $\overline{AB}$ is.

Check $AB = 4.3$ cm The estimate is about right.

Try This Estimate the lengths. Use a ruler to check, and give the length.

a. $CD = \underline{\ ?\ }$ cm

b. $DE = \underline{\ ?\ }$ cm

C ——— D ——— E

You can often find an unknown length by solving an equation.

Example 2

Write and solve an equation to find the length of $\overline{CD}$.

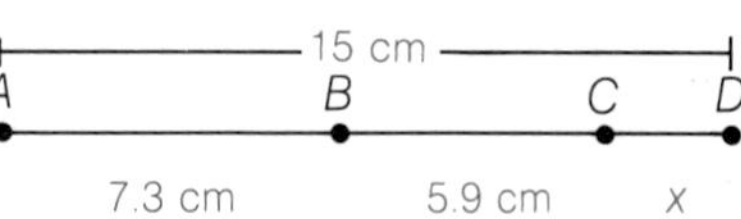

Solution Let $x = CD$. Then Let x be the unknown length.

$$7.3 + 5.9 + x = 15$$
$$13.2 + x = 15$$
$$-13.2 + 13.2 + x = -13.2 + 15$$
$$x = 1.8$$

$CD = 1.8$ cm

Try This c. Write and solve an equation to find the length of $\overline{BC}$.

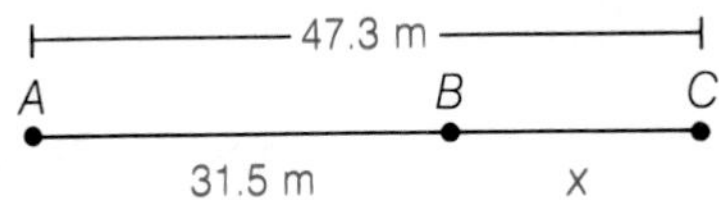

The total distance around a figure is called its **perimeter.** The perimeter of a rectangle is equal to twice its length plus twice its width. The formula is written as $P = 2l + 2w$.

You can find the perimeter of a nonrectangular figure by adding the lengths of the sides.

Example 3

Find the perimeter.

Solution $P = 2l + 2w$

$= 2(14.7) + 2(7.4)$

$= 29.4 + 14.8$

$= 44.2$

The perimeter is 44.2 cm.

14.7 cm

7.4 cm

Try This

d. Find the perimeter.

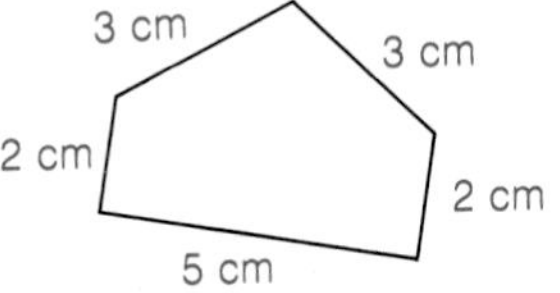

When you know the perimeter of a figure but not the length of one side, you can write and solve an equation to find the unknown length.

Example 4

Write and solve an equation to find the length of $\overline{AB}$.

Solution Let $x = AB$.

$x + 1.3 + 2.5 + 0.4 + 0.9 = 7.2$

$x + 5.1 = 7.2$

$x + 5.1 - 5.1 = 7.2 - 5.1$

$x = 2.1$

$AB = 2.1$ m

Perimeter = 7.2 cm

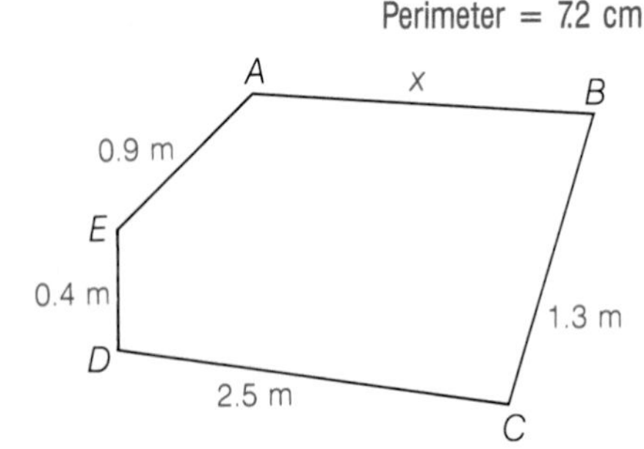

Try This

e. Write and solve an equation to find the unknown length.

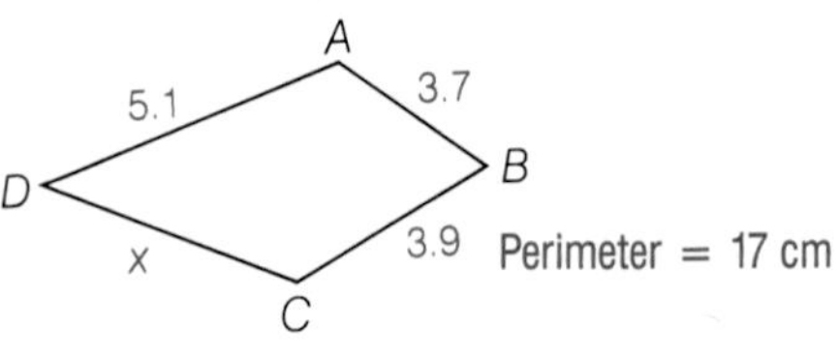

Class Exercises

Give an equation that is suggested by each figure.

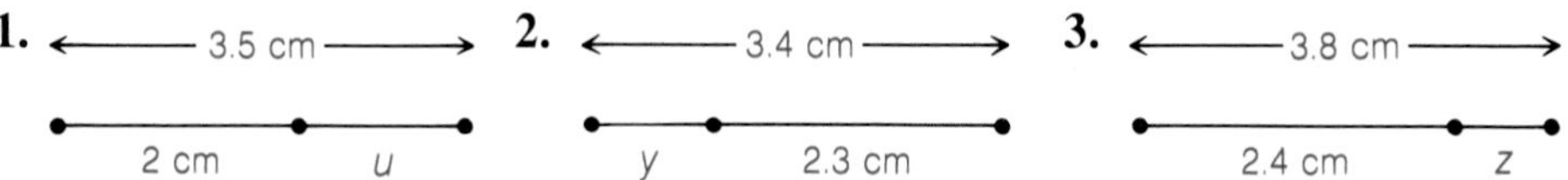

Discuss the Ideas

4. Suppose you know that one side of a figure is 23.4 cm long and the perimeter of the figure is 65.3 cm. Can you determine the shape of the figure? Explain.

Exercises

Practice and Apply

Estimate the length of each segment to the nearest centimeter. Use a ruler to check your measure, and give the length.

A B C D E

1. AC = ?
2. BD = ?
3. CE = ?
4. BC = ?
5. BE = ?
6. AE = ?

Write and solve an equation to find each unknown length.

7.
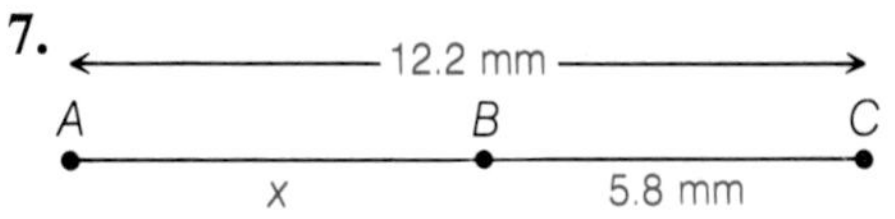

8.
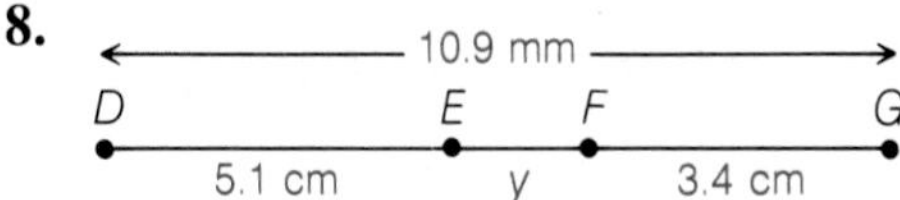

9.
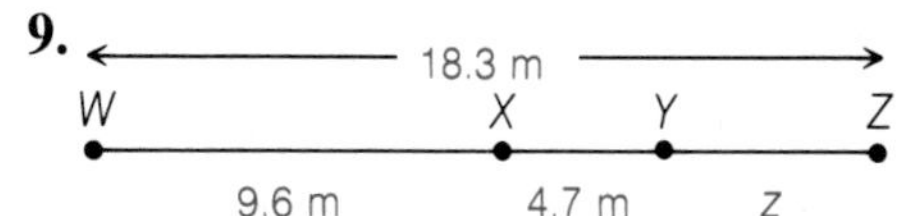

10.
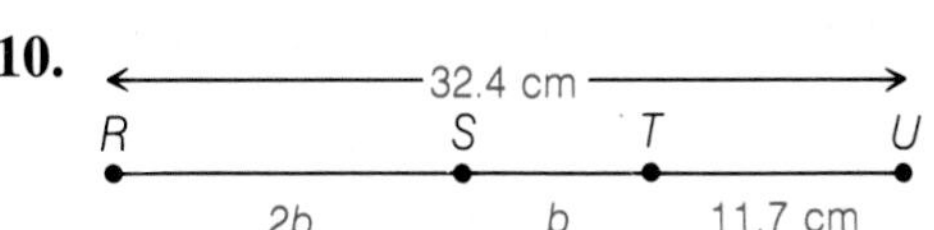

Find the perimeter.

11. 12.
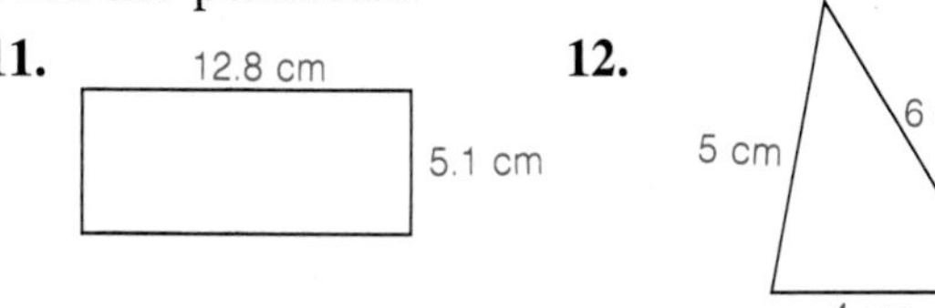

13.
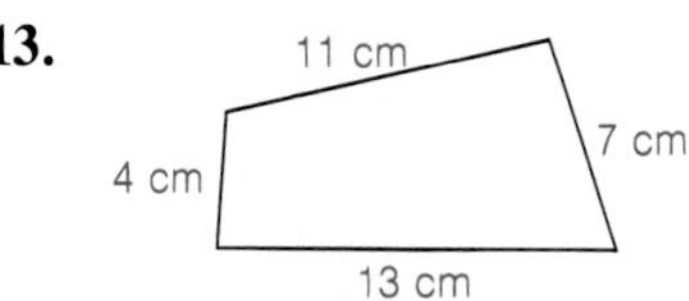

14. Find the perimeter of a picture that is 48 cm long and 33 cm wide.
15. If the picture frame is 2 cm wide what is the perimeter of the completed picture frame?

Write and solve an equation to find the unknown length.

16.

8 cm
8 cm
13 cm
x
5 cm
30 cm

Perimeter = 86

17.

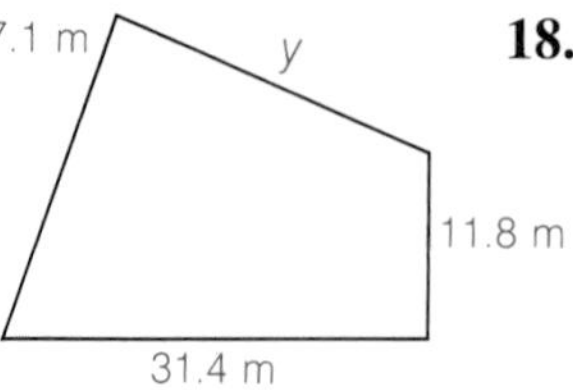

Perimeter = 76.7

18.

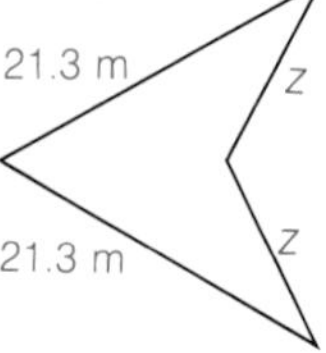

Perimeter = 68.6

Extend and Apply

19. The perimeter of the triangle at the right is 14 cm. Write and solve an equation to find the lengths of the sides.

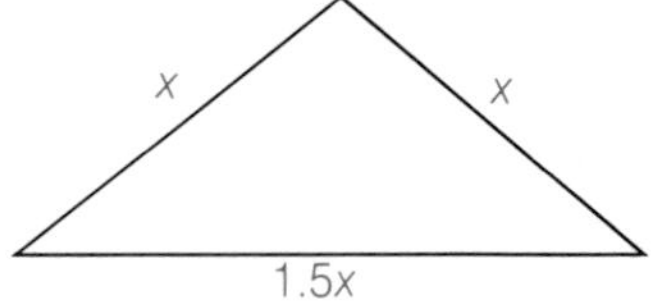

20. An 8.9 km cross-country course has an 0.8 km section that is flat, a 2.3 km section on a slight grade, a section on a steep uphill grade, a 4.5 km section on a slight downhill grade, and an 0.8 km section on rough ground. Write and solve an equation to find the length of the steep uphill grade.

21. A rectangle with a perimeter of 96 cm has a length 3 times its width. Write and solve an equation to find the lengths of the sides.

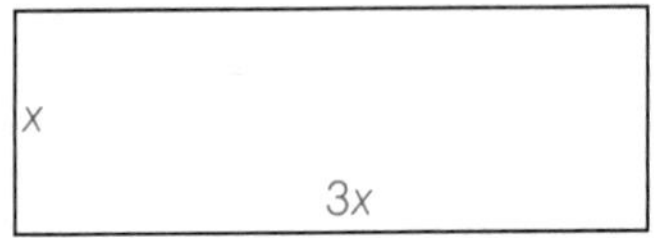

Use Mathematical Reasoning

Write and solve equations to find x and y in each figure below. Then find the perimeter of the figure. Assume all angles are right angles.

22.

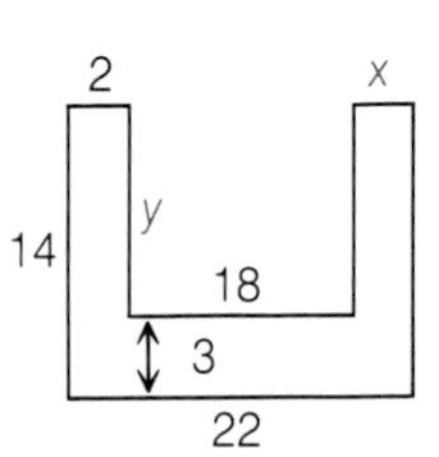

23.

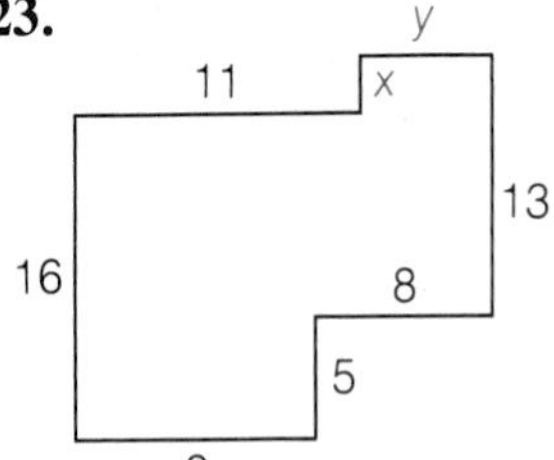

24.

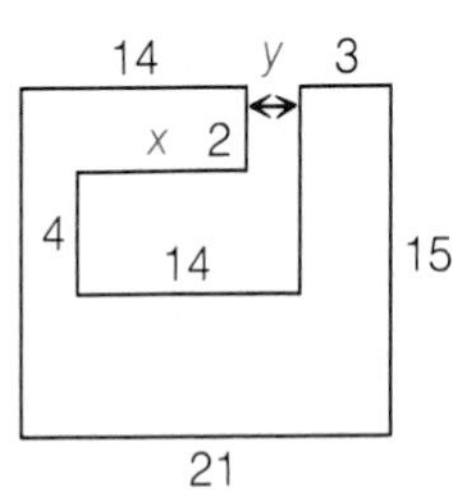

Mixed Review

Write each percent as a fraction or mixed number in lowest terms.

25. 140% **26.** 250% **27.** 108% **28.** 70% **29.** 37%

Write an equation to find each. **30.** 60% of 12 **31.** 0.5% of 60

32. 16 is what percent of 40? **33.** 27 is what percent of 18?

12-3

Angles and Angle Measures

Objective To measure angles; to classify angles as right, acute or obtuse; to write equations to find angle measures.

Application

Many skilled professionals draw and measure angles in their work. This navigator uses angles and angle measures to plot a ship's course. (See Example 1.)

Understand the Ideas

An **angle** consists of two rays with a common endpoint called the **vertex.** Each ray is called a side of the angle.

Figure	Name	Symbol
X, Y, Z, 3	angle *XYZ* or angle *Y* or angle 3	$\angle XYZ$ or $\angle Y$ or $\angle 3$

A **protractor** is used to measure angles. The unit of angle measure is the **degree** (°). To measure an angle, place the protractor at the vertex of the angle and the baseline of the protractor along one side of the angle as shown. Then read the number of degrees from the other side of the angle. In the drawing at the right, the measure of $\angle ABC$ is 50°. We write: $m\angle ABC = 50°$.

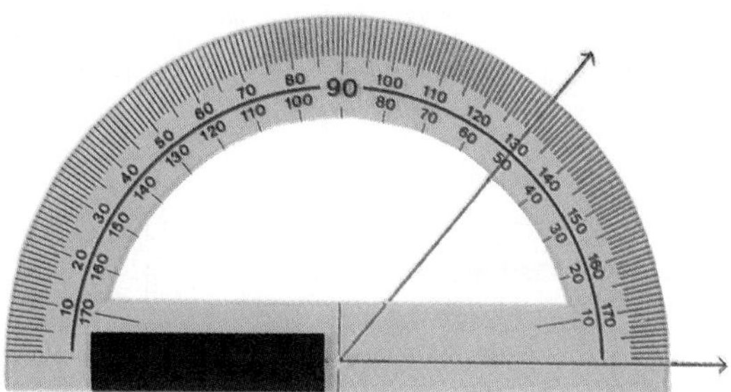

Angles are classified into three groups according to their measures. The measure of an **acute angle** is less than 90°. The measure of a **right angle** is 90°. The measure of an **obtuse angle** is greater than 90°.

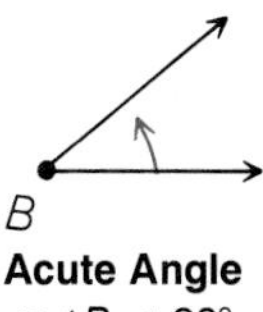

Acute Angle
$m\angle B < 90°$

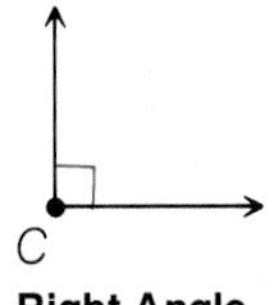

Right Angle
$m\angle C = 90°$

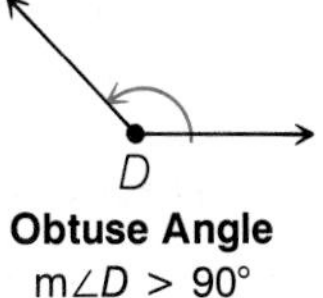

Obtuse Angle
$m\angle D > 90°$

Example 1

The navigator in the **application** may draw a figure like the one at the right to plot a ship's course. Name the following:

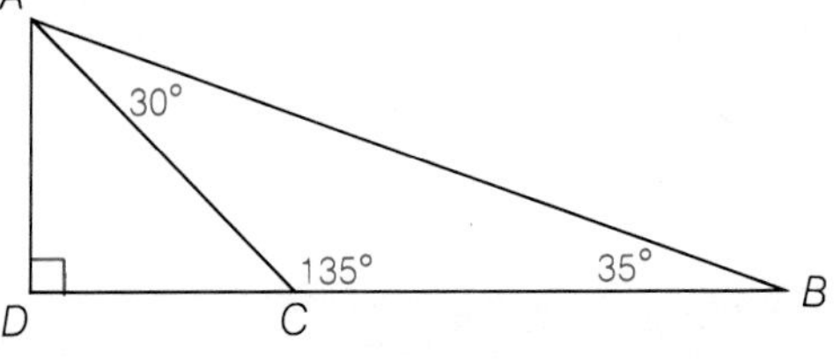

a. one acute angle

b. one obtuse angle

Solution **a.** $\angle CAB$ **b.** $\angle ACB$

Try This Refer to the figure to name the following:

a. two other acute angles **b.** a right angle

Example 2

Write and solve an equation to find $m\angle ABD$.

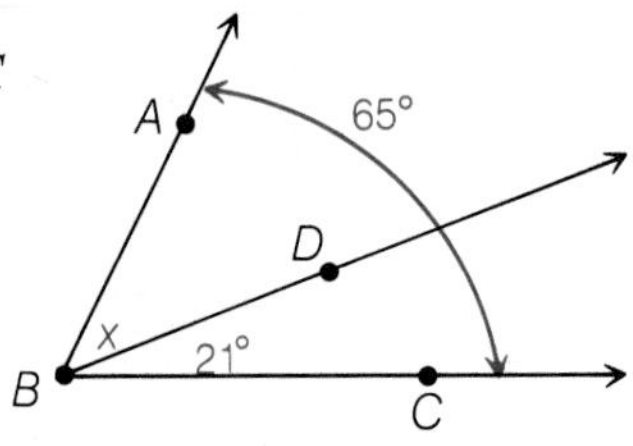

Solution

$$m\angle ABC = m\angle ABD + m\angle DBC$$
$$65 = x + 21$$
$$65 - 21 = x + 21 - 21$$
$$44 = x$$

$m\angle ABD = 44°$

Try This For the figure above, write and solve an equation to find each.

c. $m\angle DBC$ if $m\angle ABD$ is 28° **d.** $m\angle ABD$ if $m\angle DBC$ is 49°

Two angles are **complementary** if the sum of their measures is 90°. Two angles are **supplementary** if the sum of their measures is 180°.

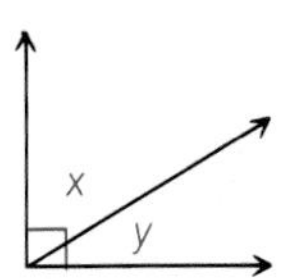

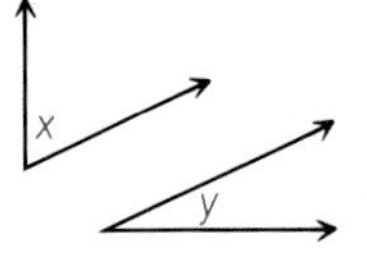

Complementary angles
$x + y = 90$

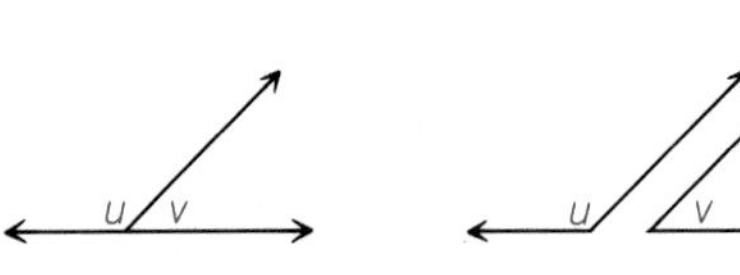

Supplementary angles
$u + v = 180$

Example 3

Write and solve an equation to find the complement of a 49° angle.

Solution

$x + 49 = 90$	Let x = the measure of the complement. The sum of the measures of an angle
$x + 49 - 49 = 90 - 49$	and its complement is 90°.
$x = 41$	The complement of a 49° angle is a 41° angle.

Try This Write and solve an equation to find:

e. the supplement of a 119° angle. **f.** the complement of a 48° angle.

Class Exercises

State whether an angle with the given measure is acute, right, or obtuse.

1. 10° **2.** 90° **3.** 175° **4.** 1° **5.** 95°

6. 80° **7.** 18° **8.** 100° **9.** 89° **10.** 130°

Discuss the Ideas

11. Draw a line and a point *O* on the line. Draw two rays from *O* both on the same side of the line. How do you know that your figure includes at least one acute angle and at least one obtuse angle?

Exercises

Practice and Apply

1. Position a protractor on this figure and give the measures of 5 different angles without moving the protractor. Record your measures.

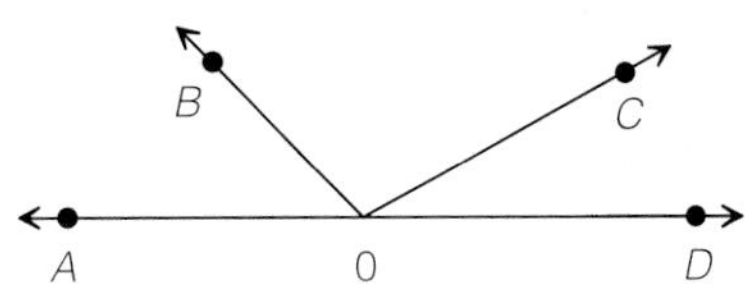

A navigator needed to read this figure.

2. Name an acute angle.

3. Name an obtuse angle.

4. Name a right angle.

5. Find m∠*ABD*.

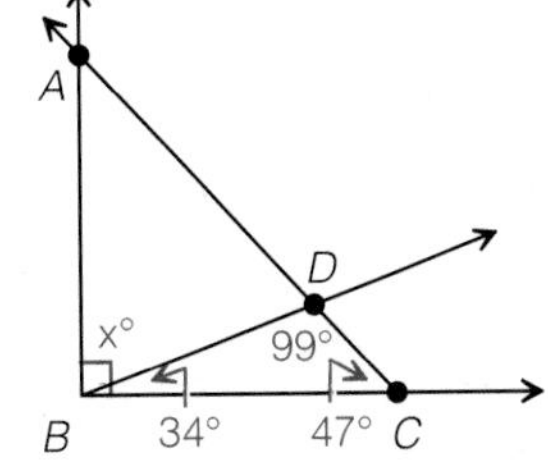

Refer to the figure at right. Write and solve an equation to find:

6. m∠*ABD* if m∠*CBD* = 15°

7. m∠*CBD* if m∠*ABD* = 31°

8. m∠*ABD* if m∠*CBD* = 21°

9. m∠*CBD* if m∠*ABD* = 35°

10. m∠*ABD* if m∠*CBD* = 19.2°

11. m∠*CBD* if m∠*ABD* = 27.5°

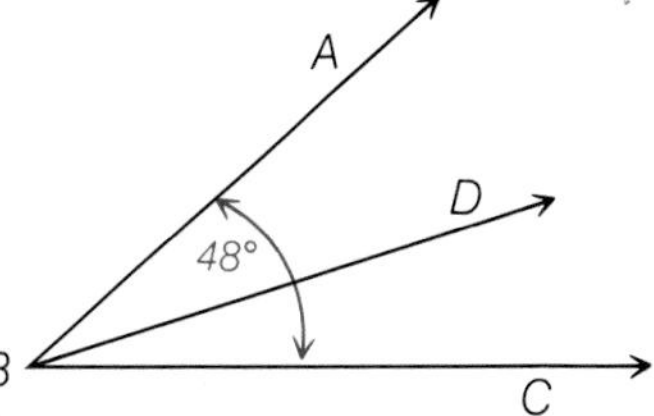

12. An airline pilot flying due west makes a 20° turn. If you drew the plane's path, what angle would it form?

13. A telescope is directed 78° above the horizon. If its direction is lowered by 12°, what is its angle to the horizon?

Write and solve an equation to find:

14. the complement of a 23° angle.

15. the complement of a 53° angle.

16. the supplement of a 123° angle.

17. the supplement of a 153° angle.

Extend and Apply

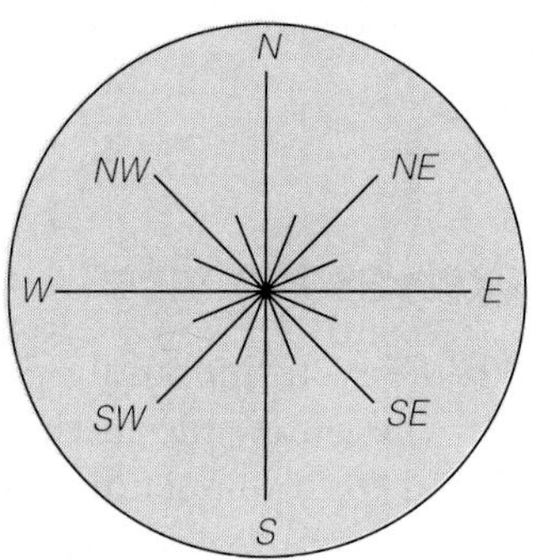

18. What is the measure of the angle between east and northeast?

19. What is the measure of the angle between northeast and north-northeast?

20. Two supplementary angles have measures of $2x$ and $3x$. Write and solve an equation to find the measure of the angles.

21. Two complementary angles have measures of y and $5y$. Write and solve an equation to find the measure of angle y.

Use Mathematical Reasoning

22. A ship travels in a direction 12° east of due north until it reaches a lighthouse. It then turns 30° to the left. How many degrees from due north is the ship now traveling?

23. After a ship travels due east for several hours, it turns 21 degrees to the left. How many degrees east of north is the ship now traveling?

Mixed Review

Write as a fraction in lowest terms. **24.** 40% **25.** 35%

Solve and check. **26.** $4.5n + 16.3 = 21.7$ **27.** $-6.2m + 18.3 = 6m$

Estimation

Use the 60°, 45°, and 30° angles to estimate the measures of the angles below.

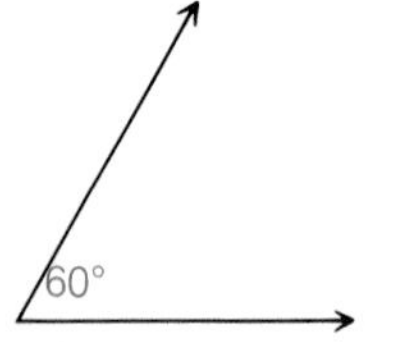

$\frac{2}{3}$ of a right angle

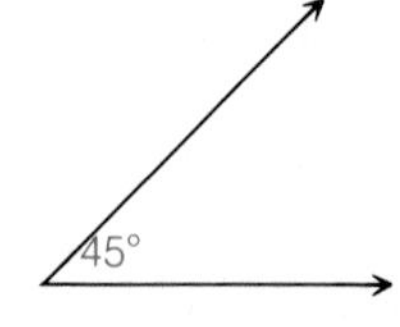

$\frac{1}{2}$ of a right angle

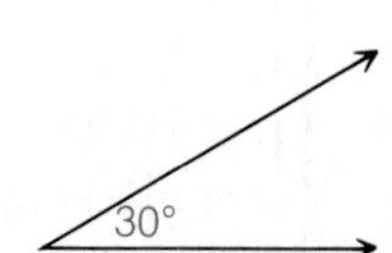

$\frac{1}{3}$ of a right angle

1.

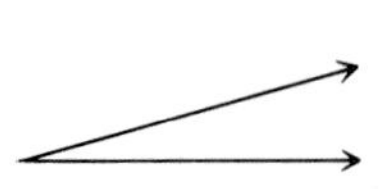

2.

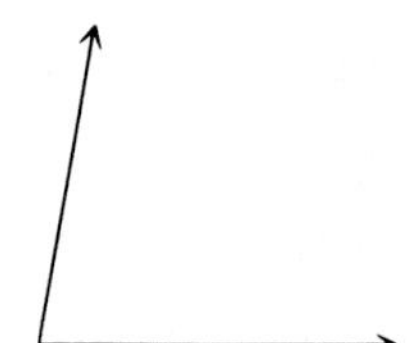

3.

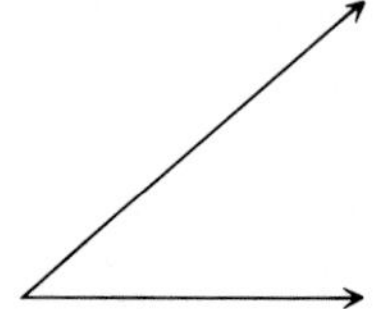

12-4 Parallel and Perpendicular Lines

Objective To identify lines as parallel or perpendicular; to find measures of vertical and corresponding angles.

Explore

Lines p and q are drawn by using the two sides of a ruler. Draw three of these figures where the line r has a different slope in each case. Label the angles as shown at the right.

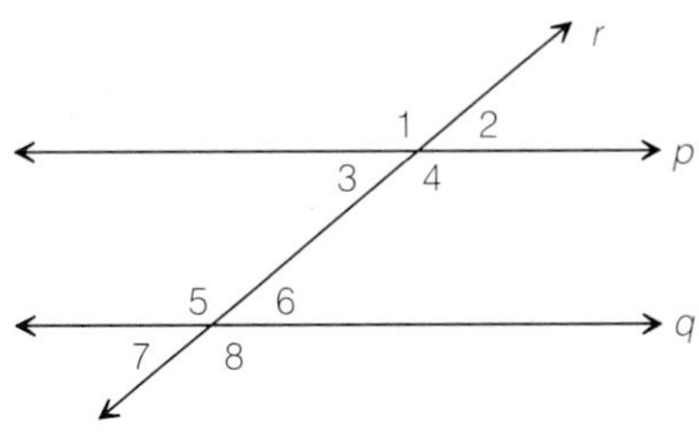

Measure all of the angles with a protractor and make a guess about which pairs have equal measures.

Understand the Ideas

Two lines in the same plane are **parallel** if they have no points in common. Two segments or rays in the same plane are parallel if the lines containing them are parallel. Lines in the same plane that are not parallel are called **intersecting** lines. Lines that intersect to form right angles are called **perpendicular** lines.

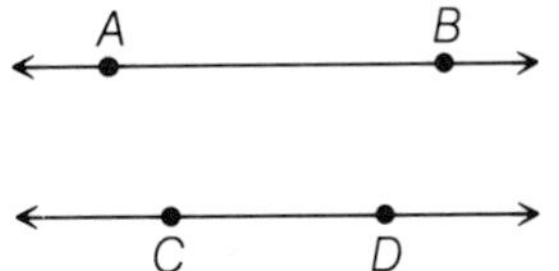

parallel lines
$\overleftrightarrow{AB}$ is parallel to $\overleftrightarrow{CD}$
$\overleftrightarrow{AB} \parallel \overleftrightarrow{CD}$

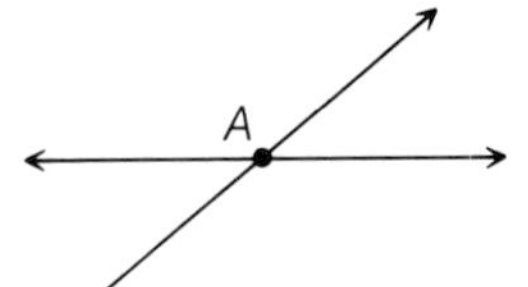

lines intersect at *A*
A is a point
of intersection

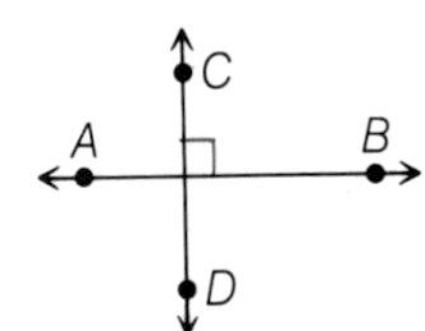

perpendicular lines
$\overleftrightarrow{AB}$ is perpendicular to $\overleftrightarrow{CD}$
$\overleftrightarrow{AB} \perp \overleftrightarrow{CD}$

Two intersecting lines form two pairs of **vertical angles.** In the figure at right, $\angle 2$ and $\angle 4$ are vertical angles, and $\angle 1$ and $\angle 3$ are vertical angles.

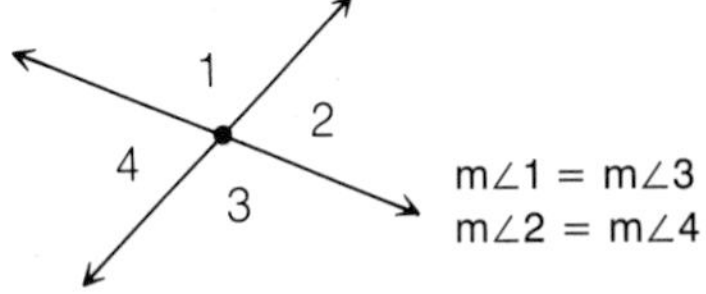

$m\angle 1 = m\angle 3$
$m\angle 2 = m\angle 4$

Measure of Vertical Angles

Vertical angles have the same measure.

When lines intersect, you can sometimes use vertical angles to find the measure of an angle not given.

Example 1

Find m∠1 on the figure at right.

Solution m∠1 = 29° ∠1 is vertical to an angle of 29°. Vertical angles have the same measure.

Try This

a. Find m∠2 on the figure at right.

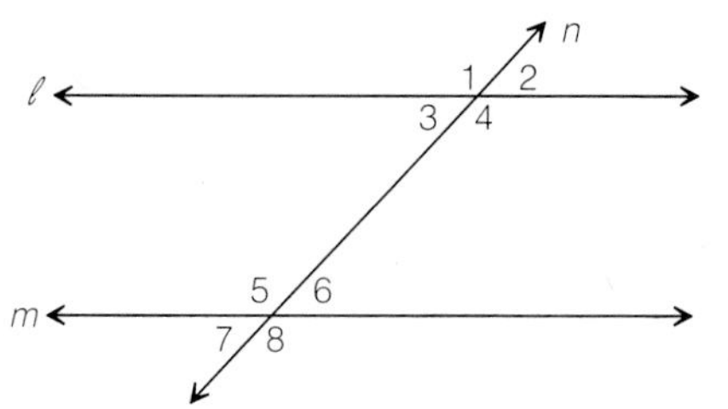

A line that intersects two other lines is called a **transversal.** When a transversal intersects a pair of parallel lines, the pairs of **corresponding angles** formed have the same measure.

Corresponding angles in this figure are ∠1 and ∠5, ∠2 and ∠6, ∠3 and ∠7, and ∠4 and ∠8.

m∠1 = m∠5
m∠2 = m∠6
m∠3 = m∠7
m∠4 = m∠8

The pairs of **alternate interior angles** also have the same measure. Alternate interior angles in the above figure are ∠3 and ∠6, and ∠4 and ∠5.

Measures of Corresponding Angles and Alternate Interior Angles

Where a transversal intersects a pair of parallel lines, corresponding angles have the same measure and alternate interior angles have the same measure.

Example 2

Lines *a* and *b* are parallel. Find the measures of ∠1, ∠2, and ∠3.

Solution

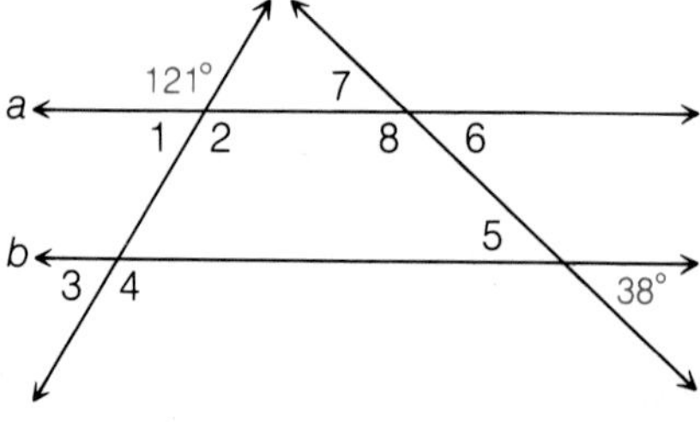

m∠1 + 121 = 180 ∠1 is supplementary to the angle measuring 121°
m∠1 = 59°

m∠2 = 121° Vertical angles have equal measures.

m∠3 = 59° Corresponding angles have equal measures.

Try This

b. Find the measures of ∠5, ∠6, ∠7, and ∠8.

Class Exercises

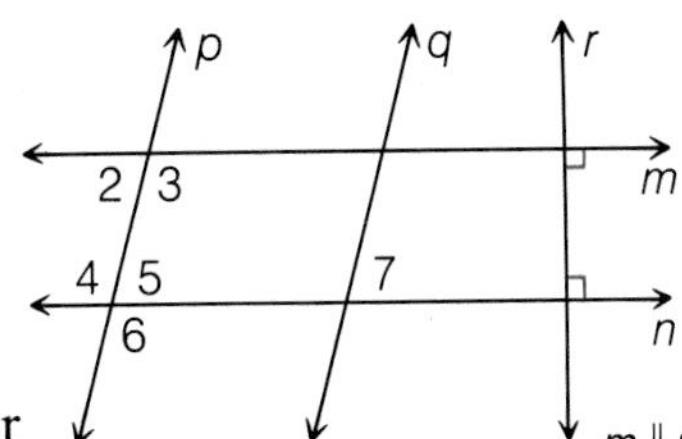

1. Name a pair of parallel lines.
2. Name a pair of perpendicular lines.
3. Name an angle that is vertical to $\angle 4$.
4. Name an angle corresponding to $\angle 3$.
5. Name an angle that is an alternate interior angle to $\angle 5$.

Discuss the Ideas

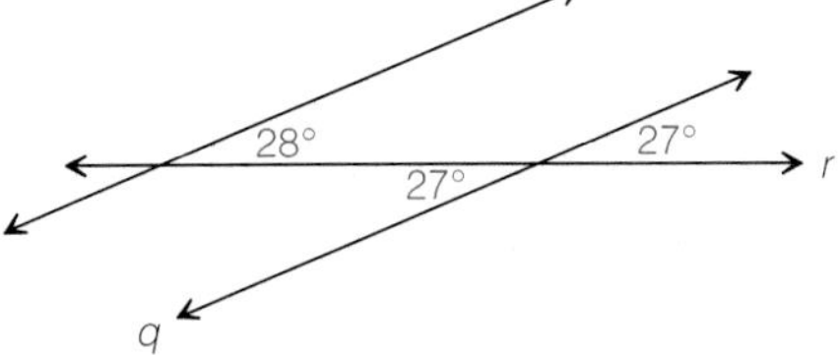

6. Discuss how you can tell that lines p and q are not parallel.

Exercises

Practice and Apply

Find the measures of $\angle 1$, $\angle 2$, $\angle 3$, and $\angle 4$.

1. 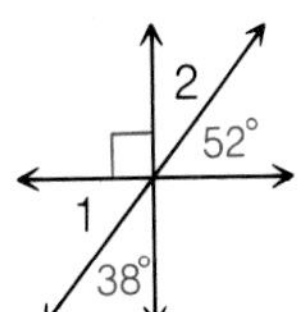

2. 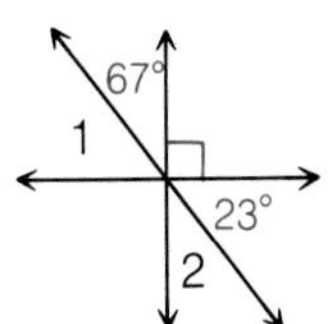

3. 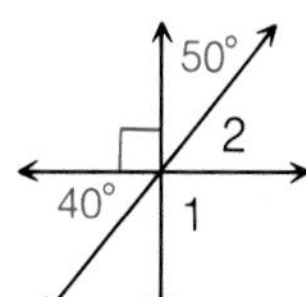

4. 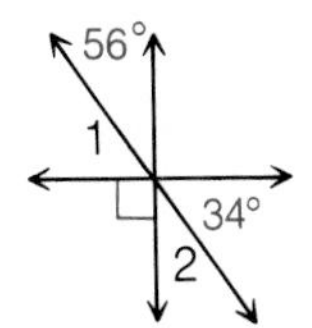

5. 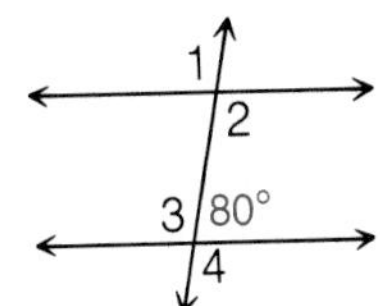

6. 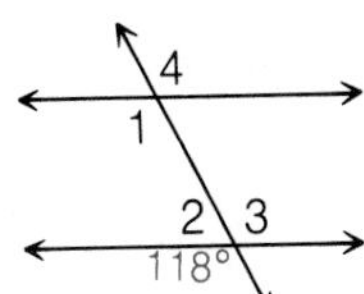

7. 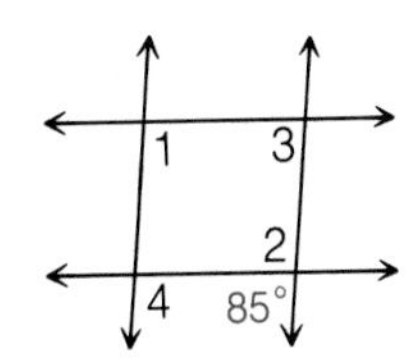

8. 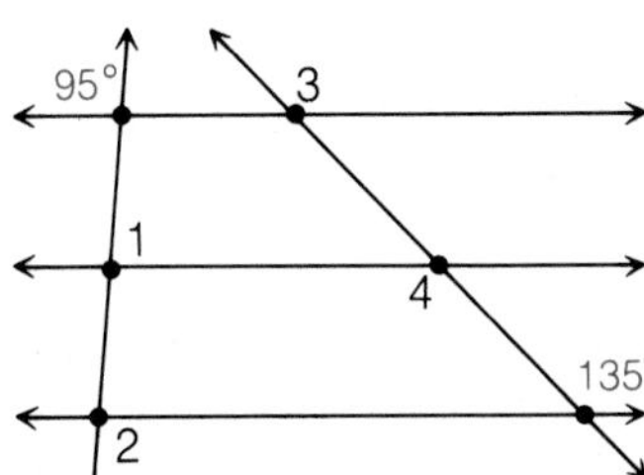

9. A hiker walking north makes a 30° turn to the right. Afer walking for 30 minutes she turns 150° to the right. In which direction is she walking?
10. A ship crosses the equator at a 28° angle. If the ship continues in the same direction, at what angle will it cross the 5° latitude line? (Assume that a small portion of the earth's surface is like a plane surface.)

The figure at the right shows a plan for making a fence gate. It includes several parallel lines.

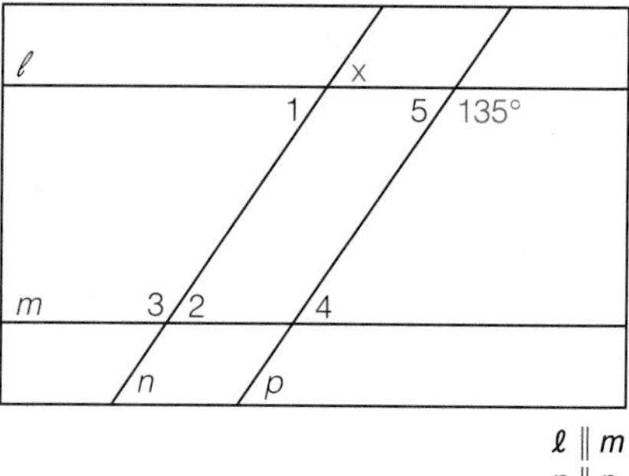

11. How do you know that m∠5 = 45°?

12. How are angles 1 and 5 related? How do their measures compare?

13. What are the measures of angles 3 and 4?

14. How do you know that m∠1 and m∠x are equal? How do you know that m∠x and m∠2 are equal?

15. How do you know that m∠4 and m∠5 are equal?

Extend and Apply

Write and solve an equation to find the measure of ∠ABC.

16.

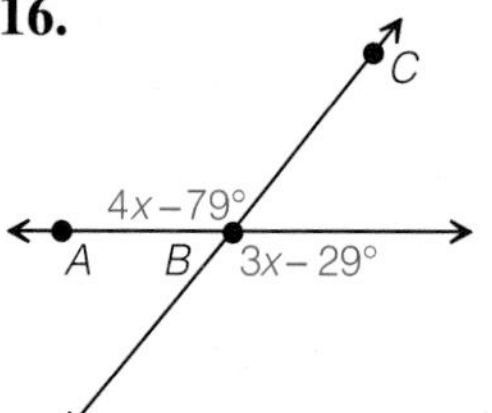

17.

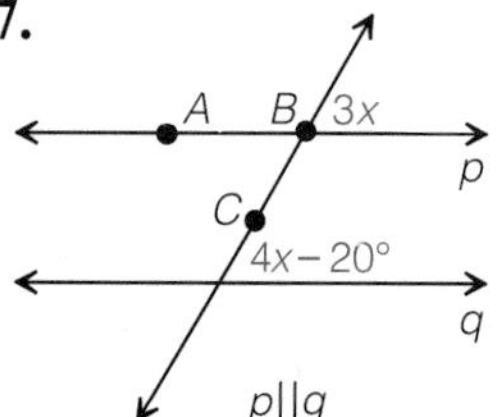

18.

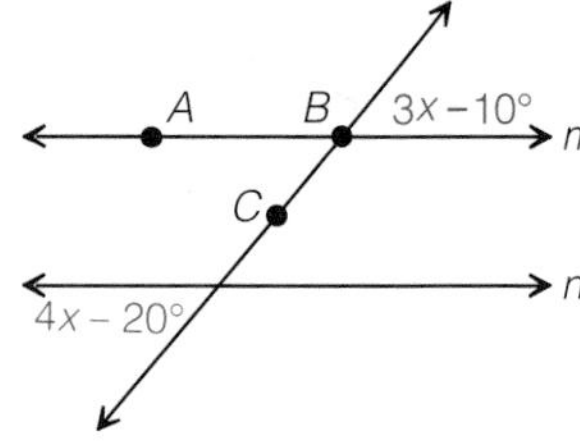

19. Communicate Write a paragraph that describes vertical angles, corresponding angles, and alternate angles that can be seen in your classroom or on your school campus.

Use Mathematical Reasoning

20. Show that lines p and q are not parallel if m∠ABC is 72°.

21. If lines p and q are parallel, then x = __?__ and m∠ABC = __?__ .

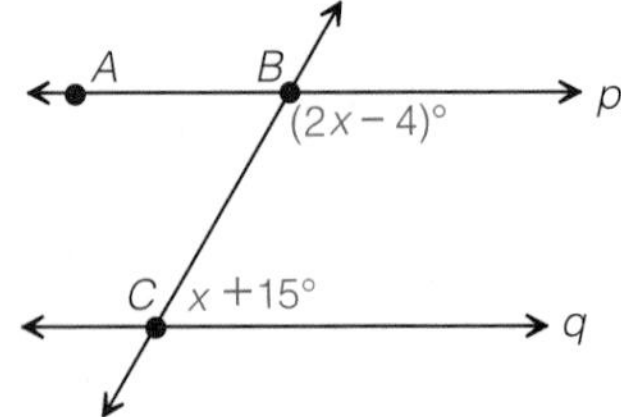

Mixed Review

Use a proportion to write each of the following as a percent.

22. $\frac{4}{5}$ **23.** $\frac{1}{8}$

24. What percent of 16 is 12? **25.** What percent of 45 is 27?

26. What number is 80% of 120? **27.** What number is 65% of 230?

Using Deductive Reasoning

Objective To decide whether conclusions based on conditional statements are correct.

Statements like the one shown in the ad with an "if" part and a "then" part are used throughout everyday life and in mathematics. They are called "if-then" or **conditional** statements.

The following activity will help you think about drawing correct conclusions in situations involving conditional statements.

Group Activity Assume that the conditional statement is true. Work in groups to answer the questions about conclusions. Justify your decisions.

If you get an A on every Pre-Algebra test, then you get an A in the course.

1. Suppose Diem did not get an A on every Pre-Algebra test. Can you conclude that she did not get an A in the course?
2. Suppose Jordan got an A on every Pre-Algebra test. Can you conclude that he got an A in the course?
3. Suppose Ziat did not get an A in the Pre-Algebra course. Can you conclude that he did not get an A on every test?

The situation above illustrates that you must think carefully about the conclusions you draw from conditional statements. Some conclusions seem logical, but do not necessarily follow from the information given.

Apply Mathematical Reasoning

1. Assume that the conditional statement and facts are true. Decide which of the conclusions are correct.
   Conditional: *If you live in Houston, then you live in Texas.*
   a. Shobana lives in Houston. Conclusion: She lives in Texas.
   b. Danny does not live in Texas. Conclusion: He does not live in Houston.
   c. Pedro does not live in Houston. Conclusion: He does not live in Texas.
   d. Rose lives in Texas. Conclusion: She lives in Houston.

12-5 Triangles

Objective To classify triangles according to type, using specific names; to write equations to find angle measures in triangles.

Understand the Ideas

A **triangle** is a figure in a plane, made up of three segments meeting at endpoints. In the triangle at right, $\overline{AB}$, $\overline{BC}$, and $\overline{AC}$ are called the **sides**. Points A, B, and C are called **vertices.**

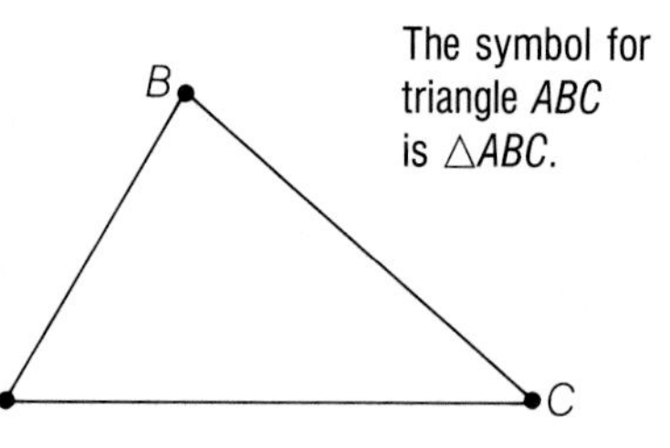

The symbol for triangle *ABC* is $\triangle ABC$.

Triangles are classified by the measures of their angles or the lengths of their sides.

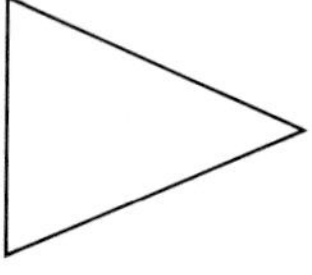

Acute
all acute angles

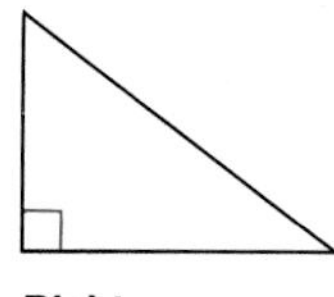

Right
one right angle

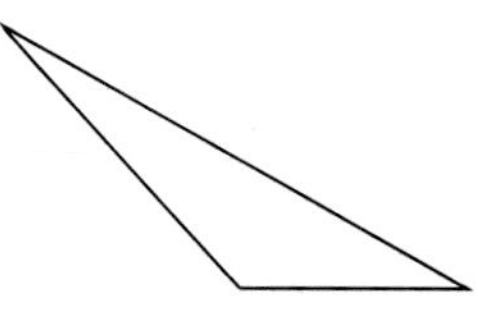

Obtuse
one obtuse angle

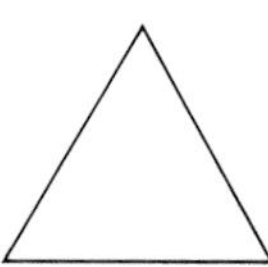

Equilaterial
all sides equal in length

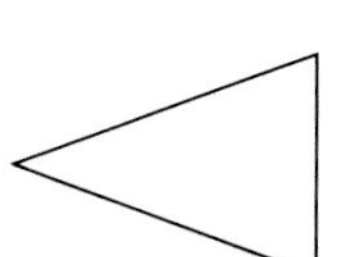

Isosceles
at least two sides equal in length

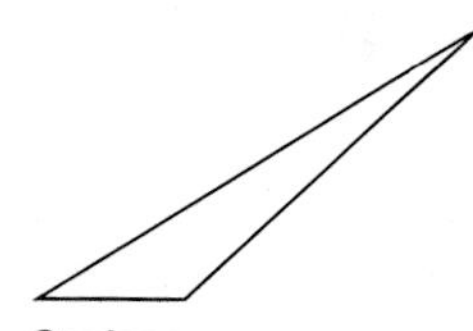

Scalene
no two sides equal in length

Example 1

Classify $\triangle ABC$ and $\triangle DEF$ by the measures of their angles and the lengths of their sides.

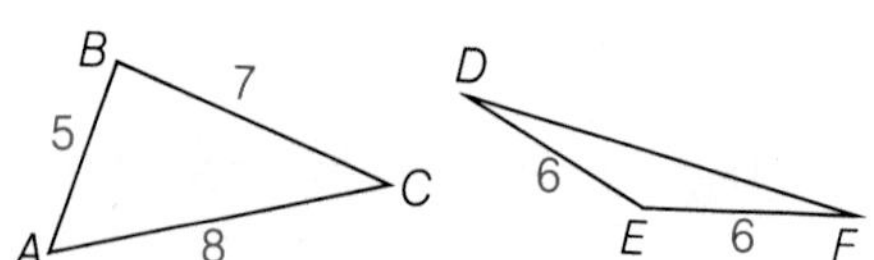

Solution

$\triangle ABC$ is acute and scalene. All angles are acute and no two sides are equal in length.

$\triangle DEF$ is obtuse and isosceles. Angle *E* is obtuse; two sides are equal in length.

Try This **a.** Classify $\triangle XYZ$ and $\triangle BCD$ by the measures of their angles and the lengths of the sides.

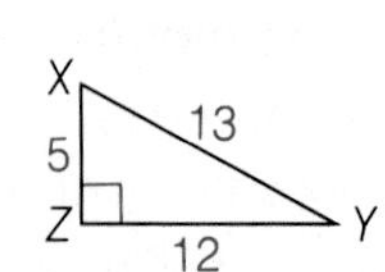

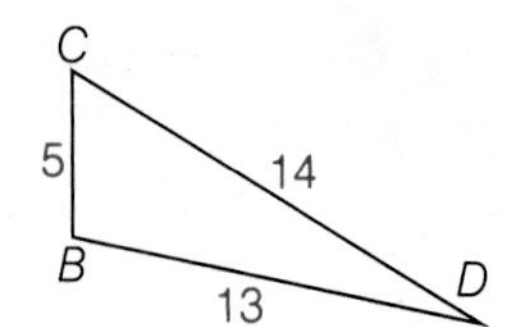

The picture below suggests an important property of triangles.

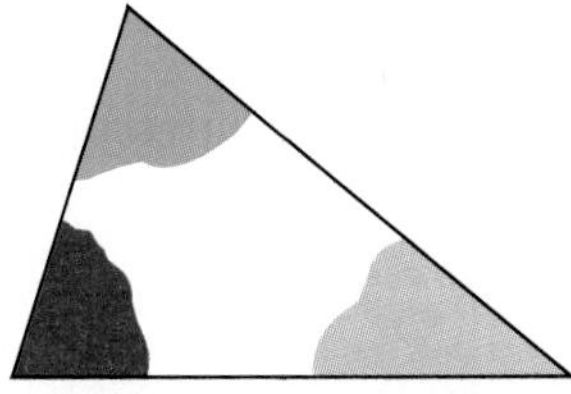

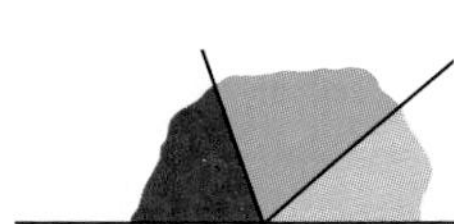

Sum of the Angle Measures of a Triangle

The sum of the angle measures in any triangle is 180°.

$m\angle A + m\angle B + m\angle C = 180°$

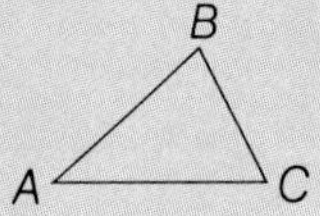

Example 2

Write and solve an equation to find $m\angle A$.

Solution $x + 30 + 130 = 180$

$x + 160 = 180$

$x = 20$

$m\angle A = 20°$.

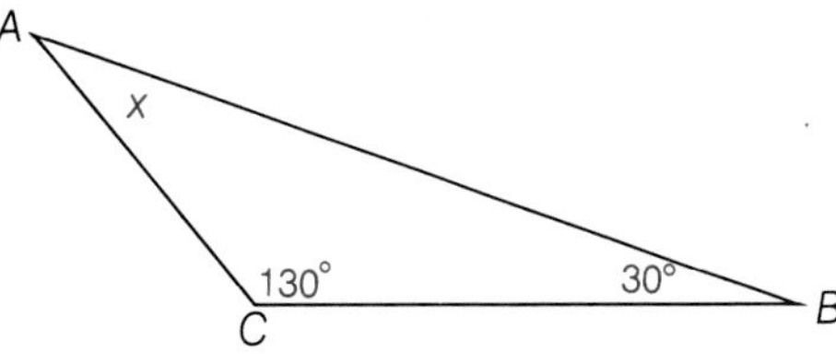

Try This

b. Two angles of a triangle have measures 37° and 92°. Write and solve an equation to find the measure of the third angle.

Class Exercises

On the figure at right, name the following:

1. an obtuse triangle.

2. three right triangles.

3. two acute triangles.

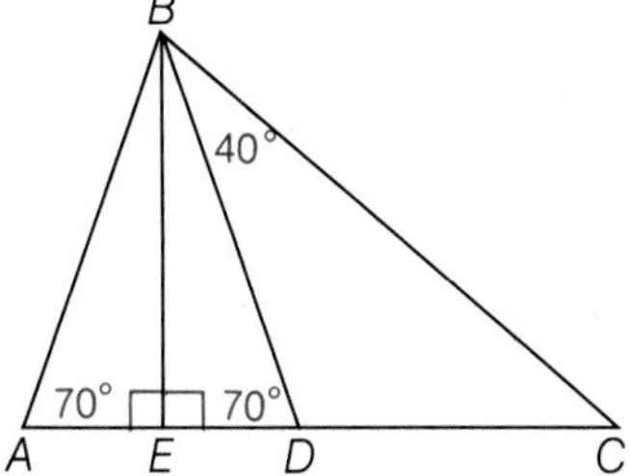

Discuss the Ideas

Discuss how many ways you can fill in the blanks to make a true statement if replacements for the blanks are chosen from among: acute, right, obtuse, equilateral, isosceles, and scalene.

4. A(n) ______ triangle is sometimes a(n) ______ triangle.

5. A(n) ______ triangle is always a(n) ______ triangle.

Exercises

Practice and Apply

Classify each triangle by the measures of its angles and the lengths of its sides.

1. T R 8 8 S

2. 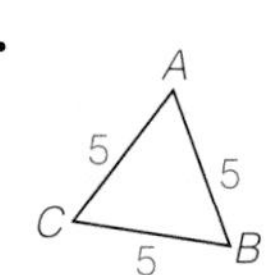

3. 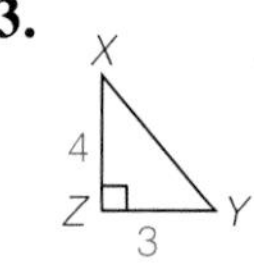

4. 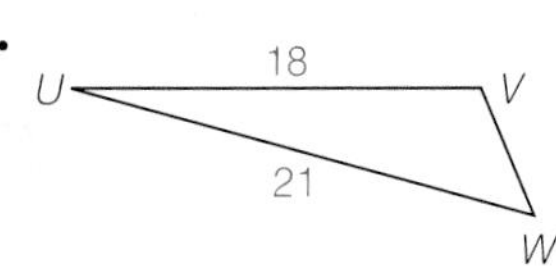

Write and solve an equation to find m∠A.

5. 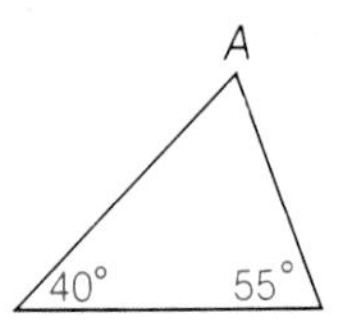

6. 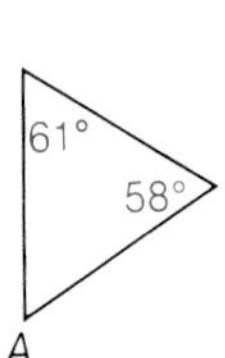

7. 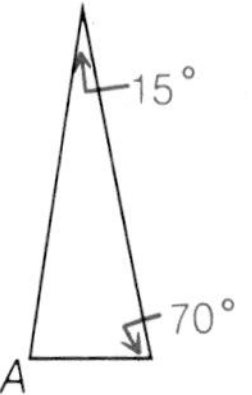

8. 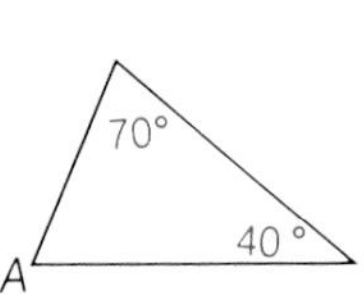

Write and solve an equation to find the measure of the third angle.

9. Two angles of a triangle have measures of 70° and 32°.

10. Two angles of a triangle have measures of 119° and 25°.

Extend and Apply

Write and solve an equation to find the measure of each angle.

11. 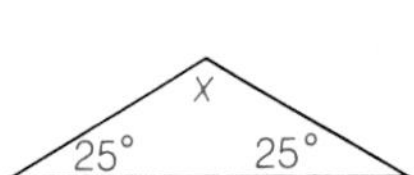

12. 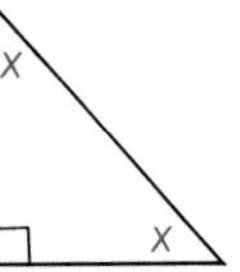

13. 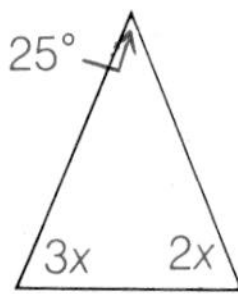

14. A surveyor is marking the boundaries of a triangular plot of land. He starts at one corner of the property and walks due east to the next corner. He then turns 60° north and proceeds to the third corner. What conclusion can you draw about this triangular plot of land?

Use Mathematical Reasoning

Find the pattern and use the variable n to complete the following: x = __?__

15. 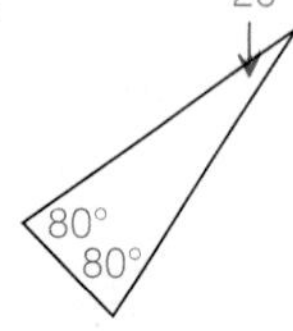

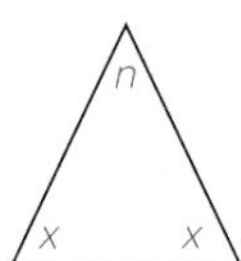

n x x

Mixed Review

16. What percent of 20 is 4?

17. What percent of 20 is 17?

12-6 Polygons

Objective To classify polygons according to type, using specific names; to write and solve equations to find the measure of an angle in a polygon.

Application

An interior designer encounters examples of geometry when selecting fabric designs, floor coverings, and wallpaper. The floor covering shown here has a pattern that is made from repeating polygons. (See Example 1.)

Understand the Ideas

A **polygon** is a plane figure formed by three or more segments that intersect only at their endpoints so that exactly two segments meet at each endpoint. A polygon is named according to the number of its sides or angles.

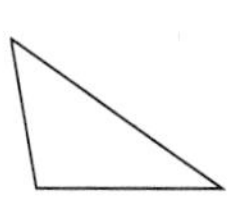

triangle
3 sides

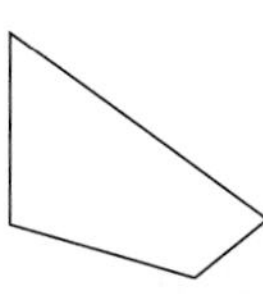

quadrilateral
4 sides

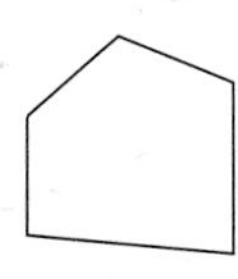

pentagon
5 sides

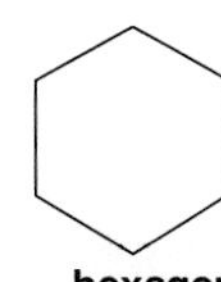

hexagon
6 sides

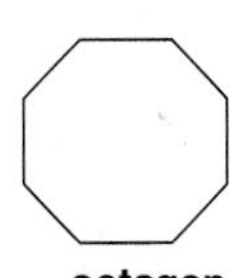

octagon
8 sides

In a **regular polygon,** all sides and all angles have the same measure. The hexagon and octagon above are regular polygons.

A **quadrilateral** is a polygon with four sides. Some quadrilaterals have specific names.

rectangle
4 right angles

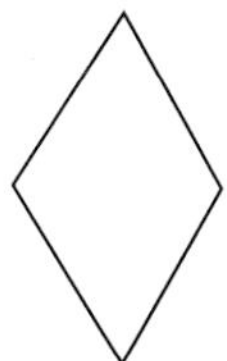

rhombus
all sides the same length

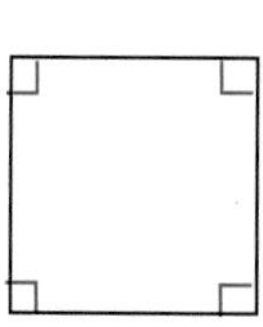

square
4 right angles; all sides the same length

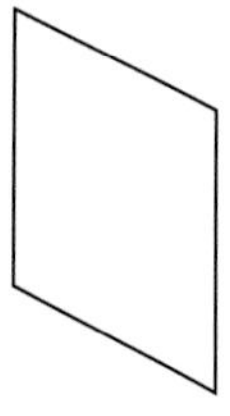

parallelogram
2 pairs of parallel sides

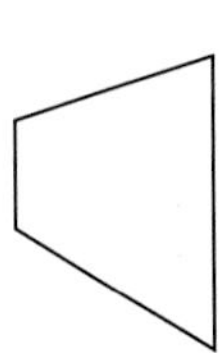

trapezoid
1 pair of parallel sides

Example 1

Name each type of polygon in the floor covering seen in the **application**, and tell whether it is regular. Use specific names for quadrilaterals.

Solution

Regular octagon
Square

Try This Name each polygon and indicate whether it is regular. Use specific names for quadrilaterals.

a.

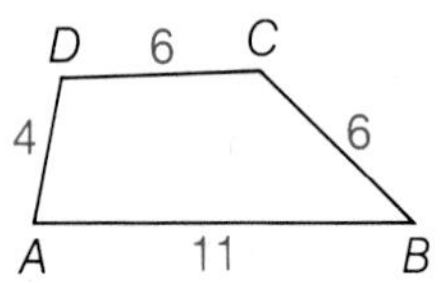

b.

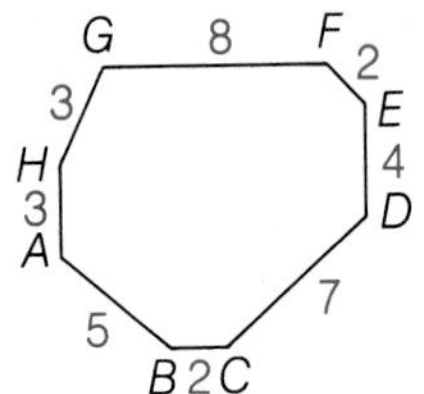

The figure below shows an important property of quadrilaterals.

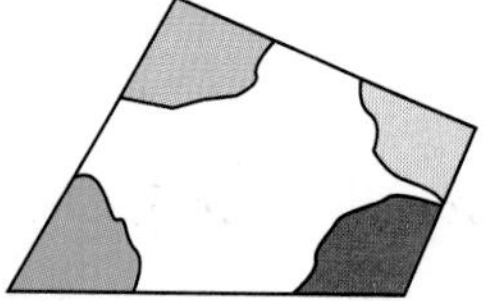

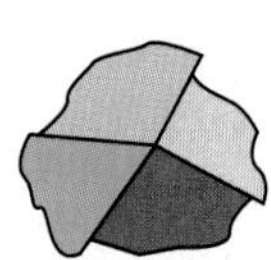

Sum of the Angle Measures of a Quadrilateral

The sum of the measures of the angles in any quadrilateral is 360°.

$m\angle A + m\angle B + m\angle C + m\angle D = 360°$

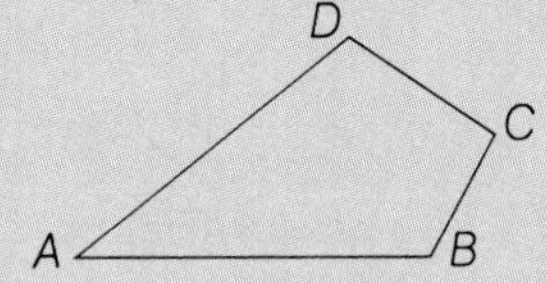

Example 2

Write and solve an equation to find $m\angle A$.

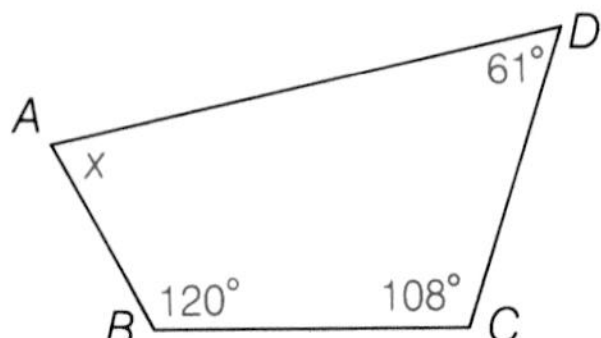

Solution

$x + 120 + 108 + 61 = 360$ — The sum of the measures of the angles in a quadrilateral is 360°.

$x + 289 = 360$ — Combine terms.

$x + 289 - 289 = 360 - 289$

$x = 71$

$m\angle A = 71°.$

Try This **c.** Write and solve an equation to find m∠A.

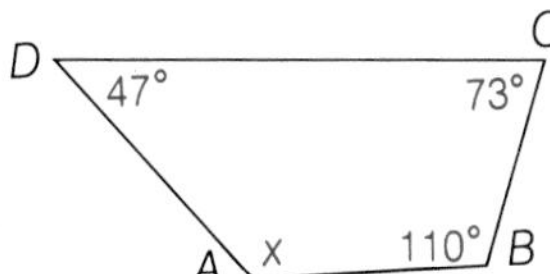

Class Exercises

Name a polygon that has:

1. 5 sides. **2.** 4 sides. **3.** 6 sides. **4.** 3 sides. **5.** 8 sides.

6. When is a polygon a regular polygon?

7. What is another name for a regular triangle?

8. What is another name for a regular quadrilateral?

Discuss the Ideas

9. Is it possible to draw a quadrilateral that has two pairs of sides the same length but is not a parallelogram? Explain.

Exercises

Practice and Apply

Name each polygon and indicate whether it is regular. Use any special names for quadrilaterals.

1.

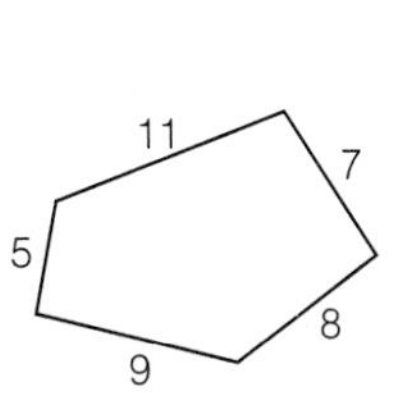

2.

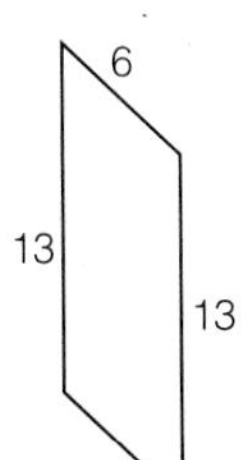

3.

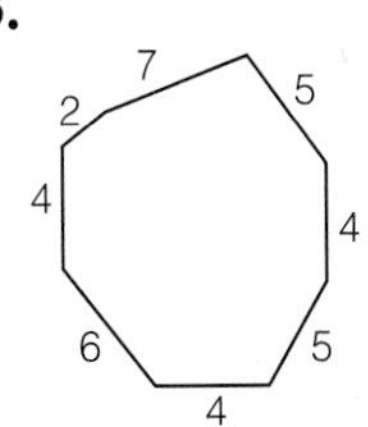

4.

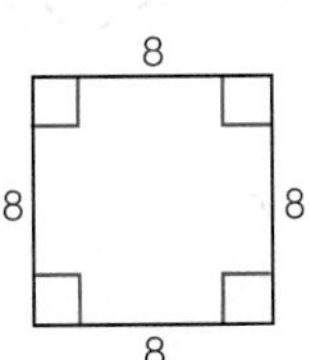

Write and solve an equation to find m∠A.

5.

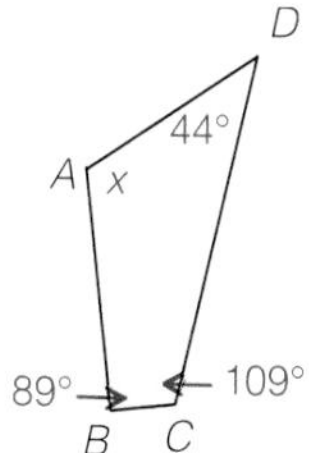

6.

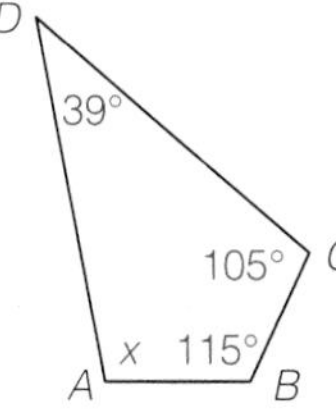

7.

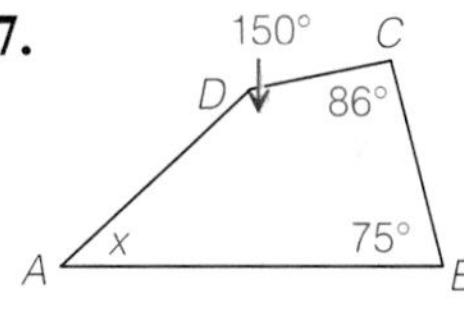

8.

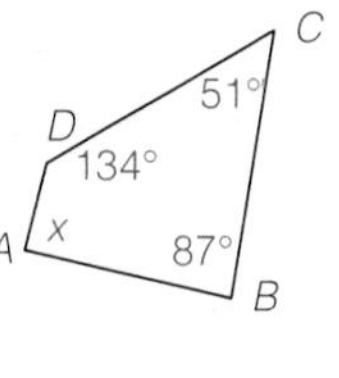

9. A quadrilateral has two right angles and the measure of the third angle is twice the measure of the fourth angle. What is the measure of each angle?

10. If a kite has a 68° angle and two right angles, what is the measure of the fourth angle?

Extend and Apply

Write and solve an equation to find each angle measure.

11.

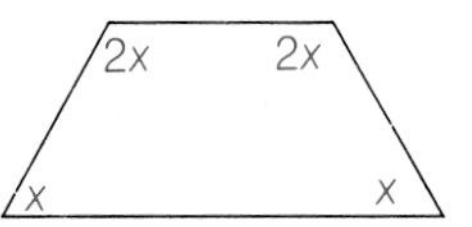

12.

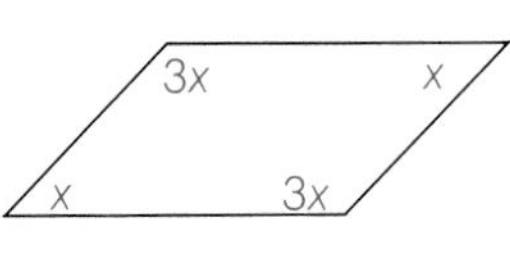

13.

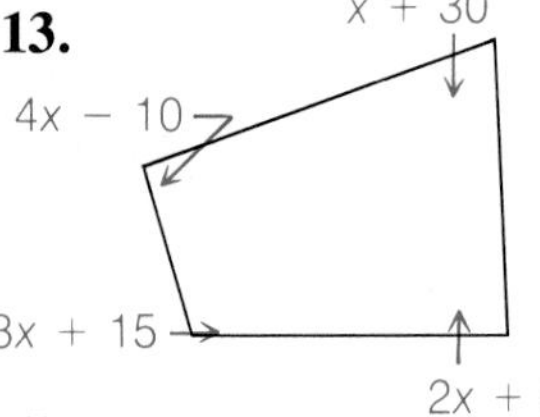

14. Name a quadrilateral that is not regular but has all:

a. sides the same length **b.** angles the same measure

15. Write to Learn You have learned that a quadrilateral might be classified as a rectangle, rhombus, square, parallelogram, or trapezoid. Write a specific step-by-step procedure that you could use to program a robot to draw a quadrilateral that does not belong to any of the above classifications.

Use Mathematical Reasoning

16. Draw a quadrilateral, a pentagon, and a hexagon. Find the number of diagonals from a single vertex needed to divide each figure into triangles. What generalization can you make about the number of diagonals and the number of triangles?

Mixed Review

Give the greatest common factor (GCF). **17.** 20, 32, 8 **18.** 15, 21, 36

19. What percent of 70 is 105? **20.** What percent of 200 is 1?

Numbers to Algebra

You can find a general formula for the sum of the measures of the angles of a polygon with n sides by generalizing from the number patterns shown.

Numbers			Algebra
			Polygon with n sides
3 sides 1×180	4 sides 2×180	5 sides 3×180	n sides $(n - 2) \times 180$

1. Find the sum of the angle measures of a polygon with 12 sides.

2. Find the sum of the angle measures of a polygon with 150 sides.

Using a Road Map

Objectives To solve applied problems, using road maps, mileage charts, and formulas.

A road map gives information about distances between cities. On the map below, the interstate highway is shown in blue. Notice the red arrowheads at exits 18 and 33. About halfway between these two arrowheads is a red number 40. This means the distance between the arrowheads is 40 miles. Notice the small numbers in black between each pair of exits. Between exits 23 and 26 is a small black 8. This means that the distance between these two exits is 8 miles.

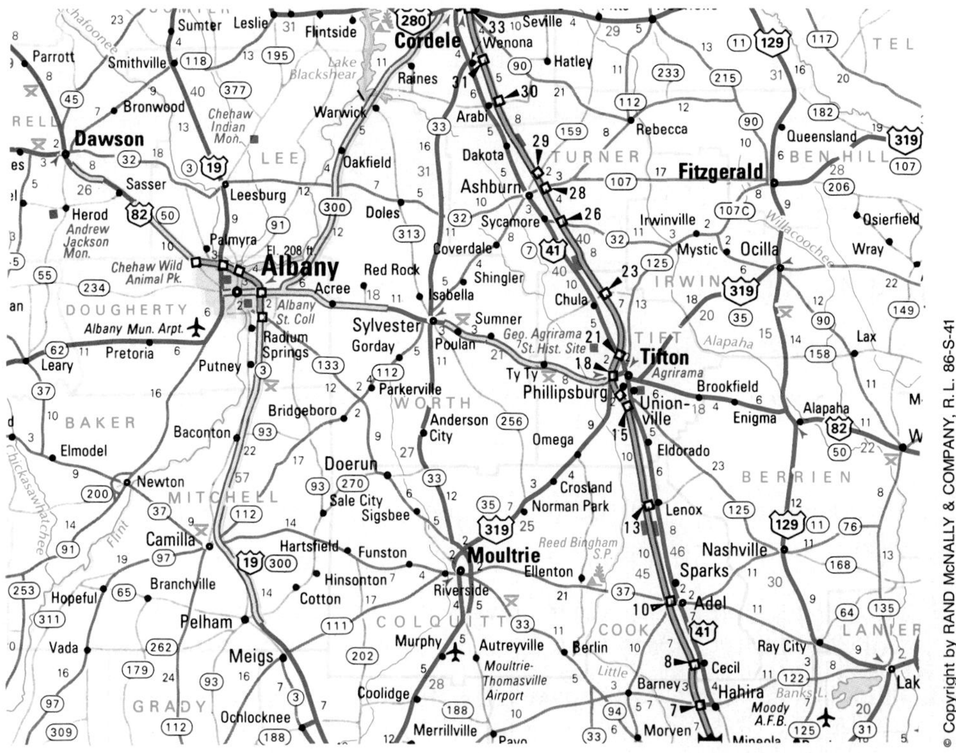

Problems

Solve. Use the map and the formula *distance* = *rate* × *time* as needed.

1. How far is it from Moultrie to Sylvester along highway 33? (Note the red arrows at these towns and the red number between them.)
2. How far is it from Tifton to Ocilla on highway 319?
3. How far is it from Albany to Tifton on highway 82?

4. How far will a car traveling at 55 mi/h drive in $1\frac{1}{2}$ hours?

5. Would a car traveling at 55 mi/h be able to drive from exit 18 to exit 33 on the map in less than 45 minutes?

6. How long does it take to travel 125 miles at 55 mi/h?

7. The distance from San Francisco to New York is about 2,800 miles. About how long will it take for a jet to fly from San Francisco to New York at an average speed of 620 mi/h?

8. A truck driver averages 50 mi/h. If he drives $10\frac{1}{2}$ hours a day, about how many days will it take him to travel 1,500 miles?

9. A family drove a distance of about 3,000 miles from Boston, MA, to Los Angeles, CA. They averaged 500 miles a day. Traveling costs were $35 a day for food and $40 for a motel each night. If it cost $0.17 per mile to operate their car, what was their total expense for the trip if they stayed in a motel the night of their arrival?

Use the mileage chart to answer problems 10–12.

	Chicago	Dallas	St. Louis	Wash., D.C.
Chicago		921	289	709
Dallas	921		655	1307
St. Louis	289	655		862
Wash., D.C.	709	1307	862	

10. How many miles is it from Washington, D.C. to Dallas and back?

11. How many miles is it from Dallas to St. Louis and back?

12. How many more miles is it to travel through St. Louis on the way from Dallas to Chicago than to go directly?

13. **Data Search** For a driver averaging 50 miles per hour, how long would it take to drive from Kansas City, Missouri, to Denver Colorado?

What's Your Decision?

Suppose you are planning to travel from New Orleans, LA, to Detroit, MI on interstate highways. To travel the minimum number of miles, what route should you take? If you average 50 miles per hour, how many hours will you drive?

12-8 Circles and Circumference

Objective To find the circumference, radius, or diameter of a circle.

Explore

Use several different cylindrical shaped containers for this activity. For each container, follow these three steps and record your data in a table. What conclusion can you draw about the ratio of L to d?

- Measure the diameter (d) of the cylinder to the nearest millimeter.
- Measure the distance around the cylinder by first wrapping a piece of string around it and then measuring the string's length (L) to the nearest millimeter.
- Calculate the ratio $\frac{L}{d}$.

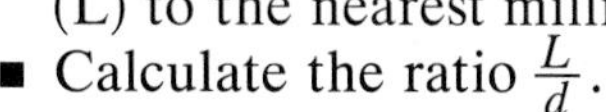

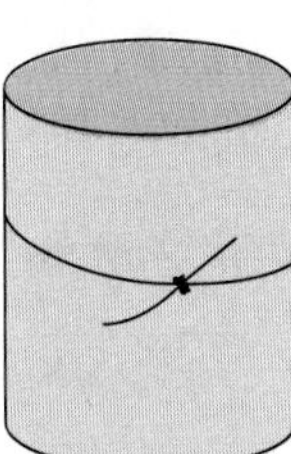

Understand the Ideas

A **circle** is the set of all points in a plane that are a fixed distance from a point called the **center.** Any segment that joins the center to a point on the circle is called a **radius** (r) of the circle. The **diameter** (d) of the circle is a segment that passes through the center and has endpoints on the circle.

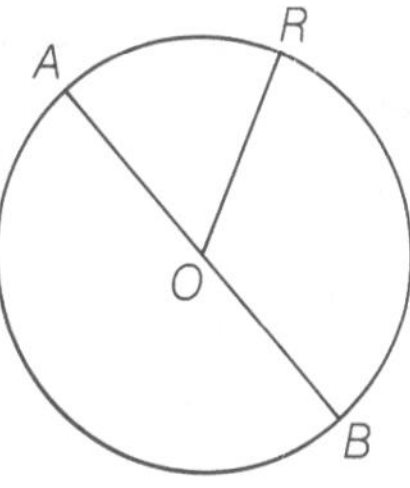

O is the center
$\overline{OR}$ is a radius
$\overline{AB}$ is a diameter

The distance around a circle is called the **circumference** (C) of the circle. The ratio $\frac{C}{d}$ is the same number for all circles, and is represented by the Greek letter π. The number $\pi \approx 3.14$.

Formula **Circumference of a Circle**

The circumference of a circle is π times the diameter, or 2 times π times the radius.

$C = \pi d$ or $C = 2\pi r$

Example 1

Find the circumference of a circle with diameter 4 cm. Use 3.14 for π.

Solution $C = \pi d$

$C \approx 3.14 \times 4 \approx 12.56$ cm Substitute 3.14 for π and 4 for d.

Try This Find the circumference of a circle with the given diameter or radius. Use 3.14 for π.

a. diameter = 3.2 cm   **b.** radius = 8.2 cm

Most calculators have a key [π] that displays the value of π to seven or more decimal places. When using a calculator to find the circumference of a circle, you will need to round your answer.

Example 2

Find the circumference of a circle with radius 8 cm. Use a calculator and round to the nearest hundredth.

Solution $C = \pi d = 2\pi r$

2 [×] [π] [×] 8 [=] 50.265482

50.27 cm   Round to the nearest hundredth.

Try This Use a calculator and round to the nearest hundredth.

c. Find the circumference of a circular tank whose radius is 21 feet.

Example 3

Find the radius of a tin can that has a 9-inch long label wrapped around it. Use 3.14 for π.

Solution $C = 2\pi r$

$9 \approx 2(3.14)r$ Substitute 9 for C and 3.14 for π.

$r \approx \frac{9}{6.28} \approx 1.43$

The radius of the can is approximately 1.43 inches.

Try This Use 3.14 for π.

d. Find the radius of a circle with circumference 12 m.

e. Find the diameter of a circle with circumference 18 cm.

Class Exercises

For the figure at right:

1. name the center.

2. name three radii.

3. give the length of a radius.

4. name a diameter.

5. name another diameter.

6. give the length of a diameter.

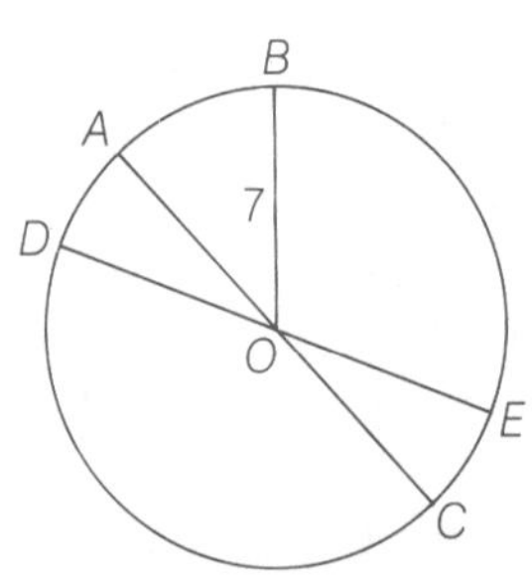

Discuss the Ideas

7. If a diameter of a circle is doubled, what will happen to its circumference?

Exercises

Practice and Apply

For Exercises 1–18, use 3.14 for π and round to the nearest hundredth.

Find the circumference of a circle with the given diameter or radius.

1. diameter = 5 cm **2.** diameter = 12 cm **3.** diameter = 20 cm

4. diameter = 4.8 cm **5.** radius = 6.1 m **6.** radius = 8.3 m

Find the diameter of a circle with the given circumference (C) or radius (r).

7. $C = 5$ cm **8.** $C = 8$ mm **9.** $C = 12$ m

10. $C = 4.6$ m **11.** $r = 35.7$ cm **12.** $r = 99.8$ m

Find the radius of a circle with the given circumference (C) or diameter (d).

13. $C = 9$ cm **14.** $C = 4$ m **15.** $C = 15$ cm

16. $d = 452.8$ cm **17.** $d = 32.84$ m **18.** $C = 14.8$ m

19. Estimate the circumference of a 28-inch diameter bicycle wheel. Find the circumference with a calculator.

Extend and Apply

Use 3.14 for π in Exercises 20–23.
Find the perimeter of each figure. All curves are parts of circles.

20.

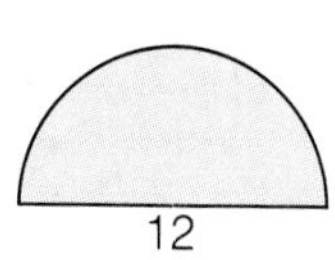

21.

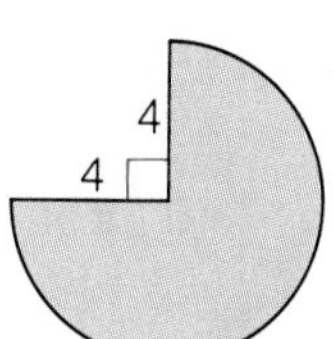

22.

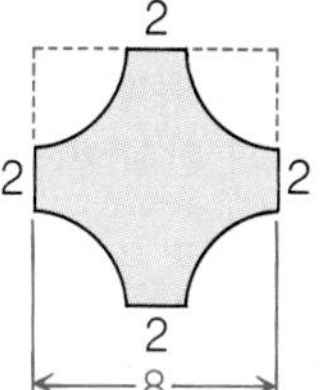

23. How many feet does a bicycle travel with each revolution of a 28-inch diameter wheel? How many revolutions does the wheel make to travel one mile (5,280 feet/mile)?

24. Determine Reasonable Answers Is the perimeter of the diamond-shaped curve at the right a) about 16 cm, b) less than 16 cm, or c) greater than 16 cm? Explain your answer.

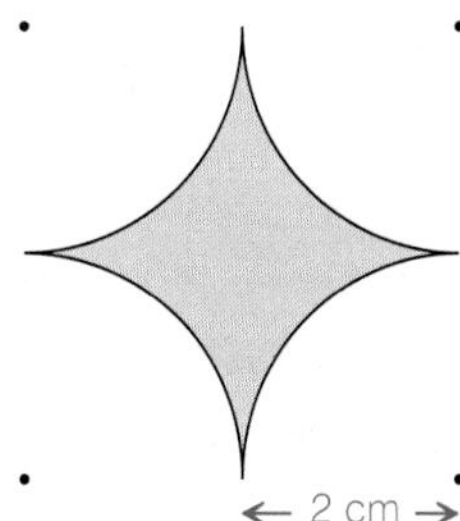

Use Mathematical Reasoning

25. The radius of the earth is approximately 6,380 kilometers. Imagine that a steel ring is looped tightly around the equator. Suppose the steel ring is made 6 meters longer. Will this make the ring loose enough so that:

an ant could walk under the ring?
a finger would fit under the ring?
a cat could walk under the ring?
a truck could be driven under the ring?

Mixed Review

There are 36 students in Mrs. Ward's class. 20 students are boys. 6 students are left-handed.

26. What is the ratio of boys to girls?

27. What percentage of the students are left-handed?

28. What is the ratio of left-handed to right-handed students?

Computer Activity

This program calculates an approximation for π by calculating the perimeter of a polygon that is inscribed in the circle.

```
10  PRINT "HOW MANY SIDES DO YOU WANT THE
    APPROXIMATING POLYGON TO HAVE?"
20  INPUT S
30  LET NM=INT(S/4)
40  LET AR=0:X0=0:Y=1:X=0:ST=1/NM
50  FOR N=1 TO NM
60  LET X1=X0+N*ST:
    LET Y1=SQR(1-X1*X1)
70  LET L=SQR((X1-X)*(X1-X)+
    (Y1-Y)*(Y1-Y))
80  LET AR=AR+L
90  LET X=X1:Y=Y1
100 NEXT N
110 PRINT "PI IS APPROXIMATELY "; 2*AR
120 END
```

$r = 1$

The circumference is π. The perimeter of the polygon is approximately π.

Run the program to find about how many sides are required for the approximation of π to round to:

1. 3.14 **2.** 3.141 **3.** 3.1415

12-9 Problem Solving: Writing Equations

Practice Solving Problems

Objective To practice solving word problems by writing and solving equations.

Problems

Practice and Apply

Solve by writing an equation.

1. This week Rosa worked only 25% of the hours she usually works in a week. She worked 9 hours this week. How many hours does she usually work in a week?
2. The length of one side of a rectangular lot is $2\frac{1}{2}$ times as long as the width. How long is each side if the perimeter is 56 m?
3. One angle of a triangular sign is 45°. The second angle is 2 times the measure of the third angle. What are the measures of the three angles?

Extend and Apply

4. Teriko worked at a restaurant for 5 hours on Saturday and earned \$7.50 in tips. The total of her wages and tips was \$31.25. What is her hourly wage?
5. Arnie and Maria each collected the same number of aluminum cans in a clean-up project. When they turned their cans in, they were told they had collected 25% of the total number of cans brought in that day. Arnie and Maria each collected 158 cans. What was the total number of cans brought in that day?
6. The cost to develop film at a store decreases for more than one roll. The second roll costs 10% less than the first roll and the third roll costs 20% less than the first roll. The cost for 3 rolls is \$23.76. What is the cost for 1 roll?

Use Mathematical Reasoning

7. Write a word problem that would be solved using the equation
   a. $\frac{2}{3}x = 4$ **b.** $x - 15 = 120$

Mixed Review

Solve and check. **8.** $4.5t + 1.9t = 3.2$ **9.** $-16 = 21m + 5$
10. $14x = 4x - 30$ **11.** $r + 63 = 8r$ **12.** $17c + 4c = 84$

12-10 Congruent Figures

Objective To write statements about congruent figures, vertices, and sides; to use SAS, SSS, and ASA properties to show congruence in triangles.

Application

Matching keys must be made identical in size and shape. That means that $\triangle ABC$ must be congruent to $\triangle DEF$.

Understand the Ideas

Two figures are **congruent** if they are identical in size and shape. Segments are congruent if they have the same length. Angles are congruent if they have the same measure. The symbol $\cong$ means "is congruent to."

Imagine that one congruent polygon is lifted and placed upon the other. The matching vertices are called **corresponding vertices,** and the matching sides are called **corresponding sides.** In the figures below, vertex A corresponds to vertex G and $\overline{CD}$ corresponds to $\overline{EH}$.

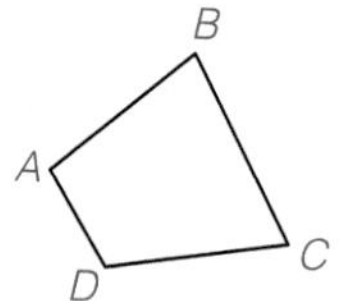

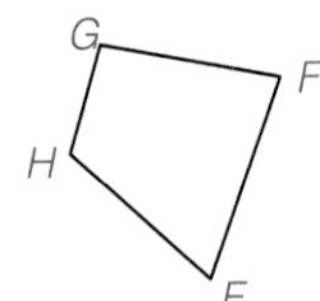

For any two congruent figures, corresponding vertices are congruent and corresponding sides are congruent. When naming two figures as congruent, list corresponding vertices in the same order. If $\triangle ABC \cong \triangle JKL$, then A and J, B and K, C and L are corresponding vertices.

Example 1

In the **application**, triangles ABC and DEF are congruent. That is: $\triangle ABC \cong \triangle DEF$. List all congruent angles and sides.

Solution $\angle A \cong \angle D$ $\quad \overline{AB} \cong \overline{DE}$

$\angle B \cong \angle E$ $\quad \overline{AC} \cong \overline{DF}$

$\angle C \cong \angle F$ $\quad \overline{BC} \cong \overline{EF}$

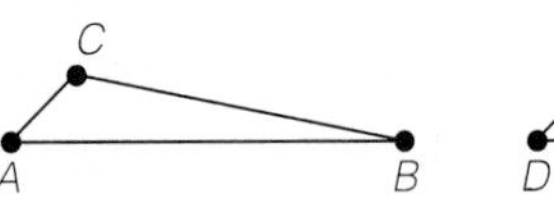

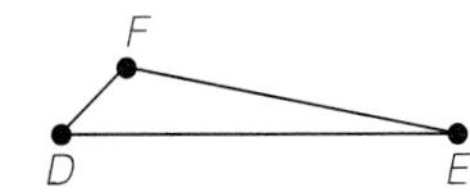

Try This

a. Write all statements about congruent angles and sides. $ABCDEF \cong GHIJKL$

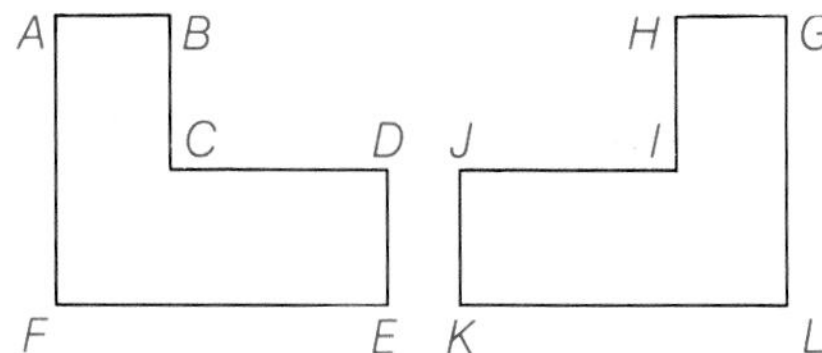

When two triangles are congruent, they have six pairs of congruent parts. To be sure that two triangles are congruent, you do not need to show that all six congruence statements are true. You can use any of the following three congruence properties to decide. The red marks in the figures below show the corresponding sides and angles.

Congruence Properties

1. **Side-Angle Side (SAS)**
If two sides and the included angle (the angle between the two sides) of one triangle are congruent to two sides and the included angle of another triangle, then the two triangles are congruent.

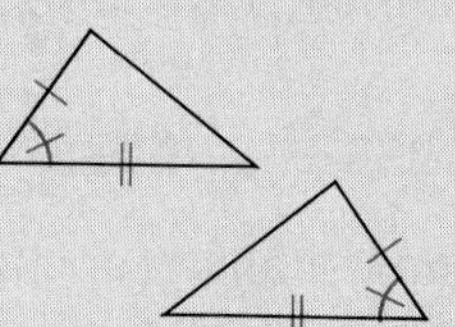

2. **Side-Side-Side (SSS)**
If the three sides of one triangle are congruent to the three sides of another triangle, then the two triangles are congruent.

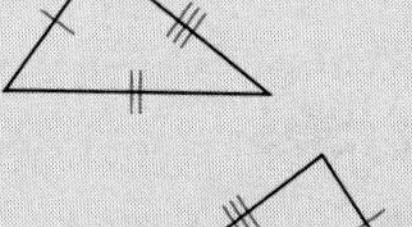

3. **Angle-Side-Angle (ASA)**
If two angles and the included side of one triangle are congruent to two angles and the included side of another triangle, then the two triangles are congruent.

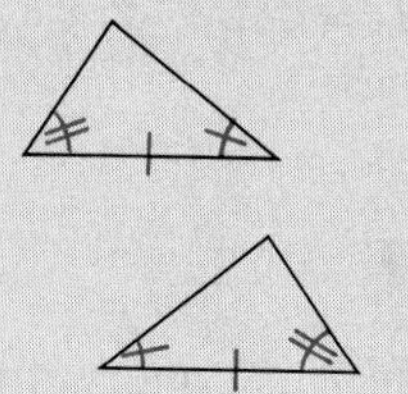

Example 2

Use the SAS, SSS, or ASA Property to show that the pair of triangles at right is congruent.

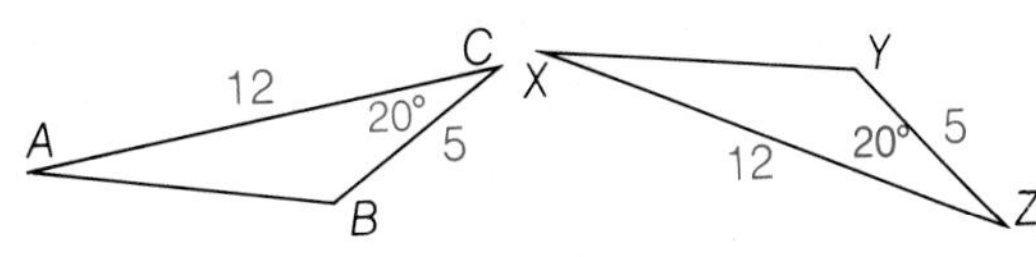

Solution $\overline{AC} \cong \overline{XZ}$

$\angle C \cong \angle Z$

$\overline{BC} \cong \overline{YZ}$ Since lengths of two sides and the included angle are given, use the SAS Property.

$\triangle ABC \cong \triangle XYZ$ by the SAS Property.

Try This **b.** Use the SAS, SSS, or ASA Property to show that the pair of triangles is congruent.

C 80° A 30° B U 30° V 80° W

Class Exercises

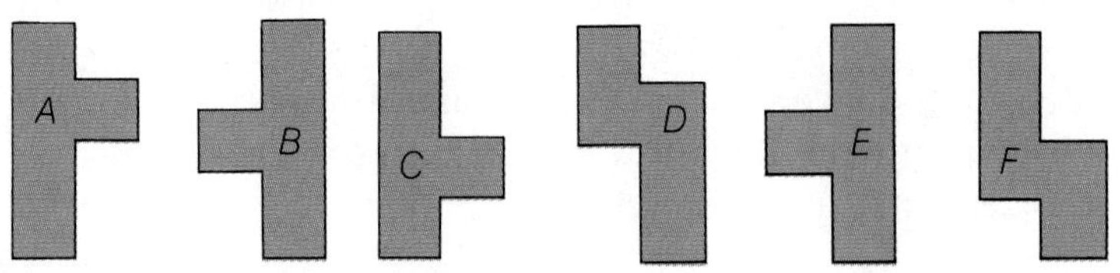

1. Which polygon seems to be congruent to polygon A?
2. Which polygon seems to be congruent to polygon E?
3. Which polygon seems to be congruent to polygon D?

Discuss the Ideas

4. How many examples of congruent parts can you think of on an automobile?

Exercises

Practice and Apply

$\triangle RST \cong \triangle UVW$. Complete each statement.

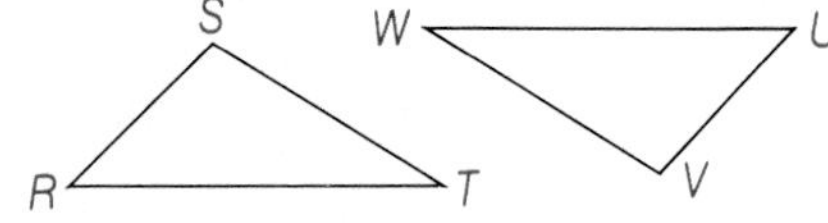

1. $\angle R \cong$ ___?___
2. $\overline{RS} \cong$ ___?___
3. $\angle W \cong$ ___?___
4. $\overline{VW} \cong$ ___?___

ABCDEF is congruent to *RSTUVW*. Complete each statement.

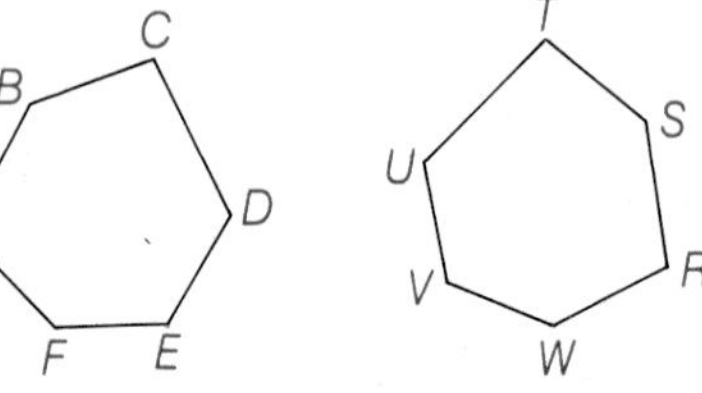

5. $\angle A \cong$ ___?___
6. $\angle U \cong$ ___?___
7. $\overline{EF} \cong$ ___?___
8. $\overline{ST} \cong$ ___?___
9. $\angle S \cong$ ___?___
10. $\angle E \cong$ ___?___
11. $\overline{CD} \cong$ ___?___
12. $\angle D \cong$ ___?___
13. $\overline{RS} \cong$ ___?___
14. $\overline{AB} \cong$ ___?___

Use the SAS, SSS, or ASA Property to show that each pair of triangles is congruent.

15. 8 18 19 8 18 19

16. 19 68° 7 19 68° 7

17. 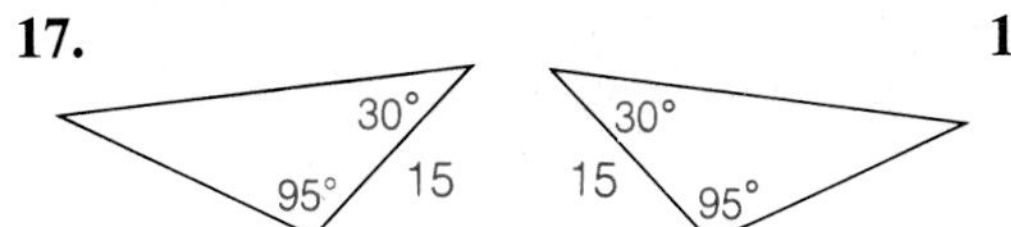

18. 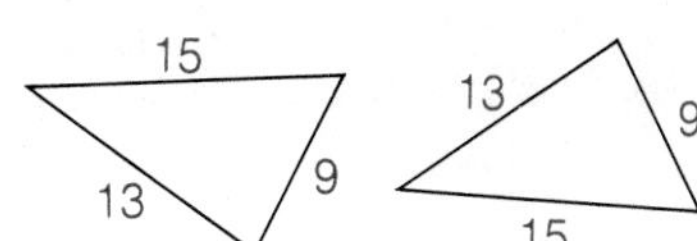

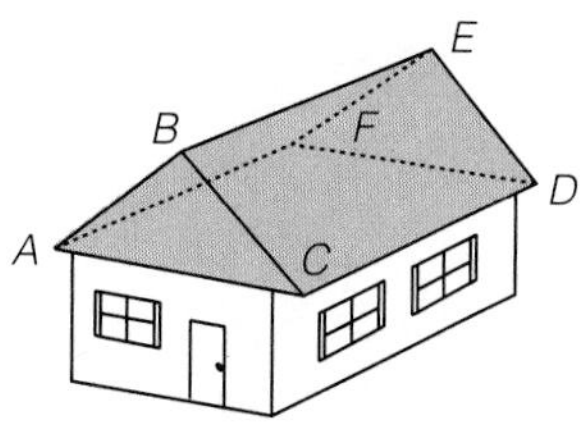

19. Name a pair of congruent triangles that you find on this diagram of a roof.

20. Name a pair of congruent rectangles that you find on the diagram.

Extend and Apply

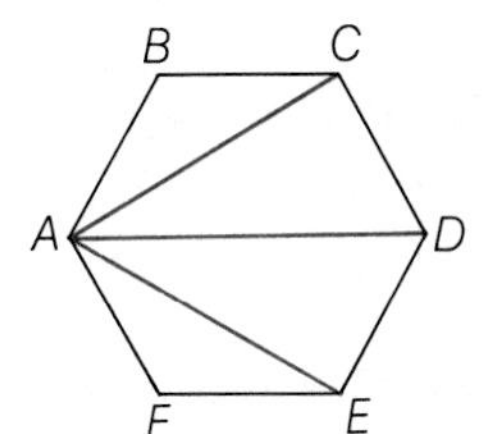

The figure at right is a regular hexagon.

21. Name a triangle congruent to $\triangle ABC$. What congruence property shows this?

22. Name a triangle congruent to $\triangle ACD$. What congruence property shows this?

Use Mathematical Reasoning

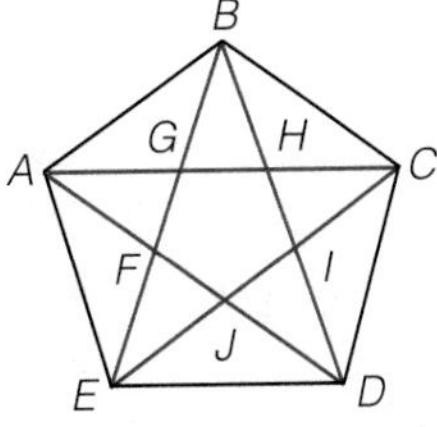

The five-pointed star is drawn in a regular pentagon.

23. Name all the triangles that are congruent to $\triangle ABD$.

24. List five triangles in this figure that are not congruent to each other.

Mixed Review

Write as a decimal. Use a bar for a repeating decimal. **25.** $\frac{3}{16}$ **26.** $\frac{2}{3}$

Solve and check. **27.** $45c - 17 = 140.5$ **28.** $5m \div 6 = 10$

29. $m + 1.7m = 0.54$ **30.** $r - 16 = -373$ **31.** $26t - 14 = 18.5$

Estimation

Use estimation to decide whether each pair of triangles is congruent.

1. 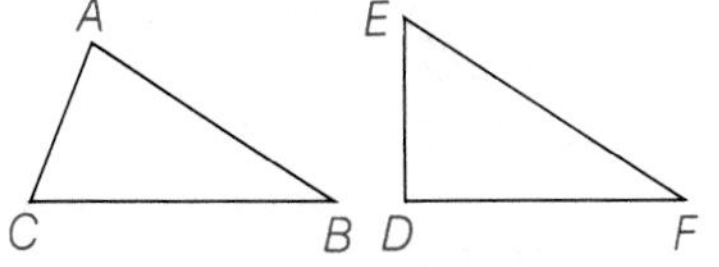

2. 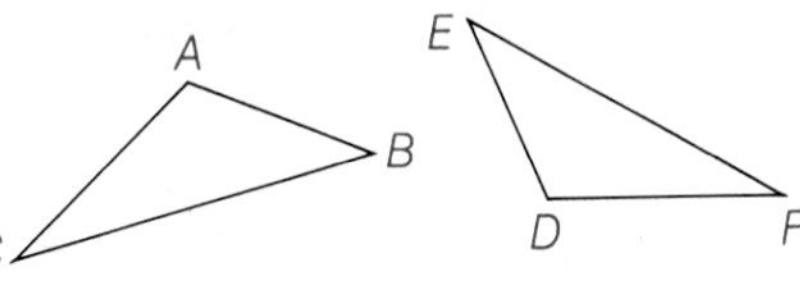

3. 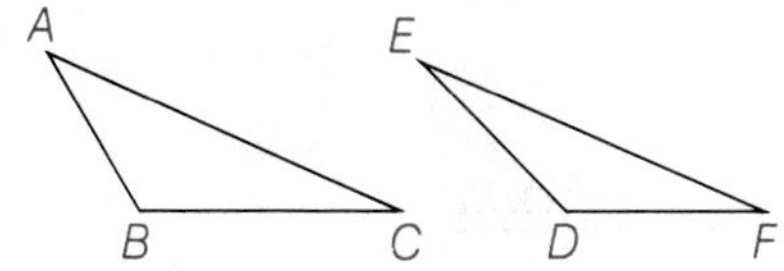

4. 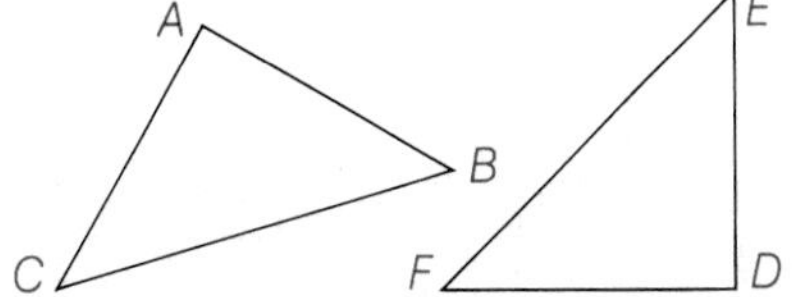

12-11 Data Collection and Analysis

Glyphs

Objective To draw and interpret glyphs.

A **glyph** is a picture or symbol that shows selected data at a glance. It allows us to combine and visually display several bits of information.

A **circle-ray glyph** is a circle with rays connected on the outside. The length of the rays give information about the data. A **facial glyph** is a glyph that uses a picture of a face to display information. Glyphs using other types of recognizable objects are also useful.

Making a Circle-Ray Glyph

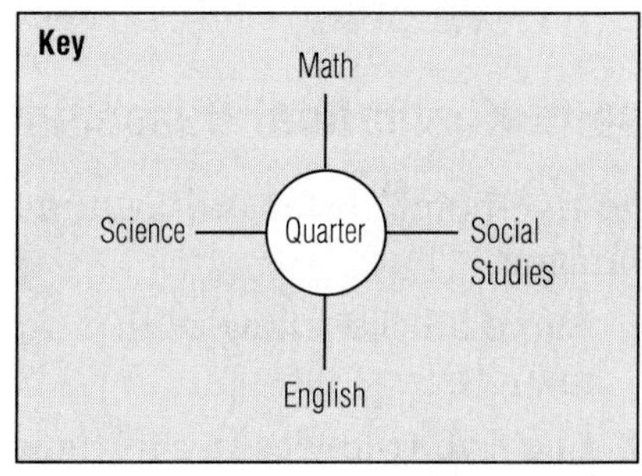

Teri received the following grades for the past 4 quarters.

Math C, C, B, A
Social Studies C, B, B, B
Science F, D, D, B
English C, B, A, A

To make glyphs to show the grades, she let A = 4, B = 3, C = 2, D = 1 and F = 0. Then she drew the rays on the glyphs, letting $\frac{1}{8}$ inch equal 1 grade point.

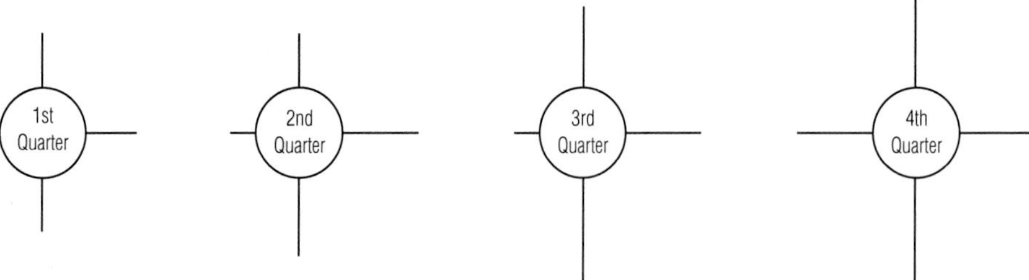

Interpreting the Circle-Ray Glyphs

Use only the glyphs and the key to answer these questions.

- During which quarter did Teri make the worst grades? the best grades?
- Do you think her grades improved from quarter to quarter? Explain.
- Did Teri get an F? If so, during which quarter?

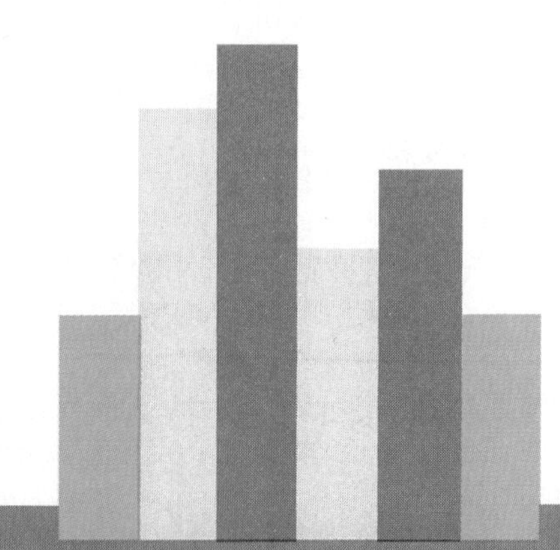

Project

1. Create a key and draw a circle-ray glyph for each student to show the four test scores shown at the right.

   Bob: 59, 85, 95, 80
   Jane: 65, 90, 79, 81
   Carlos: 76, 94, 99, 86

2. Look at the glyphs and make statements to interpret the data. The top student is the one with the longest combined length of rays. Do the glyphs show the top student?
3. Choose some data of your own and make glyphs to show it.

Making a Facial Glyph

Matt and his friends made these facial glyphs to show some things about themselves. They used three levels, *below average, average,* and *above average* to determine the size of the facial characteristics that show the data. The key shows the average size.

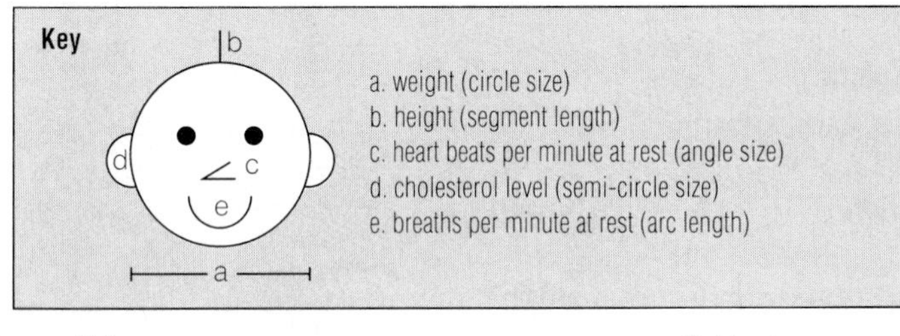

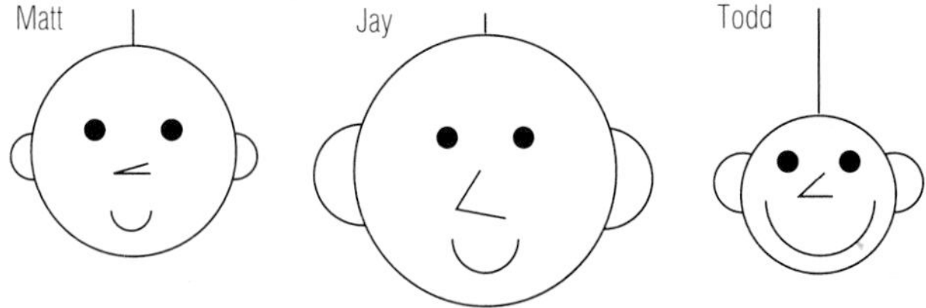

Interpreting the Facial Glyphs

- Who is short with above average weight?
- Who is tall and thin?
- Who has the lowest cholesterol level and the slowest heartbeat?
- Who do you think is probably in the best physical shape? Explain.

Project

4. Use the key above and make a facial glyph for a person with average weight, above average height, very low cholesterol level, above average heartbeat count per minute when at rest, and below average breaths per minute at rest.
5. Select some data, create a key, and make a facial glyph to show the data. Make some statements that interpret the glyph.

12-12 Geometric Constructions

Objective To construct segments, angles, triangles, perpendicular lines and angle bisectors.

To do a geometric construction, you use only a compass and straightedge. Below are some basic constructions.

Example 1

Construct a copy of $\overline{AB}$.

Solution

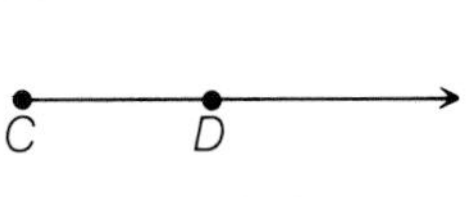

Use a straightedge to draw $\overrightarrow{CD}$.

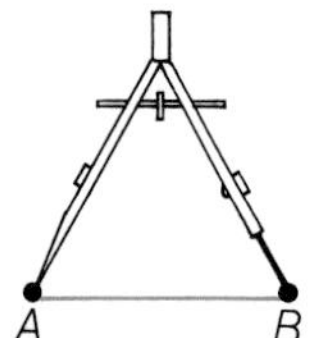

Place the sharp tip of the compass at A and the writing tip at B.

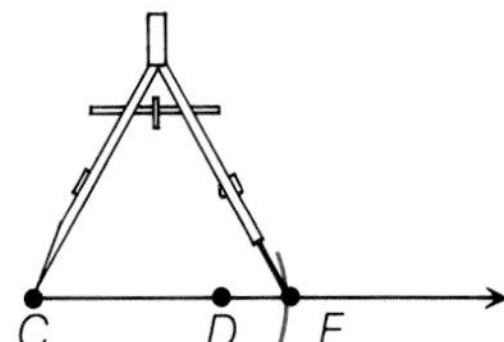

With the same setting, place the sharp tip of the compass at C and draw an arc. Label point E. $\overline{CE} \cong \overline{AB}$.

Try This

a. Draw a segment and construct a copy of the segment.

Example 2

Construct a copy of $\angle ABC$.

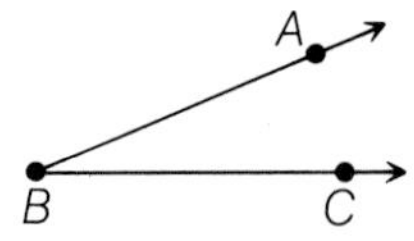

Solution

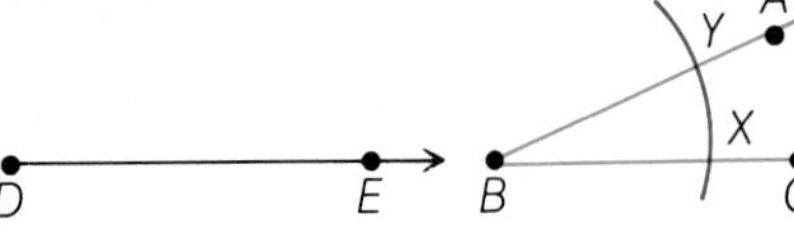

Use a straightedge to draw $\overrightarrow{DE}$.

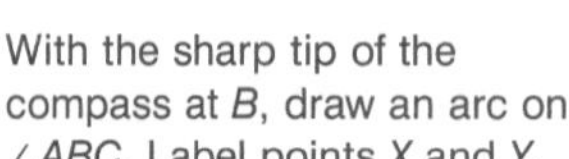

With the sharp tip of the compass at B, draw an arc on $\angle ABC$. Label points X and Y.

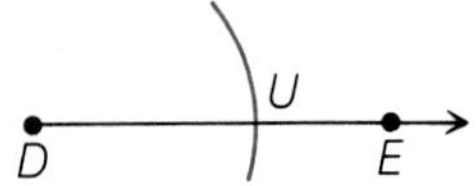

With the same setting, place the sharp tip of the compass at D and draw an arc. Label point U.

Place the sharp point on X and the writing point on Y.

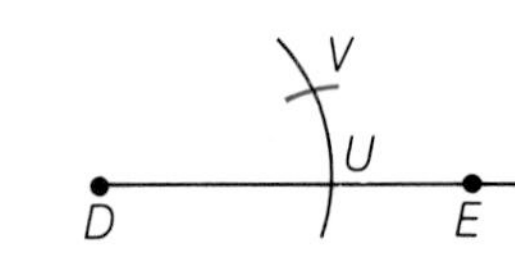

With the same setting, place the sharp point at U and draw an arc. Label point V.

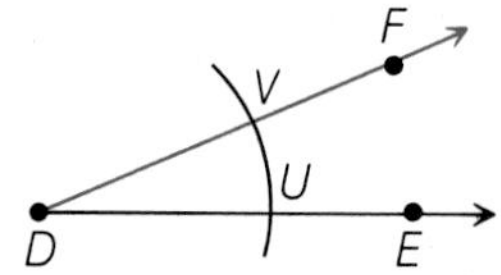

Draw ray DF through point V. $\angle FDE \cong \angle ABC$

Try This

b. Draw an angle and construct a copy of it.

Example 3

Construct a line perpendicular to the given line through point P.

Solution

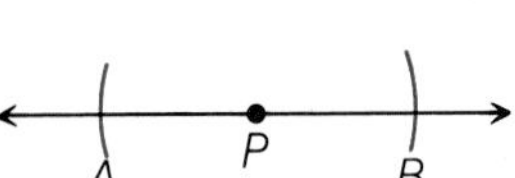

Place the sharp point of the compass at P and draw 2 arcs with the same setting, intersecting the line at A and B.

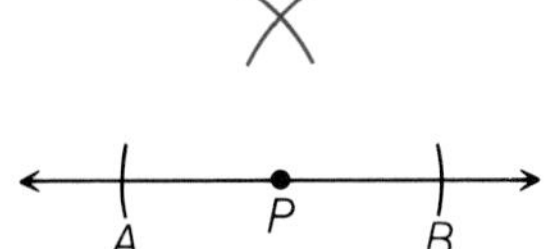

Place the sharp point at A, open it to beyond P, and draw an arc. With the same setting place the sharp point at B and draw an arc intersecting the first arc. Label point C.

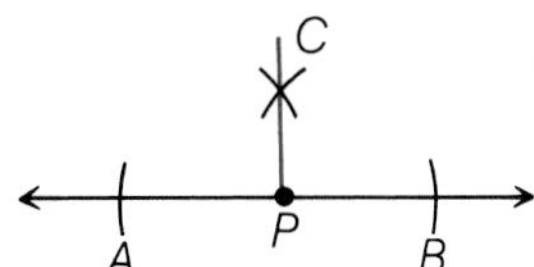

Draw line PC. It is perpendicular to line AB.

Try This **c.** Copy the line at the right. Construct a perpendicular line through point P.

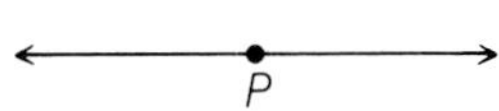

Example 4

Construct a triangle with side lengths a, b, and c.

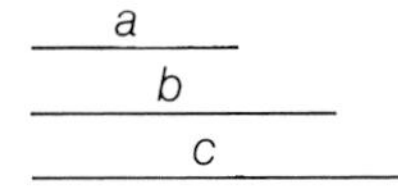

Solution

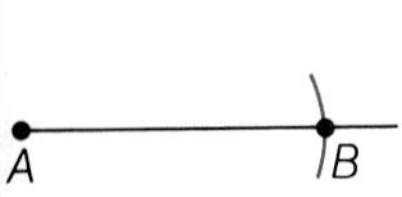

Draw a ray and copy the segment of length b.

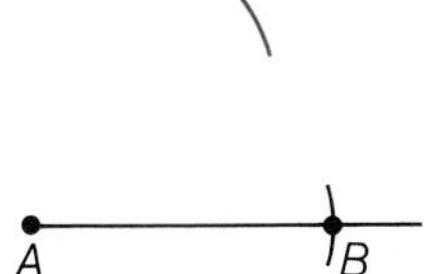

Set the compass opening by length c. Then place the sharp point at A and draw an arc.

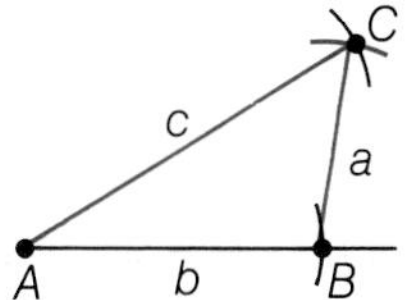

Set the compass opening by length a. Then place the sharp point at B and draw an arc to form point C. Draw segments $\overline{AC}$ and $\overline{BC}$.

Try This **d.** Construct an equilateral triangle.

An **angle bisector** is a ray that divides an angle into two congruent angles.

Example 5

Draw an angle ABC and bisect it.

Solution

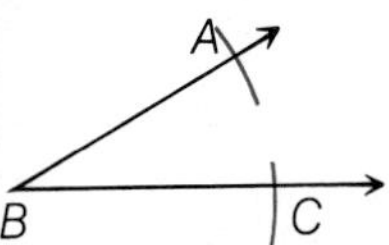

Place the sharp point of the compass at B and draw an arc intersecting the sides of the angle at A and C.

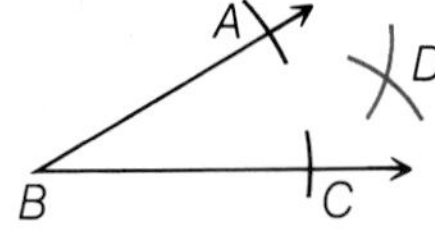

Open the compass more than half the distance from C to A and draw arcs from A and C. Label the point D.

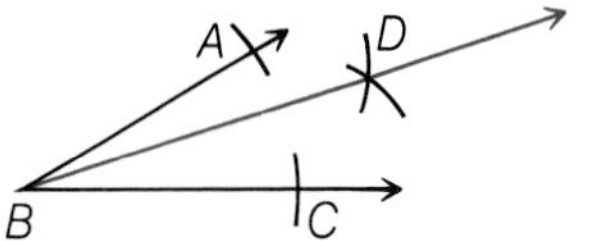

Draw ray $\overrightarrow{BD}$. It is the bisector of the angle.

Try This **e.** Construct a right angle and bisect it to form a 45° angle.

Exercises

Practice and Apply

Copy the segments and construct a perpendicular at point M.

1. A M B

2. A M

3. M A

Copy the angle and construct a bisector.

4.
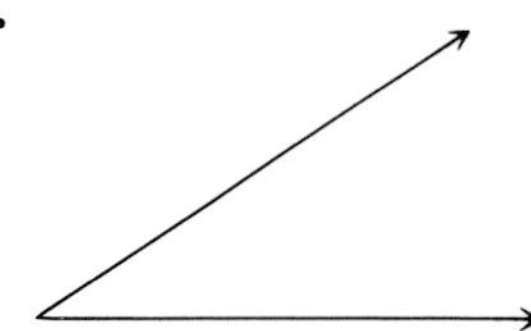

5.
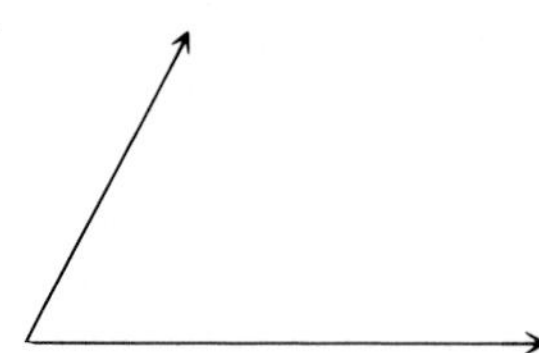

6.
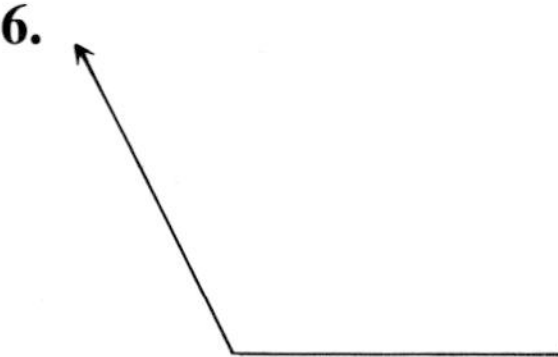

Construct a triangle with sides the lengths of the segments given.

7.

8.

9.

Extend and Apply

Construct:

10. a 45° angle. **11.** a 30° angle. **12.** a 60° angle.

13. a $22\frac{1}{2}°$ angle. **14.** a 15° angle. **15.** a $7\frac{1}{2}°$ angle.

16. a square.

17. an isosceles right triangle.

18. a pair of perpendicular lines.

Use Mathematical Reasoning

19. Draw a circle. Construct points A, B, C, D, E, F on it to make a regular hexagon.

20. Draw a circle. Construct points A, B, C, D, E, F, G, H on it to make a regular octagon.

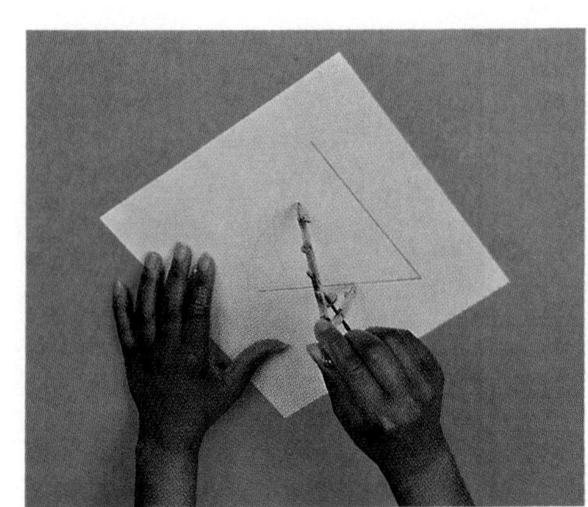

Mixed Review

Solve and check. **21.** $2x + 10 = 4x$

22. $14 - 9x = -4$

23. $36 = 15c - 24$

24. What percent of 90 is 65?

25. 38 is 200% of what number?

12-13 Problem Solving: Strategies

Using Special Insight

Objective To solve nonroutine problems that require special insight.

Solving some problems requires special insight. If you use the strategies and your first attempts are not successful, try thinking about the problem in a different way. A new point of view may help a solution to pop into your head. Try the following problem.

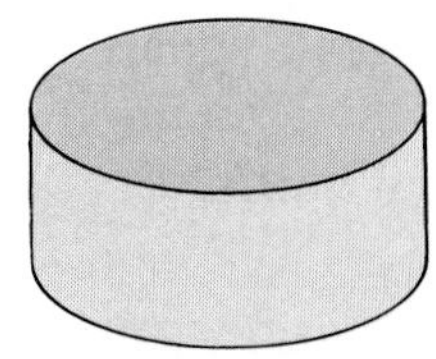

Sample Problem A waitress had always used 4 straight cuts to cut a cylinder of cheese into 8 identical pieces. One day, she suddenly realized that she could do it with only 3 straight cuts! How did she do it?

When looking for a solution to the problem, you might first think about cutting the cheese with 4 cuts, as in figure A below. Then you might think about ways to make 3 straight cuts across the top as in figure B. After several unsuccessful tries, you might try to think about the problem in a different way. Perhaps, suddenly, you will decide to try horizontal cuts as well as vertical cuts, and find the solution shown in figure C.

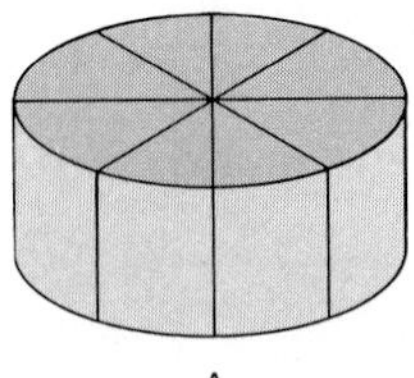

A

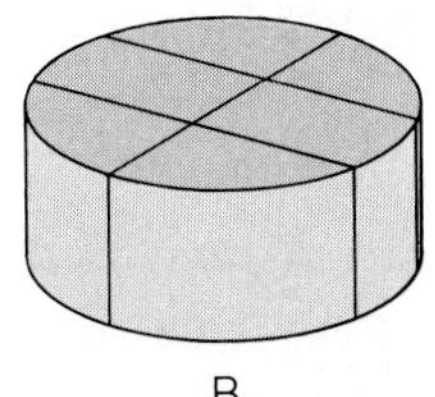

B

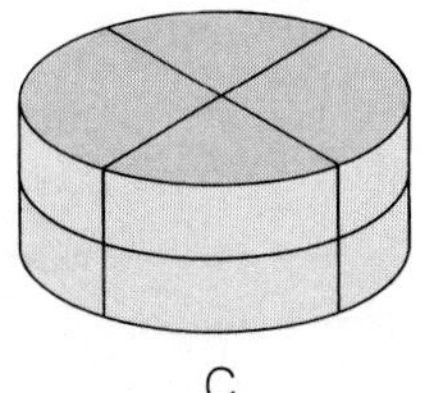

C

Problem-Solving Strategies

Choose the Operations	Make a Table	Make an Organized List
Guess, Check, Revise	Look for a Pattern	Use Logical Reasoning
Draw a Diagram	Write an Equation	Work Backward
	Simplify the Problem	

Problems

Solve. Allow yourself time to think about problems in different ways.

1. A very honest teenager said, "Two days ago I was 13, but next year I'll be 16." When is the teenager's birthday?

2. Copy these nine dots. Draw four connected straight lines through all nine dots without lifting your pencil or retracing any part of a line.

3. How can these two square quilts be cut and sewn back together to form one square quilt with twice the area of one of the original quilts?

4. You have an 8-ounce can and a 3-ounce can, with no markings on either can. How can you measure out 4 ounces of juice using only these two cans?

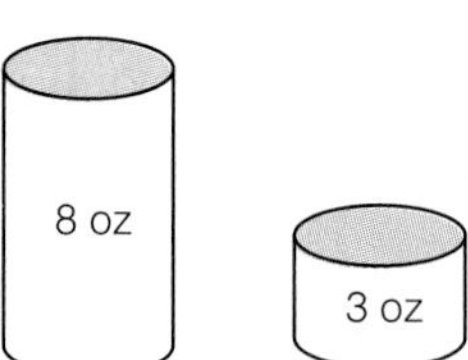

5. Where should you put the fences to divide this field into 4 congruent fields that are the same shape as the original field?

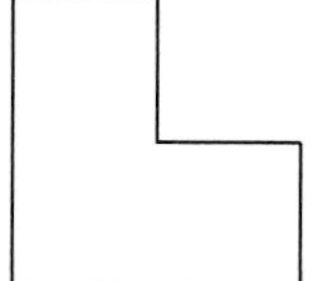

Group Decision Making

6. Work in a group. Discuss and decide.

Situation Your older brother has agreed to drive you and 2 of your friends to summer camp. The camp is 175 miles from your home. Your parents will pay your brother \$0.15/mi round trip. You want to find out how much he will have left after he pays for the gasoline and any oil that the car needs during the trip.

Guidelines for Planning

- **Formulate Problems** you will need to solve.
- Discuss **Assumptions** you will make and **Data** you will need.

a. What decision or decisions do you need to make in this situation?

b. Formulate problems you need to solve to make the decision(s).

c. List any assumptions you need to make to arrive at a decision.

d. What data, if any, do you need to collect to make a decision?

e. Write a paragraph summarizing what your group did, what decisions you made, and why.

Extend Key Ideas

Motion in Geometry

There are three basic motions in the plane that move a geometric figure to a new position without distorting its size and shape. A figure and its image after one of these motions are congruent.

Exploration 1 Slide or Translation

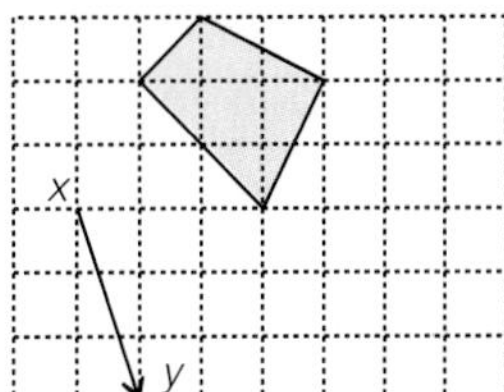

1. Draw this quadrilateral on graph paper. Then draw its position after it is slid in the direction and distance of arrow XY.
2. Draw another arrow UV. Then draw the quadrilateral position after it is slid in the direction and distance of arrow UV.
3. Calculate the length of each side of the quadrilateral in its original position and in its new positions. Are they equal?

Exploration 2 Flip or Line Reflection

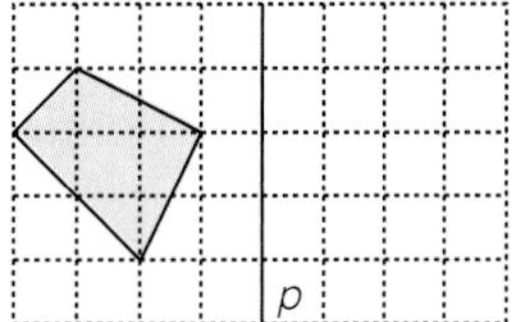

4. Draw this quadrilateral and line p on graph paper. Then imagine that line p is a mirror and draw the reflection of the quadrilateral in line p.
5. The quadrilateral and its reflection should fall upon each other when the paper is folded along line p. Show this is true for your drawing.

Exploration 3. Turn or Rotation

6. Draw this figure and point O on graph paper. Then draw the figure in its position after a 90° clockwise turn about point O.
7. Draw the figure's position after a 180° turn about point O.
8. Place tracing paper over your drawing and draw the original figure on your tracing paper. Then place your pencil on point O and turn the tracing paper 90° clockwise. Does the tracing coincide with the figure you drew in Problem 7?

Chapter 12 Review/Test

Understanding

Complete each statement.

12-1 **1.** A segment PQ includes endpoints P and Q and all points ______ .

12-3 **2.** Two angles are supplementary if the sum of their measures is ______ .

12-4 **3.** Two lines in the same plane are parallel if they have no ______ .

12-6 **4.** A polygon is regular if all sides and all angles ______ .

12-10 **5.** Two polygons are congruent if they have the same ______ .

Skill

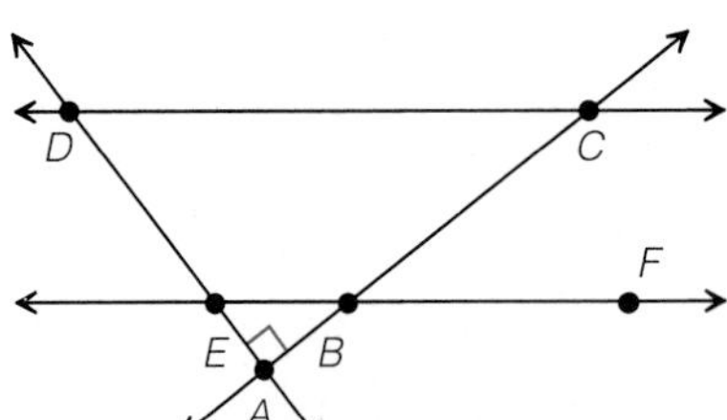

12-1 12-2 12-3 12-4 Refer to the figure for Exercises 6–11.

6. Estimate the length of $\overline{BF}$.

7. Name a line.

8. Name a segment.

9. Name an acute angle.

10. Name an obtuse angle.

11. Name a pair of parallel lines.

Classify each triangle by the measures of its angles and the lengths of its sides.

12-5 **12.** $\triangle EFG$ has a 90 degree angle and no sides are equal in length.

12-5 **13.** $\triangle VWX$ has an obtuse angle and two sides equal in length.

12-6 Name the polygon.

14.

15.

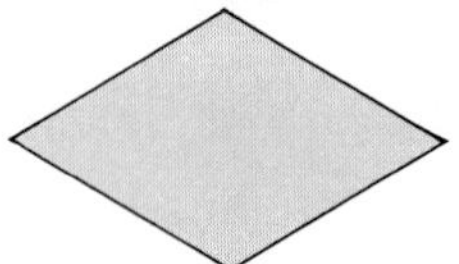

Application

12-7 Solve. Use the formula *distance* = *rate* × *time.*

16. Albert averaged 11 miles per hour on a $3\frac{1}{2}$ hour bicycle ride. How many miles did he ride?

Solve by writing an equation. Use 3.14 for π in Exercise 18.

12-11 **17.** Sandy attended 65% of the school basketball games. If she attended 13 games, what was the total number of games the team played?

12-8 **18.** The General Sherman tree, the world's largest tree in volume of wood, is in Sequoia National Park. The base of its trunk has a circumference of 30.97 meters. What is its diameter?

Cumulative Review

8-7 Solve.

1. $4x - 2 = 2x + 16$ **2.** $12f = 16f - 16$

3. $25 + 6d = 5d$ **4.** $30k + 8 = 22k + 24$

8-10 Solve each inequality.

5. $7 > p - 6$ **6.** $6m < -48$

7. $9n - 5n > 20$ **8.** $\frac{w}{3} - 6 > 12$

9-7 **9.** Find the slope of a line that contains the points $A(-1, 20)$ and $B(2, -4)$.

9-12 **10.** Graph the inequality $y < 2 - x$. Is point $(4, -1)$ a solution?

10-1 Write each ratio as a fraction in lowest terms.

11. 7:17 **12.** 30 to 40 **13.** $\frac{72}{18}$

10-2 Solve. Check your answers.

14. $\frac{a}{35} = \frac{2}{7}$ **15.** $\frac{7}{8} = \frac{y}{56}$ **16.** $\frac{2}{3} = \frac{16}{p}$

10-2 Solve by using a proportion.

17. The ratio of Amy's height to Rita's height is 11 to 9. Amy is 66 inches tall. How tall is Rita?

18. The ratio of trumpets to trombones in a band is 4 to 3. The band has 16 trumpets. How many trombones does it have?

10-3 Simplify each rate using a proportion.

19. 159 km/3 h **20.** $600/5 days **21.** 192 beats/3 min

10-3 Solve.

22. Paul charges $90 for 5 hours of labor. What is his hourly rate?

23. Shari drove 204 miles on 6 gallons of gas. How many miles per gallon did she get?

11-1 Solve by using a proportion or writing an equation.

24. 25% of 84 **25.** 120% of 50 **26.** 12.5% of 72

11-2 Find the percent.

27. What percent of 20 is 9? **28.** 25 is what percent of 125?

29. What percent of 96 is 24? **30.** 18 out of 120 is what percent?

11-3 Find the missing number. Round to the nearest tenth if necessary.

31. 7 is 5% of what number? **32.** 80% of what number is 64?

33. 25% of what number is 19? **34.** 36 is 75% of what number?

13 Area and Volume Formulas

Kyle can jump over a row of cones on his skateboard. Find the height of a cone if the area of its base is 25 square inches and it has a volume of 125 cubic inches.

13-1 Area of Rectangles and Parallelograms

Objective To use formulas to find the areas of rectangles and parallelograms.

Application

A pool cover costs $5 per square meter. To find the replacement cost of their pool cover, the Thorpes must find the area of the surface of their pool.

Understand the Ideas

The **area** of a region is the number of unit squares needed to cover the region. The unit square used to measure the area of the rectangle below is a square centimeter. Since 15 square centimeters (cm^2) are used to cover the rectangle, its area is 15 cm^2.

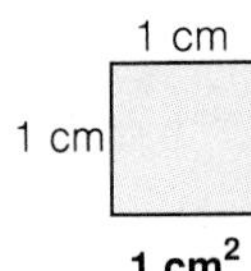

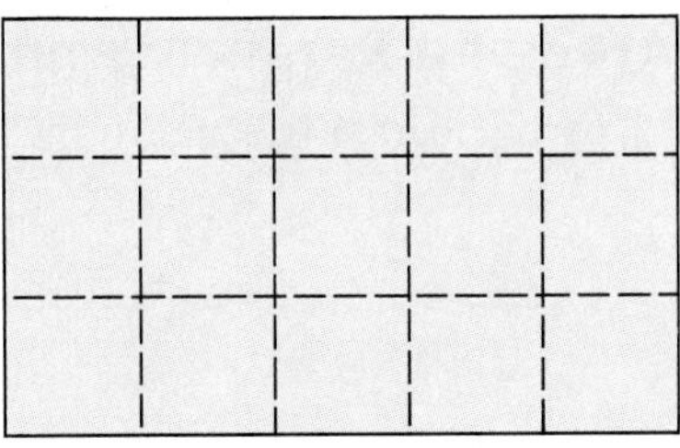

Area = 15 cm^2

In the rectangle above, there are 3 rows of 5 unit squares. Note that the product of the length and the width of the rectangle gives its area, $5 \times 3 = 15$, and the area is 15 cm^2. This suggests the following formula for the area of a rectangle.

Formula **Area of a Rectangle**

The area of a rectangle is equal to the length times the width.

$A = lw.$

Example 1

The Thorpes' pool in the **application** is 18.5 m long and 5.5 m wide. Find the area of the surface of the pool.

Solution $A = lw$

$A = 18.5 \times 5.5$ Replace l with 18.5 and w with 5.5.

$A = 101.75$

The area of the surface of the Thorpes' pool is 101.75 m^2.

Try This

a. An official basketball court is 28 yards long and 15.25 yards wide. What is the area of a basketball court?

The formula for the area of a parallelogram is similar to that for a rectangle. The length of one side of a parallelogram is called the *base* (b). The perpendicular distance between a pair of parallel bases is called the *height* (h). Any parallelogram can be cut into two pieces and rearranged to form a rectangle. The area of the parallelogram is equal to the area of the resulting rectangle.

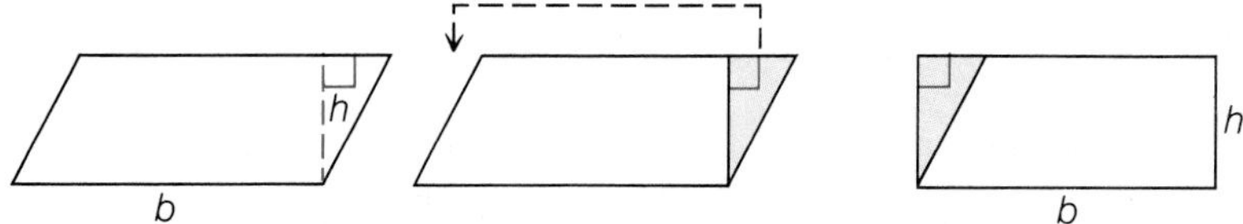

This illustration suggests the following formula.

Formula **Area of a Parallelogram**

The area of a parallelogram is equal to the base times the height.

$$A = bh$$

Example 2

A parking garage was designed to have slanted spaces. Each parking space was to be 20 ft long and 9 ft wide. Find the area of one parking space.

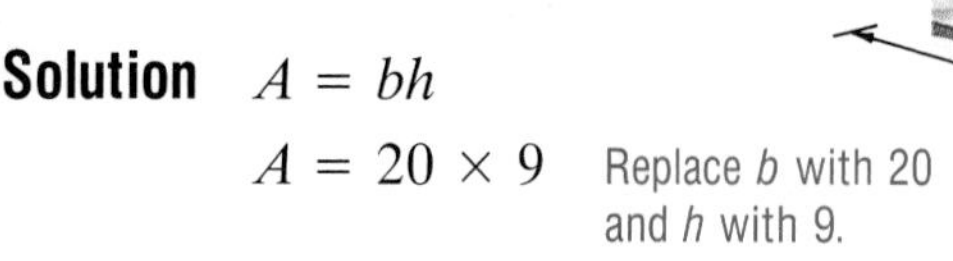

Solution $A = bh$

$A = 20 \times 9$ Replace b with 20 and h with 9.

$A = 180$

The area of one parking space is 180 ft^2.

Try This

Find the area of a parallelogram with the dimensions given.

b. 24 m long and 9 m high **c.** 48.3 cm long and 51.5 cm high

Class Exercises

Give the dimensions you would use to find the area.

1.

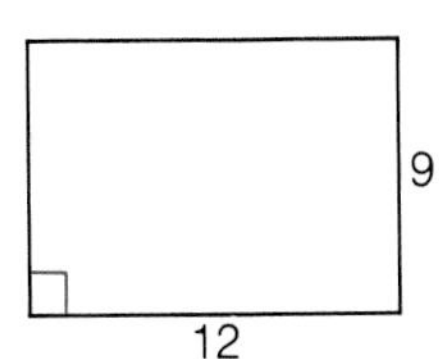

2.

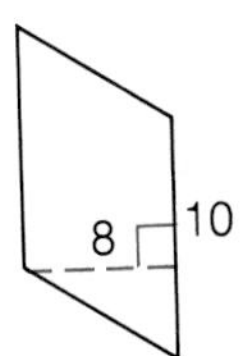

3.

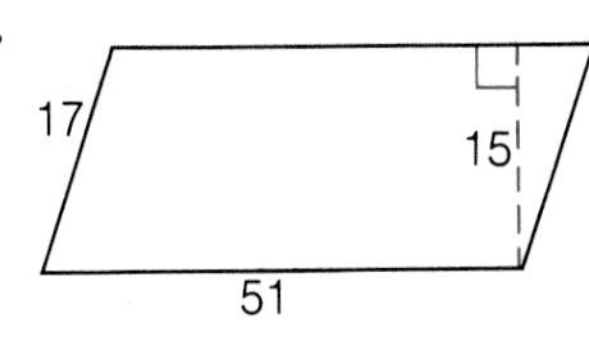

Discuss the Ideas

4. Do you think that if two parallelograms have the same area they must have equal bases and equal heights? Explain.

Exercises

Practice and Apply

Find the area of each figure. Assume all units are centimeters.

1.

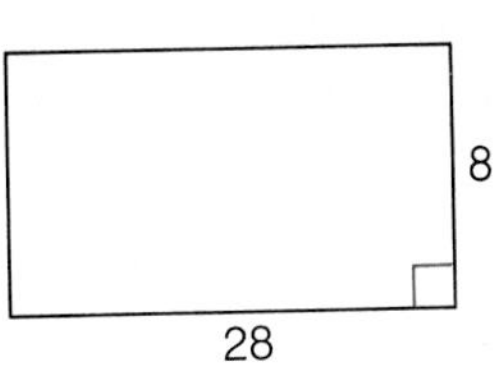

2.

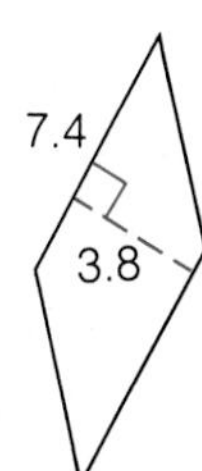

3.

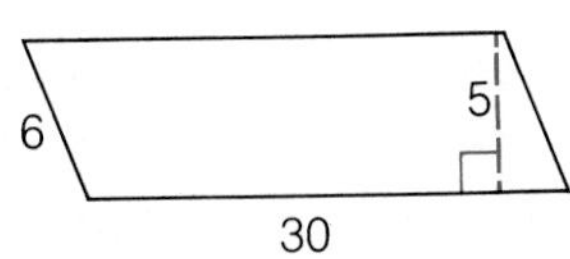

4.

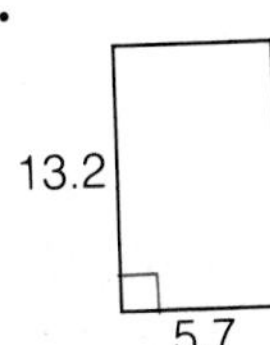

Find the area of a parallelogram with the dimensions given.

5. base = 14.3 cm, height = 5.8 cm
6. base = 123 mm, height = 18 mm
7. base = 1.56 km, height = 0.23 km
8. base = 2.51 m, height = 6.89 m

Solve.

9. A football field is 120 yd long and 53 yd wide, while a soccer field is 110 yd long and 80 yd wide. Which field has a larger playing area?
10. Atsuko wants to put wallpaper on one wall of her bedroom. The wall is 18 ft wide with an 8-ft ceiling. Assuming the wall has no windows or doors, how many square feet of wallpaper does she need?

Extend and Apply

Find the area of each parallelogram. All units are centimeters.

11. 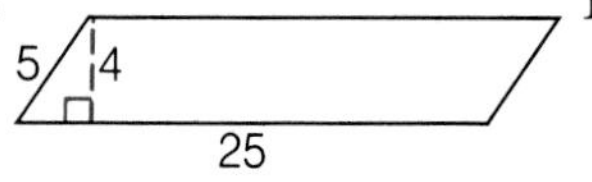

12. 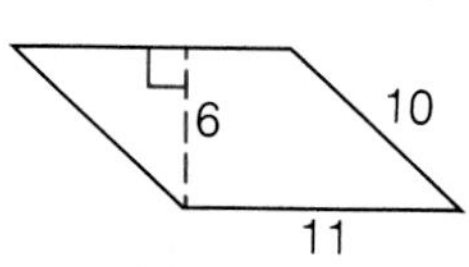

13. 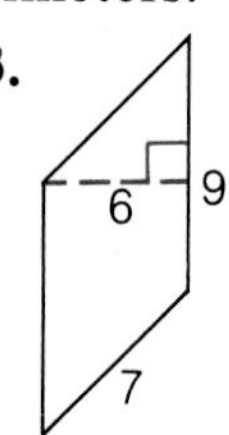

Find the base or height of a parallelogram with the measures given.

14. area = 4851 cm^2, h = 21 cm

15. area = 172.2 m^2, b = 12.3 m

16. area = 43.8 m^2, b = 36.5 m

17. area = 24.91 mm^2, h = 5.3 mm

Each unit of length is associated with a unit of area. The length units inch, foot, and yard become the area units square inch (in^2), square foot (ft^2), and square yard (yd^2). To calculate area, you must use the same unit for length and width. If units are different, use the smaller unit in your solutions to the following problems.

18. A rectangle has length of 12.5 in. and width of 0.5 ft. What is its area?

19. A rectangle has area 45 in^2. If its length is 9 inches, what is its width?

20. A gallon of paint covers about 450 ft^2. How many gallons are needed to paint the walls of a room that is 32 ft long, 16 ft wide, and 12 ft high? (The windows and doors take up 33 ft^2.)

21. Carpet costs \$18/yd^2. What is the cost to carpet a room 12 ft by 16 ft?

Use Mathematical Reasoning

22. A rectangle has a length of 25 cm and a perimeter of 70 cm. Find its area.

23. Complete the table to find which rectangle with perimeter 100 has the largest area. What generalization can you make from your answer?

perimeter	100	100	100	100	100	100	100
width	5	10	15	20	?	?	35
length	45	40	?	?	?	?	?
area	225	400	?	?	?	?	?

Mixed Review

Evaluate for $n = -\frac{1}{3}$. **24.** $2n + \frac{1}{2}$ **25.** $\frac{4}{5}n$ **26.** $-6n$ **27.** $\frac{3}{4} - n$

28. 16 is what percent of 24?

29. 28 is what percent of 24?

30. 15 is what percent of 24?

31. 21 is what percent of 24?

13-2 Area of Triangles and Trapezoids

Objective To use formulas to find the areas of triangles and trapezoids.

Application

A furniture manufacturer needs to calculate the area of the tops of these tables so that she can order plastic laminate for them. (See Example 2.)

Understand the Ideas

Any side of a triangle can be called a **base.** The **height** is the perpendicular distance from a vertex to the base.

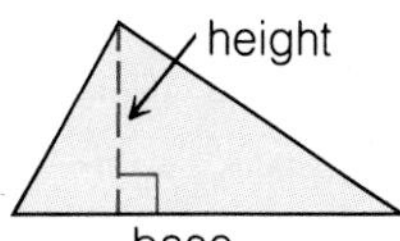

Study the figures at right. Since two congruent triangles can form a parallelogram, the area of the triangle must be one half the area of the parallelogram that has the same base and height.

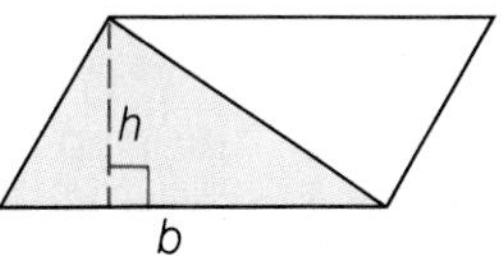

Formula Area of a Triangle

The area of a triangle is equal to $\frac{1}{2}$ the base times the height.

$$A = \frac{1}{2}bh$$

Since any side of a triangle can be a base, each triangle has three bases and three heights. When calculating the area of a triangle, you must use the correct height for the chosen base.

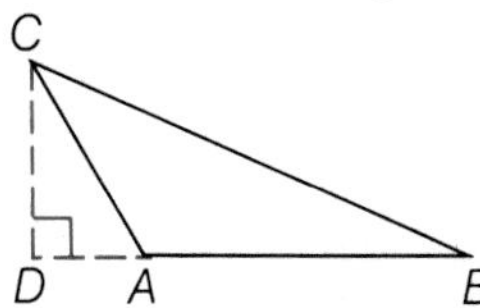

If $\overline{AB}$ is the base, then $\overline{CD}$ is the height.

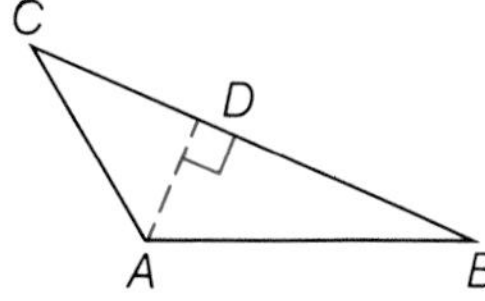

If $\overline{BC}$ is the base, then $\overline{AD}$ is the height.

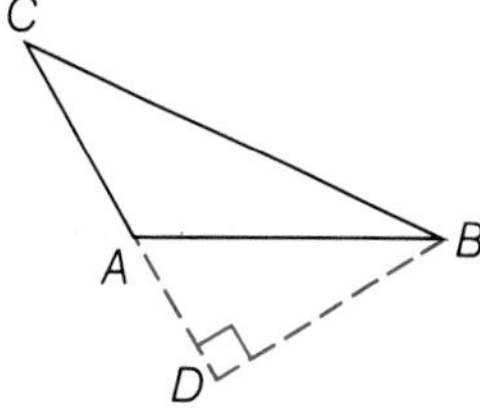

If $\overline{AC}$ is the base, then $\overline{BD}$ is the height.

Example 1

Find the area of the triangle.

Solution $A = \frac{1}{2}bh$

$A = \frac{1}{2}(23 \times 12)$ Replace b with 23 and h with 12.

$= 138$

The area is 138 cm^2.

Try This Find the area of each triangle.

a.

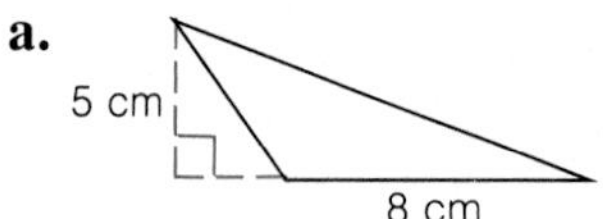

b.

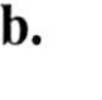

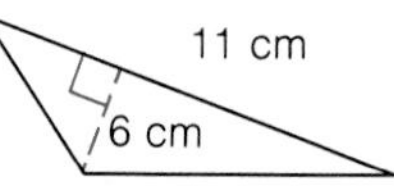

You learned earlier that a trapezoid is a quadrilateral with one pair of parallel sides, called bases. Since two congruent trapezoids can form a parallelogram, the area of one of the trapezoids is one half the area of the resulting parallelogram.

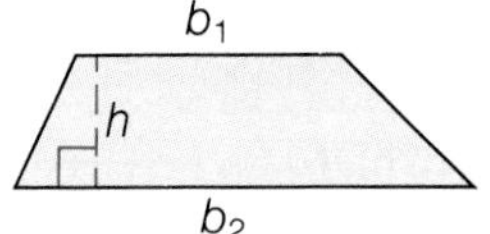

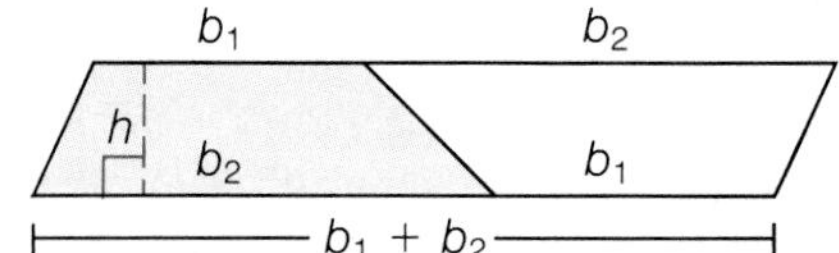

If the bases of the trapezoid have lengths b_1 and b_2, the parallelogram formed has a pair of sides with length $b_1 + b_2$.

Formula **Area of a Trapezoid**

The area of a trapezoid is equal to $\frac{1}{2}$ the height times the sum of the bases.

$$A = \frac{1}{2}h(b_1 + b_2)$$

Example 2

Each trapezoid-shaped table shown in the **application** measures 6 ft on its long side, 4 ft on its short side, and 3.5 ft between the two sides. What is the area of each table top?

Solution $A = \frac{1}{2}h(b_1 + b_2)$

$A = \frac{1}{2}(3.5)(6 + 4)$

$= 17.5$

The area of each table top is 17.5 ft^2.

Try This Draw a trapezoid and label it with the lengths given. All units are meters. Find the area.

c. $b_1 = 9, b_2 = 23, h = 29$ **d.** $b_1 = 5, b_2 = 28, h = 14$

Class Exercises

Select the base or height that you could use with the given base or height.

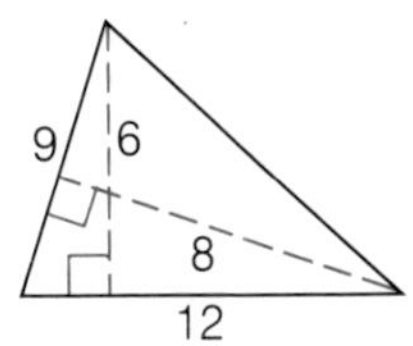

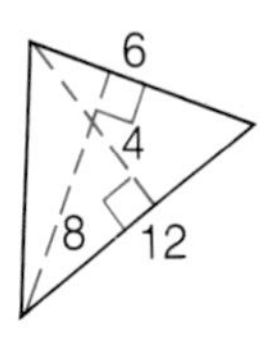

1. $b = 12, h = ?$
$h = 8, b = ?$

2. $h = 3, b = ?$
$b = 12, h = ?$

3. $b = 12, h = ?$
$b = 6, h = ?$

Discuss the Ideas

4. Discuss how you can find the area of this triangle without using the area formula in this lesson. Notice that the distance between two neighboring dots is 1 unit.

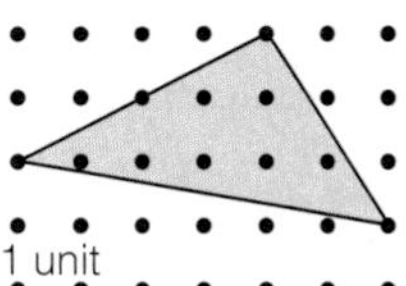

Exercises

Practice and Apply

Find the area of each triangle. All units are centimeters.

1.

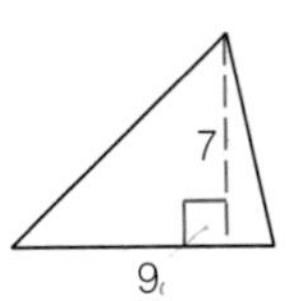

2.

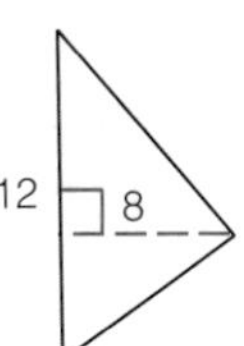

3.

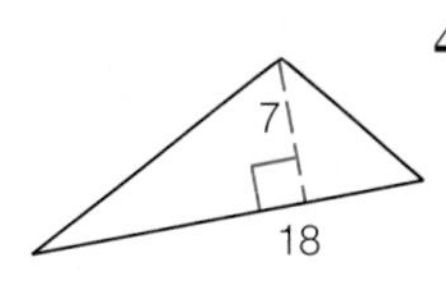

4.

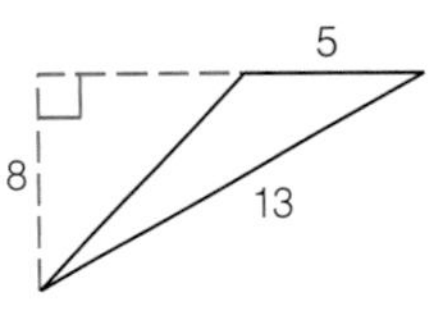

Draw a triangle and label it with the base and height given. Find the area.

5. $b = 23$ m; $h = 9$ m **6.** $b = 18$ m; $h = 2$ m **7.** $b = 34$ m; $h = 2$ m

Find the area of each trapezoid. All units are meters.

8.

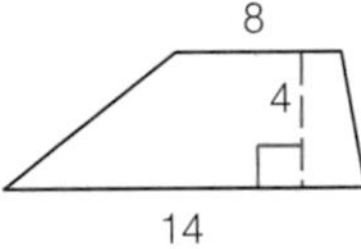

9.

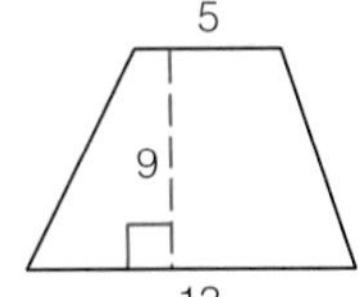

10.

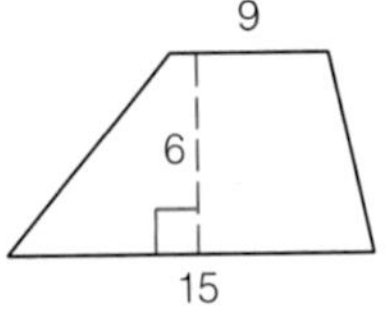

Draw a trapezoid and label it with the lengths given. Find the area.

11. $b_1 = 8$ m, $b_2 = 15$ m; $h = 5$ m **12.** $b_1 = 9$ cm, $b_2 = 17$ cm; $h = 5$ cm

Extend and Apply

13. A triangle has an area of 30 cm^2 and a height of 5 cm. Find the length of the base.

14. A trapezoid has bases of 15 cm and 48 cm. The area is 79.2 cm^2. Find the height.

Use Mathematical Reasoning

15. Use an equilateral triangle as the unit of area to find the pattern. Complete the next three columns of this table. What is the area of an equilateral triangle with side length n?

Side length	1	2	3	4	5	6
Area	1	4	9	16	25	36

Mixed Review

Solve and check. **16.** $3.4t + 5.2 = -3.3$ **17.** $3(y + 2) = 3$

18. Evaluate the formula $2a + 3(b + 4)$ for $a = 17, b = 9$.

Connections Numbers to Algebra

Replacing variables in a formula with specific numbers can help you see how to solve a formula for one variable in terms of the other variables. The example shows how to solve the formula $A = \frac{1}{2}bh$ for h by using numbers for a triangle with an area of 45 square units and a base of 9 units.

Numbers		Algebra	
$A = \frac{1}{2}bh$		$A = \frac{1}{2}bh$	
$45 = \frac{1}{2}(9)h$	Replace A with 45 and b with 9.		
$2(45) = 9h$	Multiply both sides by 2.	$2A = bh$	Multiply both sides by 2.
$\frac{2(45)}{9} = h$	Divide both sides by 9 to solve for h.	$\frac{2A}{b} = h$	Divide both sides by b to solve for h.

1. Solve $A = bh$ for h. **2.** Solve $P = 2l + 2w$ for w.

13-3 Area of Circles

Objective To use formulas to find the areas of circles.

Explore

On square grid paper draw a circle with a radius of 4 as shown. Estimate the area of the circle by counting the number of whole unit squares and fractions of unit squares in the circle.

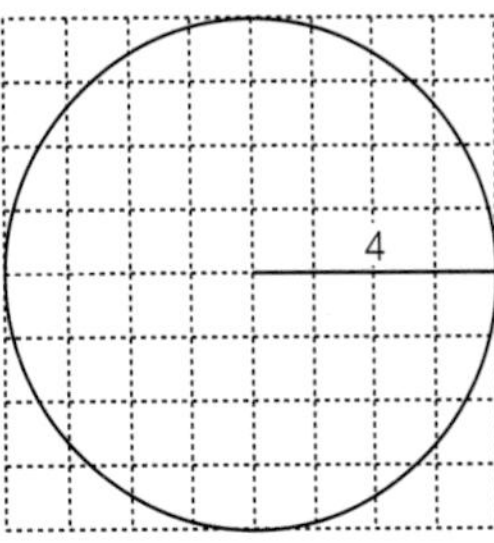

Is your estimate a little more than 3 times the radius squared, or a little more than 4 times the radius squared?

Understand the Ideas

The circumference, C, of a circle with radius r is found by using the formula $C = 2\pi r$. This formula is used to develop a formula for the area of a circle.

In the figure below, a circle of radius r has been divided into pie-shaped pieces. The pieces have been rearranged into a parallelogram-like shape. This "parallelogram" has a height r and a base that is about half the circumference of the circle. Therefore, the approximate area is $(\pi r)r$, or πr^2. Since the area of the "parallelogram" would be the same as the area of a circle, the area of the circle is also πr^2.

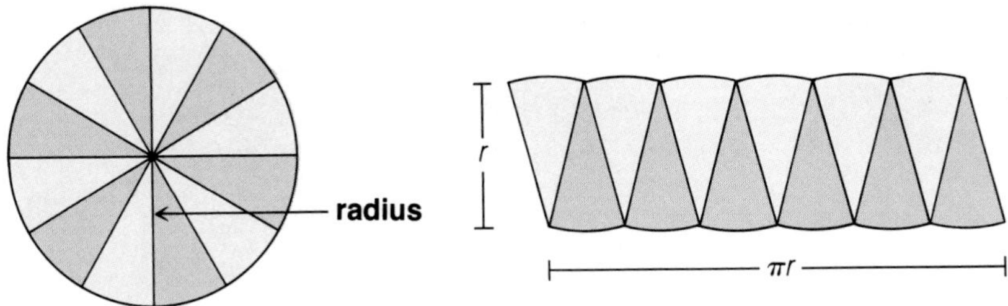

Formula **Area of a Circle**

The area of a circle is equal to π times the radius squared.

$$A = \pi r^2$$

Example

A city engineer knows that the radius of each water pipe is 15 cm. Calculate the area of the end of a pipe using the formula $A = \pi r^2$ to help determine the amount of water that a pipe carries.

Solution $A = \pi r^2$

$A \approx (3.14)15^2$ Replace π with 3.14 and r with 15.

$A \approx 706.5 \text{ cm}^2$

The area of the end of the pipe is 706.5 cm^2.

Try This Find the area of the circle.

a. radius = 3 ft **b.** diameter = 8 m

You can also use a calculator to solve area problems. The answer will vary depending upon the value for π stored in your calculator.

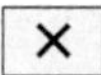  15 [x^2] [=] 706.85835

Class Exercises

Give the radius and diameter of each figure.

1.

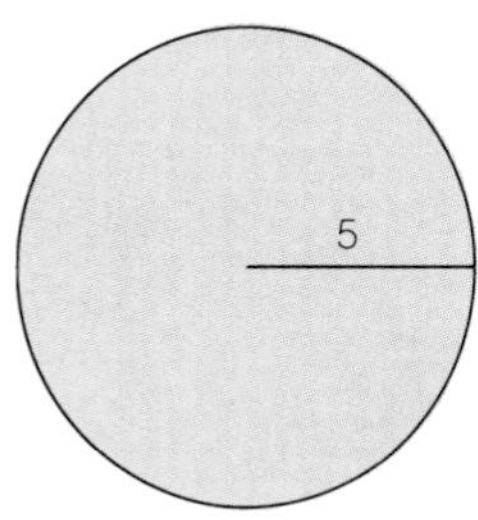

2.

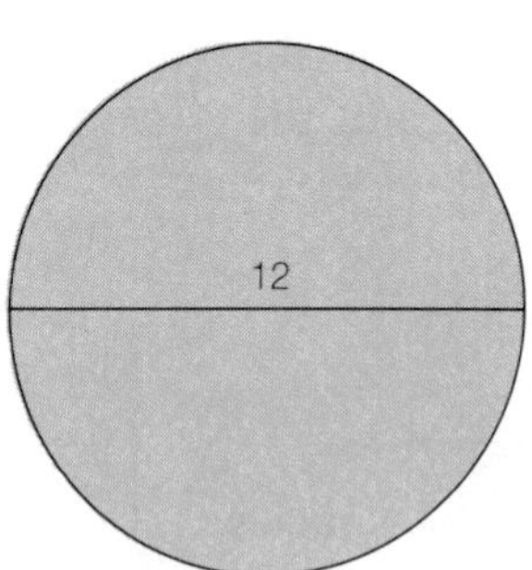

3.

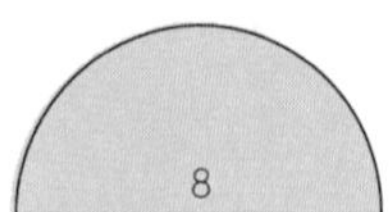

4.

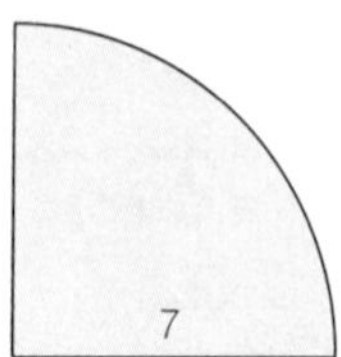

Discuss the Ideas

5. If the diameter of a circle is doubled:

a. its circumference is increased by a factor of __?__ .

b. and its area is increased by a factor of __?__ .

Exercises

Practice and Apply

Find the area of each circle. Use 3.14 as an approximation for π.

1. $r = 5$ cm

2. $r = 8$ cm

3. $d = 10$ cm

4. $d = 4.8$ cm

5. $r = 3.9$ m

6. $d = 500$ m

7. $r = 50$ cm

8. $r = 4.8$ m

9. $d = 3$ m

10. $r = 25$ m

11. $d = 12$ mm

12. $r = 250$ cm

13. Many imported record albums are called 8-inch singles because they have a diameter of 8 inches and only one song on each side. Find the area of an 8-inch single album.

14. Most record albums have a radius of 6 inches. Find the area of a traditional record album.

Use a calculator to find the area of a circle in Exercises 15–20.

15. $r = 523.6$ cm

16. $r = 83.5$ m

17. $r = 14.2$ cm

18. $d = 25.2$ cm

19. $d = 4.5$ m

20. $d = 18.8$ cm

Extend and Apply

21. Estimate, then give the area of a computer disk with diameter of:

a. 8 inches **b.** 5 inches **c.** $3\frac{1}{2}$ inches

22. Estimate whether the area of an 8-inch disk is about 2 times, 3 times, 4 times, or 5 times the area of a $3\frac{1}{2}$-inch disk. Check your estimate with a calculator.

Find the area of each shaded region. Express the answer in terms of π. Assume that semicircular regions are half-circles.

23.

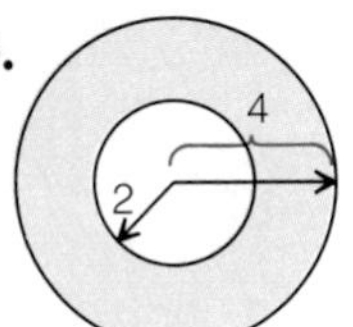

24.

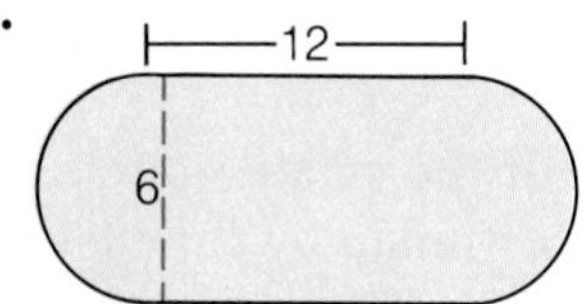

25.

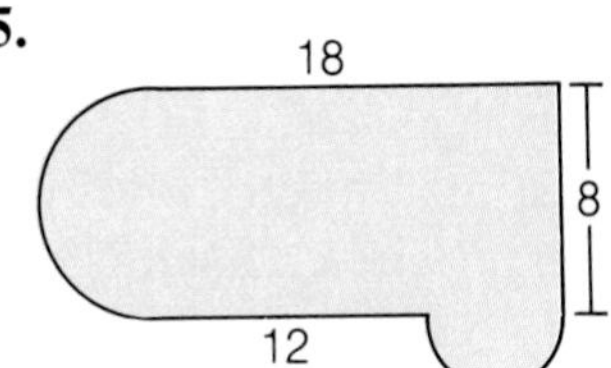

26. This dog tag has a diameter of 2.5 cm. The circular cutout at the top has a diameter of 0.4 cm. Find the area of the dog tag.

27. An archery target is divided into three circles. The bull's-eye has a diameter of 4 inches and the largest circle has a diameter of 20 inches. How much greater is the area of the largest circle (including the bull's-eye) than the area of the bull's-eye?

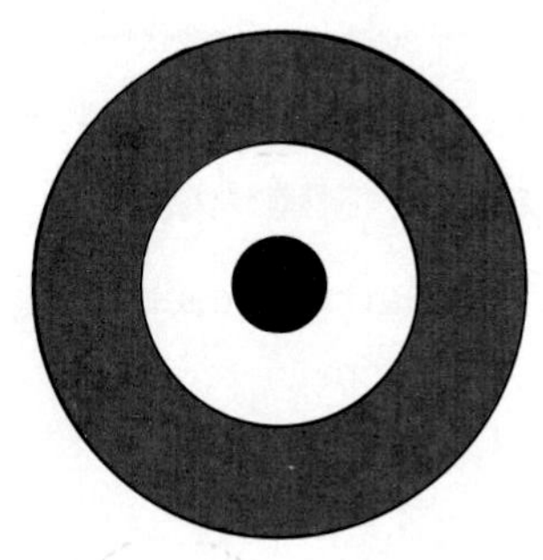

Use Mathematical Reasoning

28. Mr. Green divides a square-mile field into quarters, with a circular irrigation system on each quarter. Ms. Peabody has one large circular irrigation system. Guess which farmer irrigates the greater percentage of land. Check your guess by calculating.

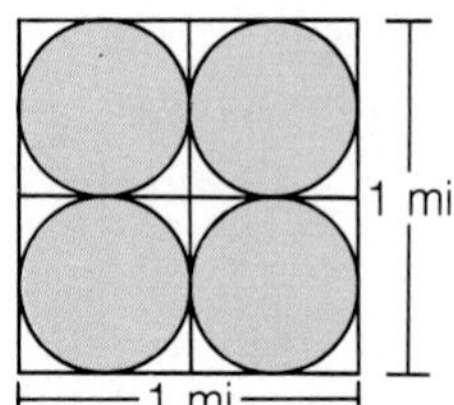

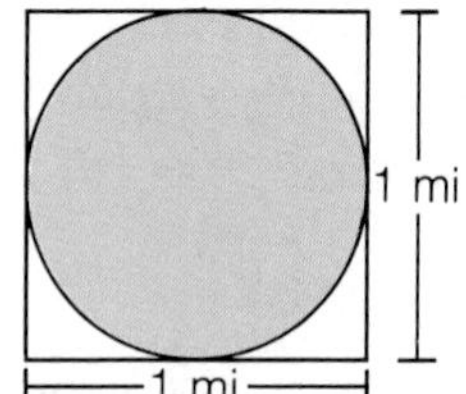

Mixed Review

Solve by writing an equation. Leonetti's Fruit market is selling apples for 25¢/lb and oranges for 35¢/lb.

29. What is the cost of 3 lb of apples and 3 lb of oranges?

30. How many lb of apples can you buy for $3.50?

Write as a fraction in lowest terms. **31.** 24% **32.** 15% **33.** 11%

Give the least common multiple (LCM). **34.** 2, 3, 4, 8 **35.** 2, 4, 6, 12

Evaluate for $x = 2, y = 24$. **36.** x^2y **37.** $3(x - y)$ **38.** $x(y - 1)$

Solve and check. **39.** $1.4 - n = 0.28$ **40.** $4m + 9 = m$

Estimation

Estimate the ratio of the area of the smaller circle to the area of the larger circle. Then check your estimate by calculating.

1.

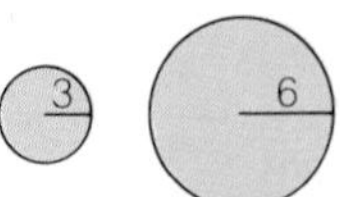

2.

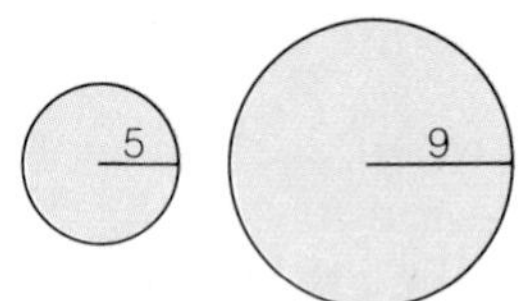

3.

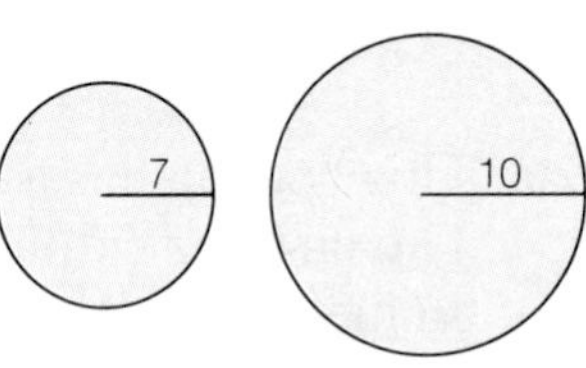

13-4 Area of Figures of Irregular Shape

Objective To find areas of figures of irregular shapes by dividing them into familiar shapes.

Explore

- Draw these polygons on graph paper.
- Estimate the area of each figure by counting the number of shaded squares.
- Find another way to estimate the area of each figure.

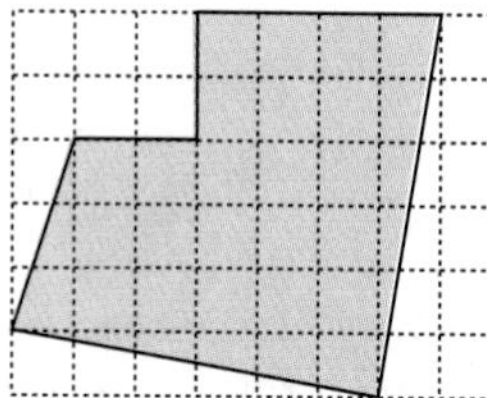

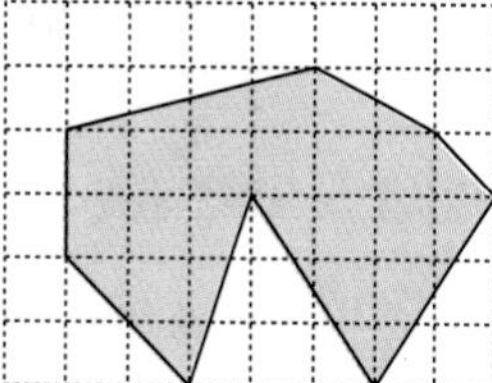

Understand the Ideas

An architect will often design a floor plan for a house that is irregular in shape. To find the area of such a figure, divide it into smaller regions that have familiar shapes. Find the area of each region and then add the areas together.

Example

Find the area of a house with the floor plan shown at the right.

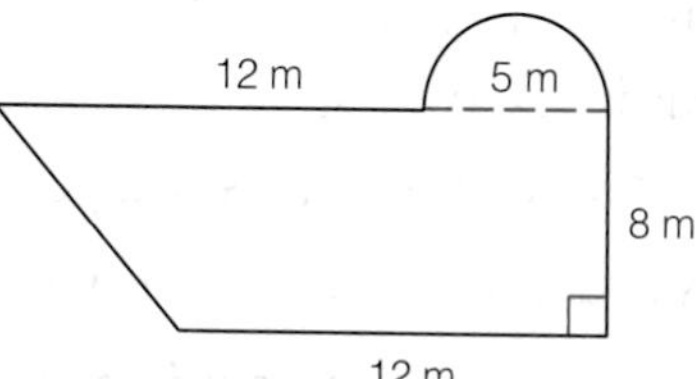

Solution

$A_T = \frac{1}{2}(8)(12 + 17)$
$= 116 \text{ m}^2$

First find the area A_T of the trapezoid, using the formula $\frac{1}{2}h(b_1 + b_2)$.

$A_{SC} = \frac{1}{2}\pi\left(\frac{5}{2}\right)^2$
$\approx \frac{25}{8}(3.14) = 9.8125 \text{ m}^2$

Next find the area A_{SC} of the semicircle. The area of a semicircle is $\frac{1}{2}$ the area of the whole circle. The radius is $\frac{5}{2}$.

$A = A_T + A_{SC} \approx 116 + 9.8125 = 125.8125 \text{ m}^2$

The house has an area of approximately 125.8 m^2.

Try This Find the area of each figure. All units are meters.

a.

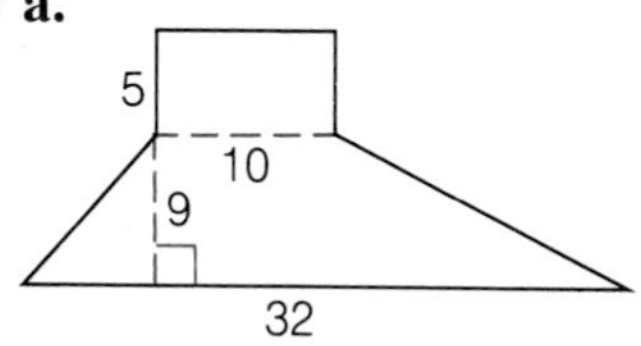

b.

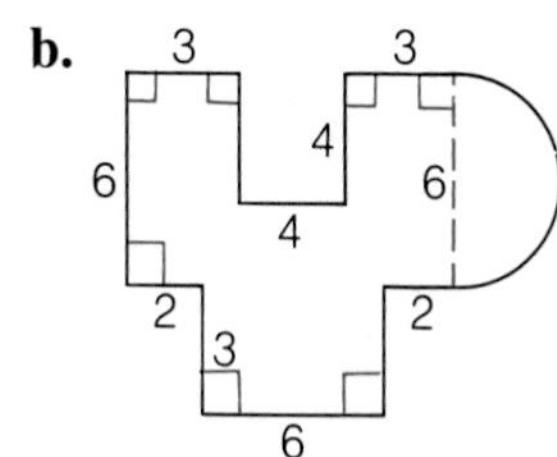

Class Exercises

First name the shapes into which each figure could be divided. Then find lengths x and y in each figure.

1.

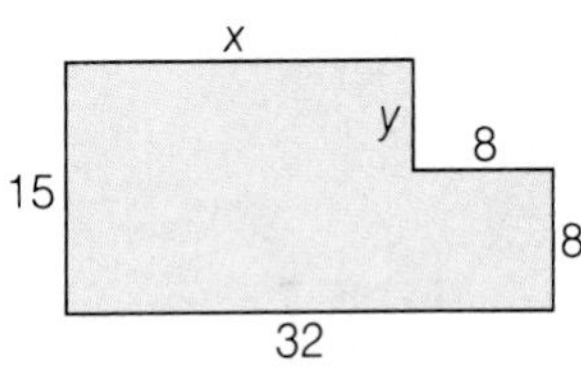

2.

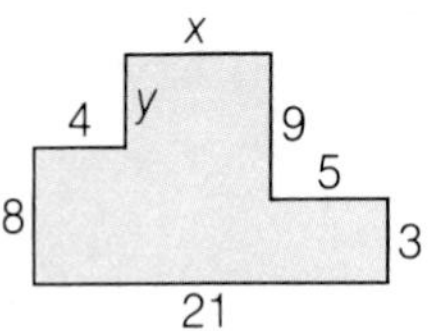

Discuss the Ideas

3. Often there are several ways to divide a region into triangles, rectangles, trapezoids, and circles. Draw a region of your own creation that can be divided in more than one way. Explain the ways the region can be divided.

Exercises

Practice and Apply

Find the area of each figure. All units are meters.

1.

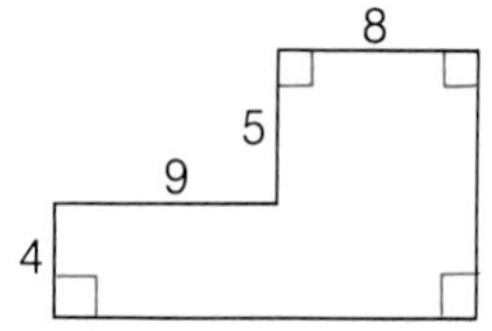

2.

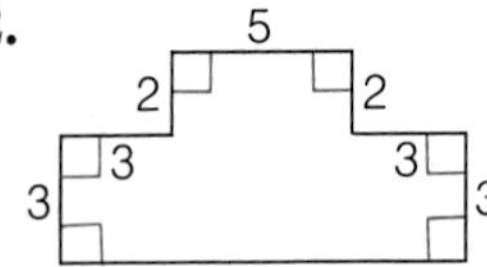

3.

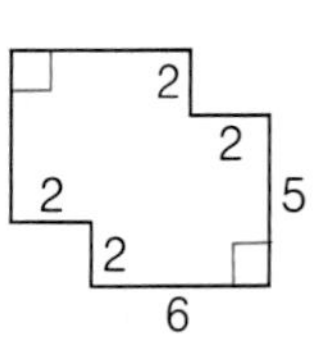

4.

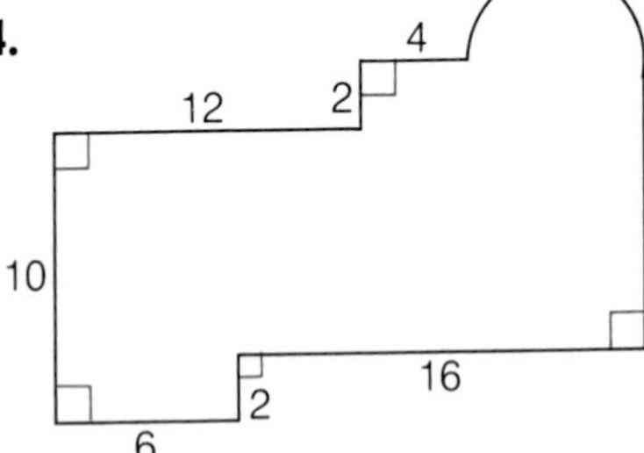

Find the area of the top of each machine part. All units are centimeters.

5.

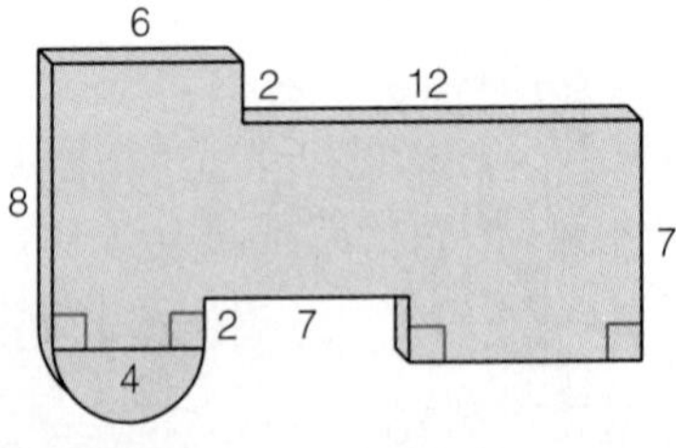

6.

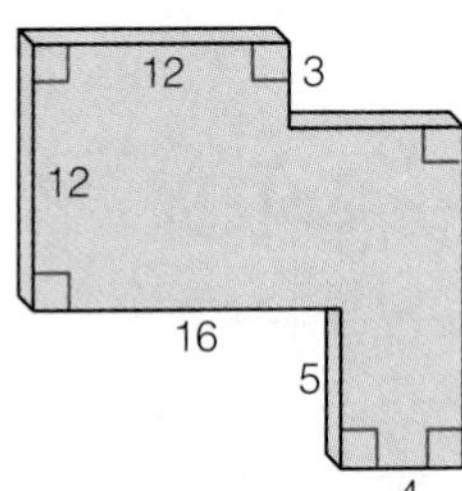

Jaian Quinones 5-20-97

pg. 571 1-6
570 - 1-4
Do pg. 320

1- (-4,1)
2. (3,3)
3-
4-
5. (-3,-2)
(pg. 570 (1-4)

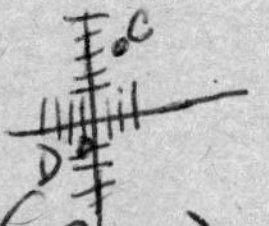

1- 12
2-
3- -9
4-

pg. 320

1- slope - $\frac{2}{5}$
2-
3- slope - -2

Extend and Apply

Find the area of each figure. All units are feet.

7.

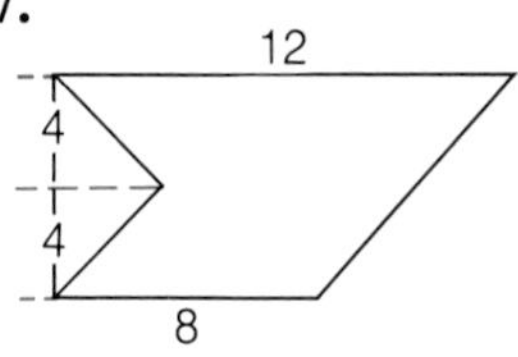

8.

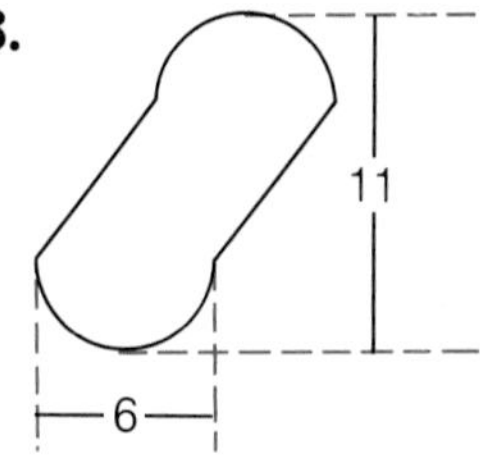

9.

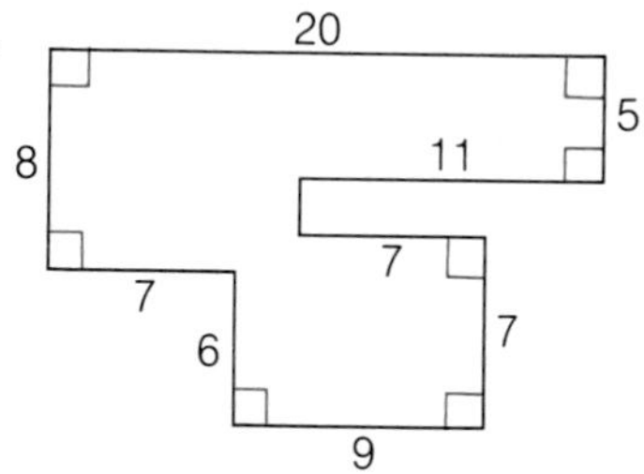

10.

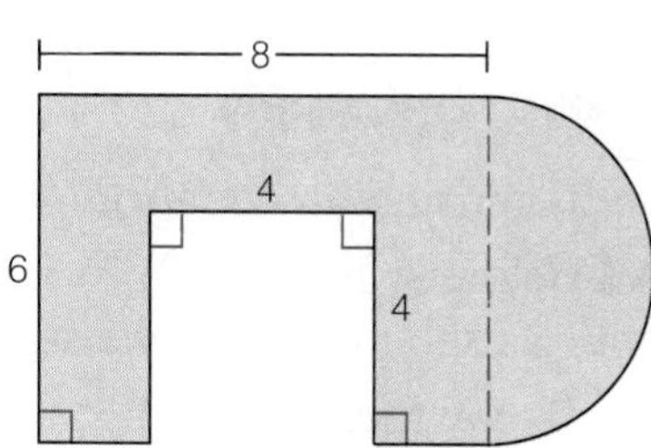

11. Missing Data What data are needed to find the area of the shaded region? Supply data and find the area of the shaded region.

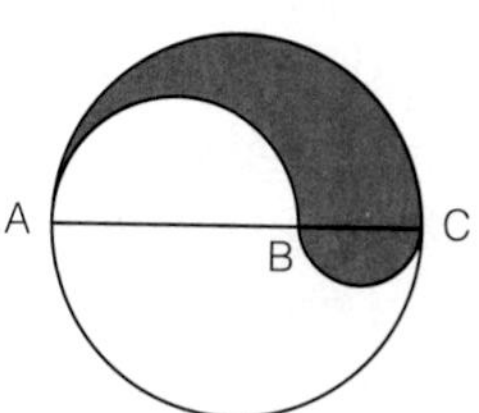

Use Mathematical Reasoning

Find the area of each shaded region. All units are meters.

12.

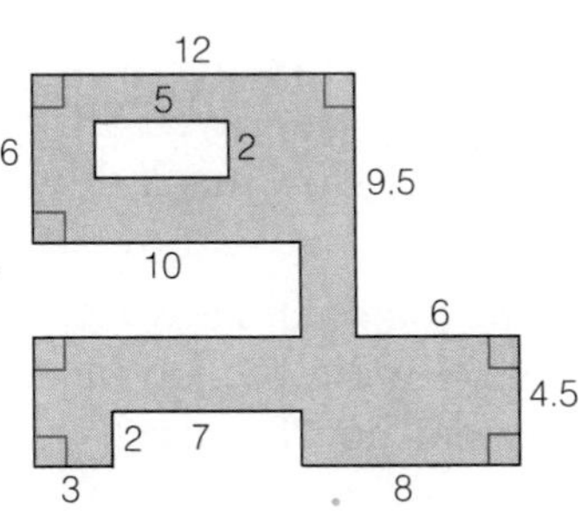

13.

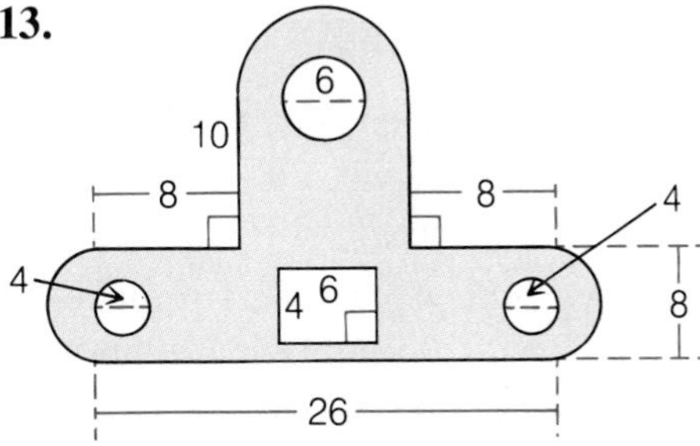

14. Communicate Suppose you are a carpet salesperson who has just sold carpet for a room the shape of the figure in Exercise 9. Write a paragraph to the carpet installer with instructions on how to cut a 12 foot wide roll of carpet to cover the floor.

Mixed Review

Write as a decimal. **15.** 16% **16.** 12.5% **17.** 120% **18.** 7%

Solve and check. **19.** $4(2n + 1) = 10$ **20.** $0.3n + 16.5 - 3n = 3$

13-5 Problem Solving: Writing Equations

Practice Solving Problems

Objective To write and solve equations to solve word problems.

Exercises

Practice and Apply

Solve by writing an equation.

1. A bricklayer makes $15.75 an hour. She makes 3 times as much per hour as she did when she started. What was her starting hourly wage?
2. Fred's pay was 4 times his assistant's. Together, they earned $675 for building a greenhouse. How much did each earn?
3. A shovel was priced at $3.74 less than a saw. A carpenter bought one shovel and one saw and paid $24.50. What was the price of the shovel?
4. The length of a garage is 3 times the width. The perimeter is 144 ft. What are the length and width?
5. Students raised money to visit a museum. This year, they earned $50 more than twice the amount they raised last year. This year they collected $1,000. How much more did they collect this year than last year?

Extend and Apply

6. Three boys saved a total of $75 for carpentry tools. Tim saved $10 more than Kyle, and Jeff saved $5 more than Kyle. How much did each boy save?
7. A worker repaired a fireplace. Since he did the job on a Saturday, his fee was $20 plus twice his normal hourly wage. He did the job in 5 hours and charged $87.50. What was his regular hourly wage?

Use Mathematical Reasoning

8. Write a word problem that could be solved by the equation.

   a. $2x - 5 = 43$ **b.** $x + 3x = 58$.

Mixed Review

Write <, >, or = for each □. **9.** -0.633 □ -0.632 **10.** -0.4 □ 0.5

Solve and check. **11.** $0.45c = 1.8$ **12.** $t - 0.6t = 3.6$

13-6 Volume of Prisms and Cylinders

Objective To use formulas to find the volumes of prisms and cylinders.

Understand the Ideas

The **volume** of a solid is the number of cubic units needed to occupy the amount of space the solid occupies. The rectangular solid at right has 8 cubic centimeters in the base layer and a height of 2 layers, making a volume of $8 \times 2 = 16$ cubic centimeters. This volume is written 16 cm^3.

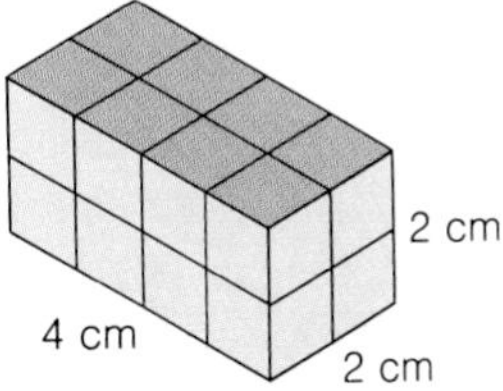

A **prism** is a solid that has a pair of bases that are congruent and parallel; its sides are parallelograms. A prism with triangles as bases is called a triangular prism. A prism with hexagons as bases is called a hexagonal prism.

Formula **Volume of a Prism**

The volume of a prism is equal to the area of a base times the height.

$$V = Bh$$

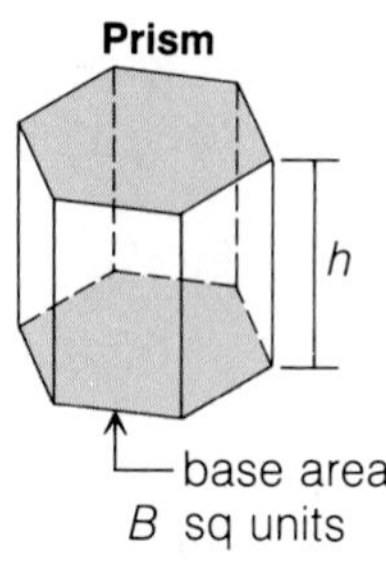

Example 1

Find the volume of the triangular prism.

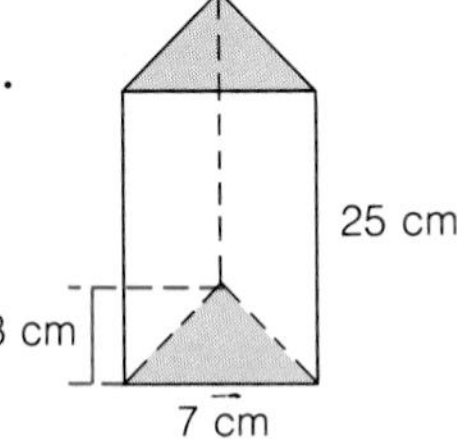

Solution

$V = Bh$

$= \frac{1}{2} \times 7 \times 8 \times 25$ The bases are triangles. $B = \frac{1}{2} \times 7 \times 8$.

$V = 700 \text{ cm}^3$

The volume of the prism is 700 cm^3.

Try This **a.** Find the volume of the prism at right.

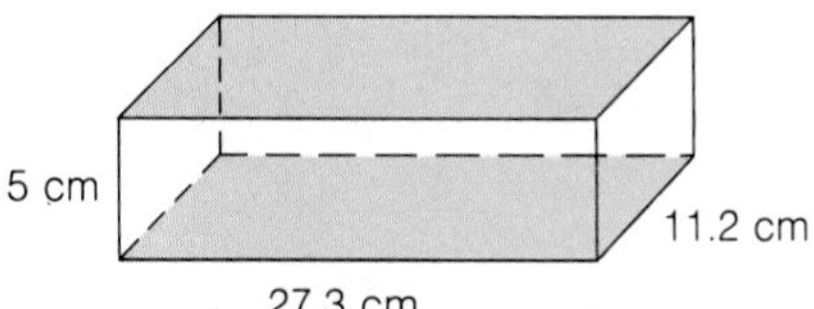

A **cylinder** has a pair of parallel circular bases with the same radius.

Formula **Volume of a Cylinder**

The volume of a cylinder is equal to the area of the base (πr^2) times the height.

$$V = \pi r^2 h$$

Cylinder

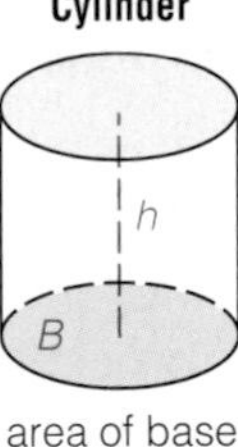

area of base is πr^2 sq units

Example 2

Find the volume of the water tank shown. The tank has a 20 m diameter and a height of 8 m.

Solution $V = \pi r^2 h$

$\approx (3.14) \times 10^2 \times 8$

$V \approx 2512$

The volume of the water tank is approximately 2,512 m^3.

Try This Find the volume of a cylinder with the dimensions given.

b. $d = 10$ cm, $h = 8$ cm **c.** $r = 5$ cm, $h = 1.8$ cm

Class Exercises

Give the height of each prism.

1.

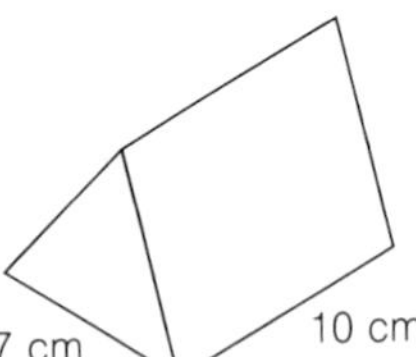

2.

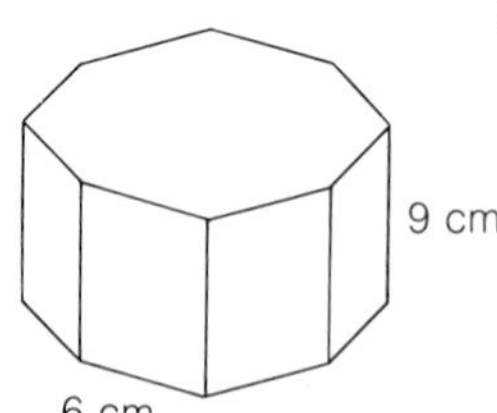

3.

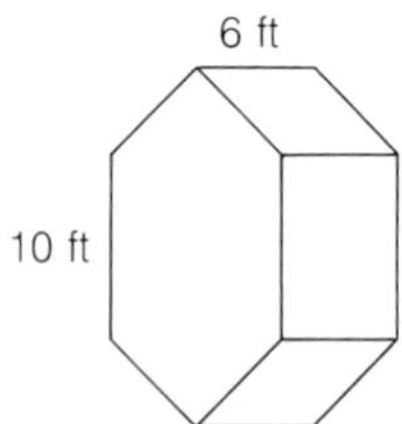

Give the radius and height of each cylinder.

4.

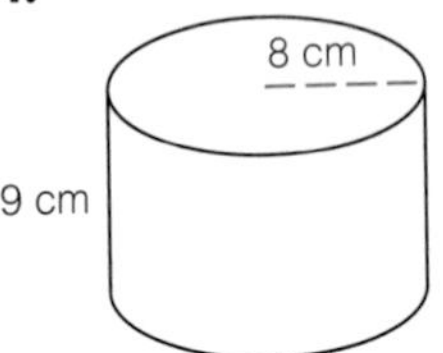

5.

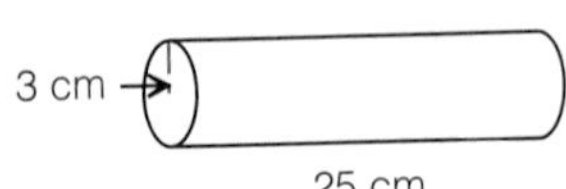

6.

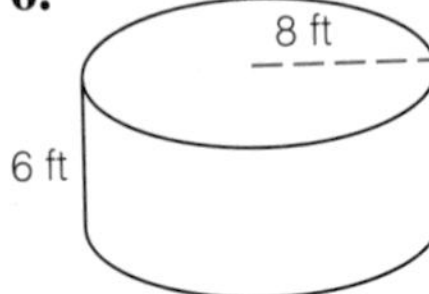

Discuss the Ideas

How does the volume of a cylinder change if:

7. the height is doubled and the radius is kept the same?
8. the radius is doubled and the height is kept the same?

Exercises

Practice and Apply

Find the volume of each prism or cylinder. Use 3.14 for π.

1.

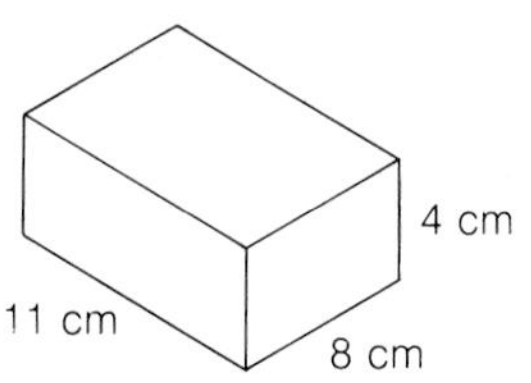

2.

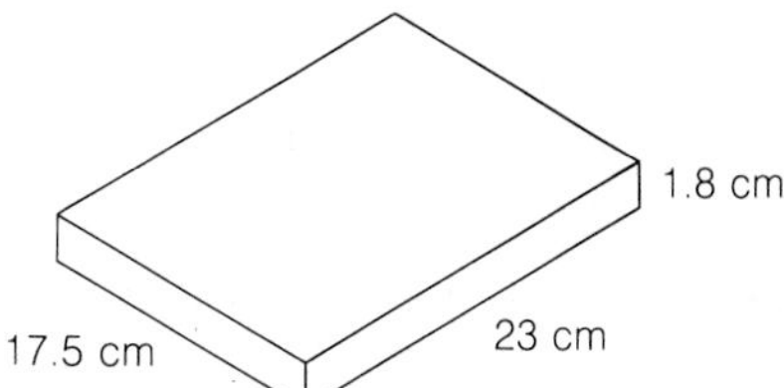

3.

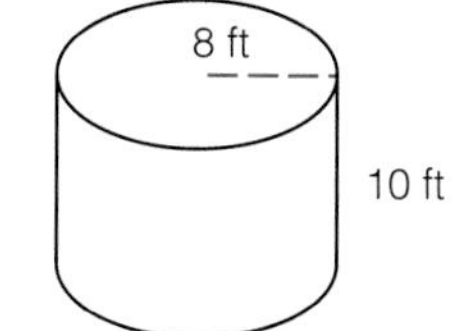

4.

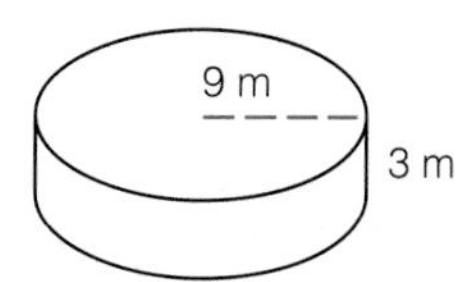

5. $B = 25\text{ cm}^2$
   $h = 12\text{ cm}$

6. $B = 192\text{ in}^2$
   $h = 24\text{ in}$

7. $B = 126\text{ ft}^2$
   $h = 4\text{ ft}$

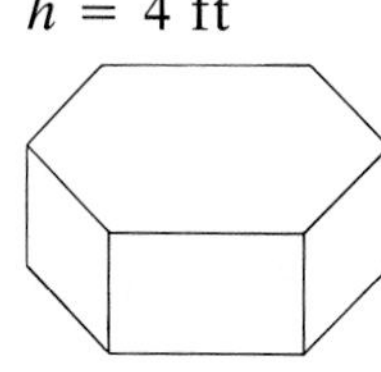

8. A cylindrical can of soup is 8 cm in diameter and 12 cm tall. What is the volume of the can of soup?
9. A one-gallon can of paint is a cylinder 15 cm in diameter and 19 cm tall. Approximately how many cm^3 are in one gallon?

Extend and Apply

For Exercises 10–25, be sure to use consistent units when computing. Express the answer in the smaller unit. Use the formula $V = lwh$ to find the volume of a rectangular prism with the dimensions given.

10. $l = 5$ m, $w = 12$ cm, $h = 18$ cm
11. $l = 25$ cm, $w = 8$ dm, $h = 36$ cm
12. $l = 23.4$ cm, $w = 12.3$ cm, $h = 12.6$ cm
13. $l = 7$ m, $w = 2.3$ m, $h = 1.8$ m

Find the volume of a cylinder with the dimensions given. Use 3.14 for π.

14. $r = 12$ cm
$h = 8$ cm

15. $r = 11$ m
$h = 19$ m

16. $r = 2$ m
$h = 3$ m

17. $r = 4$ dm
$h = 12$ dm

18. $r = 2.4$ cm
$h = 3.1$ cm

19. $r = 56$ cm
$h = 2$ m

20. $r = 8$ m
$h = 40$ cm

21. $r = 3$ cm
$h = 2$ dm

22. $r = 8$ mm
$h = 2.1$ cm

23. Find the base area of a cylinder with volume 500 cm^3 and height 5 cm.

24. Find the height of a prism with volume 125 m^3 and a base area of 5 m^2.

25. A cylindrical hole with radius 4 cm is cut through a solid cube whose edges are 10 cm long. What is the total volume of this solid?

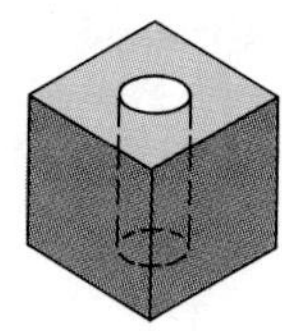

Use Mathematical Reasoning

Mentally count unit cubes to find the volume of each figure. The hidden back view of each looks like the corner of a box.

26.

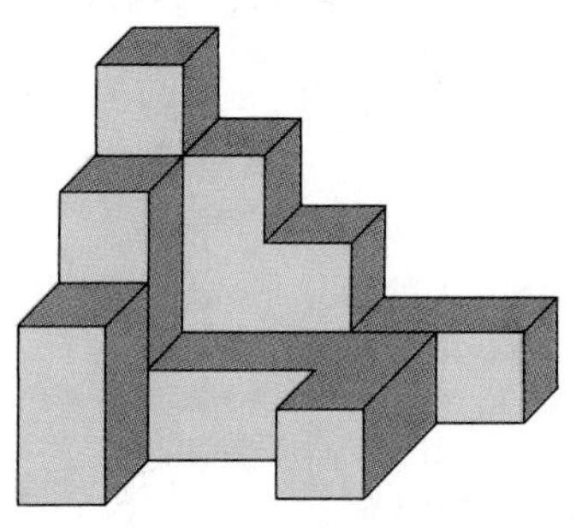

27.

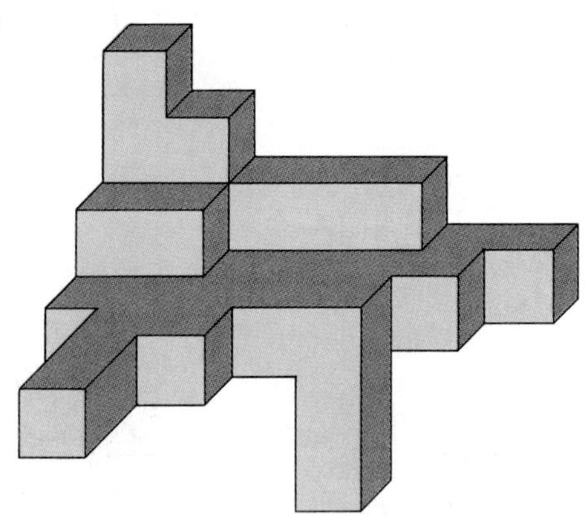

Mixed Review

Give the greatest common factor (GCF). **28.** 18, 42, 90 **29.** 15, 72, 111

Write as a decimal. **30.** $3\frac{4}{5}$ **31.** $-1\frac{3}{4}$ **32.** $\frac{15}{12}$ **33.** $\frac{1}{3}$

Write as a percent. **34.** $\frac{16}{5}$ **35.** $\frac{24}{8}$ **36.** $-\frac{3}{4}$ **37.** $\frac{7}{10}$

Solve and check. **38.** $30 = 5(x - 2)$ **39.** $9 = 2.5 + y$

Reduce. **40.** $\frac{9}{6}$ **41.** $\frac{35}{7}$ **42.** $\frac{16}{64}$

Solve. **43.** Alicia bought a computer program for $240.00. If the sales tax was 6.5%, what was the total amount that Alicia paid for the program?

13-7 Problem Solving: Applications

Building a House

Objective To solve applied problems involving area and volume.

The table below gives costs of some building materials and services for building a house.

Building Materials and Services	
Item	**Cost**
Excavation	\$ 1.30/cubic yard
Carpet	12.00/square yard
Concrete	45.00/cubic yard
Wallpaper	18.00/roll
Roofing plywood	8.85 per 4′ × 8′ sheet

To find costs for materials and services, you need to find the area or volume of the space being built. You may need to change the units of a dimension to make them consistent.

Sample Problem

How many cubic yards of concrete are needed to pour a floor 81 feet long, 42 feet wide, and 4 inches thick?

Solution $V = lwh$

$= 81 \times 42 \times \frac{1}{3}\text{ ft}^3$ Express 4 inches as $\frac{1}{3}$ foot. Replace the l with 81, w with 42, and h with $\frac{1}{3}$.

$= 1{,}134\text{ ft}^3$

$= \frac{1{,}134}{27}\text{ yd}^3$ There are 27 ft^3 in one yd^3. To change cubic feet into cubic yards, divide by 27.

$= 42\text{ yd}^3$

The volume is 42 yd^3.

Problems

Use the data in the table above to solve.

1. An excavator digs a hole 34 feet by 120 feet by 4 feet for the foundation of a building. How many cubic yards of earth are moved? What is the cost?

2. What is the cost for a concrete floor 56 ft long, 40 ft wide, and 4 in thick?

3. How many cubic yards of concrete are needed for a wall 48 inches high, 125 feet long and 10 inches thick? How much will the concrete cost?

Use this figure for Exercises 4 and 5.

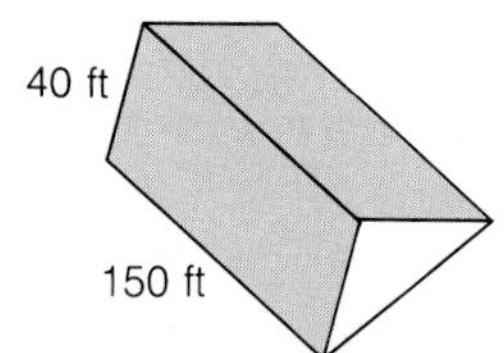

4. A roof is 40 feet from edge to peak and 150 feet long. What is the area of the roof (the shaded region on both sides)?

5. How much will the plywood for the roof in Problem 4 cost?

6. Wallpaper comes in rolls 20 inches wide and 24 feet long. How much will the wallpaper cost for a wall 8 feet high by 12 feet wide? The wall has no windows or doors.

7. Estimate the cost of carpeting a two-story house with a rectangular foundation that measures 30 feet by 42 feet.

8. **Data Search** Find the cost of a gallon of interior paint at a store near your school. Find out how many square feet a gallon covers and estimate the cost of the paint needed for two coats of paint on the walls of your classroom.

What's Your Decision?

The Malone family wants to carpet a room that is shaped as shown. The carpet salesman says they need to order 30 square yards. At \$12/yd this would cost them \$360. They find a pre-cut carpet piece that is 12 ft by 19 ft for \$250. Should the Malones buy the pre-cut piece and save \$110, or order the 30 square yards? Why?

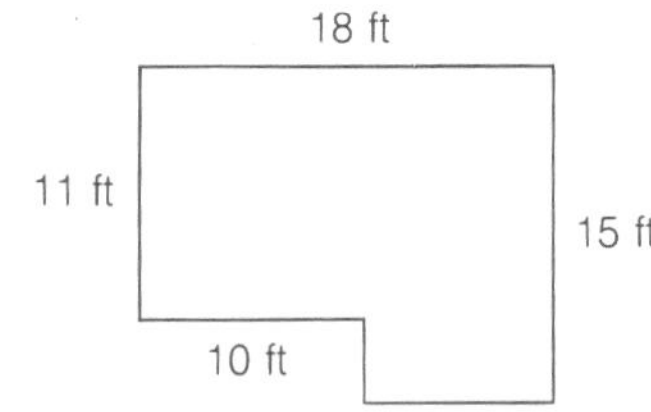

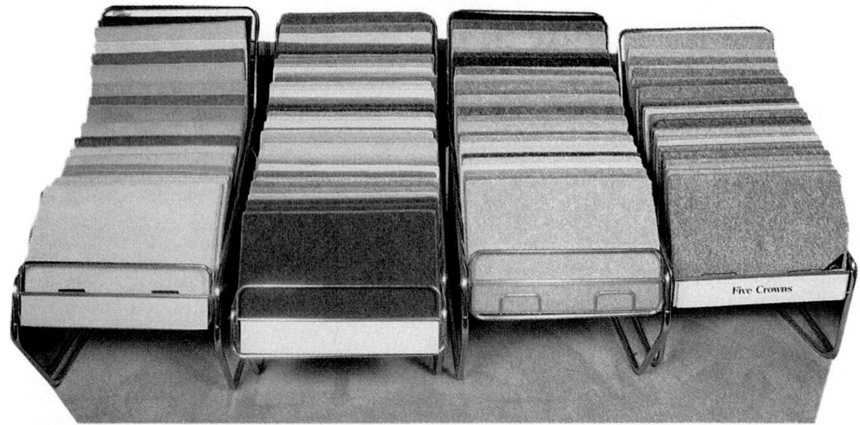

13-8 Volume of Pyramids and Cones

Objective To use formulas to find the volumes of pyramids and cones.

Understand the Ideas

A **pyramid** has a polygon as a base and triangular sides. A **cone** has one circular base. The height of a pyramid or a cone is the perpendicular distance from its vertex to its base.

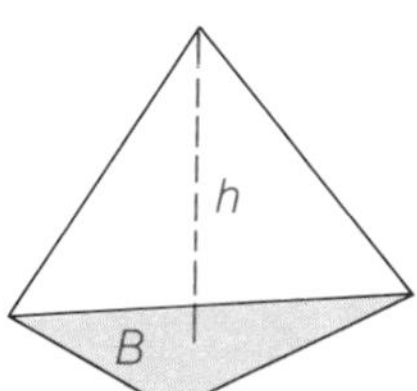

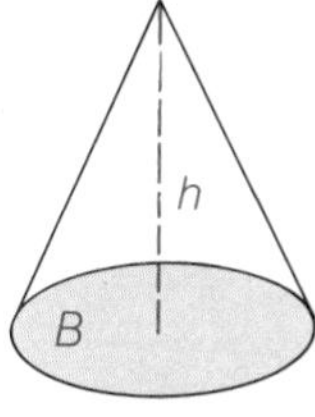

Three cones fill a cylinder.

The volume of a cone or a pyramid can be found by using the same formula.

Formula **Volume of a Pyramid or Cone**

The volume of a pyramid or a cone is equal to one-third the area of the base times the height.

$$V = \frac{1}{3}Bh$$

Example

Find the volume of a cone with radius 4 cm and height 8 cm.

Solution $V = \frac{1}{3}Bh$ — The volume of a cone is $\frac{1}{3}$ the area of the base times the height.

$\approx \frac{1}{3} \times 3.14 \times 4^2 \times 8$ — The area of the base is πr^2. Substitute 3.14 for π and 4 for r. Substitute 8 for h.

$= \frac{401.92}{3}$

$= 133.97$

The volume is 133.97 cm^3.

Try This Find the volume of a pyramid or cone with the base area or radius and the height given.

a. $B = 27 \text{ cm}^2, h = 22 \text{ cm}$ **b.** $r = 6 \text{ m}, h = 5 \text{ m}$

Class Exercises

Discuss the Ideas

Is the statement true or false? If false, explain why.

1. A cube is a pyramid.
2. The volume of a cone is $\frac{1}{3}$ the area of the base times the height.
3. Some pyramids have rectangular sides.
4. All pyramids have round bases.

Exercises

Practice and Apply

Find the volume of each figure.

1.

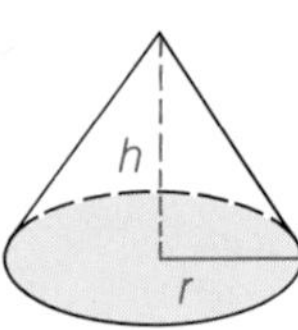

$r = 5$ cm
$h = 8$ cm

2.

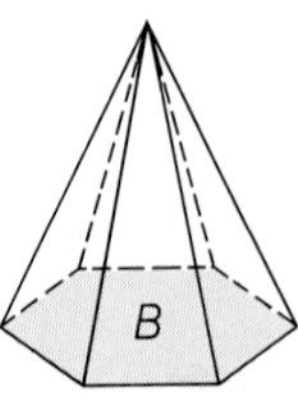

$B = 14$ cm^2
$h = 10$ cm

3.

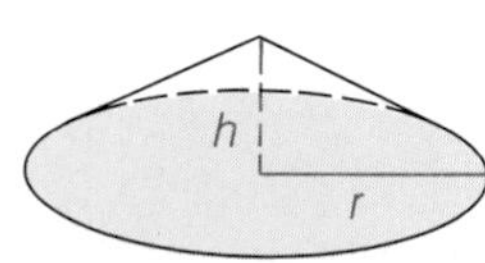

$r = 9$ cm
$h = 4$ cm

4.

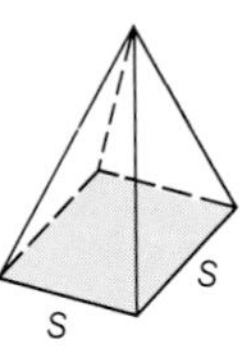

$s = 9$ cm
$h = 12$ cm

5.

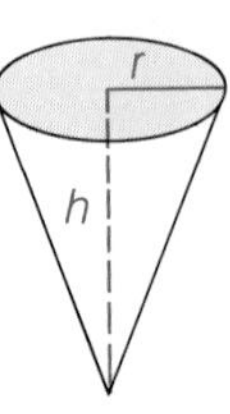

$r = 4$ in
$h = 9$ in

6.

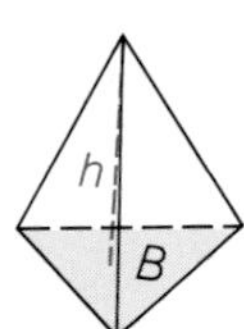

$B = 9$ cm^2
$h = 5$ cm

Find the volume of a cone with the radius and height given. Round your answer to the nearest tenth.

7. $r = 11$ cm, $h = 8$ cm
8. $r = 12$ m, $h = 4$ m
9. $r = 5$ dm, $h = 9$ dm
10. $r = 4$ cm, $h = 8$ cm

Find the volume of a pyramid with the base area and height given. Round your answer to the nearest tenth.

11. $B = 25$ cm^2, $h = 19$ cm
12. $B = 96$ m^2, $h = 23$ m
13. $B = 47$ m^2, $h = 12$ m
14. $B = 12$ cm^2, $h = 5$ cm

15. Find the approximate volume of the tip of this crayon.

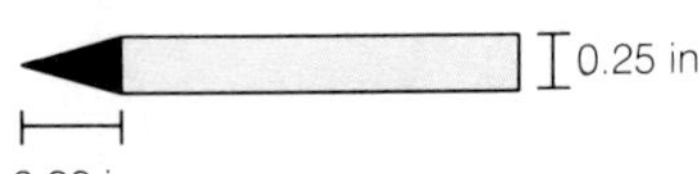

16. This machine piece has the shape of a cylinder with a cone cut into one base as shown. What is the volume of the finished machine piece?

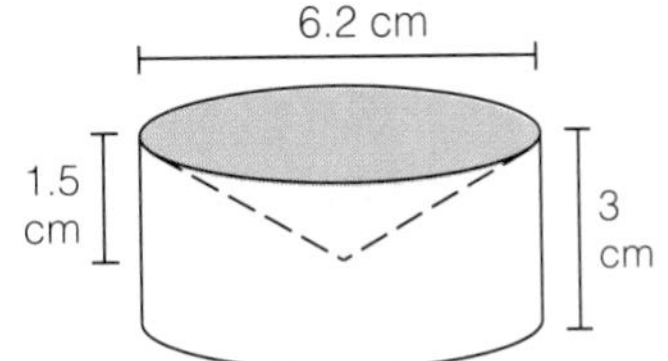

Extend and Apply

In the table below, B represents the area of the base, h the height, and V the volume of a pyramid. Find the unknown variable in each column.

	17.	**18.**	**19.**	**20.**	**21.**	**22.**	**23.**
Base area B	12π	35	?	?	36	5.3	?
height h	6	?	12	32	12	?	4.5
volume V	?	105	288	160π	?	63.6	10.35

24. What is the height of a prism if the volume is 162 m^3 and the area of the base is 9 m^2?

25. A cone and a cylinder have the same base. If the cone's height is six times the cylinder's height, how much greater is the volume of the cone?

Use the formula $V = \frac{4}{3}\pi r^3$ to find the **volume of a sphere** with the radius given. Give your answers in terms of π.

26. $r = 8$ cm **27.** $r = 6$ cm **28.** $r = 7$ m **29.** $r = 5.1$ m

Use Mathematical Reasoning

These spheres are in pyramid-shaped stacks. Find the pattern and give the next three numbers.

30.

1

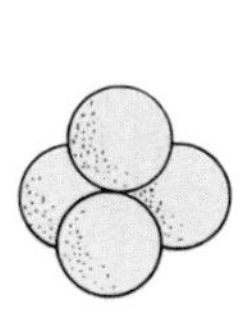

4

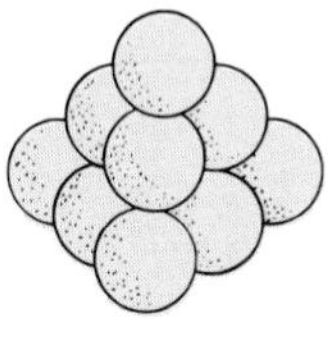

10

31.

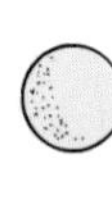

1

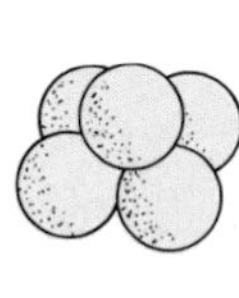

5

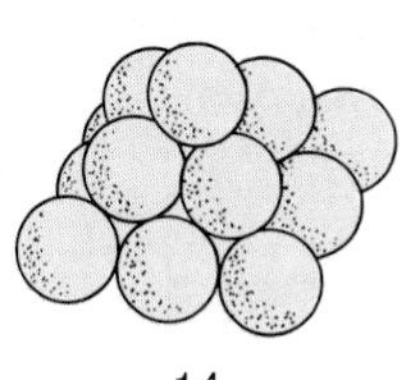

14

Mixed Review

Write as a decimal. **32.** 8% **33.** 135% **34.** 420% **35.** 19.4%

Write in scientific notation. **36.** 16,500 **37.** 0.00016 **38.** 42,300,000

Solve and check. **39.** $y \div \left(-\frac{3}{4}\right) = \frac{3}{2}$ **40.** $\frac{4}{5}c = \frac{1}{20}$

13-9 Surface Area

Objective To find the surface areas of prisms and cylinders.

Application

When considering the design of a new container, a manufacturer needs to consider both the volume of the container and the amount of material needed to make the container. A manufacturer is considering how much tin it will take to make a cylindrical container with an 8 cm radius and a height of 9 cm. (See Example 1.)

Understand the Ideas

The cylinder and prism shown below have been cut apart and laid flat. The surface area of each is equal to the area of the corresponding flat regions. The shaded regions are the bases of each figure.

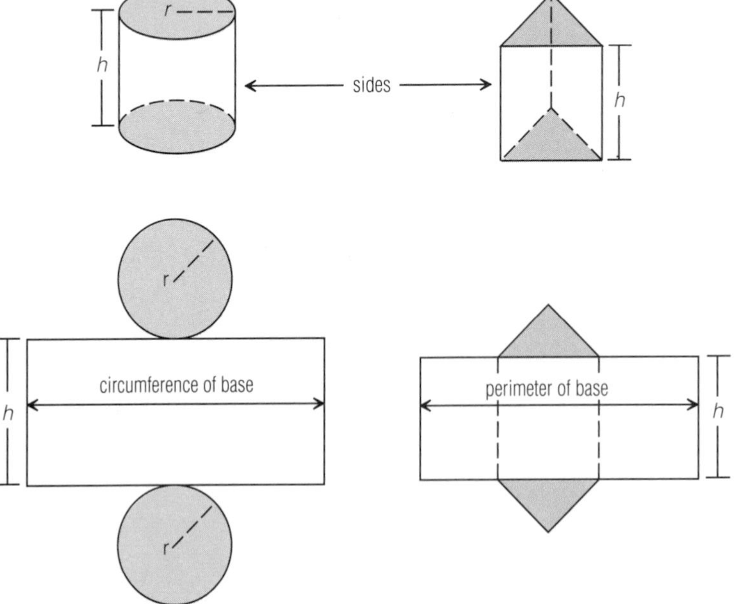

For a prism or a cylinder, surface area is equal to the area of the bases plus the area of the sides.

Example 1

Find the surface area of a cylindrical container described in the **application**. Use 3.14 for π.

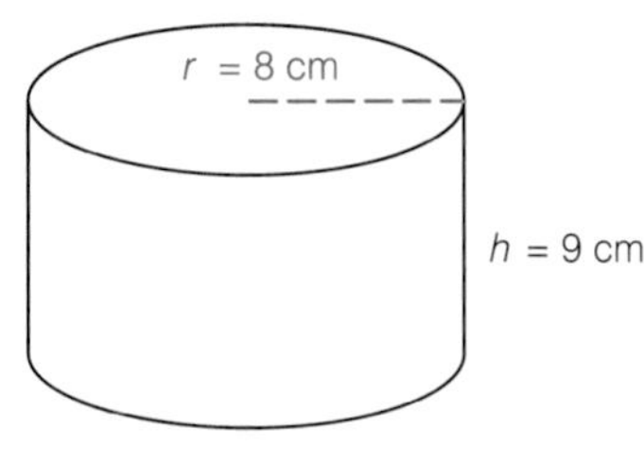

Solution Area of one base $= \pi 8^2$
$\approx 3.14 \times 64$
≈ 200.96

Area of sides $=$ circumference of base $\times$ height
$= 2\pi \times 8 \times 9 \approx 2 \times 3.14 \times 8 \times 9 \approx 452.16$

Surface area $=$ area of bases $+$ area of sides
$\approx 2 \times 200.96\ \text{cm}^2 + 452.16\ \text{cm}^2 \approx 854.08\ \text{cm}^2$

Try This Find the surface area of a cylinder with the radius and height given.

a. $r = 5$ cm, $h = 12$ cm **b.** $r = 8$ m, $h = 15$ m

Example 2

Find the surface area of the rectangular prism at right.

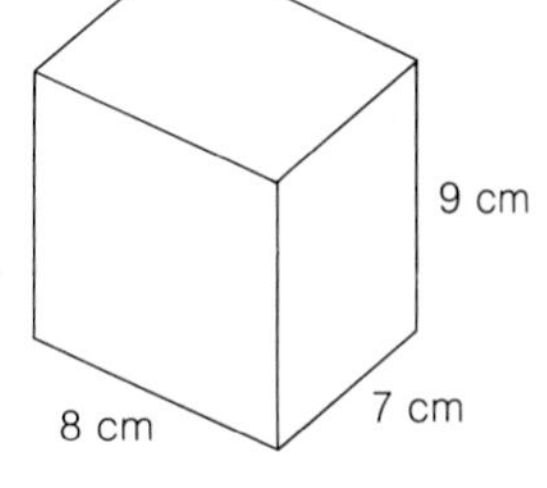

Solution

Area of one base $= 8 \times 7 = 56$
Area of sides $=$ (perimeter of base) $\times 9$
$= 30 \times 9$
$= 270$

Surface area $=$ area of the bases $+$ area of the sides
$= 2 \times 56\ \text{cm}^2 + 270\ \text{cm}^2 = 382\ \text{cm}^2$

Try This **c.** Find the surface area of the prism at right.

20 cm
12 cm
13 cm
21 cm
30 cm

Class Exercises

Give the height and the perimeter or circumference (in terms of π) of the base for each figure.

1.

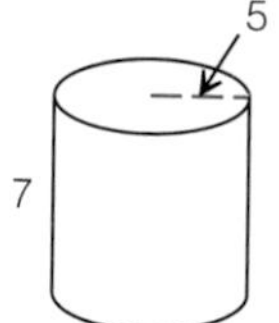

2.

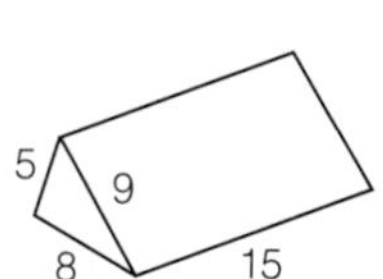

3.

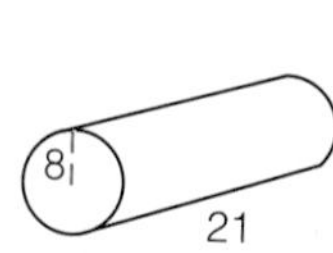

4.

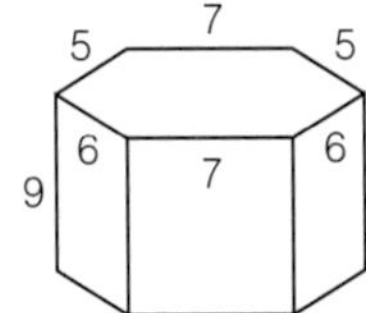

Discuss the Ideas

5. Discuss why knowing the perimeter or circumference of the base of a prism or cylinder is necessary to find the surface area of the solid.

Exercises

Practice and Apply

Find the surface area of each cylinder.

1. 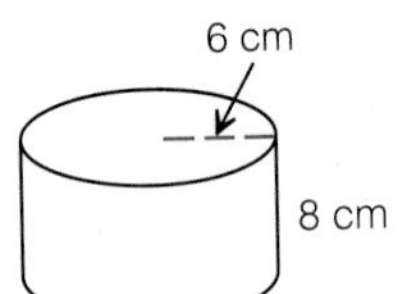

2. 5 cm, 11 cm

3. 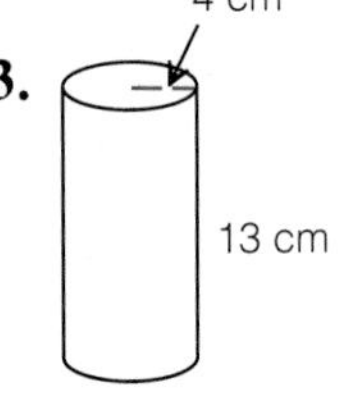

4. 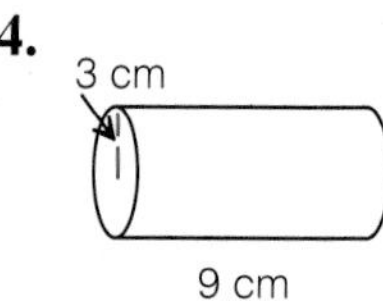

Find the surface area of a cylinder with the radius and height given.

5. $r = 8$ cm, $h = 12$ cm
6. $r = 3$ cm, $h = 5$ cm
7. $r = 90$ cm, $h = 3$ m
8. $r = 2.1$ m, $h = 83$ cm
9. $r = 5$ dm, $h = 9$ dm
10. $r = 11$ cm, $h = 25$ cm
11. $r = 12$ m, $h = 30$ m
12. $r = 8$ cm, $h = 4$ cm
13. A cylindrical tank with height 5 feet has a radius of 2 feet. What is its surface area?
14. What is the surface area of the tank in Exercise 13 in square yards?

Find the surface area of each prism.

15. 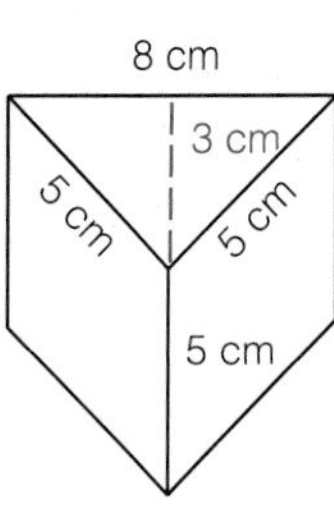

16. 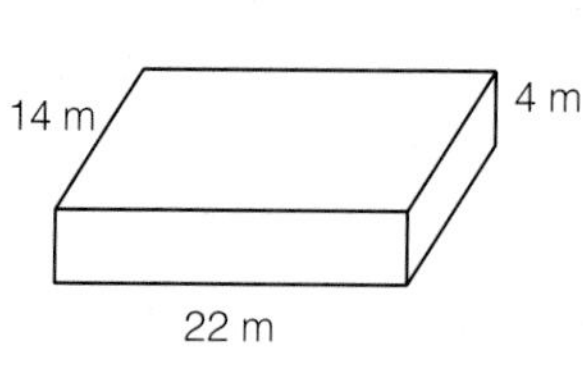

17. 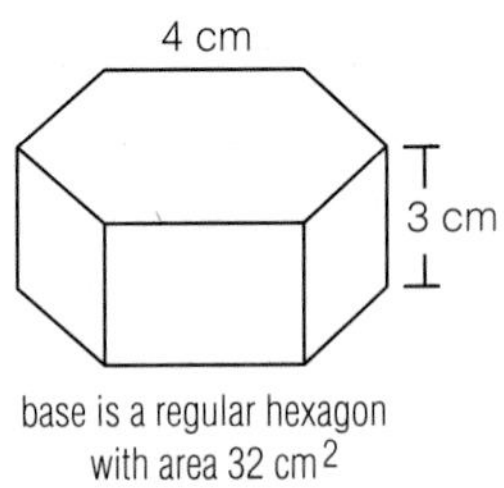

base is a regular hexagon with area 32 cm^2

Extend and Apply

18. A cylinder with height 8 cm has a volume of 288π cm^3. What is its surface area?
19. A cylinder with radius 16 cm has a volume of $2{,}560\pi$ cm^3. What is its surface area?
20. A prism with a square base has a height of 9 m and a volume of 576 m^3. What is its surface area?

The surface area of a sphere is equal to 4π times the radius squared. The formula is $A = 4\pi r^2$. Use this formula for Exercises 21–22.

21. A spherical satellite that is 2 m in diameter is covered with a thin layer of a reflective material. What is its surface area?

22. A spherical storage tank with a 30-foot radius is to be painted. If the paint covers 350 square feet per gallon, how many gallons of paint are needed?

Use Mathematical Reasoning

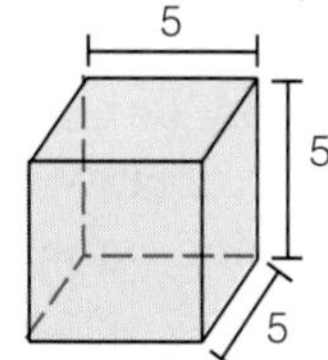

23. The hollow cube at right has a removable top and is to be painted on all surfaces, inside and out. If each edge is 5 feet long, how many square feet of surface will be painted?

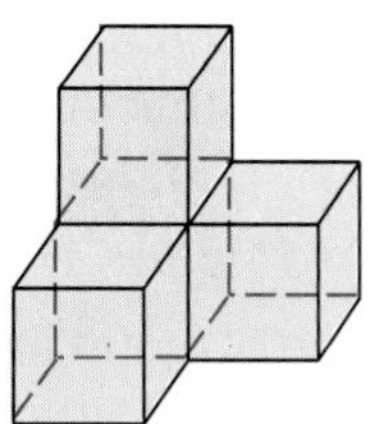

24. The solid at right is made up of 4 cubes glued together. If an edge of each cube is 2 feet, how many square feet of surface can be painted?

Mixed Review

Write as a fraction in lowest terms. **25.** 36% **26.** 65% **27.** 26%

28. 11 is 25% of what number? **29.** 12 is 150% of what number?

Solve and check. **30.** $24c + 17 = 65$ **31.** $14 = -r + 2$

Computer Activity

Almost Fresh Canning Company needs a can with the maximum volume possible given its surface area. There is a special requirement that the perimeter of the flattened label be 14 inches. The program below lists possible lengths and widths for the label.

```
10 REM MAXIMUM VOLUME FOR CAN
20 PRINT "H", "W", "VOLUME"
30 FOR H=1 TO 4 STEP 1
40 LET W=7-H
50 LET VOLUME=H*W^2/(4*3.14)
60 PRINT H, W, VOLUME
70 NEXT H
80 END
```

1. Run the program to find the maximum volume.

2. Find a more accurate answer by changing line 30 to

```
30 FOR H=1 TO 4 STEP .5
```

Critical Thinking

Spatial Relationship Decisions

Objective: To make spatial relationship decisions using critical thinking.

Critical Thinking is a process of making decisions to help you decide what to believe or do. Some questions that may help you use this process are given on page 328. Try your critical thinking skills in the following activity.

Group Activity A group of students had a disagreement about surface area and volume. Some of the statements made about a comparison between units of surface area and volume were these:

"Two figures with the same volume can't have different surface areas."
"Two figures with the same surface area can't have different volumes."

Work in a group and use a set of cubes to investigate these two statements. Write a paragraph summarizing your investigation.

Apply Critical Thinking

Work together to make decisions in each of the following situations. Write an explanation of how you made the decision and why you think it is correct. Assume that the cubes must be in contact by at least one face. Use a calculator if helpful.

1. How can you increase the surface area of this solid by two square units by moving one cube to a different position?
2. How can you make a solid whose volume is 6 cubic units and whose surface area is the same as the surface area of the solid shown at the right?
3. Roland said that the ratio of the number of units of surface area to the number of units of volume of this cube is 2 to 1. Do you agree? Why or why not?
4. Fatima said, "I can find a cube for which the ratio of the number of volume units to the number of surface area units is 2 to 1." Do you agree with Fatima? Why or why not?
5. Emiko said, "I can find a cube for which the ratio of the number of volume units to the number of surface area units is more than 100 to 1." Do you believe that she could do this? Why or why not?

Practice Solving Problems

Objective To solve nonroutine problems, using combinations of strategies.

Most problems are solved by some combination of strategies. Notice how strategies are used in the sample problem below.

Sample Problem
Amanda wants to lay out a patio in a design like the one shown below. She has 50 bricks to use. How many bricks should she place in the middle row to use the greatest number of bricks?

Solution

To solve, you can first **simplify the problem** to find the total number of bricks used if 1 brick is in the middle row, then the total with 2 bricks in the middle row, 3 bricks in the middle row, and so on. You can **draw a diagram** to determine the number of bricks used each time. You can **make a table** to record this information, and then **look for a pattern** to determine the solution.

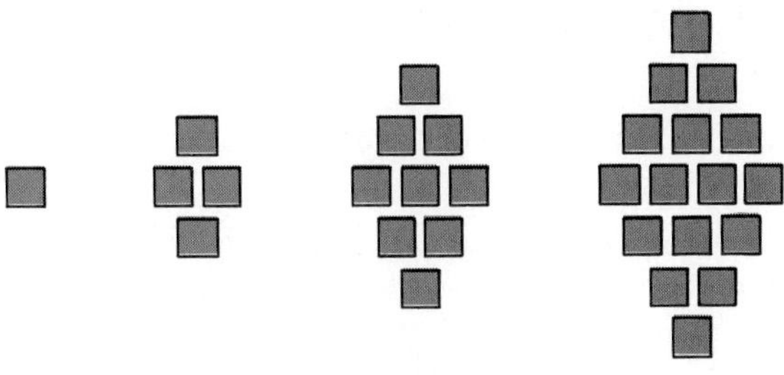

Number in Middle Row	1	2	3	4	5	6	7
Total Number of Bricks Used	1	4	9	16	25	36	49

The total number of bricks used is equal to the square of the number in the middle row. If there were 7 in the middle row, 49 bricks would be used in all.

To use the greatest number of bricks, Amanda should place 7 bricks in the middle row.

Problem-Solving Strategies

Choose the Operations	Make a Table	Make an Organized List
Guess, Check, Revise	Look for a Pattern	Use Logical Reasoning
Draw a Diagram	Write an Equation	Work Backward
	Simplify the Problem	

Problems

1. A box holding 40 pencils weighs 135 g. The same box holding 20 of the same pencils weighs 75 g. What is the weight of the box?

2. In how many different ways can a football team score 18 points?
touchdown = 6 points field goal = 3 points
point after a touchdown = 1 point safety = 2 points

3. Jane, Al, and Sally were selling school sweatshirts to raise money for a class trip. Al sold one fewer shirt than Jane, and Sally sold half as many shirts as Jane. Together the three sold 89 shirts. How many did each sell?

4. Ms. Davies gave a math quiz with 20 questions. She gave two points for each correct answer and subtracted three points for each incorrect answer. Yolanda answered all 20 questions and got a score of 0. How many did she get right and how many did she get wrong?

5. A restaurant has two types of tables. One type seats four people and one type seats six. One night, 114 people were eating at 24 tables in the restaurant, and no table with people had empty seats. How many tables of each type were used?

Group Decision Making

6. Work in a group. Discuss and decide.

Situation You are refinishing an old trunk that is 15 inches high, 16 inches wide, and 30 inches long. You have decided to line the inside of the trunk by gluing fabric to the inside surfaces. You want to find the cost of the project.

Guidelines for Planning

- **Formulate Problems** you will need to solve.
- Discuss **Assumptions** you will make and **Data** you will need.

a. What decision or decisions do you need to make in this situation?

b. Formulate problems you need to solve to make the decision(s).

c. List any assumptions you need to make to arrive at a decision.

d. What data, if any, do you need to collect to make a decision?

e. Write a paragraph summarizing what your group did, what decisions you made, and why.

Extend Key Ideas

Pick's Formula for Area

The area of polygon *ABCDE* can be found by dividing it as shown and adding together the areas of the smaller regions.

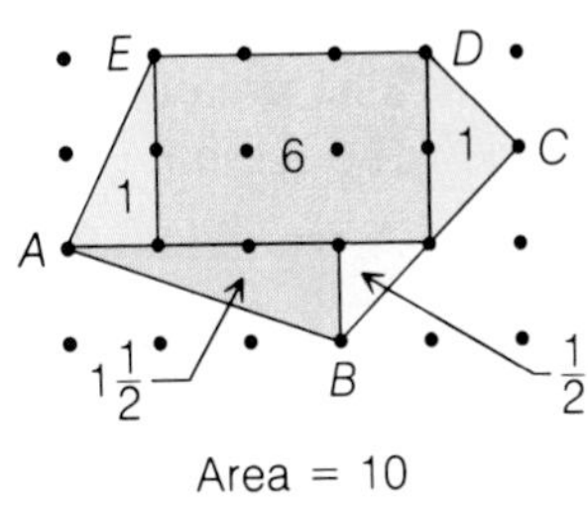

Another way to find the area of this polygon is to use Pick's Formula. The formula uses the number of dots on the boundary (***b***) and the number of dots in the interior (***i***) of the polygon.

The shaded part of the table below has been filled in for polygon *ABCDE*.

Polygon	*b*	*i*	$\frac{b}{2} + i$	Area
ABCDE	8	7	11	10
Exercise 1	10	?	?	?
Exercise 2	?	?	9	?
Exercise 3	?	?	?	5

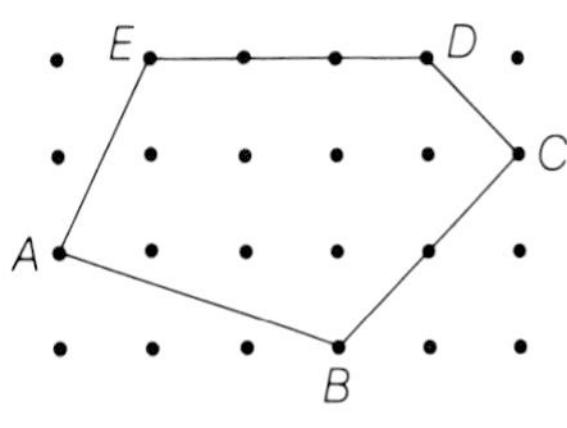

Complete the table above for the polygons in Exercises 1–3 and discover Pick's Formula.

1.

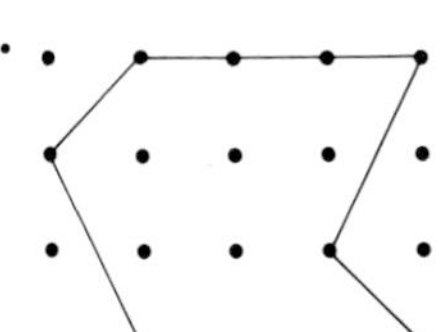

2.

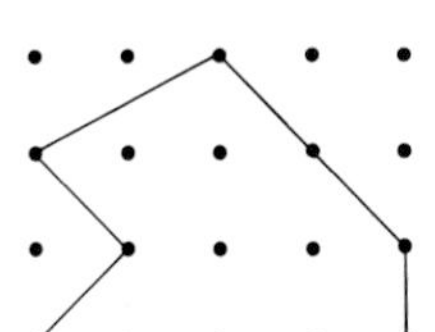

3.

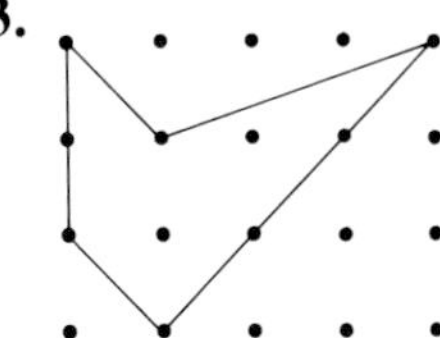

Use Pick's Formula to find the areas of each.

4.

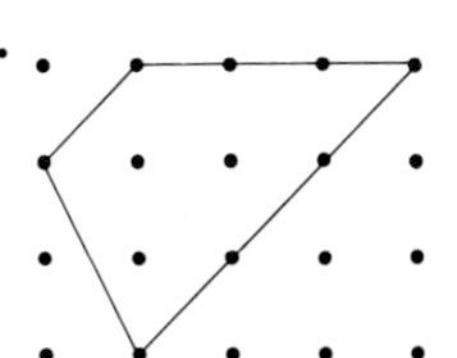

5.

Chapter 13 Review/Test

Understanding

True or false?

13-1 **1.** The area of a polygon is the number of unit squares needed to cover the region.

13-2 **2.** A triangle has exactly 1 base and 1 height.

13-3 **3.** You can find the area of a circle if you know its radius.

13-6 **4.** The volume of a solid is equal to the number of unit cubes needed to fill the solid.

13-8 **5.** A pyramid and a cone with the same base area and the same height will always have the same volume.

13-9 **6.** The volume and surface area of a solid are always equal.

Skill

13-1 Find the area of each figure. Use 3.14 for π or use a calculator.

13-2

13-3 **7.** Rectangle with length 7 cm, width 36 cm.

13-4 **8.** Triangle with base 34 m, height 8 m.

9. Parallelogram with base = 146 mm, height = 36 mm.

10. Trapezoid with bases 7 m and 18 m long and a height of 12 m.

11. Find the area of a circle with radius 4 meters.

12. Find the area of the figure at the right.

13-6 Find the volume. Use 3.14 for π or use a calculator.

13-8

13-9 **13.** A cone with a radius of 7 inches and a height of 15 inches.

14. A pyramid with a base area of 80 m^2 and a height of 22 m.

15. Find the surface area of a cylinder with radius 6 ft and height 24 ft.

16. Find the volume of this cylinder.

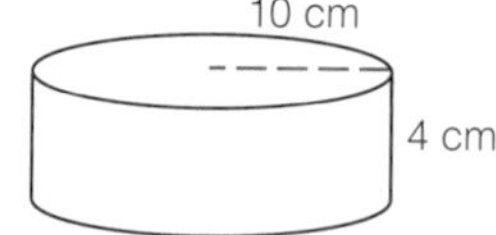

13-6 13-7 Application

17. If concrete costs \$55 per cubic yard, how much will it cost for concrete for a foundation 48 ft long, 30 ft wide, and 8 in. thick?

18. A cereal box is 19 cm wide, 6 cm deep, and 28 cm high. What is the volume of the cereal box?

19. A farmer's silo is 15 feet in diameter and 40 feet high. If silage weighs two tons per cubic yard, how many tons of silage does the silo hold?

Geometry Review

Use the figure at right for Exercises 1–5.

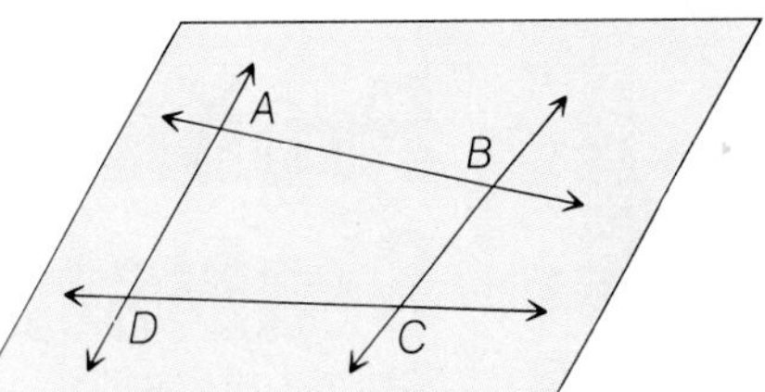

1. Name a point.

2. Name a line.

3. Name a plane.

4. Name a segment that includes point B.

5. Name a ray with vertex A.

Classify each triangle by the measures of its angles and the lengths of its sides.

6. $\triangle RST$ has all 60 degree angles and all sides are equal in length.

7. $\triangle LMN$ has one right angle and two sides equal in length.

8. Use the SAS, SSS, or ASA property to show that the pair of triangles is congruent.

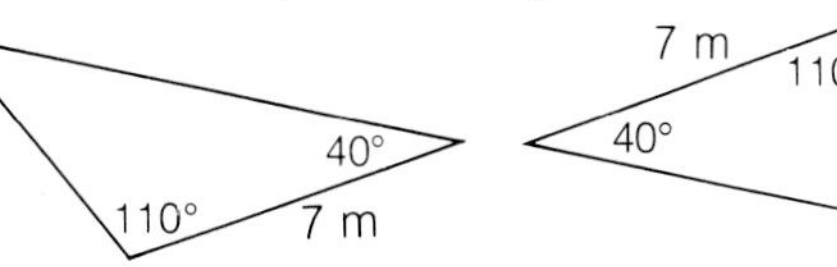

Find the area of each quadrilateral.

9. Parallelogram with base = 14.4 m, height = 6.8 m

10. Trapezoid with $b_1 = 16$ cm, $b_2 = 12$ cm, $h = 7$ cm

Find the area of each circle. Use 3.14 for π.

11. $r = 9$ m

12. $d = 3.4$ km

Find the volume of the prism or cylinder. Use 3.14 for π.

13.

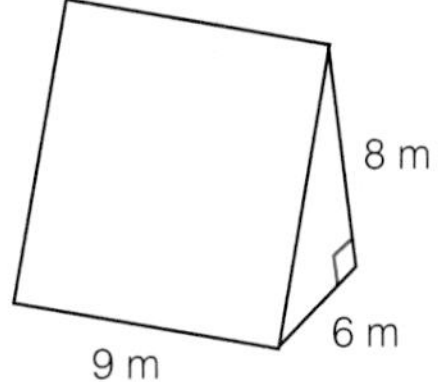

14.

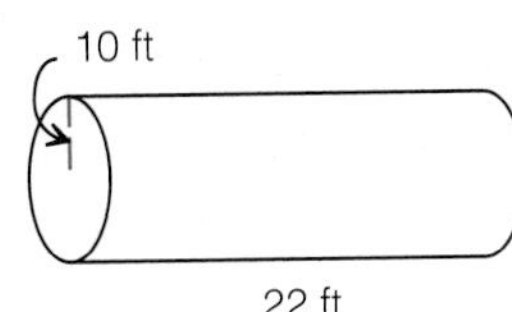

15. How many cubic yards of concrete are needed for a patio 42 feet long, 27 feet wide and 6 inches thick?

Find the volume. Use 3.14 for π.

16. A cone with a radius of 11 feet and a height of 4 feet.

17. A pyramid with a base area of 32 dm^2 and a height of 16 dm.

Find the surface area. Use 3.14 for π.

18. A cylinder with a radius of 8 cm and a height of 30 cm.

14 Probability, Statistics, and Graphs

Dana, Leona, Grace, and Lydia are hiking through the mountains. How many different ways can these hikers be arranged in a single line?

14-1 Counting Principle

Objective To use diagrams and the counting principle to find the total number of outcomes of an event.

Application

The social committee is planning the menu for the awards banquet. Sean was wondering how many different ways the committee can choose one main dish, one vegetable, and one dessert (See Example, p. 488).

Understand the Ideas

The ballot below shows one possible **outcome** of an election. One way to show all possible outcomes is to make a tree diagram as shown below. Each choice for president can be matched with either of two choices for vice-president. Each pairing of president and vice-president can be matched with either of two choices of secretary. Each "branch" shows a possible outcome.

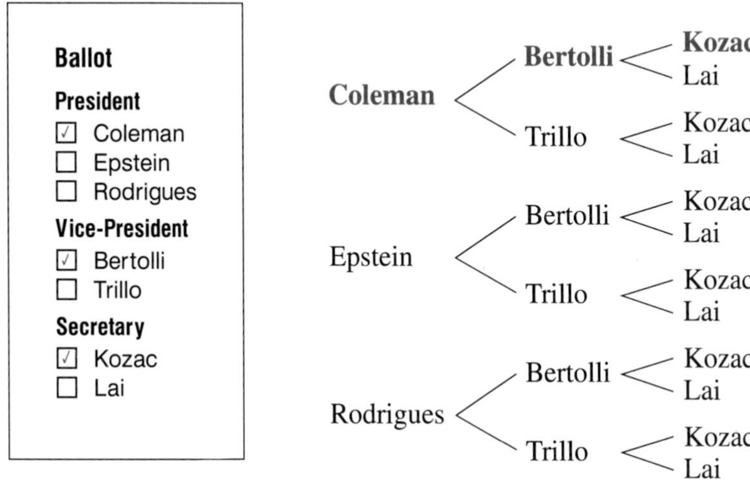

This election has 12 possible outcomes.

Since there are three choices for president, two choices for vice-president, and two choices for secretary, there are $3 \times 2 \times 2 = 12$ possible outcomes for the election. When you multiply to find the total number of outcomes, you are using the **Counting Principle.**

Rule **Counting Principle**

To find the total number of choices for an event, multiply the number of choices for each part.

Example

Suppose there were four choices each for the main dish and the vegetable, and three choices for dessert in the **application.** Use the Counting Principle to find the total number of choices possible.

Solution

$4 \times 4 \times 3 = 48$ The total is the product of the number of choices for each course.

The social committee has 48 choices for the dinner menu.

Try This Use the Counting Principle to solve.

a. Reggie needs to buy glasses. He can choose from four different styles for the frames and three tints for the lenses. How many different kinds of glasses could Reggie choose from?

Class Exercises

Use the tree diagram showing the total possible outcomes for a Frozen Yogurt Special to answer the question.

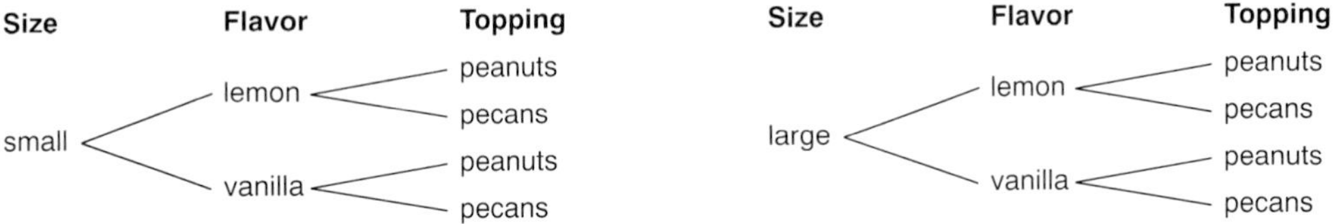

1. How many choices are there for: size? yogurt flavor? topping? a small yogurt special? a large yogurt special? a yogurt special?

Discuss the Ideas

2. When is the Counting Principle a better way to solve a problem than drawing a tree diagram? Give examples to justify your answer.

Exercises

Practice and Apply

Use the counting principle to find the total number of outcomes.

1. Select one sandwich and one drink. Sandwiches: hamburger, chicken, cheese. Drinks: juice, milk, tea.

2. Select one shirt and one tie. Shirts: white, blue, yellow, cream. Ties: striped, light blue, navy.
3. Select one club and one sport. Clubs: debate, drama, art, math. Sports: tennis, golf, volleyball.
4. Select one section of the airplane and one seat location. Sections: first class, business, coach. Locations: window, middle, aisle.
5. There are three choices for watch styles (digital, standard, Roman numerals) and there are four choices for watchbands (metal, leather, canvas, plastic). How many different choices are there for a watch?

6. A theatre has two levels (main floor, balcony) and three sections in each level (front, middle, back). How many sections are there in this theater?
7. A lineman on a football team must select one digit from among 5, 6, 7, 8, and 9 for the first digit on his jersey and one digit from among 0 through 9 for the second digit on his jersey. How many choices for two-digit numbers does he have?
8. A decorator gave Martin a choice of three wall colors and five rug colors for his room. How many choices does he have if he picks one wall color and one rug color?
9. How many different choices for a telephone are possible?
   Style: wall, desk, antique   Color: grey, white, tan, black, brown   Format: touch-tone, rotary
10. How many choices for hamburgers do you have if you are allowed to have only one condiment?
    Size: single, double, triple   Bun: whole wheat, sesame seed   Condiments: mushrooms, pickles, onions, lettuce, cheese

Extend and Apply

11. How many area codes are possible if the first digit cannot be a nine, a zero, or a one?
12. The winners of each conference in the National Basketball Association play to determine the champion. There are 13 teams in the Eastern Conference and 14 teams in the Western Conference. How many pairings are possible for the championship?

13. There are two groups participating in a school election. Each group will select a candidate for president and a candidate for vice-president from the lists below. The selected candidates will go on the final ballot. How many ways can the final ballot be filled?

Final Ballot	
The Dinosaurs Final Candidates	
President	Vice President
? ? ?	? ? ?
The Asteroids Final Candidates	
President	Vice President
? ? ?	? ? ?

The Dinosaurs	
President	Vice President
Fred	Betty
Wilma	Barney
Homer	

The Asteroids	
President	Vice President
George	Elroy
Judy	Bart
Jane	Marge

Use Mathematical Reasoning

14. Ms. Ortega wants a one-way airline ticket from Chicago to San Francisco with a stop in Denver. She wants a minimum of one hour and a maximum of three hours between flights. How many choices for pairs of flights does she have?

Flight Number	CHICAGO TO DENVER Depart	Arrive
#63	7:05 a.m.	8:20 a.m.
#1122	8:15	9:30
#34	10:10	11:25
#125	12:01 p.m.	1:16 p.m.
#456	1:40	2:55

Flight Number	DENVER TO SAN FRANCISCO Depart	Arrive
#1156	7:50 a.m.	8:51 a.m.
#92	8:50	9:51
#8	9:50	10:51
#54	12:50 p.m.	1:51 p.m.
#32	1:50	3:30

Mixed Review

Solve and check. **15.** $6(2m + 3) = 78$ **16.** $4c + 2c = 5c + 2$

What percent of 50 is: **17.** 40? **18.** 75? **19.** 15?

Look for patterns to complete the table.

20.

10	14	18	22	26	x
8	12	16			

21.

6	9	12	15	18	n
12	18	24			

14-2 Permutations

Objective To find the number of permutations of *n* objects and the number of permutations of *n* objects taken *r* at a time.

Explore

Use pieces of paper to represent books, and find how many ways these books can be arranged on a shelf side-by-side. Record your results.

2 books 3 books 4 books

Can you find a rule that tells the number of arrangements possible for any number of books? [Hint: Think about the Counting Principle.]

Understand the Ideas

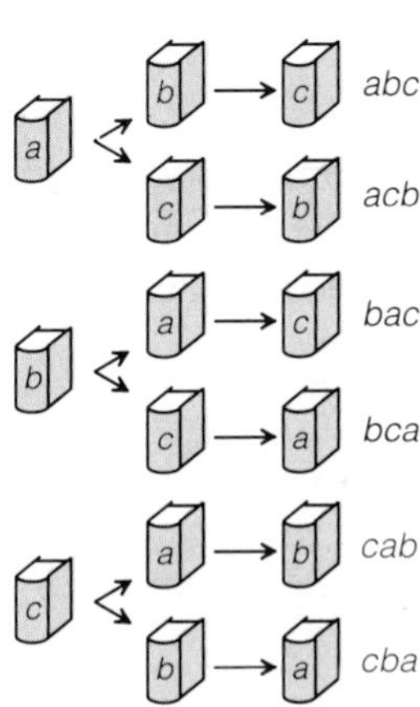

A **permutation** is an arrangement of objects in a particular order. The tree diagram at right shows permutations of 3 books. Any of the three books can be chosen for the first position. Either of the two books left can be chosen for the second position. One book is left for the third position. Using the Counting Principle, there are $3 \times 2 \times 1 = 6$ permutations of the books. The product $3 \times 2 \times 1$ can be written as **3!** This is read as **"3 factorial."**

Rule Permutations

To find the number of permutations of n objects, find the product of the numbers 1 through n.

$$n! = n \times (n - 1) \times \ldots \times 3 \times 2 \times 1$$

Example 1

There are four events in a contest between two summer camps. Campers will not go through the events in the same order. The events are the 100-meter sprint, high jump, cross country, and 50-meter swim. How many permutations of these events are possible?

Solution

$4! = 4 \times 3 \times 2 \times 1$ Since there are 4 events, the number of permutations is equal to 4 factorial.
$\quad = 24$

There are 24 possible permutations of these events.

Try This

a. Five campers are running in the first heat of the 100-meter sprint. How many different results are possible, assuming no ties?

b. How many 3-digit race numbers are possible if no digit can be repeated, using the numbers 3, 4, and 5?

The list at right shows the arrangements of two-digit numbers that can be made from the numbers 2, 4, 6, and 8, without repeating the same digit. The list shows all the permutations of two-digit numbers with 2 as the first digit, then the permutations with 4 as the first digit, and so on. There are four choices for the first digit. Then, after the first digit is chosen, there are three choices for the second digit. Using the Counting Principle, $4 \times 3 = 12$ two-digit numbers can be made.

24	**26**	**28**
42	**46**	**48**
62	**64**	**68**
82	**84**	**86**

Example 2

Five campers swam in each heat of the 50-meter swim, with the top three swimmers advancing. In how many ways could first, second, and third place be won for each heat?

Solution

$5 \times 4 \times 3 = 60$ There are 5 choices for first place, 4 choices for second, and 3 choices for third. Multiply to find the number of permutations.

There are 60 possible finishing orders.

Try This

c. Four people applied for two jobs. In how many ways could the jobs be filled, assuming the same person cannot fill both jobs?

Class Exercises

Use $n! = n \times (n - 1) \times \ldots \times 3 \times 2 \times 1$ to restate each expression.

1. 5! **2.** 6! **3.** 11!

4. $1 \times 2 \times 3 \times 4 \times 5 \times 6 \times 7$

5. $1 \times 2 \times 3 \times \ldots \times 9 \times 10$

6. $1 \times 2 \times 3 \times \ldots \times 19 \times 20$

Discuss the Ideas

7. Tell which of these situations is asking for the number of permutations. Explain. Do not solve.

- **a.** How many ways can you select 3 books off of a list of 5 books?
- **b.** Five cars are in a race. How many finishing orders are possible?

Exercises

Practice and Apply

Find the number of permutations.

1. In how many ways can five paintings be arranged in a straight line on a wall?
2. There are six finalists in an archery contest. Ribbons will be awarded for each place. How many different finishing orders are possible?
3. Five wires need to be connected to a machine, but the mechanic forgot the order. How many different orders are possible for connecting these wires?
4. In how many ways can you arrange an Ace, a King, and a Queen?
5. How many different scheduling orders are possible for your four major classes: math, history, English, and art?
6. How many ways can Huey, Dewey, and Louie sit in a row?
7. Eight students ran in a marathon. How many different finishing orders are possible for first, second, and third places, with no ties?
8. How many 3-song arrangements can be made from a list of 7 songs?
9. How many ways can president, vice-president, and secretary be selected from a list of six candidates?
10. A band, a float, and an antique car are in a parade. In how many ways can they be lined up in the parade?

Extend and Apply

11. How many 2-digit track jersey numbers can be made from 3, 5, 7, and 9? You may use the same digit twice in an arrangement.
12. How many 6-digit zip codes are possible if no digit can be repeated?
13. How many different license plates are possible if the plates have two letters followed by four numbers and no letter or number is used twice?
14. **Suppose** In Exercise 13, suppose that letters and numbers are allowed to be repeated. How many more license plates are possible? (Hint: Use the Counting Principle.)

Use Mathematical Reasoning

15. How many different 3-digit telephone area codes are possible if the first digit cannot be a 0 or a 1?
16. How many different 7-digit phone numbers are possible in each area code if the following restrictions apply: the first digit cannot be a 0 or a 1, the middle digit in the prefix cannot be a 0 or a 1, and the 3-digit prefix cannot be 555 or 911?

The expression $\frac{n!}{(n-r)!}$ gives the number of permutations of n objects taken r at a time. For Example 2 on page 492, the expression is

$$\frac{5!}{(5-3)!} = \frac{5!}{2!} = 5 \times 4 \times 3.$$

Use the expression to solve Exercises 17–19.

17. Eight basketball teams are in a tournament. In how many ways can first, second, third, and fourth place be determined? There are no ties.

18. Nine people entered the pie eating contest at the county fair. In how many ways can first, second, and third place be determined if there are no ties?

19. A shirt company has ten new colors of their most popular shirt. Each day they have a different arrangement of four shirts on display. How many days can they go without having to repeat a display of shirts?

Mixed Review

Simplify. **20.** $(6 + 3t) + 15$ **21.** $m + 6m - 4m$ **22.** $12 + 3c - 9$
23. $26n - 19n + 2n$ **24.** $3 + 6r - 12$ **25.** $4x + 3y + 2x - 9y$

Give the circumference. Use 3.14 for π. **26.** radius = 4 **27.** diameter = 5

Solve and check. **28.** $3(x + 4) - 3 = 15$ **29.** $0.4c + 0.7c = 22$
30. $14 = 2t - 8$ **31.** $6m = m - 10$ **32.** $27 + 6(y - 2) = 3$

Find the slope of the line. **33.** $y = -4x + 2$ **34.** $3x + 6y = 9$

Numbers to Algebra

You can use variables to write expressions for consecutive numbers.

Numbers	Algebra
The next three even numbers after 4. 4: 6, 8, 10	The next three even numbers after an even number n. n: $(n + 2)$, $(n + 4)$, $(n + 6)$

Write expressions for each of the following.

1. The next four consecutive whole numbers after whole number n.

2. The two whole numbers just before a whole number x.

3. The two even numbers just before an even number y.

4. Numbers that are 5, 10, and 15 times greater than a whole number m.

14-3 Probability

Objective To find the probability of simple events and mutually exclusive events.

Explore

When you throw two fair dice, each numbered 1 to 6, the smallest sum you can get is $1 + 1 = 2$; the largest sum possible is $6 + 6 = 12$. All whole numbers from 2 to 12 are possible.

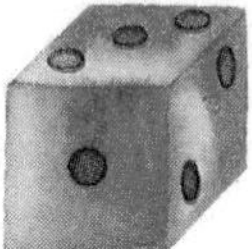

Which sums have the best chance of coming up when you throw two fair dice? Make a guess. To check your guess, list all of the ways each sum can be rolled.

$3 + 5 = 8$

Understand the Ideas

A die has sides numbered 1 through 6. If you toss a die once there are six possible outcomes: 1, 2, 3, 4, 5, and 6. Each outcome is **equally likely.** Since there are 6 equally likely outcomes, the **probability** of each outcome is $\frac{1}{6}$. If there are n equally likely outcomes from an activity, the probability of each outcome is $\frac{1}{n}$. An outcome or a combination of outcomes is called an **event.**

Rule Probability

To find the probability of an event **A,** written ***P*(A),** divide the number of ways for the event to occur by the total number of possible outcomes.

Example 1

Find the probability of each for one toss of a die.

a. $P(\text{even number})$ **b.** $P(\text{a number} < 6)$ **c.** $P(\text{a number} > 6)$

Solution

a. $P(\text{even number}) = \frac{3}{6} = \frac{1}{2}$ There are three even numbers. There are six possible outcomes. Reduce $\frac{3}{6}$ to $\frac{1}{2}$.

b. $P(\text{a number} < 6) = \frac{5}{6}$

c. $P(\text{a number} > 6) = \frac{0}{6} = 0$ It is impossible to throw a number greater than 6. The probability of an impossible event is 0.

Try This Find the probability of each for one toss of a die.

a. $P(\text{a multiple of } 2)$ **b.** $P(0 < \text{a number} < 7)$

If two events cannot occur at the same time, they are **mutually exclusive.** In one toss of a die, the events "an even number" and "an odd number" are mutually exclusive, since no number is both even and odd. The events "a number > 3" and "an even number" are not mutually exclusive, since 4 and 6 are both greater than 3 and even. This relationship is stated in the following formula.

Formula **Mutually Exclusive Events**

If two events are **mutually exclusive,** the probability of one or the other occurring is equal to the sum of the probabilities of each one occurring. If A and B are mutually exclusive events,

$$P(\text{A or B}) = P(\text{A}) + P(\text{B})$$

Example 2

Find the probability of each.

a. $P(\text{blue or green})$

b. $P(\text{blue or a multiple of } 10)$

1	2	3	4
5	10	15	20
10	20	30	40

Solution

a. $P(\text{blue or green}) = \frac{1}{3} + \frac{1}{3} = \frac{2}{3}$ The events are mutually exclusive. $P(\text{blue}) = \frac{1}{3}$ and $P(\text{green}) = \frac{1}{3}$

b. $P(\text{blue or a multiple of } 10) = \frac{1}{3} + \frac{1}{2}$

$= \frac{2}{6} + \frac{3}{6} = \frac{5}{6}$

The events are mutually exclusive. $P(\text{blue}) = \frac{1}{3}$ and $P(\text{multiple of } 10) = \frac{6}{12} = \frac{1}{2}$

Try This Find the probability of each, using the picture above.

c. $P(\text{number} < 4 \text{ or number} > 20)$

d. $P(\text{prime number or a multiple of } 10)$

Class Exercises

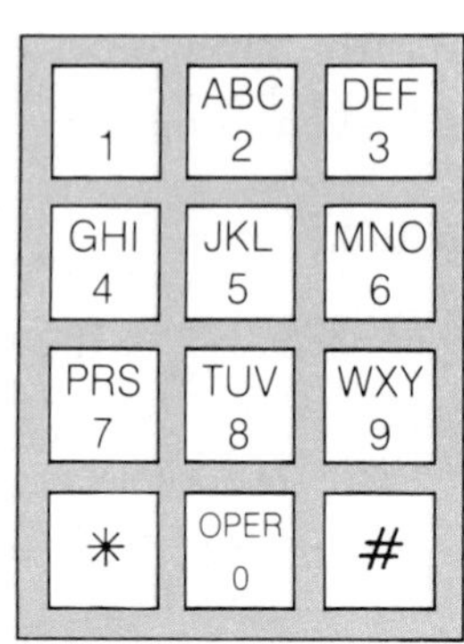

Suppose you closed your eyes and pushed one button on the telephone at random. What is the probability of pushing each?

1. 0(zero) **2.** an even number

3. a prime number **4.** a factor of 4

5. a vowel **6.** a consonant

7. the letter Z **8.** a button with no number

Discuss the Ideas

9. Replace x and y with a number to make a true statement. Explain the meaning of each.
   a. The probability of an event must be greater than or equal to x.
   b. The probability of an event must be less than or equal to y.

Exercises

Practice and Apply

One card is drawn from a deck of 52 playing cards. Find each probability.

1. P(red card)
2. P(black card)
3. P(ace)
4. P(heart)
5. P(5)
6. P(queen)
7. Find the probability of selecting the king of diamonds.
8. Find the probability of not selecting a red card.
9. What is the probability of selecting a black face card?
10. What is the probability of not selecting a heart?

Suppose there are 15 balls in a bag. All are the same size. Four are red, six are white, and five are blue. You select one ball from the bag. Find each probability.

11. P(red)
12. P(white)
13. P(blue)
14. P(not blue)
15. P(not white)
16. P(not red)

Use the spinner at right. Find each probability.

17. P(blue or white)
18. P(blue or prime)
19. P(multiple of 5 or multiple of 4)
20. P(odd or blue)
21. P(even or green)
22. P(green or blue or white)
23. P(multiple of 10 or green or red)

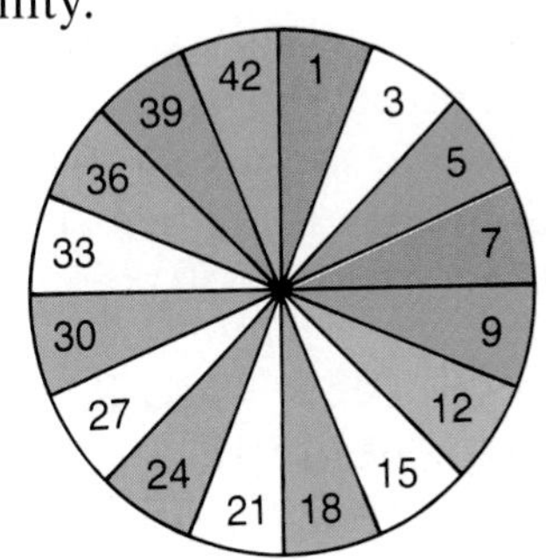

Extend and Apply

Solve.

24. One postcard will be drawn out of 500 received for a ticket to a concert. You mailed 25 postcards. What are your chances of getting the ticket if all of your postcards were received?
25. Janis and 4 of her friends are among 40 candidates for a visit to Washington, D.C. One student will be selected at random. What is the probability that Janis or one of her friends will be selected?

26. **Communicate** Solve the problem, then write a sentence describing how you made your decision.

Suppose there are 2,000 contestants in a raffle drawing. Each student in your class has entered once. Is the probability of someone from your class being selected greater than or less than 10%?

Use Mathematical Reasoning

27. One die has a blank face instead of a 1-dot face. Another die has a blank face instead of a 4-dot face. What is the probability of rolling a sum of 7 with the dice?

28. A lost-and-found office had three identical jackets. One was yours. You and two others arrived to claim your jackets. The clerk handed out the three jackets at random. What is the probability each of you got your own jacket?

Mixed Review

Give the least common multiple (LCM). **29.** 3, 5, 6 **30.** 4, 6, 9

Solve and check. **31.** $2m - 6 < -2$ **32.** $4(c + 1) = 28$

33. Give the perimeter of a square with a side length of 4.5 cm.

Computer Activity

A common probability experiment is tossing a coin. The outcomes are heads and tails. The probability for heads is one-half. In the real world, probabilities may not work out according to the formula. If you were to toss a coin 50 times you probably would not get 25 heads. This computer program simulates, or acts like, a coin tossing experiment. It performs 50 coin tosses and counts the number of heads.

```
10 REM COIN TOSSING PROGRAM
20 LET HEADS=0
30 FOR I=1 TO 50
40 LET N=INT(RND(1)*2)
50 IF N=1 THEN HEADS=HEADS+1
60 NEXT I
70 PRINT "THE NUMBER OF HEADS="; HEADS
80 END
```

1. Run the program. How many times should HEADS appear?
2. How many outcomes were HEADS?
3. Change Line 30 so that there are 100 tosses and run the program again. Did your result come closer to 50%?

14-4 Independent and Dependent Events

Objective To distinguish between and calculate the probability of independent and dependent events.

Understand the Ideas

Suppose you first spin the spinner with numbers and then the spinner with letters. The outcome of the first spin does not influence the outcome of the second. The events are **independent.**

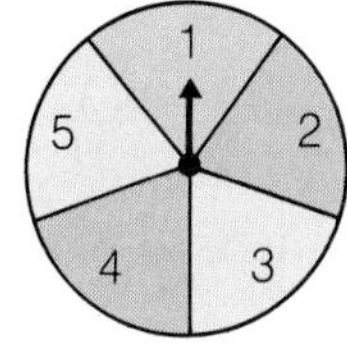

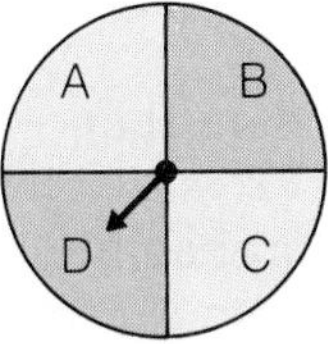

Formula **Independent Events**

When two events are independent, the probabiliity of both occurring is equal to the product of the probabilities of each event occurring.

$P(\text{A and B}) = P(\text{A}) \times P(\text{B})$

Example 1

For the two spinners above, find P(even number and vowel).

Solution

$P(\text{even number}) = \frac{2}{5}$ $\quad P(\text{vowel}) = \frac{1}{4}$

$P(\text{even number and vowel}) = \frac{2}{5} \times \frac{1}{4} = \frac{1}{10}$ Since the two events are independent, multiply their probabilities.

Try This

Find each probability for the spinners above.

a. P(odd number and consonant) **b.** P(number < 5 and a B)

Suppose you randomly choose one woman from a list of eight men and four women to serve on a committee. You then want to select another person. The probability of selecting a woman the second time is not the same as it was the first time because the size of the total group has been reduced. When the outcome of an event is influenced by the outcome of a previous event, it is a **dependent event.**

To find the **probability of dependent events,** find the probability of the first event. Then, taking the first event into consideration, find the probability of the second event. Repeat this for each dependent event. Then multiply the probabilities.

Example 2

Find the probability of picking two women in a row from a list of eight men and four women.

Solution

$P(\text{woman}) = \frac{4}{12} = \frac{1}{3}$ 4 out of 12 people are women.

$P(\text{then woman}) = \frac{3}{11}$ 3 are women but only 11 people remain.

$P(\text{woman then woman}) = \frac{1}{3} \times \frac{3}{11} = \frac{3}{33} = \frac{1}{11}$

The probability of picking two women is $\frac{1}{11}$.

Try This Suppose there are eight men and four women on a list. Find each probability.

c. P(woman then a man) **d.** P(man then a woman)

Class Exercises

State whether the pairs of activities are dependent or independent events.

1. Tossing heads on one coin and tails on another coin.
2. Taking one white sock from a drawer and then, without replacing it, taking another.
3. Seeing a blue motorcycle yesterday and a blue motorcycle today.

Discuss the Ideas

4. Give an example of a pair of independent events and a pair of dependent events. Discuss why each is independent or dependent.

Exercises

Practice and Apply

Find the probability for the spinner and for the cube numbered 1–6. Assume that the first outcome is for the spinner and the second is for the cube.

1. P(8 and 3)
2. P(even and odd)
3. P(12 and a number <6)
4. P(multiple of 5 and 5)
5. P(a number >12 and a number >4)
6. P(divisible by 7 and prime)

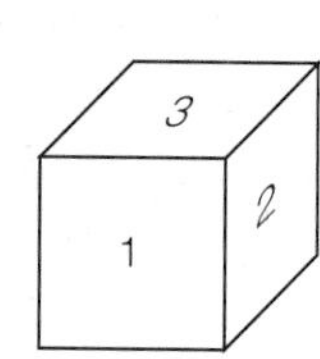

Suppose you have a standard deck of 52 playing cards. You select two cards at random without replacing the first.

7. Find the probability of picking the king of spades and then the ace of hearts.

8. Find the probability of picking a red card and then another red card.

9. Find the probability of picking a 4 and then a queen.

10. Find the probability of picking a queen and then another queen.

Extend and Apply

You have a drawer with three white shirts, four gray shirts, five green shirts, and four blue shirts. You reach in and select three shirts at random without replacing them. Find each probability.

11. P(white then gray then green)

12. P(blue then green then gray)

13. P(green then green then blue)

14. P(blue then blue then blue)

Suppose you replace each shirt each time in the situation above.

15. What is the probability of getting a white shirt and then a blue shirt and then a green shirt?

16. What is the probability of picking a gray shirt and then a gray shirt and then a gray shirt?

Use Mathematical Reasoning

The probability that person A will pass gym class is $\frac{5}{6}$, that B will pass is $\frac{3}{4}$, and that C will pass is $\frac{2}{3}$. If the probability that A will pass gym is $\frac{5}{6}$, then the probability A will not pass gym is $\frac{1}{6}$. Find each probability.

17. all three will not pass the course

18. A and C will pass but B will not

19. A and B will pass but C will not

20. A and B will not pass but C will

Mixed Review

Write as a percent. **21.** $\frac{3}{5}$ **22.** $1\frac{3}{8}$ **23.** $\frac{9}{15}$ **24.** $\frac{11}{4}$

Give the greatest common factor (GCF). **25.** 6, 24, 51 **26.** 100, 120, 135

Calculator Activity

Use a calculator to help you give each probability as a percent. Round to the nearest whole percent.

1. Of 60 previous days with atmospheric conditions like today's, it has rained on 35. What is the probability of rain today?

2. Of 150 previous days with atmospheric conditions like today's, it has rained on 20. What is the probability of rain today?

14-5 Problem Solving: Writing Equations

Practice Solving Problems

Objective To write and solve equations to solve word problems.

Practice and Apply

Solve by writing an equation.

1. The total cost of a bicycle is \$140. Glenda put \$20 down on the bicycle and will pay the rest in three equal payments. How much will each payment be?
2. Bob rode his bike from his house to a house 5 miles north. He rode at the rate of $\frac{1}{4}$ mile per minute. How far from home was he after 20 minutes?
3. A board 6 m long is to be cut into two pieces. The length of one piece must be 0.5 m more than twice the length of the other. How long should each piece be?
4. Mary made \$4.75 an hour and \$15 in overtime pay the first week of her job. Her total salary for the week was \$181.25. How many regular hours did she work?

Extend and Apply

Solve by writing an equation.

5. A carpenter measured the sides of a triangular wooden frame for a house. Each side measured one foot longer than the previous side. The perimeter of the frame was 51 feet. How long was each side of the frame?
6. 50% of the cost of a television set was \$60 more than 25% of its cost. How much did the television cost?

Use Mathematical Reasoning

7. Write a word problem that could be solved by the equation
   a. $25x - 15 = 65$ **b.** $x + 12 = 4x$

Mixed Review

Solve and check. **8.** $9x + 3x = 48$ **9.** $r = 16 + 3r$ **10.** $x + 3x = 8$

Write the prime factorization, using exponents. **11.** 504 **12.** 495

Probability Decisions

Objective To use probability and critical thinking to decide whether a game is fair.

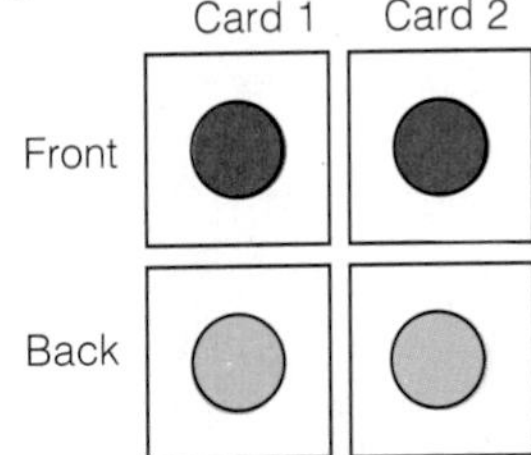

Critical Thinking is a process of making decisions about what to believe or do. Some questions that may help you use this process are given on page 328. The Example below shows how you might use critical thinking skills to analyze a game.

Sample Problem Make two small cards like those shown above. Play a game in which you mix up and drop the cards. Player 1 gets a point if the two cards match. Player 2 gets a point if the cards do not match. Do you think this is a fair game?

Solution Make a tree diagram to show the possible pairs of cards that can show.

First Card	Second Card	Pairs of cards that can appear
Red	Red	Red, Red
	Green	Red, Green
	Blue	Red, Blue
Blue	Red	Blue, Red
	Green	Blue, Green

Since the two cards match in only one of the five possible pairs of cards, the probability of a match is $\frac{1}{5}$. The probability that the cards will not match is $\frac{4}{5}$.

This is not a fair game.

Apply Critical Thinking

Work with a partner in Exercises 1 and 2.

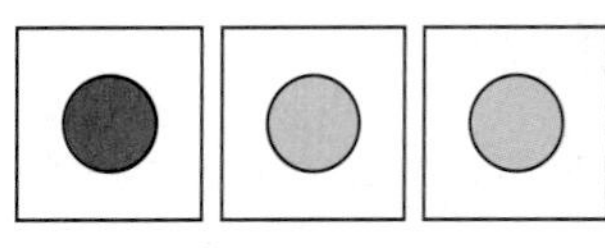
Standard Row

1. Make three small cards like the ones shown here. Play a game in which you shuffle the cards, randomly lay them out, and compare them to the standard row. Player 1 gets a point if all of the cards match those in the standard row. Player 2 gets a point if exactly one of the cards match the standard row. Do you think this is a fair game? Write a paragraph to support your decision.

2. Roll a pair of dice. Find the product of the numbers on the dice. If the product is even, Player 1 gets a point. If the product is odd, Player 2 gets a point. Is this a fair game? Write a paragraph supporting your decision.

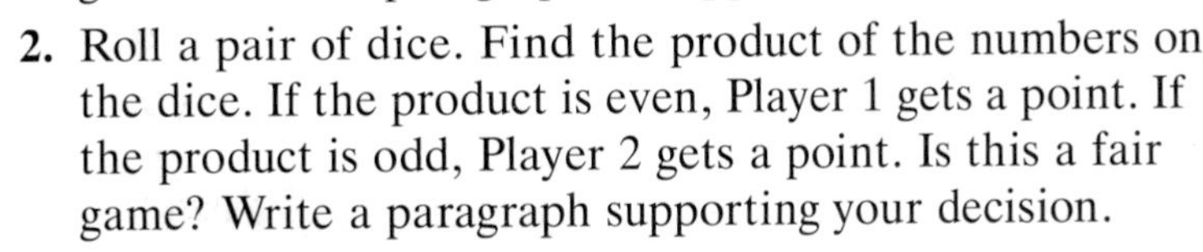

14-6 Frequency Tables, Range, and Mode

Objectives To make a frequency table for a set of data; to find range and mode.

Application

Some students wanted to know the most common starting wage paid by restaurant chains in their city. They collected data from 23 restaurants. Here are their data.

Data	$3.85	$4.00	$4.25
$4.00	$4.60	$4.00	$4.00
$4.25	$4.00	$4.25	$4.00
$4.60	$4.50	$4.25	$4.00
$3.85	$4.00	$4.50	$3.85
$4.25	$4.00	$4.50	$4.60

Understand the Ideas

Data can often be recorded using a **frequency table.** The **range** of a set of data is the difference between the greatest and the least numbers in the set. The **mode** is the number or item that appears most frequently.

Example

Make a frequency table for the wages given in the **application.** Find the range and the mode.

Solution

Hourly Wage	Tally	Frequency
$3.85	|||	3
$4.00	~~||||~~ ||||	9
$4.25	~~||||~~	5
$4.50	|||	3
$4.60	|||	3

Range = $4.60 − $3.85 = $0.75
Greatest wage − least wage = range.

Mode = $4.00
$4.00 occurs most frequently in the table.

Try This **a.** Make a frequency table for the data. Find the range and mode. Ages of girls on a soccer team: $16\frac{1}{2}$, 17, 15, 16, $15\frac{1}{2}$, $16\frac{1}{2}$, $17\frac{1}{2}$, 17, $15\frac{1}{2}$, $16\frac{1}{2}$, $16\frac{1}{2}$, 18, $16\frac{1}{2}$, $17\frac{1}{2}$, $16\frac{1}{2}$, $16\frac{1}{2}$, 16, 16, 17, 16, $16\frac{1}{2}$.

Class Exercises

In a survey, English students asked people to try to say five tongue twisters. They made a frequency table showing which ones people were able to say.

Tongue Twister	Tally	Frequency
1. The sinking steamer sank.	卌 卌 卌 卌 卌	
2. Rubber baby buggy bumpers	卌 卌 卌 卌 卌 卌 卌 I	
3. Toy boat (repeat 6 times)	卌 卌 卌 卌 卌 卌 卌 卌 I	
4. The sixth sick sheik's sixth sheep's sick.	卌 卌 III	
5. She sells seashells by the seashore.	卌 卌 卌 卌 卌 卌 卌 卌 卌 II	

1. How many people were able to say each tongue twister?
2. Which tongue twister could the most people say?
3. Which tongue twister could the fewest people say?

Discuss the Ideas

4. In the Example, suppose eight more restaurants were surveyed, and all of them reported a starting wage of $4.25 per hour. Would the range for this data change? Would the mode change? Explain.

Exercises

Practice and Apply

Make a frequency table for each set of data. Find the range and mode.

1. High temperature in degrees Celsius for May and June.

5/1	**5/4**	**5/7**	**5/10**	**5/13**	**5/16**	**5/19**	**5/22**	**5/25**	**5/28**	**5/31**
25	27	25	26	26	29	30	31	29	26	27
6/3	**6/6**	**6/9**	**6/12**	**6/15**	**6/18**	**6/21**	**6/24**	**6/27**	**6/30**	
30	31	31	32	31	31	33	34	33	32	

2. Ages of pilots on North South Airlines.

39	37	45	43	38	48	50	51	37	52	52	40
40	38	52	50	53	52	38	55	52	48	42	43

3. Number of runs per game scored by the Texas Rangers in June.

3	0	1	6	5	12	0	3	1	4	7	5	3
4	3	2	1	1	3	0	4	6	7	3	8	2

4. Scores on Chapter 13 Pre-Algebra test for Mr. Mendoza's class.

82	76	80	90	84	100	64	74	76	86	98	84	92
74	76	80	72	68	76	90	70	70	88	76	86	

5. Kisha works at a waterslide. Her job today is to record the number of people in line for the two water slides at each hour of the day. Find the range and mode for the data she collected. Combine the data for the two slides.

Slide	Time											
A	9 a.m.	10	11	12	1	2	3	4	5	6	7	8
	17	19	24	41	35	45	50	41	32	36	35	29
B	9 a.m.	10	11	12	1	2	3	4	5	6	7	8
	16	24	28	34	27	34	28	36	35	32	27	38

6. Andy works as a ski instructor. His job one day was to estimate the number of people on the different runs at several times throughout the day. Find the range and the mode for the data he collected. Combine the data for all of the ski runs.

Ski run	Estimated number of people at various times
Wine Ridge	15, 16, 27, 42, 22, 23, 34, 17, 28, 33, 30, 34, 22, 32, 19
Red Onion	41, 26, 22, 30, 18, 35, 31, 21, 23, 22, 40, 36, 37, 34, 25
Bunny Hop	2, 28, 33, 22, 18, 36, 23, 16, 22, 34, 27, 42, 17, 22, 40, 12

Extend and Apply

7. Videocassette rental fees vary greatly in the same city. For a class project, a group of students collected data on rental fees for all of the stores in town. Make a frequency table for the data. Use intervals of \$2, with \$1.00–\$2.99 as the first interval. Find the range and mode.

$3, $3.80, $2, $2.75, $4.50, $1.99, $5.75, $1, $1.50, $5, $1, $2, $5, $4.25, $5, $2.50, $3.75, $2, $3, $2, $2.75, $2.60, $2, $3.25, $2, $6, $3.25, $2, $3.50, $4.75, $4, $2.50, $4, $3.10, $1.69, $3.

Use Mathematical Reasoning

8. Add two numbers so that the mode changes.
18, 18, 18, 17, 16, 16, 15, 14

9. Add one of the numbers 20 through 24 so that the mode does not change.
24, 24, 24, 23, 23, 22, 22, 21, 21, 20, 20

10. Add two numbers so the range becomes 8.
9, 8, 8, 7, 6, 6, 6, 5, 3, 3, 3, 3, 2, 2

Mixed Review

Solve and check. **11.** $9 < 2c + 1$ **12.** $4.5y = -18$ **13.** $-6t = 3$

What percent of 40 is: **14.** 15? **15.** 10? **16.** 56?

Evaluate for $x = 2, y = 4$. **17.** $2xy$ **18.** $4x - 2y$ **19.** $x(x - y)$
20. $3x - 2y + 9$ **21.** $6(x - 9) + 3y$ **22.** $4.5x - 2.1y$

Does y vary directly with x? If it does, find the value of k.

Does y vary inversely with x? If it does, find the value of k.

23.

x	y
1	3
2	4
3	5
4	6
5	7

24.

x	y
1	5
2	10
3	15
4	20
5	25

25.

x	y
1	24
2	12
3	8
4	6
5	4.8

26.

x	y
1	3
2	2
3	1
4	0
5	−1

Estimation

Find the range and mode for the data shown in the graph. Estimate the frequency of each response.

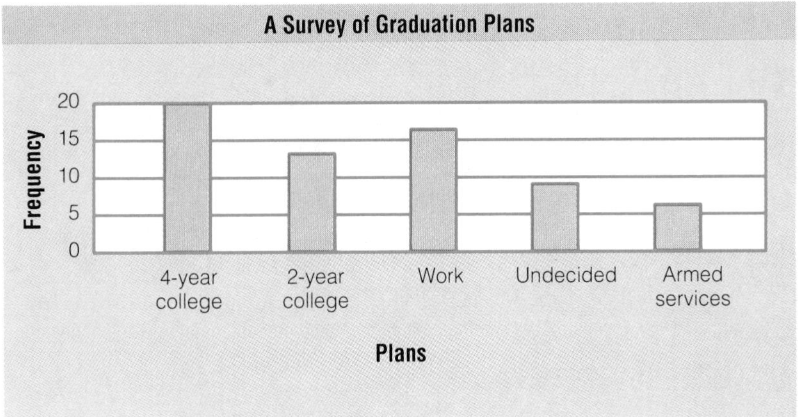

14-7 Mean and Median

Objective To find the mean and median of a set of data.

Advertising by Restaurant Chains

Restaurant	Amount Spent in 3 Months
A	\$45 million
B	\$20 million
C	\$15 million
D	\$11 million
E	\$11 million
F	\$ 6 million

Application

A consumer group collected the data shown and wants to know the mean and median advertising costs for different restaurant chains.

Understand the Ideas

In section 14-6, you learned how to find the mode. Two other measures used to determine which number in a list of numbers is "most typical" are **mean** and **median.** To find the **mean** or **average** of a list of numbers, find the total and divide by the number of items. The **median** is the middle number in a list of numbers arranged in order. If there are two middle numbers, the median is the mean of the two middle numbers.

Example

Find the mean and median for the advertising numbers given in the **application.**

Solution

$$\text{Mean} = \frac{45 + 20 + 15 + 11 + 11 + 6}{6}$$ Find the sum of the 6 numbers and divide by 6.

$$= \frac{108}{6}$$

$$\text{Mean} = 18$$ The mean is 18 million dollars.

45 20 **15** **11** 11 6 List the numbers in order.

$$\text{Median} = \frac{15 + 11}{2}$$ The median is the mean of the two middle numbers.

$$\text{Median} = \frac{26}{2}$$

$$= 13$$ The median is 13 million dollars.

The mean is \$18 million and the median is \$13 million.

Try This

a. Find the mean and median attendance at honor society meetings.

Sept	Oct	Nov	Dec	Jan	Feb	Mar	Apr	May
11	14	12	12	12	18	10	20	22

Class Exercises

Tell whether each is true or false.

1. The mean and median are always the same.
2. An equal number of numbers in a list are above and below the median.
3. The mean is always one of the numbers in a list of numbers.
4. The median is always one of the numbers in a list of numbers.
5. Mean and average are the same.
6. If there is one middle number in a list, it is the median.

Discuss the Ideas

7. In the **application,** suppose Restaurant G spent $100 million on advertising. Would you expect the mean or the median to change the most? Explain.

Exercises

Practice and Apply

Solve. Round to the nearest tenth if necessary.

1. Find the mean and the median for the number of boxes of candy sold: Boxes: 12, 56, 43, 34, 58, 62, 71
2. Find the average number of students in a school club. Numbers of students in school clubs: 12, 8, 8, 24, 15, 3, 4, 9, 10, 16
3. Find the average temperature change (degrees Celsius) for the 11-day period. Temperature change: 2.6, 3.8, 7, 4.5, 4.6, 7.8, 5.1, 8.1, 4.6, 5.6, 6.2
4. Find the mean and the median for the number of people attending performances of the school play. Attendance: 273, 485, 233, 225, 486, 387, 250, 239, 428
5. Find Todd's average for the last 10 quizzes. Quiz scores: 15, 18, 20, 14, 19, 19, 17, 19, 20, 18
6. The math teachers at Jefferson School are 24, 23, 35, 40, 42, 50, 32, and 36 years old. What is the median age for these teachers?

7. A survey shows that the number of visitors to San Francisco after the October 1989 earthquake dropped significantly compared with the previous year. Copy and complete the table below.

HOTEL & MOTEL OCCUPANCY			
Number of hotel and motel rooms occupied			
San Francisco	Nov. 1988	Nov. 1989	Percent change
All rooms (average)	___	___	___
Rooms over $110	8100	7512	
Rooms $80–$110	9672	6996	
Rooms under $80	7994	7248	

Extend and Apply

8. Restaurants in Middletown paid different starting hourly wages. A new restaurant opened and wanted to offer a starting wage greater than the median starting wage paid by other restaurants. What would be the lowest wage the new restaurant could offer? Wages: $3.65, $4.50, $4.25, $5.00, $3.65, $4.75

9. In 29 at-bats in a World Series, Roberto Clemente had 7 singles, 2 doubles, 1 triple, and 2 home runs. What was his batting average for the World Series? Batting average is the number of hits divided by the times at bat. Round the decimal to the thousandths place.

Use Mathematical Reasoning

10. Use mental math to estimate the mean for the following numbers. 87, 195, 213, 230, 298, 305, 479, 550

11. Derek's score on each math exam increased by 5 points from the previous exam. The mean for the five exams he took was 70. What were his exam scores?

Mixed Review

What percent of 24 is: **12.** 16? **13.** 9? **14.** 12? **15.** 21?

Evaluate for $x = 3, y = 4$. **16.** $\frac{x}{y}$ **17.** $\frac{2x}{3y}$ **18.** $\frac{x}{3} + \frac{y}{2}$ **19.** $\frac{1 - x}{1 - y}$

Write, <, >, or = for each □. **20.** $\frac{2}{3}$ □ $\frac{18}{25}$ **21.** -1.106 □ -1.016

14-8 Problem Solving: Applications

Managing a Computer Store

Objective To solve applied problems using information from graphs.

A manager of a computer store keeps data on sales of computers and computer materials. The data are often shown in graphs.

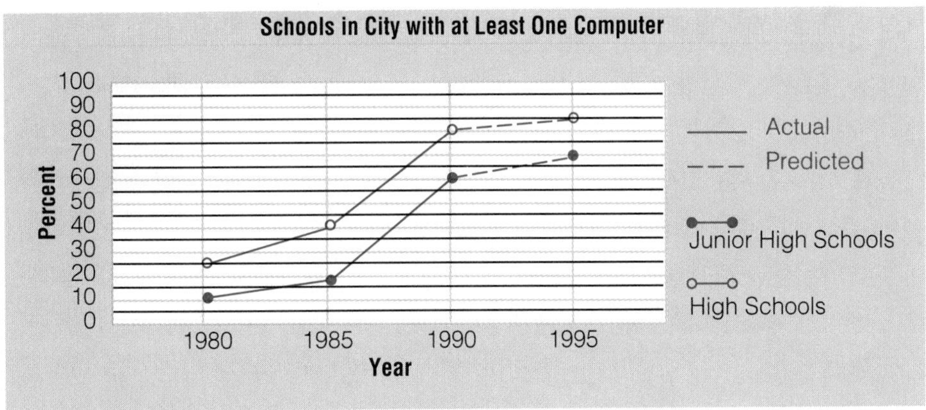

Problems

Use the graphs on pages 511 and 512 to solve.

1. In 1990, a greater percent of high schools had at least one computer than junior high schools. How many percentage points more?
2. By how many percentage points did the junior high schools having at least one computer increase from 1980 to 1990?
3. By how many percentage points did the high schools having at least one computer increase from 1980 to 1990?
4. What was the mean percentage of junior high and high schools having at least one computer in 1980?
5. What is the mean percentage of junior high and high schools expected to have at least one computer in 1995?
6. Predict what percentage of junior high schools will have at least one computer in the year 2000.
7. How many fewer computers costing less than $1,000 were sold in 1990 than were sold in 1988?
8. How many more computers costing $1,000 to $2,000 than computers costing more than $2,000 were sold in 1990?
9. What was the total number of computers sold in 1988? In 1990?

10. What was the mean number of computers sold in different price ranges in 1988? in 1990?

11. What was the approximate percentage of increase in sales of computers costing more than $2,000 from 1988 to 1990?

12. What was the approximate percentage of decrease in sales of computers costing less than $1,000 from 1988 to 1990?

13. How much greater were the sales of game software than business software?

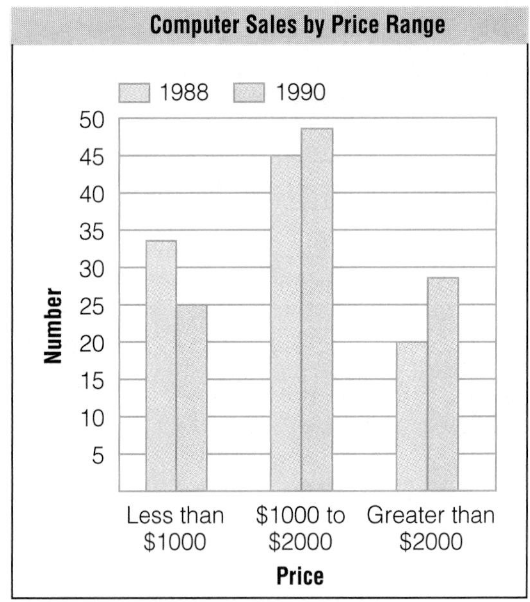

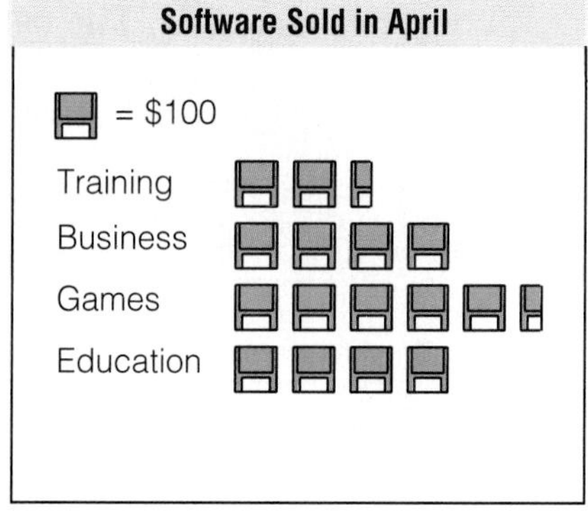

14. How much less were the sales of training software than education software?

15. What were the average sales of different types of computer software in April?

16. **Data Search** Find the number of computers in your school for each of the last 5 years. Use that information to predict how many computers your school will have next year and in 5 years.

What's Your Decision?

Your school wants to buy 20 new computers. The regular price at two stores is the same, $1,500 per computer. Store A will give the school five computers at no charge if it buys 15 at the regular price. Store B will give the school 15% off the cost of each computer. A 5% sales tax must be paid at either store. Where should your school buy the computers?

14-9 Making Bar Graphs and Line Graphs

Objective To make bar graphs and line graphs.

Application

The manager of the Pines Motel was interested in how rates have increased from 1950 to 1990. She recorded the following data. Room rates: 1950, $9.75; 1960, $18.75; 1970, $28.40; 1980, $50.40; 1990, $79.75.

Understand the Ideas

Bar graphs and line graphs are useful for comparing data. A line graph is usually used to show how something changes over time, and a bar graph is used to compare similar things. You can use these steps to make a graph.

1. Determine the scale.
   - Find the greatest and least values for the data.
   - Select a scale to fit your data.
2. Draw and label the horizontal and vertical sides of the graph.
3. Plot the points for the line graph and draw the bars for the bar graph.
4. Give the graph a title.

Example 1

Make a line graph for the room rates given in the **application.**

Solution

Greatest amount is $79.75

Least amount is $9.75

Let the scale be $10 per mark.

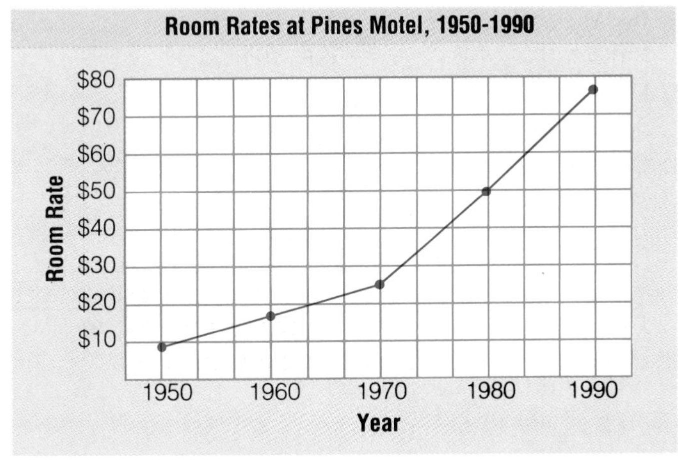

Try This **a.** Make a line graph for the data. Median heights of boys: age 11, 142 cm; age 12, 150 cm; age 13, 158 cm; age 14, 163 cm; age 15, 169 cm; age 16, 176 cm; age 17, 177 cm.

Example 2

Make a bar graph for the data. Airline tickets sold by one travel agent on a given day: Northeast, 9; Southeast, 5; Midwest, 6; Southwest, 4; Rockies, 3; West Coast, 7.

Solution

Greatest number is 9

Least number is 3

Let the scale be 1 ticket per mark.

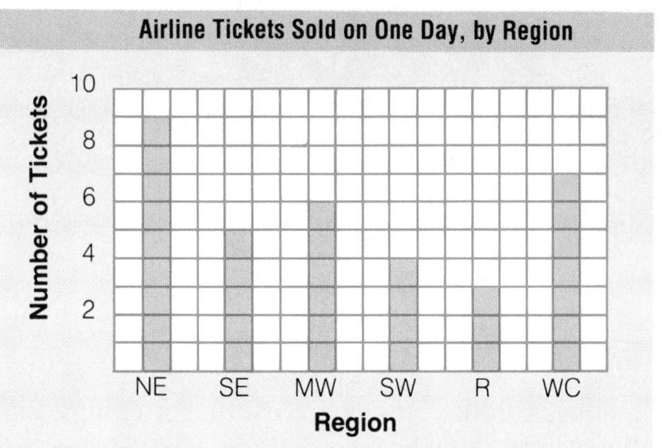

Try This **b.** Make a bar graph for the data. Take-offs and landings at busy airports each year: Chicago, 600,000; Atlanta, 580,000; Los Angeles, 480,000; Denver, 475,000; Dallas, 440,000.

Class Exercises

Use the graph to answer the questions.

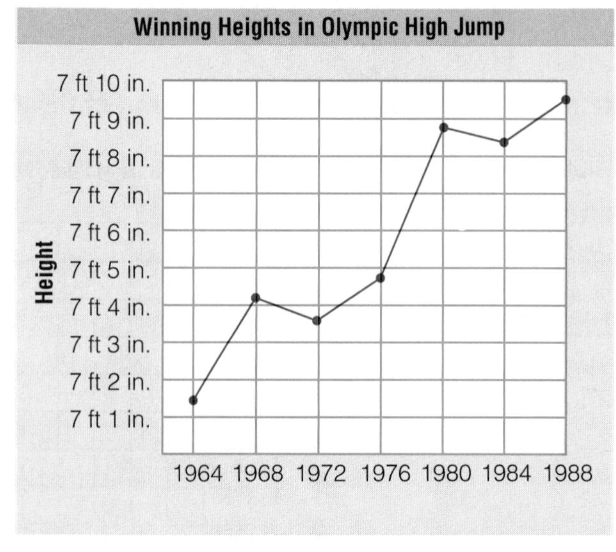

1. How many inches does each line on the vertical scale represent?
2. How many years does each line on the horizontal scale represent?
3. In what year was the highest jump? The lowest jump?
4. Between which years did the winning height drop?
5. Between which years was the change in the winning height greatest?

Discuss the Ideas

6. Look at the graph with the Class Exercises. Why does the distance between the vertical lines representing the years have to be the same?

Exercises

Practice and Apply

Make a bar graph for the data in Exercises 1 and 2.

1. Number of students using a computer lab at lunchtime. Monday, 7; Tuesday, 6; Wednesday, 4; Thursday, 5; Friday, 5. Let each mark on the scale represent one student.
2. Average wind velocities, in miles per hour: Boston, 12.5; Chicago, 10.3; Honolulu, 11.8; San Francisco, 10.5; Washington, D.C., 9.4. Let each mark on the scale represent 0.5 mi/h.

Make a line graph for the data in Exercises 3 and 4.

3. Average monthly rainfall in a town, in centimeters: January, 1.8; February, 2.2; March, 4.0; April, 7.6; May, 8.2; June, 5.4; July, 3.6; August, 2.8; September, 4.2; October, 4.2; November, 2.6; December, 2.0. Let each mark on the scale represent 0.4 cm.
4. Price of gold, per ounce: 1978, $194; 1979, $308; 1980, $613; 1981, $460; 1982, $376; 1983, $424; 1984, $361; 1985, $318; 1986, $368; 1987, $448; 1988, $438. Let each mark on the scale represent $50.

Extend and Apply

5. Make a line graph for the data. Then make another line graph, using the same data but changing the scale so that the graph is almost a straight line.

Leaded Regular Gasoline Prices, 1973–1982									
1973	1974	1975	1976	1977	1978	1979	1980	1981	1982
$0.40	$0.53	$0.57	$0.59	$0.62	$0.63	$0.86	$1.19	$1.31	$1.26

Use Mathematical Reasoning

6. Make up a story that could explain the changes in the graph below.

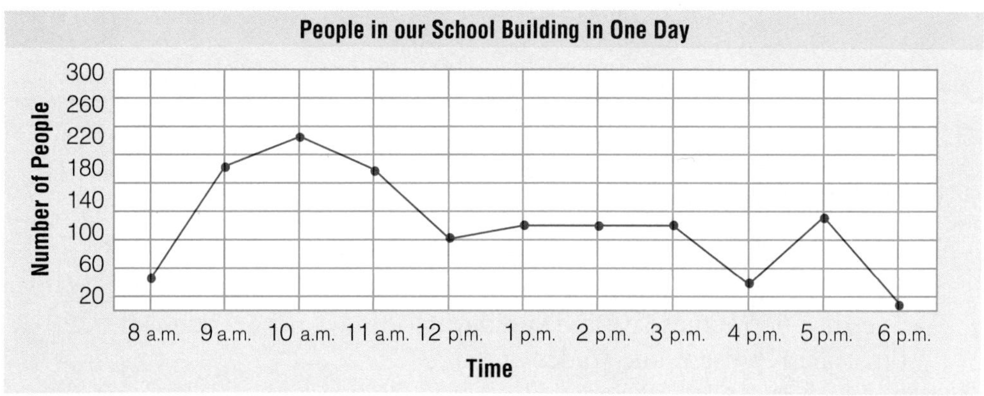

Mixed Review

Simplify. **7.** $16n + 3n - 9 - 10n$ **8.** $2(a + 6) - 8$

Solve and check. **9.** $2t = 16 - 2t$ **10.** $3c = c + 5$ **11.** $-42 = 6y$

12. $2m < 3m + 1$ **13.** $t + 2t = 21$ **14.** $-18 = 6 + 4n$

15. $\left(\frac{3}{16}\right)y = -\frac{3}{4}$ **16.** $r - \frac{1}{2} = \frac{5}{16}$ **17.** $\frac{m}{6} = \frac{25}{15}$ **18.** $\frac{2}{3} = z + \frac{4}{5}$

A square has one side = 6 m. **19.** Give the perimeter. **20.** Give the area.

21. Give the perimeter of a regular pentagon with one side = 7.5 cm.

22. Give the perimeter of an equilateral triangle with one side = 11 m.

Estimation

Estimate the winning times for this race for the next three years.

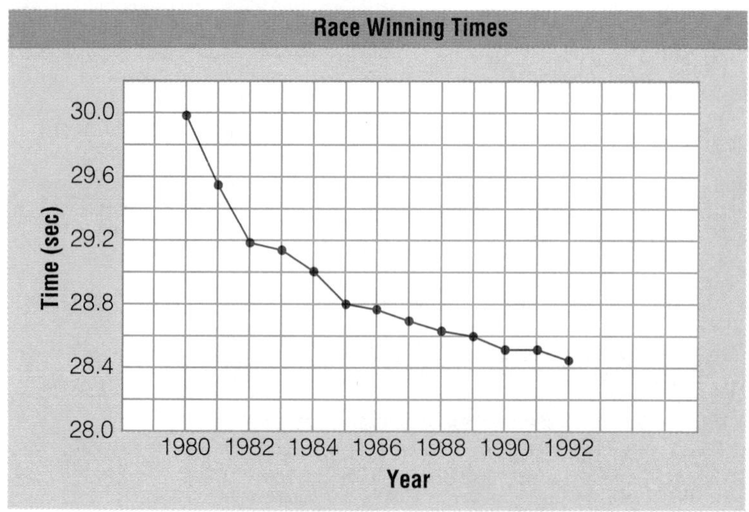

14-10 Making Pictograms

Objective To make pictograms.

Application

The following numbers of coins were made at the Denver mint in 1982. Coins: half-dollars, 6 million; quarters, 120 million; dimes, 54 million; nickels, 19 million; pennies, 60 million.

Understand the Ideas

Pictograms are used to help make comparisons. Follow these steps to make a pictogram.

1. Determine the scale:
   - Find the greatest and least values for the data.
   - Select a scale to fit the data.
2. Round the data; draw and label the pictures for the graph.
3. Show the scale for the graph.
4. Give the graph a title.

Example

Make a pictogram for the coin data given in the **application**.

Solution Greatest number = 120. Least number = 6.

Let (\$) = 10 million coins and (half coin) = 5 million coins.

Rounded data: Half dollars, 5 — 6 is closer to 5 than to 10.
Quarters, 120
Dimes, 55 — 54 is closer to 55 than to 60.
Nickels, 20 — 19 is closer to 20 than to 15.
Pennies, 60

Coins Made at Denver Mint in 1982

Half-dollars

Quarters

Dimes

Nickels

Pennies

= 10 million coins

Try This **a.** Make a pictogram for the data. Favorite breakfast meals: cereal, 88; eggs, 39; pancakes, 129; toast, 138; fruit, 70.

Class Exercises

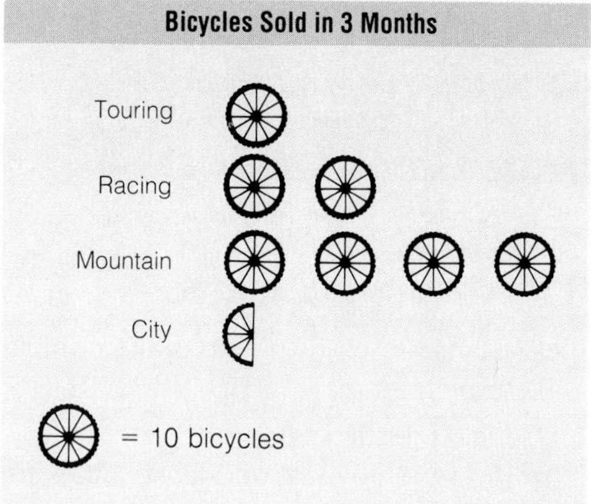

1. What does each wheel represent?
2. What does each half-wheel represent?
3. Which type of bicycle sold most?
4. How many city bikes were sold?

Discuss the Ideas

5. Do pictographs always show exact data? Explain.

Exercises

Practice and Apply

Make a pictogram for the data.

1. Favorite sports at the Simmonsville Racquet Club: racquetball, 18 members; tennis, 32 members; handball, 12 members; squash, 10 members. Let each picture represent four people.
2. Campers on Labor Day weekend: Camp Pine, 125; Camp Timber, 75; Tent City, 150; Mountain Trees, 105. Let each picture represent 25 campers.
3. Favorite forms of exercise: running, 125 people; walking, 58 people; swimming, 29 people; bicycling, 46 people; exercise class, 15 people. Let each picture represent 15 people.

Make a pictogram for the data.

4. Size (in acres) of National Parks in Alaska: Wrangell-St. Elias, 8,945,000; Gates of the Arctic, 7,500,000; Denali, 4,700,000; Katmai, 3,716,000; Glacier Bay, 3,225,000; Lake Clark, 2,875,000; Kobuk Valley, 1,750,000. Let each picture represent one million acres.

5. Populations of cities: New York, 7,072,000; Tokyo, 8,336,000; Mexico City, 9,191,000; Sydney, 3,281,000; London, 6,696,000; Bombay, 8,227,000; Nairobi, 1,048,000; Moscow, 7,831,000. Let each picture represent one million people.

Extend and Apply

6. Use the graph on campers during Labor Day weekend (Exercise 2) to find the mean number of people at a camp.

7. Use the graph on populations of cities (Exercise 5) to find the mean and median number of people living in the cities.

Use Mathematical Reasoning

8. Make up two different sets of data that, when rounded, would be shown by the graph below.

Mixed Review

Write <, >, or = for each □. **9.** $-0.33 \square -0.32$ **10.** $9.01 \square 9.1$

11. $3(n-4) \square 3n - 3(4)$ **12.** $6(2) \square -6(-2)$ **13.** $ab \square ba$

Solve and check. **14.** $9.6n + 1.4n = 27.5$ **15.** $3.5c = 14.7$

What percent of 64 is: **16.** 36? **17.** 20? **18.** 72?

14-11 Problem Solving: Strategies

Practice Solving Problems

Objective To solve nonroutine problems.

Problem-Solving Strategies

Choose the Operations	Make a Table	Make an Organized List
Guess, Check, Revise	Look for a Pattern	Use Logical Reasoning
Draw a Diagram	Write an Equation	Work Backward
	Simplify the Problem	

Problems

Solve.

1. The owner of a car rental business buys gasoline at $1.05 per gallon. Each of the 25 rental cars holds 15 gallons. If the tank in each car is between empty and one-quarter full, about how much would it cost to fill all 25 cars with gasoline?

2. A shipment of three boxes of machine parts weighed a total of 65 kg. The heaviest box weighed three times as much as the second box, which was three times heavier than the lightest box. How much did each box weigh?

3. The owner of a furniture factory set up a plan for training new employees. The first training session was to be for one employee. Each of the following sessions was to hold two more people than the previous one. The factory had 30 new employees. How many training sessions were needed?

4. A secret-service agent has been told to find all possible routes from the airport to the state capitol building. Each route has to be studied and the safest one selected. The figure below shows the streets from the airport to the capitol. All streets are one-way, as shown by the arrows. How many different routes are possible?

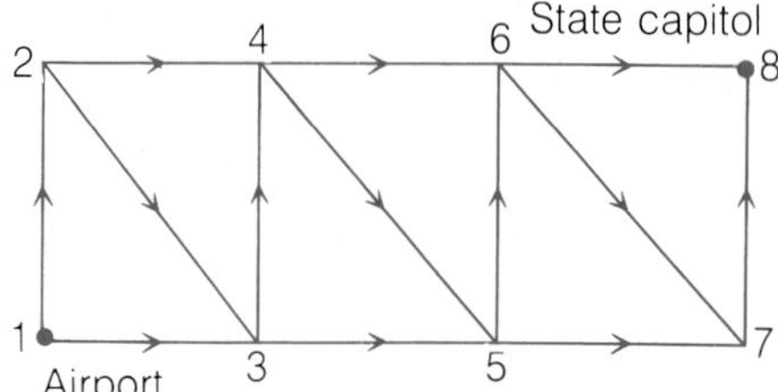

5. A printer who made envelopes and stationery for Companies A, B, and C mixed up the shipments. Each company received another company's envelopes and yet another company's stationery. Company A received Company C's stationery. What envelopes and whose stationery did each company receive?

6. Ms. Wells had a stack of math papers to grade. She graded $\frac{1}{4}$ of the papers during lunch break. She graded $\frac{1}{2}$ of what was left after school. She took the rest of the papers home with her and graded only $\frac{1}{6}$ of those. She had 20 papers left to grade the next morning. How many papers did she have in the beginning?

7. At Peter's Pizza Pan, customers can order thin or deep-dish pizza with whole-wheat or regular crust. They can choose either one or two of the following toppings: pepperoni, sausage, mushrooms. How many different pizzas could a customer order?

8. A paint salesperson visits a store every eighth working day. Another salesperson visits the same store every sixth working day. The store is open Monday through Saturday. Today is Tuesday, May 2nd. Both visited the store today. On what date will they both visit the store again? Can one of them change his schedule and never meet the other in the store again? Explain.

Group Decision Making

9. Work in a group. Discuss and decide.

Situation For your birthday you received an aquarium that is 60 cm by 40 cm by 30 cm with all the accessories (gravel, light, filter, pump), but you must buy fish and water conditioner. You need to find out how many fish you can put in your aquarium, how much water conditioner to put in, and the cost to do this.

Guidelines for Planning

- **Formulate Problems** you will need to solve.
- Discuss **Assumptions** you will make and **Data** you will need.

a. What decision or decisions do you need to make in this situation?

b. Formulate problems you need to solve to make the decision(s).

c. List any assumptions you need to make to arrive at a decision.

d. What data, if any, do you need to collect to make a decision?

e. Write a paragraph summarizing what your group did, what decisions you made, and why.

Extend Key Ideas

Combinations

Tanya's class must select two students out of five candidates as class representatives. How many different pairs can be selected from the five candidates?

Candidates (choose 2)
(A) Alvarez (B) Barnes (C) Carlsen (D) Dickinson (E) Ebel

You learned in this chapter that there are $5 \times 4 = 20$ ways to select 2 out of 5 people. Here is an *organized list* of the 20 ways.

	AB	**AC**	**AD**	**AE**
BA		**BC**	**BD**	**BE**
CA	**CB**		**CD**	**CE**
DA	**DB**	**DE**		**DE**
EA	**EB**	**EC**	**ED**	

Alvarez-Barnes (AB) and Barnes-Alvarez (BA) are both included in the list above. Since the *order* of the students does not matter, you need to divide the total number of permutations by the number of permutations of two people ($2! = 2 \times 1 = 2$). The list below shows all 10 ways in which 2 out of the 5 people can be selected. An arrangement of objects in which *the order of the objects does not matter* is called a **combination.**

AB	**AC**	**AD**	**AE**
	BC	**BD**	**BE**
		CD	**CE**
			DE

Use objects or draw a diagram to help you complete each Exercise.

1. How many ways can you select three books from a list of five books?
2. How many ways can you select 3 movies from the 8 movies currently playing at the cinemaplex?
3. You have enough money to buy six CDs, but there are eight that you would like. How many different ways can you select six CDs?
4. A table tennis club has 10 members. How many games would be played if each member played each other member one time?
5. How many teams of 4 boys and 3 girls can be made from 5 boys and 7 girls?
6. Write a **rule** or a formula that tells how to numerically find the number of combinations.

Chapter 14 Review/Test

Understanding

14-2 Tell whether each is asking for the number of permutations. Do not solve.

1. How many ways can five runners finish a race if there are no ties?
2. How many 3-person committees can be made from a list of 12 people?

True or False?

14-3 **3.** The probability of an event is less than or equal to 1.

14-6 **4.** The mode would be affected by adding 100 to this list of numbers: 38, 45, 50, 45, 48, 52

Skills

14-1 Use the Counting Principle to find the total number of outcomes.

5. Select one date and one show time. Dates: June 10, June 11, June 17, June 18, June 24, June 25. Times: 6:00 p.m., 8:00 p.m., 10:00 p.m.

14-3 There are 10 tennis balls in a bag. Two are green, three are white, and five are yellow. You select one ball from the bag without looking. Find each probability.

6. P(yellow) **7.** P(not green) **8.** P(green or white)

14-4 Find the probability of each for one toss of two dice.

9. P(2 and 5) **10.** P(a number $>$ 5 and an even number)

Applications

14-6, 14-7 **11.** The volleyball team members' ages are 20, 20, 20, 22, 23, 25, 25, 26, and 26. Find the mean, median, and mode for their ages.

14-3 **12.** Randy bought 6 tickets in a raffle. A total of 275 tickets were sold. Give an estimate for the probability of Randy winning.

14-1 **13.** Beatrice is selecting a kite from among three shapes and 6 different colors. How many choices does she have?

14-2 **14.** There are six dogs in a dog show. A ribbon will be awarded to each contestant. How many different finishing orders are possible?

14-9 **15.** Make a bar graph for the data. Mountain heights in feet: McKinley, 20,320; Whitney, 14,494; Mauna Kea, 13,796; Granite Peak, 12,799; Rainier, 14,410.

14-10 **16.** Make a pictogram for the data. Trees on schoolgrounds: maple, 9; birch, 15; pine, 6; oak, 12.

15 Square Roots and Special Triangles

The peak of Cayuga Hill is 500 ft higher than the base of the hill. Kevin biked 1,500 ft to get to the top of the hill. Use the Pythagorean Theorem to find the horizontal distance he traveled.

15-1 Square Roots

Objective To find square roots and evaluate expressions including square roots.

Explore

Use a calculator.

- Guess, then check. What whole number times itself is
  a. 576? **b.** 961? **c.** 2,809?
  Repeat until you find the correct answer.
- Find the decimal that is the best answer to each question. What number times itself is approximately
  a. 20? **b.** 53? **c.** 72?
  Repeat until you find the answer to the nearest hundredth.

Understand the Ideas

A **square root** of 36 is 6 since $6 \cdot 6 = 36$. In general, a square root of a number x is the number y if $y^2 = x$. The symbol $\sqrt{}$, called a **radical sign,** is used to indicate the positive square root. We write $\sqrt{36} = 6$. We call 36 a **perfect square** because it has a whole number square root.

Each positive number has two square roots. For example, 64 has square roots of 8 and -8 since $8^2 = 64$ and $(-8)^2 = 64$.

8 is the positive square root of 64, written as $\sqrt{64} = 8$.
-8 is the negative square root of 64, written as $-\sqrt{64} = -8$.

Example 1

Find $\sqrt{49}$.

Solution $\sqrt{49} = 7$

Try This

Find the square root. **a.** $-\sqrt{25}$ **b.** $\sqrt{81}$

Example 2

Find $\sqrt{\frac{9}{4}}$.

Solution $\sqrt{\frac{9}{4}} = \frac{\sqrt{9}}{\sqrt{4}} = \frac{3}{2}$

Try This

Find the square root. **c.** $\sqrt{\frac{16}{9}}$ **d.** $-\sqrt{\frac{9}{64}}$

When numbers are added or subtracted under a single radical sign, carry out the operation before finding the square root.

Example 3

Evaluate each expression. **a.** $\sqrt{29 + 7}$ **b.** $\sqrt{81} - \sqrt{36}$

Solution

a. $\sqrt{29 + 7} = \sqrt{36}$ Since both numbers are under the same radical sign, add before finding the square root.
$= 6$

b. $\sqrt{81} - \sqrt{36} = 9 - 6$ Find the square root of each number before subtracting.
$= 3$

Try This Evaluate each expression.
e. $\sqrt{49} + \sqrt{121}$ **f.** $\sqrt{121 - 40}$

Class Exercises

State whether the following are true or false.

1. $\sqrt{25} = 5$ **2.** $\sqrt{9} = 3$ **3.** $\sqrt{36} = -6$ **4.** $-\sqrt{16} = 4$
5. $\sqrt{36} = 6$ **6.** $\sqrt{16} = -4$ **7.** $-\sqrt{25} = -5$ **8.** $\sqrt{49} = 7$

Discuss the Ideas

9. Discuss why it does not make sense to talk about the square root of a negative number. For example, $\sqrt{-25}$ is not defined.

Exercises

Practice and Apply

Find the square root.

1. $\sqrt{25}$ **2.** $-\sqrt{81}$ **3.** $\sqrt{4}$ **4.** $\sqrt{9}$ **5.** $\sqrt{144}$
6. $\sqrt{64}$ **7.** $-\sqrt{16}$ **8.** $-\sqrt{4}$ **9.** $\sqrt{16}$ **10.** $\sqrt{100}$
11. $\sqrt{\frac{1}{9}}$ **12.** $\sqrt{\frac{4}{25}}$ **13.** $-\sqrt{\frac{16}{49}}$ **14.** $\sqrt{\frac{9}{100}}$ **15.** $-\sqrt{\frac{144}{25}}$

16. A square has an area of 49 cm^2. What is the length of each side of the square?

17. If the area of a circle is 16π cm^2, what is the radius of the circle?

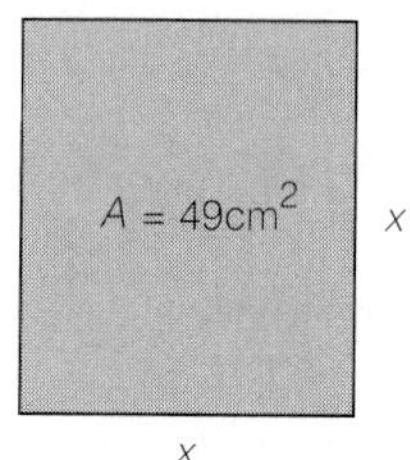

Evaluate each expression.

18. $\sqrt{25} + \sqrt{81}$ **19.** $\sqrt{41 - 5}$ **20.** $\sqrt{55 - 6}$

21. $\sqrt{74 + 26}$ **22.** $\sqrt{81} - \sqrt{100}$ **23.** $\sqrt{221 - 100}$

24. $\sqrt{23 + 58} - \sqrt{36}$ **25.** $\sqrt{81 - 17} - \sqrt{81}$ **26.** $\sqrt{16 + 9} - \sqrt{9}$

27. $\sqrt{12 + 13} + \sqrt{49}$ **28.** $\sqrt{81} - \sqrt{45 - 20}$ **29.** $\sqrt{64} - \sqrt{36 + 28}$

Extend and Apply

Write $<$, $>$, or $=$ in place of □ to make a true statement.

30. $\sqrt{25} + \sqrt{36}$ □ $\sqrt{25 + 36}$ **31.** $\sqrt{81} - \sqrt{4}$ □ $\sqrt{81 - 4}$

32. $\sqrt{16 - 9}$ □ $\sqrt{16} - \sqrt{9}$ **33.** $\sqrt{16 + 9}$ □ $\sqrt{16} + \sqrt{9}$

34. Evaluate the expression $3\sqrt{a} + \sqrt{b}$ for $a = 25$ and $b = 81$.

35. Evaluate the expression $\sqrt{\frac{a}{b}}$ for $a = 243$ and $b = 3$.

Use Mathematical Reasoning

Find the pattern and give the next two terms. Then complete the nth term.

36. $\sqrt{2^4} = 4$, $\sqrt{3^4} = 9$, $\sqrt{4^4} = 16$, ___?___ , ___?___, $\sqrt{n^4} =$ ___?___

37. $\sqrt{2^6} = 8$, $\sqrt{3^6} = 27$, $\sqrt{4^6} = 64$, ___?___ , ___?___ , $\sqrt{n^6} =$ ___?___

Mixed Review

Give the probability of drawing from a standard deck of 52 playing cards:

38. a diamond **39.** the king of spades **40.** a red ten

Connections Numbers to Algebra

Check to see that the number examples are true. Then replace a and b with other perfect squares to test the generalization given.

Numbers	Algebra
$\sqrt{4} \cdot \sqrt{9} = \sqrt{4 \cdot 9}$ $\sqrt{4} \cdot \sqrt{16} = \sqrt{4 \cdot 16}$ $\sqrt{9} \cdot \sqrt{16} = \sqrt{9 \cdot 16}$	For non-negative numbers a and b, $\sqrt{a}\sqrt{b} = \sqrt{ab}$

Use the generalization above to express each product as an integer.

1. $\sqrt{2} \cdot \sqrt{32}$ **2.** $\sqrt{18} \cdot \sqrt{2}$ **3.** $\sqrt{3} \cdot \sqrt{48}$ **4.** $\sqrt{5} \cdot \sqrt{20}$

5. $\sqrt{2} \cdot \sqrt{50}$ **6.** $\sqrt{8} \cdot \sqrt{18}$ **7.** $\sqrt{3} \cdot \sqrt{27}$ **8.** $\sqrt{6} \cdot \sqrt{24}$

15-2 Approximating Square Roots

Objective To approximate square roots that are irrational using a calculator or a square root table.

Application

Engineers often need to evaluate formulas that involve square roots. For example, the formula $t = \frac{\sqrt{d}}{4}$ can be used to calculate the time in seconds for an object to fall d feet. (See Example 2.)

Understand the Ideas

In the last section, you learned how to find the square root of a perfect square. But what about numbers that are not perfect squares, such as $\sqrt{7}$? We know that $\sqrt{4} = 2$ and $\sqrt{9} = 3$. Since 7 is between 4 and 9, $\sqrt{7}$ should be between $\sqrt{4}$ and $\sqrt{9}$. That is, $\sqrt{7}$ should be between 2 and 3.

The square root of any number that is not a perfect square is an *irrational* number, and we can only approximate it with a decimal. Using a calculator with a $\sqrt{}$ key or a square root table, you will find that $\sqrt{7} \approx 2.646$.

Example 1

Between what two consecutive integers does $\sqrt{18}$ lie?

Solution $4 < \sqrt{18} < 5$ Since $4^2 = 16$ and $5^2 = 25$, $\sqrt{18}$ is between 4 and 5.

Try This Between what two consecutive integers does each square root lie? **a.** $\sqrt{28}$ **b.** $\sqrt{53}$

Example 2

Use a calculator to evaluate the formula in the **application** to find the time (t), in seconds, it takes for an object to fall a distance (d) of 52 feet. Round to the nearest tenth of a second.

Solution $t = \frac{\sqrt{d}}{4}$

$t = \frac{\sqrt{52}}{4}$ Replace the variable d with 52. Evaluate.

$t = 52$ [√] [÷] 4 [=] 1.80277

It takes an object ≈ 1.8 seconds to fall 52 feet.

Try This

Evaluate the formula above for the values given.

c. $d = 256$ feet **d.** $d = 1{,}000$ feet **e.** $d = 5{,}280$ feet

Example 3

Use the table to find an approximation for $\sqrt{13}$.

Solution $\sqrt{13} \approx 3.606$

Look down the left column of the table to find 13. Then look across to the square root column to read 3.606.

Number n	Square Root $\sqrt{n}$	Square $\sqrt{n^2}$
7	2.646	49
8	2.828	64
9	3	81
10	3.162	100
11	3.317	121
12	3.464	144
13	3.606	169
14	3.742	196
15	3.873	225
16	4	256

Try This Use this table to find an approximate value for each.

f. $\sqrt{15}$ **g.** $\sqrt{11}$

Class Exercises

Give the closest integer estimate for each square root.

1. $\sqrt{12}$ **2.** $\sqrt{17}$ **3.** $\sqrt{24}$ **4.** $\sqrt{39}$

5. $\sqrt{27}$ **6.** $\sqrt{80}$ **7.** $\sqrt{50}$ **8.** $\sqrt{10}$

Discuss the Ideas

9. Compare the different methods of approximating the square root of a number. Which method gives the most accurate answer?

Exercises

Practice and Apply

Between what two consecutive integers does each square root lie?

1. $\sqrt{7}$ **2.** $\sqrt{12}$ **3.** $\sqrt{17}$ **4.** $-\sqrt{5}$ **5.** $\sqrt{43}$

6. $\sqrt{39}$ **7.** $-\sqrt{42}$ **8.** $\sqrt{38}$ **9.** $\sqrt{29}$ **10.** $-\sqrt{41}$

11. $\sqrt{24}$ **12.** $\sqrt{37}$ **13.** $\sqrt{85}$ **14.** $\sqrt{57}$ **15.** $\sqrt{112}$

Use the formula $D = 1.2\sqrt{A}$ to find the distance D (in miles) to the horizon from an airplane that is the given altitude A (in feet) above the ground. Round to the nearest mile.

16. $A = 3{,}600$ **17.** $A = 5{,}280$ **18.** $A = 15{,}000$ **19.** $A = 24{,}649$

Use the formula $t = \frac{\sqrt{d}}{4}$ to find the time t (in seconds) it takes for a parachutist to free-fall the given distance d (in feet). Round to the nearest tenth of a second.

20. $d = 400$ **21.** $d = 625$

22. $d = 2{,}304$ **23.** $d = 3{,}600$

Use the formula $T = 2\sqrt{L}$ to find the time T (in seconds) that it takes a pendulum with length L (in meters) to swing back and forth once. Round to the nearest tenth of a second.

24. $L = 3$ **25.** $L = 8.5$

26. $L = 1.2$ **27.** $L = 14.7$

Use the table on page 560 to find each square root.

28. $\sqrt{2}$ **29.** $\sqrt{5}$

30. $\sqrt{14}$ **31.** $\sqrt{17}$

32. $\sqrt{27}$ **33.** $\sqrt{10}$

34. $\sqrt{47}$ **35.** $\sqrt{93}$

Extend and Apply

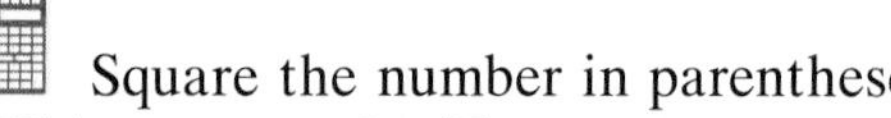

Square the number in parentheses. Write < or > for $\square$.

36. $(3.606)^2 \square 13$ **37.** $(1.414)^2 \square 2$

38. $(1.732)^2 \square 3$ **39.** $(2.828)^2 \square 8$

40. $(3.317)^2 \square 11$ **41.** $(3.873)^2 \square 15$

42. $(5.764)^2 \square 33$ **43.** $(4.444)^2 \square 20$

44. $(6.602)^2 \square 44$ **45.** $(5.454)^2 \square 30$

A square root can be multiplied by another number. For example, $6\sqrt{25} = 6 \times 5 = 30$. In Exercises 46–47, write <, >, or = in place of $\square$ to make a true statement.

46. $2\sqrt{16} \square \sqrt{32}$ **47.** $3\sqrt{9} \square \sqrt{27}$

Evaluate each formula.

48. $r = \sqrt{\frac{a}{\pi}}$ for $a = 121\pi$.

49. $D = \sqrt{a^2 + b^2 + c^2}$ where $a = 3$, $b = 7$, and $c = \sqrt{63}$. Hint: $c^2 = 63$.

Use Mathematical Reasoning

50. Choose nonzero whole numbers for a, b, and c so that $\sqrt{a} \cdot \sqrt{b} = \sqrt{c}$.

51. Find two solutions to $\sqrt{x} = x$.

Mixed Review

Use the figure at right for Exercises 52–55. Write and solve an equation to find each.

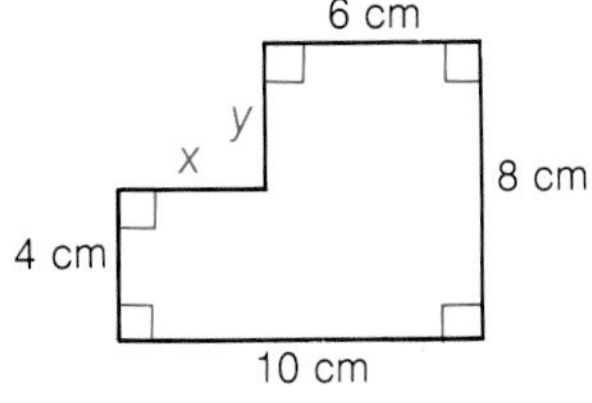

52. The length of x.
53. The length of y.
54. The perimeter of the figure.
55. The area of the figure.

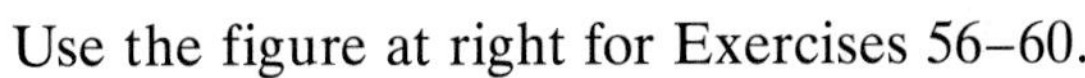

Use the figure at right for Exercises 56–60.

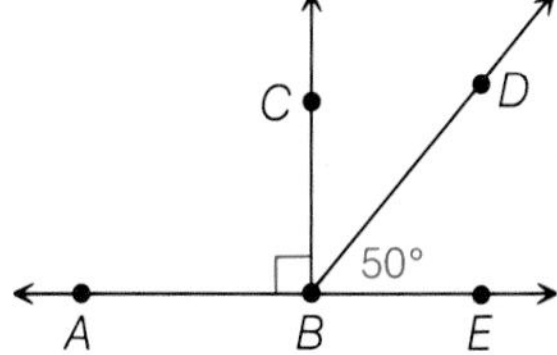

56. Name a pair of supplementary angles.
57. Name a pair of complementary angles.
58. Name a right angle.

Write an equation to find the measure of: **59.** $\angle CBD$ **60.** $\angle ABD$

Solve and check. **61.** $5m - 2m = 27$ **62.** $4.5c + 6.9c = 45.6$

63. $11 = 9x + 6.5$ **64.** $3t = 12 - 5t$ **65.** $21m + 16 = 79$

Computer Activity

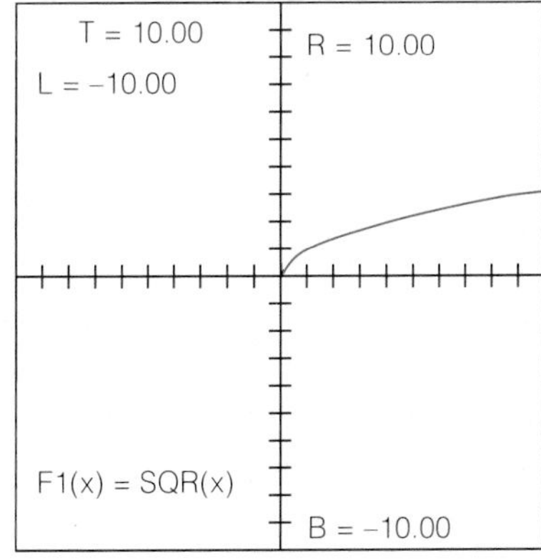

The square root function can be graphed using a computer graphing utility, such as Master Grapher or a graphing calculator. The function is $f(x) = \sqrt{x}$. There is no square root symbol on the keyboard so a function name such as SQR is used, $f(x) =$ SQR(x). The values of the square root are the y-coordinates in the ordered pair $(x, f(x))$.

Special features of the graphing utility can be used to find square roots. You can change the units on the axes and you can zoom in on points. Use a graphing utility to find the following to the nearest tenth.

1. $\sqrt{4}$ **2.** $\sqrt{8}$ **3.** $\sqrt{79}$

15-3 Solving Equations: Using Square Roots

Objective To solve equations of the form $x^2 = k$.

Understand the Ideas

To solve equations of the form $x^2 = 25$, you need to use the property shown by these equations.

$$\sqrt{5^2} = \sqrt{25} = 5 \qquad \sqrt{(-7)^2} = \sqrt{49} = |-7| = 7$$

The general property is stated as follows.

The Square Root Property

For any number x, $\sqrt{x^2} = |x|$.

When both sides of an equation are positive, you can find the square root of both sides and the equality is maintained. These equations have two solutions since there is both a positive and a negative square root.

Example 1

Solve and check. $x^2 = 25$

Solution

$x^2 = 25$

$\sqrt{x^2} = \sqrt{25}$ — Undo squaring by finding the square root of both sides.

$|x| = \sqrt{25}$ — Use the property $\sqrt{x^2} = |x|$ on the left side.

$x = 5$ or $x = -5$

Check $5^2 = 25$ and $(-5)^2 = 25$

Try This

Solve and check.

a. $x^2 = 49$ **b.** $x^2 = 100$

Remember that the square root of any whole number that is not a perfect square is an irrational number, and we can only approximate it with a decimal. Therefore, the exact value of such a square root is represented using the radical sign.

Example 2

Solve and check. Give both an exact and an approximate solution.
$w^2 = 17$.

Solution

$$w^2 = 17$$
$$\sqrt{w^2} = \sqrt{17}$$
$$|w| = \sqrt{17}$$
$$w = \sqrt{17} \text{ or } w = -\sqrt{17}$$ When $\sqrt{w^2}$ is not an integer, write the exact answer using the $\sqrt{\ }$ symbol.

$w = 17$ [$\sqrt{\ }$] [4.1231056] Use the $\sqrt{\ }$ key.

≈ 4.123 or -4.123 Write the approximate positive and negative answers.

Check

$$(\sqrt{17})^2 \stackrel{?}{=} 17$$ Replace x with $\sqrt{17}$ and $-\sqrt{17}$ in $x^2 = 17$.
$$(-\sqrt{17})^2 \stackrel{?}{=} 17$$
$$17 = 17 \checkmark$$

Try This

Solve and check. Give an exact and an approximate solution.

c. $x^2 = 39$ **d.** $x^2 = 73$

Example 3

Solve and check. $x^2 - 5 = 20$

Solution

$$x^2 - 5 = 20$$
$$x^2 - 5 + 5 = 20 + 5$$ Add 5 to both sides.
$$x^2 = 25$$
$$\sqrt{x^2} = \sqrt{25}$$ Find the square root of both sides.
$$x = 5 \text{ or } x = -5$$

Check $5^2 - 5 = 20$ and $(-5)^2 - 5 = 20$

$25 - 5 = 20 \checkmark$ and $25 - 5 = 20 \checkmark$

Try This

Solve and check.

e. $x^2 - 9 = 0$ **f.** $x^2 + 3 = 19$

Class Exercises

State whether the equation has integer solutions.

1. $x^2 = 16$ **2.** $x^2 = 64$ **3.** $x^2 = 85$ **4.** $x^2 = 48$

5. $x^2 = 121$ **6.** $x^2 = 144$ **7.** $x^2 = 81$ **8.** $x^2 = 65$

Discuss the Ideas

9. Does $x^2 + 46 = 0$ have a solution? Explain.

Exercises

Practice and Apply

Solve and check. Give both an exact and an approximate solution when appropriate. Round to the nearest hundredth.

1. $x^2 = 16$ **2.** $x^2 = 36$ **3.** $x^2 = 81$

4. $x^2 = 47$ **5.** $x^2 = 121$ **6.** $x^2 = 38$

7. $x^2 = 56$ **8.** $x^2 = 196$ **9.** $x^2 = 132$

10. $x^2 = 144$ **11.** $x^2 = 53$ **12.** $x^2 = 99$

13. $x^2 - 25 = 0$ **14.** $x^2 + 7 = 43$ **15.** $x^2 + 11 = 111$

16. $x^2 + 15 = 40$ **17.** $x^2 - 9 = 40$ **18.** $x^2 + 34 = 70$

19. $x^2 + 3 = 52$ **20.** $x^2 - 8 = 41$ **21.** $x^2 + 9 = 90$

22. Ben said, "If I square my age, I am 225 years old." How old is Ben?

23. Ben's sister is only 121 when you square her age. How old is she?

Extend and Apply

Solve and check. Give both an exact answer and an estimate.

24. $x^2 - 13 = 100$ **25.** $x^2 + 5 = 60$ **26.** $x^2 - 9 = 90$

27. $3x^2 = 90$ **28.** $4x^2 = 88$ **29.** $5x^2 = 160$

Use Mathematical Reasoning

Find two solutions to each equation.

30. $x^2 = x$ **31.** $x^2 = x + 2$ **32.** $x^2 = -x$

Mixed Review

What percent of 60 is: **33.** 33? **34.** 45? **35.** 12? **36.** 20?

Solve and check. **37.** $16t + 13t = 15t + 28$ **38.** $4.2c - 11 = 1.6$

Solve. **39.** How many cubic yards of concrete are needed for a driveway 54 feet long, 12 feet wide and 6 inches thick?

40. You throw a die twice. Find the probability of rolling a 3 and then a 4.

Estimation

To estimate the square root of a number that is not a perfect square, you can choose compatible numbers. For example, $\sqrt{26} \approx \sqrt{25} = 5$, so $\sqrt{26} \approx 5$.

Use compatible numbers to estimate these square roots.

1. $\sqrt{37}$ **2.** $\sqrt{80}$ **3.** $\sqrt{99}$ **4.** $\sqrt{10}$ **5.** $\sqrt{15}$

15-4 Pythagorean Theorem

Objective To use the Pythagorean Theorem to find unknown lengths of sides of right triangles.

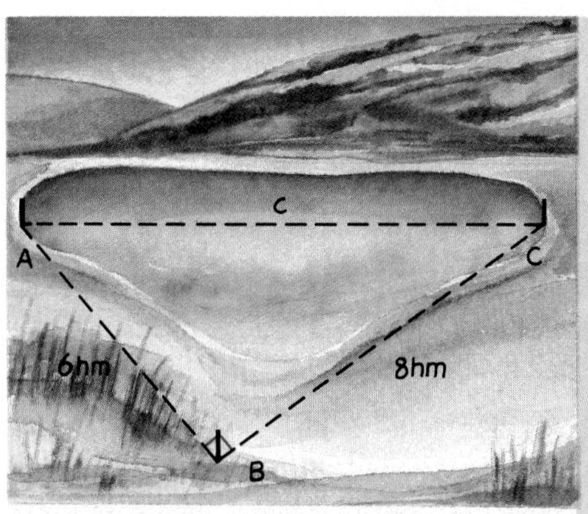

Application

A surveyor had poles at points marked A, B, and C. The distances that could be measured are shown on the diagram. What is the approximate distance across the pond?

Understand the Ideas

The longest side of a right triangle, the side opposite the right angle, is called the **hypotenuse**. The two shorter sides are called the **legs** of the triangle.

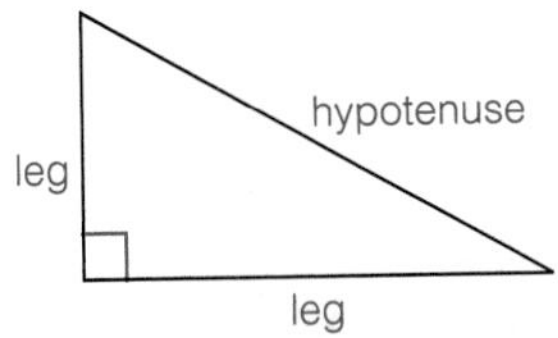

The triangle in the figure below has sides that are 3, 4, and 5 units long. The areas of the squares that have been constructed on each side show that the square of the hypotenuse is equal to the sum of the squares of the two legs.

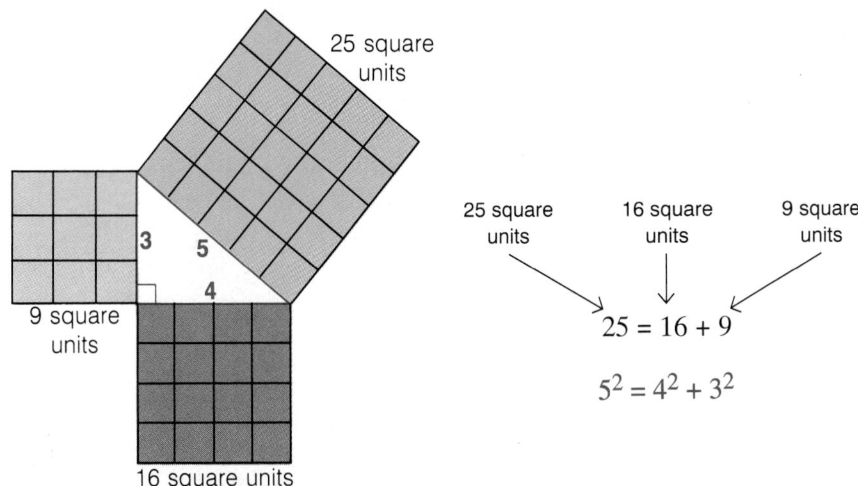

This suggests the following theorem.

The Pythagorean Theorem

In a right triangle, the square of the length of the hypotenuse is equal to the sum of the squares of the lengths of the two legs. If c is the length of the hypotenuse and a and b are the lengths of the two legs,

$c^2 = a^2 + b^2$

Example 1

Find the distance AC across the pond shown in the **application.**

Solution

$c^2 = a^2 + b^2$	Use the Pythagorean Theorem.
$c^2 = 6^2 + 8^2$	Substitute 6 for a and 8 for b.
$c^2 = 36 + 64$	Square terms and add.
$c^2 = 100$	
$c = \sqrt{100} = 10$	Since c represents a length, its value is the positive square root.

The distance across the pond is 10 hm.

Try This Draw a right triangle with hypotenuse c and legs a and b.

a. Find length c if $a = 5$ and $b = 12$.

b. Find length c if $a = 7$ and $b = 15$.

Example 2

Find the length of leg a. Express your answer in radical form.

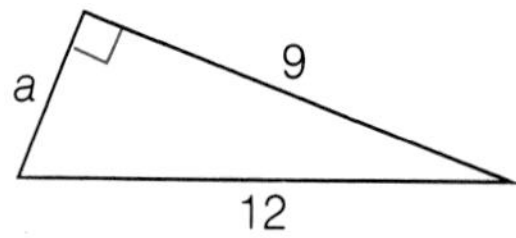

Solution

$a^2 + b^2 = c^2$	Use the Pythagorean Theorem.
$a^2 + 9^2 = 12^2$	Substitute 9 for b and 12 for c.
$a^2 + 81 - 81 = 144 - 81$	
$a^2 = 63$	
$a = \sqrt{63}$	The length of leg a is $\sqrt{63}$.

Try This Draw a right triangle with hypotenuse c and legs a and b.

c. Find the length of leg a if $c = 15$ and $b = 8$.

d. Find the length of leg a if $b = 6$, $c = 14$.

Class Exercises

Which statements about legs a and b and hypotenuse c of a right triangle are true and which are false?

1. $c^2 = a^2 + b^2$

2. $a^2 = b^2 + c^2$

3. $b^2 = c^2 - a^2$

4. $a^2 = b^2 - c^2$

5. $b^2 = a^2 - c^2$

6. $a^2 = c^2 - b^2$

Discuss the Ideas

7. Do you think the Pythagorean Theorem can be used to find the length of the third side of any triangle when the lengths of two sides are known? Explain.

Exercises

Practice and Apply

Find the length of the hypotenuse.

1.

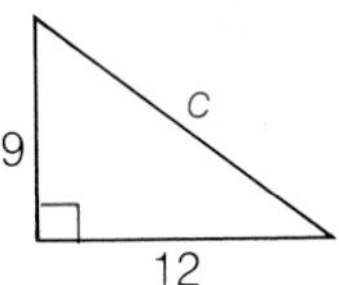

2.

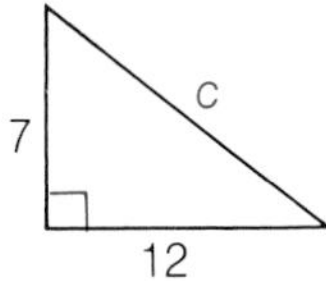

3.

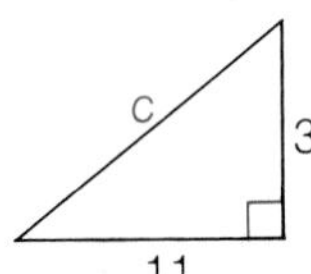

Draw a right triangle with legs a and b and hypotenuse c for Exercises 4–9. Find the length of c. If c is not an integer, express in radical form.

4. $a = 8$ and $b = 12$. Find c.

5. $a = 8$ and $b = 15$. Find c.

6. $a = 12$ and $b = 5$. Find c.

7. $a = 9$ and $b = 40$. Find c.

8. $a = 10$ and $b = 16$. Find c.

9. $a = 15$ and $b = 6$. Find c.

Find the missing length of leg a.

10.

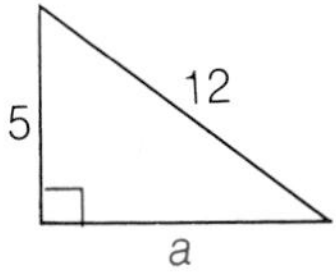

11.

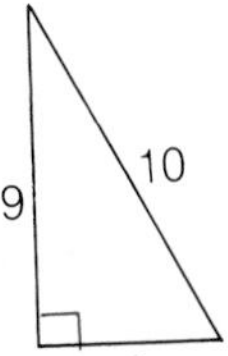

12.

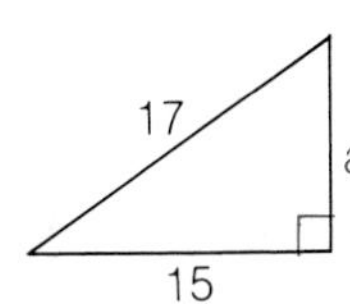

Draw a right triangle with legs a and b and hypotenuse c to use for Exercises 13–18. Find the length.

13. $a = 6$ and $c = 13$. Find b.

14. $a = 10$ and $c = 20$. Find b.

15. $b = 13$ and $c = 15$. Find a.

16. $b = 6$ and $c = 12$. Find a.

17. $a = 18$ and $c = 23$. Find b.

18. $a = 12$ and $c = 15$. Find b.

19. The base of a 32-foot ladder is 10 feet from the building. How high above the ground is the top of the ladder?

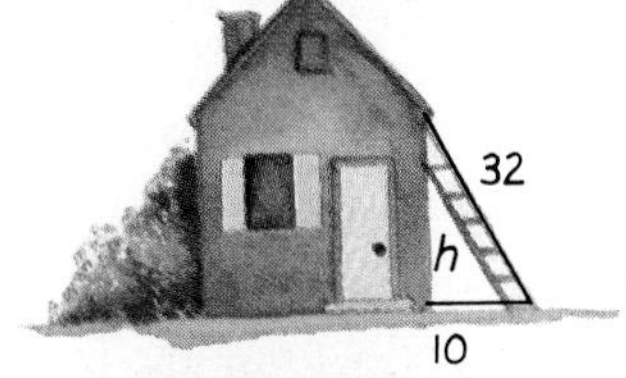

20. What is the diagonal distance across the garden shown at the right?

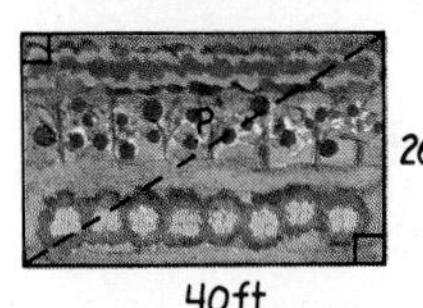

The **converse** of the Pythagorean Theorem allows you to determine if a triangle is a right triangle when you are given the lengths of the sides. If a triangle has side lengths a, b, and c, and $a^2 + b^2 = c^2$, then you have a right triangle. Which of these triples are sides of a right triangle?

21. 40, 50, 60 **22.** 5, 12, 13 **23.** 7, 15, 21 **24.** 8, 15, 17

25. 9, 11, 17 **26.** 7, 24, 25 **27.** 20, 21, 29 **28.** 9, 29, 36

Extend and Apply

29. A person travels 8 mi due north, 3 mi due west, 7 mi due north, and 11 mi due east. How far is that person from the starting point?

30. A door is 6 ft 6 in. by 36 in. Can a thin piece of plywood 7 ft wide be carried through the doorway?

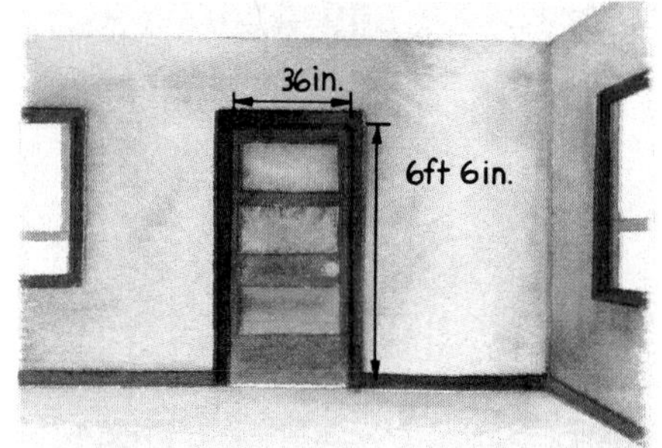

31. A road climbs 800 ft as you travel a horizontal distance of 3 mi. How much longer is the road surface than the horizontal distance? (5,280 ft = 1 mi)

32. How high was the telephone pole before it was broken?

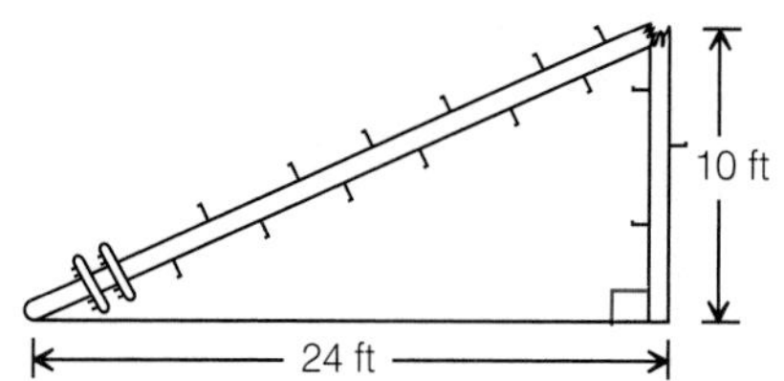

Use Mathematical Reasoning

Suppose that u and v are any two whole numbers. Let x, y, and z be the following three numbers: $x = 2uv$, $y = u^2 - v^2$, $z = u^2 + v^2$. For which of these values of u and v are x, y, and z sides of a right triangle?

33. $u = 4, v = 1$ **34.** $u = 4, v = 3$ **35.** $u = 5, v = 2$

Mixed Review

Simplify. **36.** $6t + 9 - 4t - 1$ **37.** $9c - 6c - 12$ **38.** $2n + 4n + 12$

Solve and check. **39.** $3.6y = 5y - 0.7$ **40.** $9x + 6 = 8.7$

Mental Math

These equations show a way to square mentally a 2-digit number ending in 5. Study the pattern.

$15 \cdot 15 = (10 \cdot 20) + 25 = 225$ $25 \cdot 25 = (20 \cdot 30) + 25 = 625$

$35 \cdot 35 = (30 \cdot 40) + 25 = 1225$ $45 \cdot 45 = (40 \cdot 50) + 25 = 2025$

Use mental math to find each product.

1. $55 \cdot 55$ **2.** $65 \cdot 65$ **3.** $75 \cdot 75$ **4.** $85 \cdot 85$ **5.** $95 \cdot 95$

15-5 Problem Solving: Applications

Sports Playing Areas

Objective To solve word problems.

Many sports are played in rectangular areas. The table below lists the dimensions commonly used for several sports.

Playing Area Dimensions	
Sport	**Dimensions**
Boxing	20 ft × 20 ft
Karate	26 ft × 26 ft
Wrestling	39 ft 3 in. × 39 ft 3 in.
Judo	52 ft 6 in. × 52 ft 6 in.
Basketball	28 yd × 15 yd 9 in.
Ice Hockey	200 ft × 100 ft
U.S. Football	120 yd × 53 yd
Soccer	110 yd × 80 yd

Problems

Use the data from the table to solve.

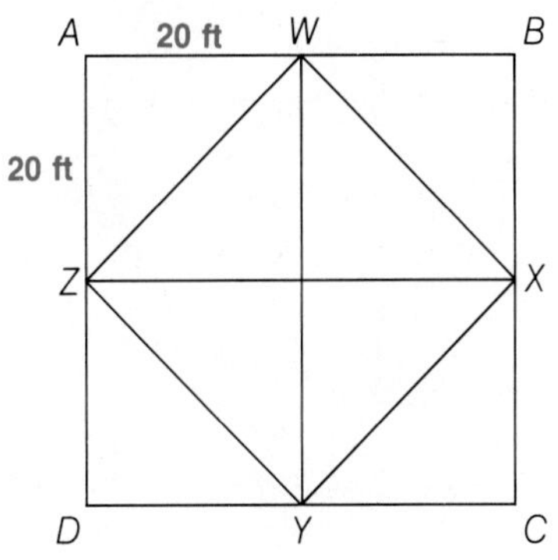

1. This gymnasium floor has overlapping areas drawn to allow for several different sports. The square *ABCD* is divided into quarters for use as four boxing areas. Is the square *WXYZ* large enough for karate?

2. Suppose that in the figure above, $AW = AZ = 39$ ft 3 in. and the square is used for wrestling. Is square *WXYZ* large enough to be used for judo?

3. How many basketball courts could fit on a football field?

4. When a basketball court *QRST* is laid out, *QRST* must be a rectangle. A way of checking this is to measure the diagonals *QS* and *RT* to make sure they are the same length. How long are these diagonals?

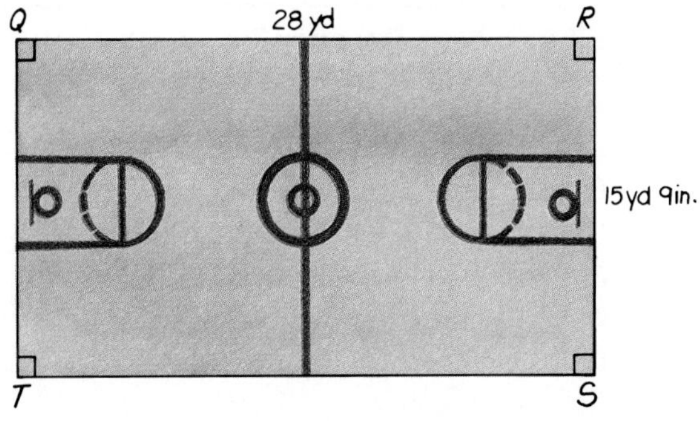

5. What is the length of the diagonal of a soccer field? (This is the longest possible kick that would keep the ball in play.)
6. Suppose that in the top figure on page 539, $AW = AZ = 26$ ft and the square is used for karate. Is square $WXYZ$ large enough to be used for wrestling?
7. A football field $ABCD$ and a soccer field $WXYZ$ are to be laid out in overlapping fashion, as shown (O is the center of both fields). The people painting the lines want to know the length AW. What is it?

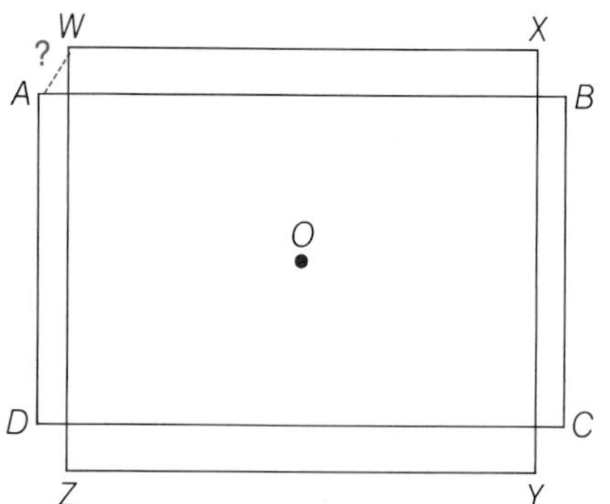

8. The ratio of length to width for the ice hockey field is 2 to 1. Which playing field listed in the table has the greatest length to width ratio?
9. **Data Search** Find the cost of grass seed in your area and estimate the cost of grass seed for a soccer field and a football field.

What's Your Decision?

A school board bought a piece of land with the dimensions shown. On the land, they want to lay out football and soccer practice fields and six basketball courts. How would you arrange these playing fields on the land?

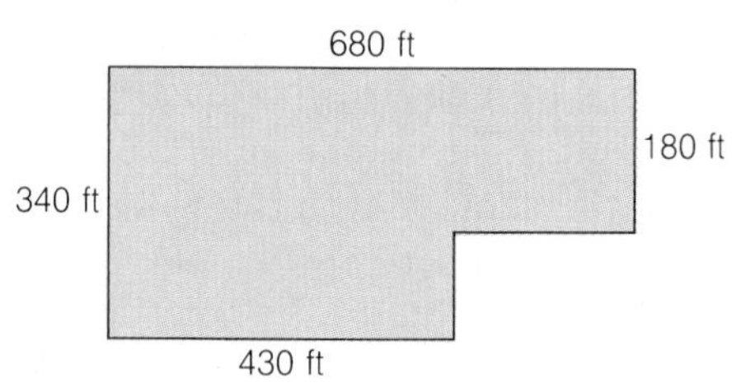

15-6 Similar Polygons

Objective To determine lengths of corresponding sides of similar polygons.

Explore

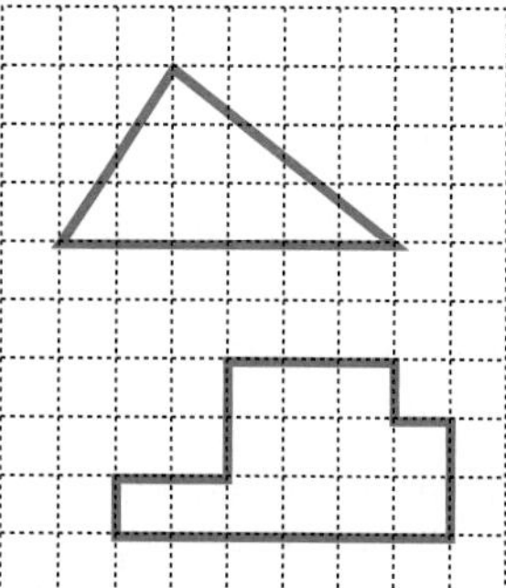

- Copy the triangle at the right on graph paper. Draw another triangle with each side twice as long.
- Find the area of both triangles. What is the ratio of the area of the large triangle to the area of the small triangle?
- Copy the polygon at the right on graph paper. Draw another polygon with each side three times as long.
- Find the area of both polygons. What is the ratio of the area of the large polygon to the small polygon?

Understand the Ideas

Polygons that are the same shape but not necessarily the same size are called **similar** polygons. Two triangles that are similar have matching congruent angles, called corresponding angles. Corresponding angles are shown by matching arc symbols.

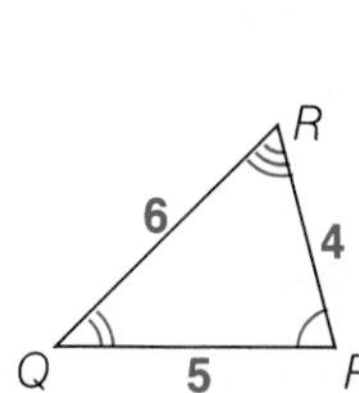

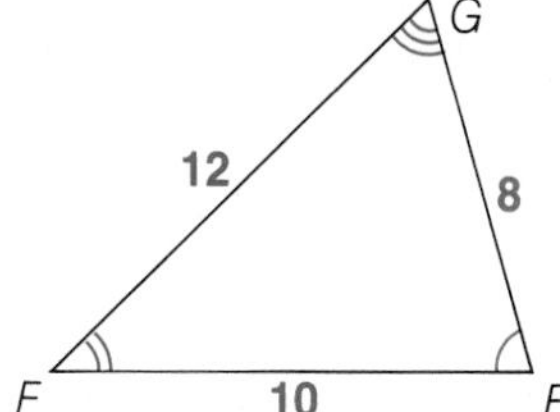

Corresponding angles
$\angle P$ and $\angle E$
$\angle Q$ and $\angle F$
$\angle R$ and $\angle G$

The following generalization is true for all pairs of similar triangles.

Lengths of corresponding sides of similar triangles are proportional.

In the above figures the three ratios of corresponding sides all equal $\frac{1}{2}$.

$$\frac{QR}{FG} = \frac{6}{12} = \frac{1}{2} \qquad \frac{PR}{EG} = \frac{4}{8} = \frac{1}{2} \qquad \frac{PQ}{EF} = \frac{5}{10} = \frac{1}{2}$$

You can use this idea to find lengths of sides of similar triangles. The symbol $\sim$ means *is similar to*. We write $\triangle \boldsymbol{PQR} \sim \triangle \boldsymbol{EFG}$.

Example

$\triangle PQR \sim \triangle XYZ$. Use a proportion to find r.

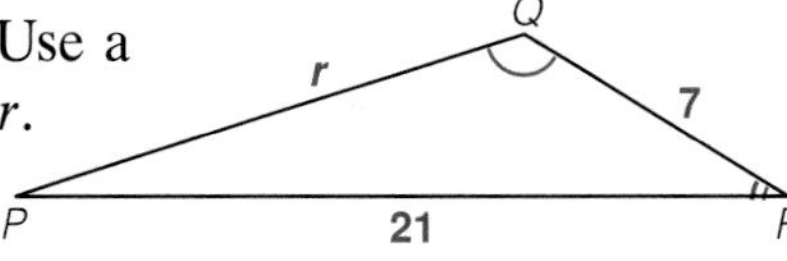

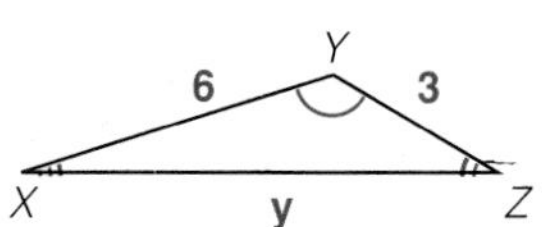

Solution

$\frac{QR}{YZ} = \frac{PQ}{XY}$ QR corresponds to YZ. PQ corresponds to XY. Lengths of corresponding sides are proportional.

$\frac{7}{3} = \frac{r}{6}$ Substitute lengths of sides in the proportion.

$7 \cdot 6 = 3 \cdot r$

$42 = 3r$

$14 = r$

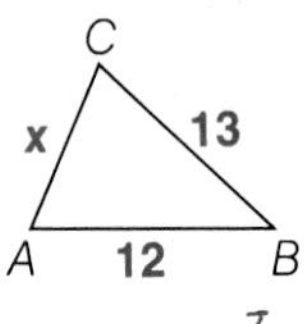

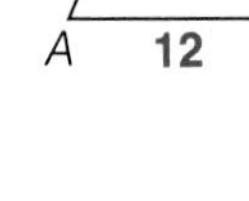

Try This $\triangle ABC \sim \triangle XYZ$

Use the proportion to find:

a. x **b.** y

Class Exercises

Name the corresponding angles and sides for these similar triangles.

1.

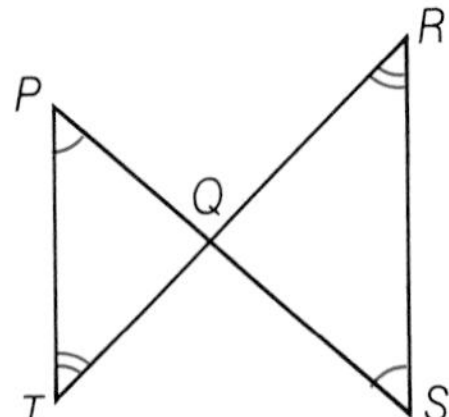

2.

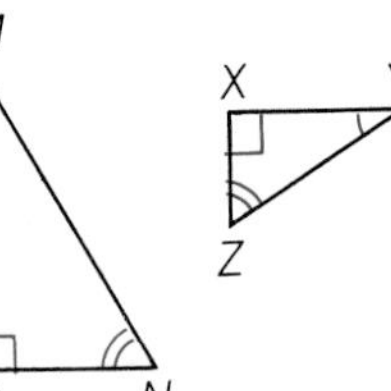

3.

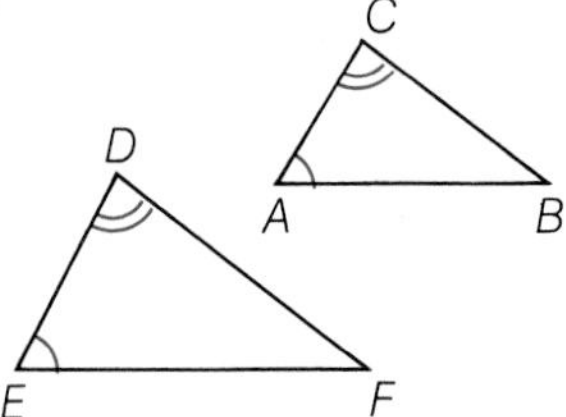

Discuss the Ideas

4. Explain why these rectangles are not similar.

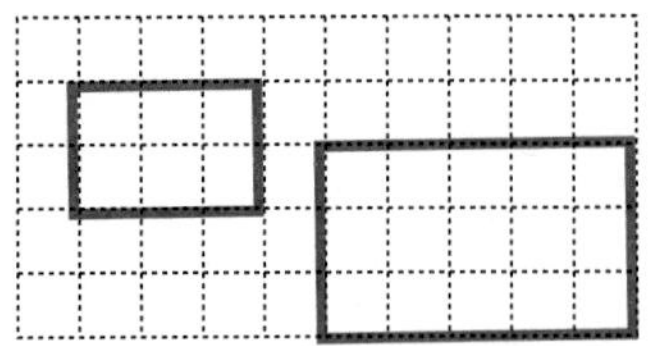

Exercises

Practice and Apply

Use proportions to find the unknown lengths for these similar triangles.

1.

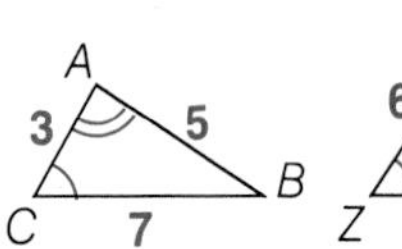

2.

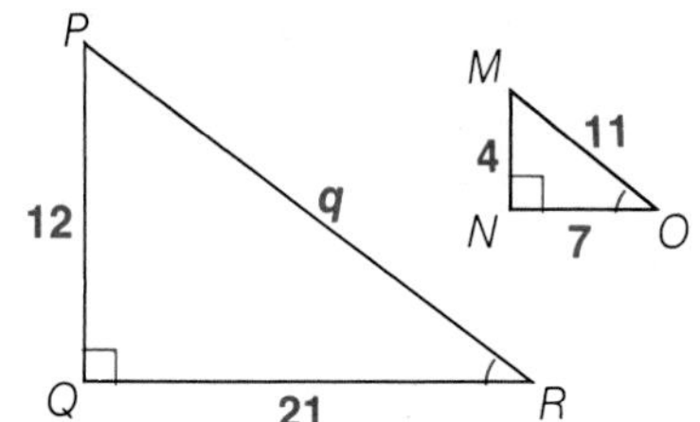

3.

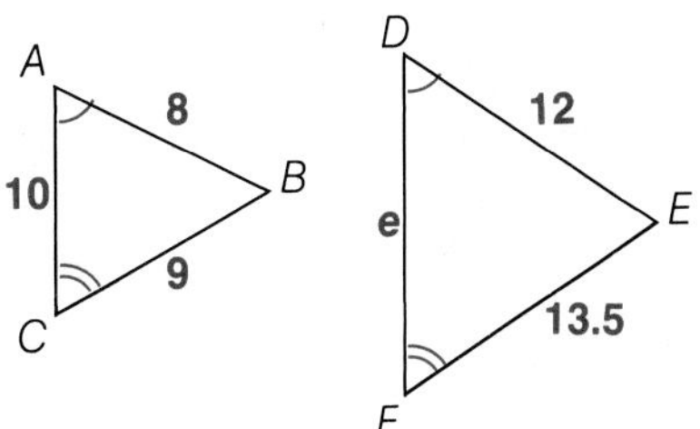

4.

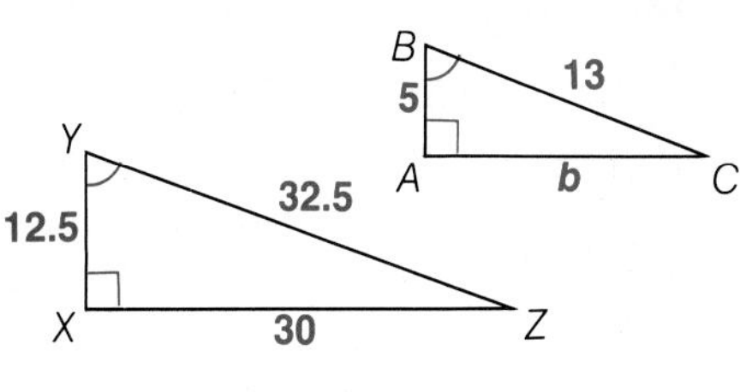

5. The distance across a river can be found by laying out two similar right triangles. What is the distance across the river?

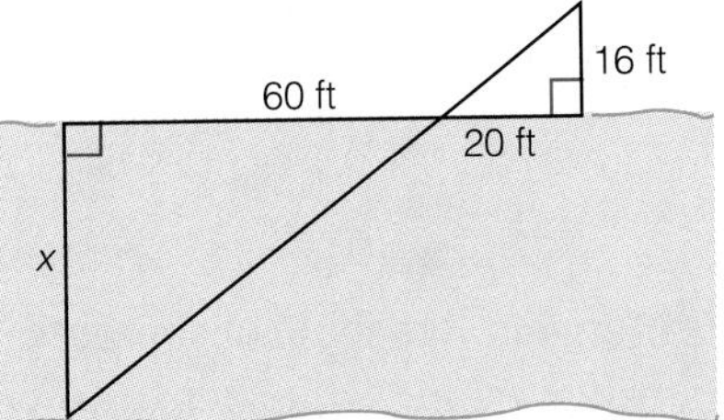

6. Melvin is 1.8 m tall. On a sunny day, his shadow was 2 m long at the same time that the shadow of a lamppost was 7 m long. Find the height of the lamppost.

Extend and Apply

Use a proportion to find the unknown lengths for these similar triangles.

7.

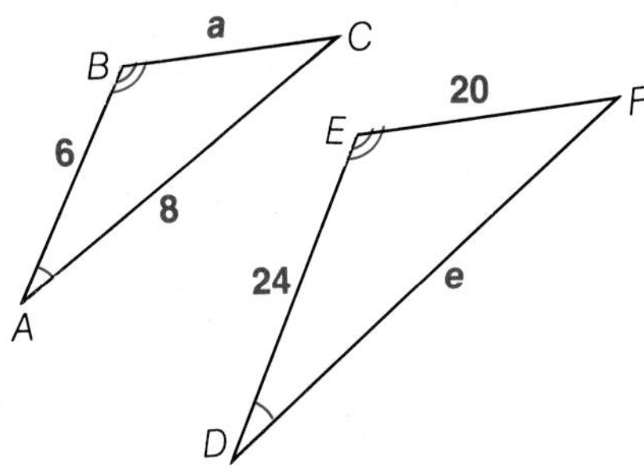

8.

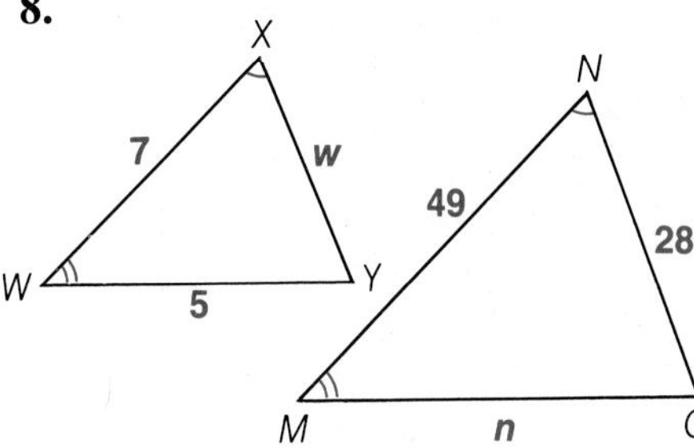

9.

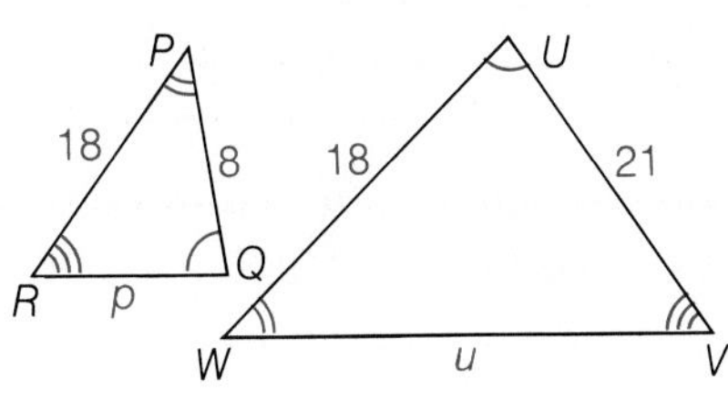

10.

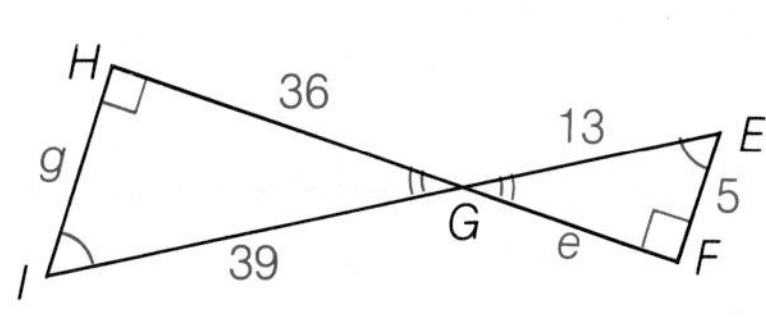

11. Find the distance (d) across the pond if the small triangle is similar to the large triangle.

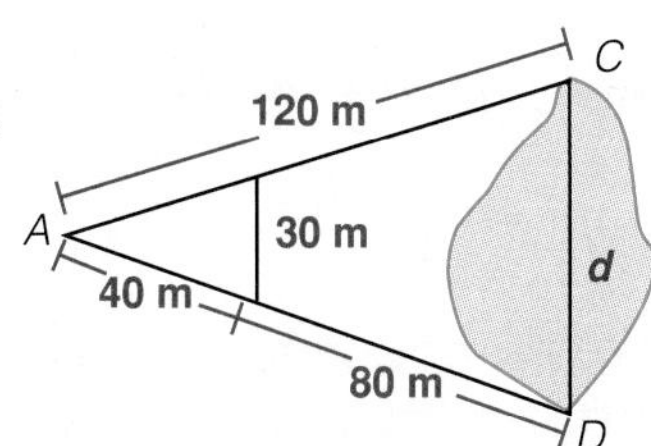

12. Find the height (h) of the wall.

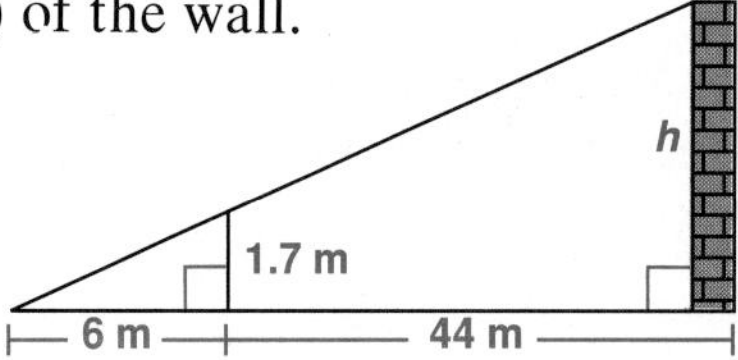

13. A surveyor needs to find the length AB, but the garage is in the way. $\triangle ABC \sim \triangle DEC$. What is the length of AB?

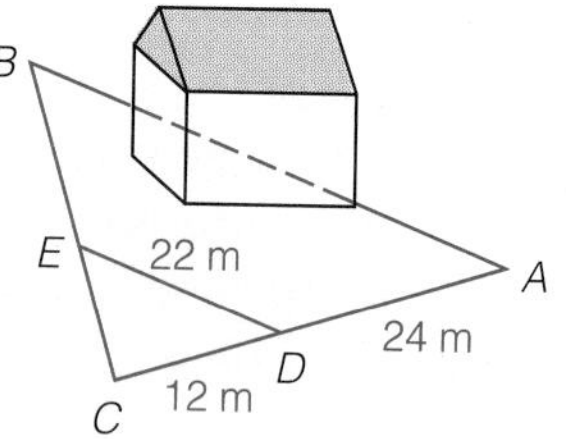

14. **Determine Reasonable Answers** Use graph paper to draw pairs of similar triangles to help you complete the following statement.

In its final approach, an airplane loses about 300 feet of altitude for every 1,500 feet of horizontal distance traveled. If that rate of descent continues over 10 miles, the plane's altitude will decrease about:

a. 2,000 ft **b.** 5,000 ft **c.** 10,000 ft **d.** 30,000 ft

Use Mathematical Reasoning

15. Triangle ABC at right is similar to a larger triangle PQR (not shown). The ratio of corresponding sides is 2:1. What is the area of each triangle?

16. This table shows the areas of rectangles of given lengths and widths.

length	2	4	8	...	x	$2x$
width	3	6	12	...	y	$2y$
area	6	24	96	...	xy	$4xy$

Complete the following generalization. If the length and width of a rectangle are both doubled, the area of the rectangle is increased by a factor of __?__

Mixed Review

Reduce to simplest terms. **17.** $\frac{18}{84}$ **18.** $\frac{52}{65}$ **19.** $\frac{45}{63}$ **20.** $\frac{54}{6}$

Solve and check. **21.** $4n + 9n = 10 + 12n$ **22.** $2.4y = y + 7$

Solve. **23.** Leslie worked for $5\frac{1}{2}$ hours on Saturday and $6\frac{3}{4}$ hours on Sunday. How many hours did she work all together for these two days?

15-7 Special Triangles

Objective To find lengths of sides of special triangles.

Understand the Ideas

The two acute angles of an isosceles right triangle are both 45° angles. An isosceles right triangle is called a **45°-45° right triangle.**

You can use the Pythagorean Theorem to show that the length of the hypotenuse of the 45°-45° right triangle ABC is $\sqrt{2}$ when the legs are length 1.

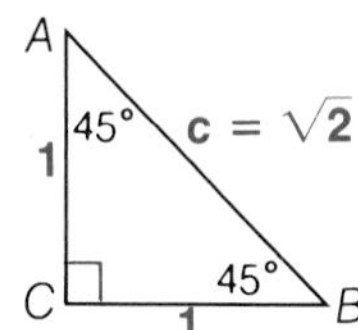

$$c^2 = 1^2 + 1^2$$
$$c^2 = 2$$
$$c = \sqrt{2}$$

$\triangle DEF$ below is a 45°-45° right triangle with legs a units long. We use the fact that $\triangle ABC \sim \triangle DEF$ to write the proportion below.

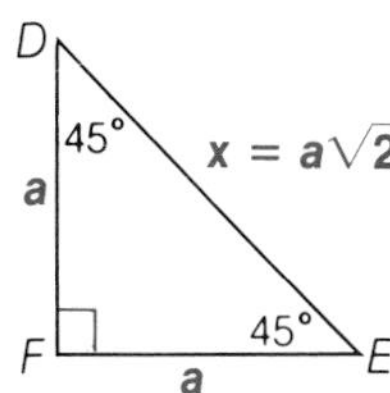

$$\frac{a}{1} = \frac{x}{\sqrt{2}} \quad \text{or} \quad x = a\sqrt{2}$$

Formula **45°-45° Right Triangle**

If a 45°-45° right triangle has legs $\boldsymbol{a}$ units long, then the hypotenuse is $\boldsymbol{a\sqrt{2}}$ units long.

Example 1

Find length x.

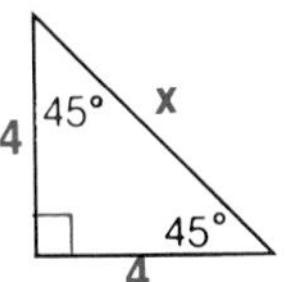

Solution

$x = 4\sqrt{2}$ x is equal to the length of the leg times $\sqrt{2}$.

Try This

a. Draw a 45°-45° triangle. Find the length of the hypotenuse if the length of each leg is 5.

An **altitude** of an equilateral triangle bisects an angle and a base to form two right triangles. Each of these triangles has a 30° angle and a 60° angle and is called a **30°-60° right triangle.**

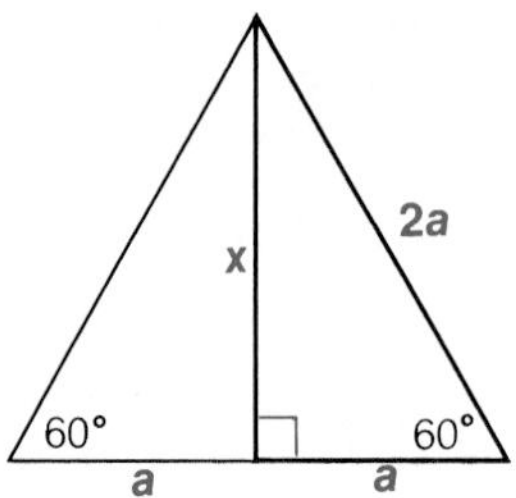

The short leg of the 30°-60° right triangle is half as long as the hypotenuse. If the hypotenuse is length **2*a*,** the short leg has length ***a*.**

You can use the Pythagorean Theorem to find the length of the long leg of the 30°-60° right triangle.

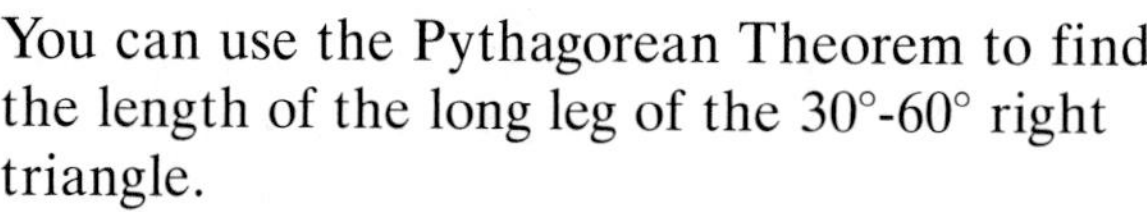

$$(2a)^2 = x^2 + a^2$$
$$4a^2 = x^2 + a^2$$
$$3a^2 = x^2$$
$$\sqrt{3}a = x$$

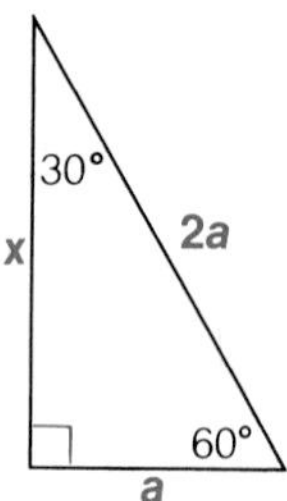

Formula 30°-60° Right Triangles

If a 30°-60° right triangle has a shorter leg ***a*** units long, then the longer leg is ***a*$\sqrt{3}$** units long and the hypotenuse is **2*a*** units long.

Example 2

Find lengths x and y.

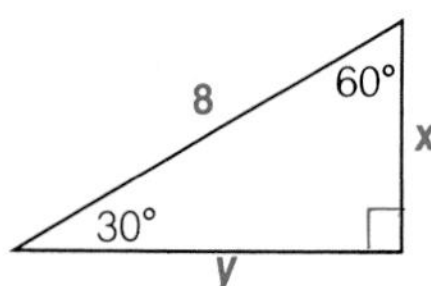

Solution

$x = \frac{8}{2} = 4$ The short leg of a 30°-60° right triangle is half the length of the hypotenuse.

$y = 4\sqrt{3}$ The long leg of a 30°-60° right triangle is $\sqrt{3}$ times the length of the short leg.

Try This **b.** Draw a 30°-60° right triangle. Find the lengths of the legs if the hypotenuse is 5.

Class Exercises

Is it possible for a right triangle to have side lengths as shown?

1.

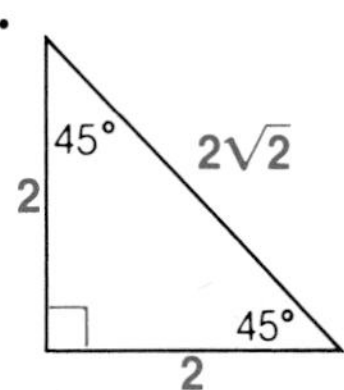

2.

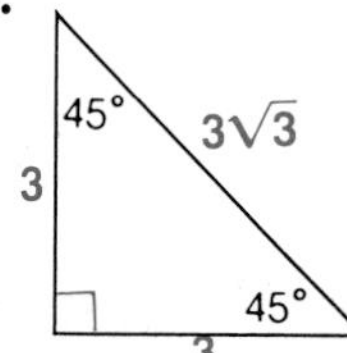

3.

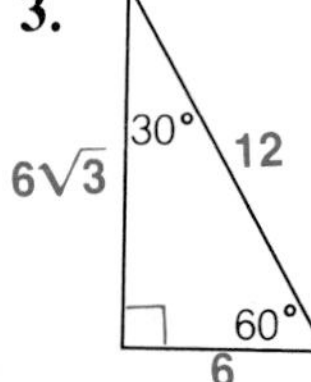

4.

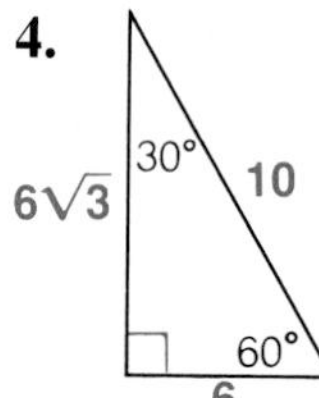

Discuss the Ideas

5. A 45°-45° right triangle is sometimes called an isosceles right triangle. Discuss why this is also an appropriate title.

Exercises

Practice and Apply

Find the unknown lengths.

1. 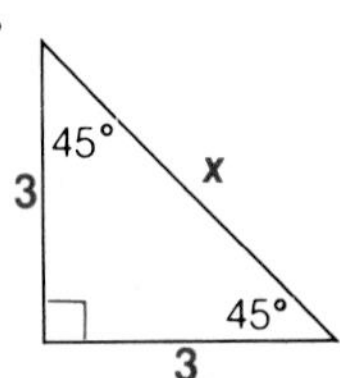

2. 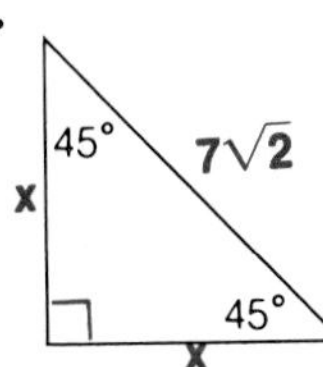

3. 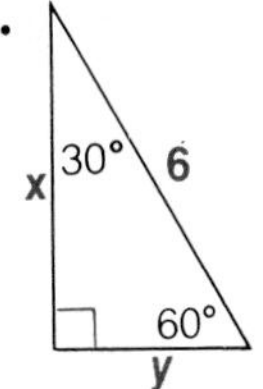

4. 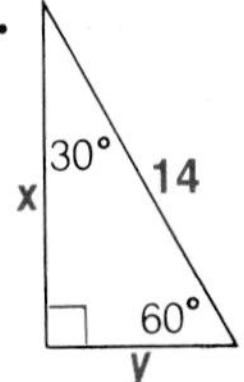

5. Draw a 45°-45° right triangle. What is the length of the hypotenuse if the length of each leg is 5? 4.3?.
6. Draw a 30°-60° right triangle. What is the length of the legs if the length of the hypotenuse is 25? $2\sqrt{3}$?
7. On a baseball diamond, the distance between bases is 90 ft. Find the approximate distance from home plate to second base.
8. The end of a tent is shaped like an equilateral triangle. If the base of the tent is 5 feet across, how high is the tent?

Extend and Apply

Solve. Use the approximations $\sqrt{2} \approx 1.414$ and $\sqrt{3} \approx 1.732$.

Refer to the planter box at right for Exercises 9 and 10. The side of a planter box is shaped like a trapezoid, with dimensions as shown.

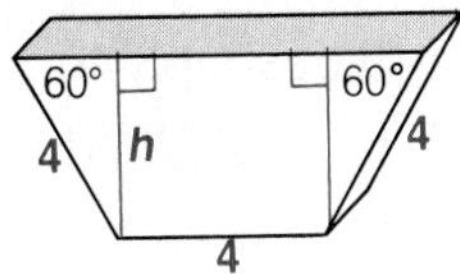

9. Find the height of the planter.
10. Find the length of the upper edge of the side of the planter.

Use Mathematical Reasoning

11. Triangle ABC is drawn on the surface of a box whose length, width, and height are all 1. What is the length of AB?
12. What is the area of $\triangle ABC$?

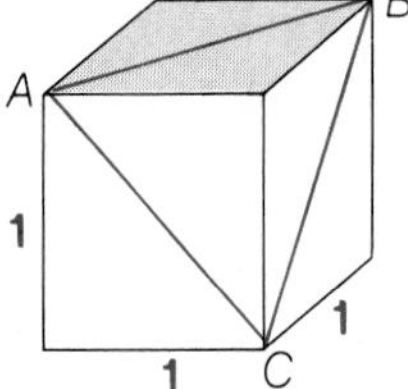

Mixed Review

Solve and check. **13.** $35 = 5c + 2c$ **14.** $m + 16 = 17$

15. $10 + 2m = 13$ **16.** $t + 6t = -42$ **17.** $14 - 2m = 18$

15-8

More About Functions

Objective To explore nonlinear functions.

Explore

Examine the graphs below. Guess which graph represents $y = x^2$, which represents $y = \sqrt{x}$ (for positive values of x only), and which represents $y = |x|$. Explain your guesses.

A.

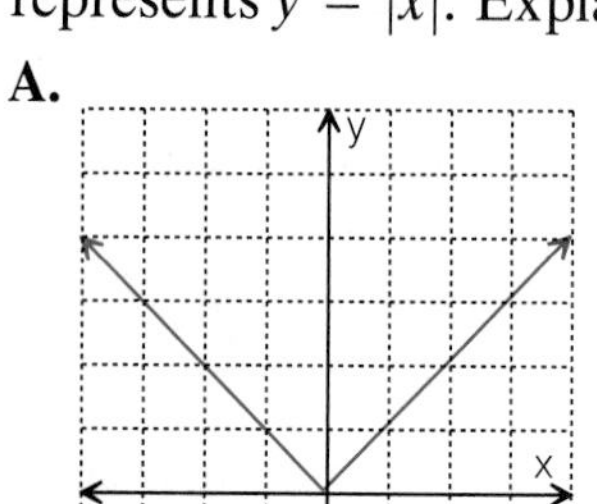

B.

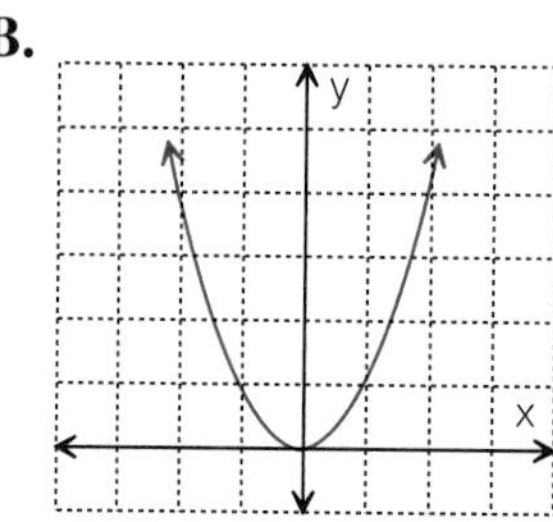

C.

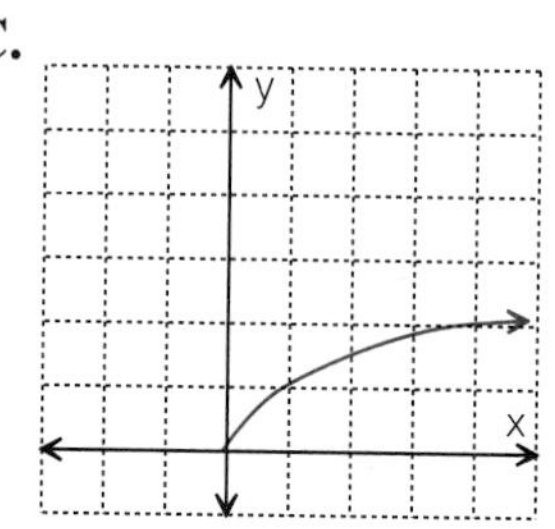

Use a computer or a graphing calculator to graph each of the equations above and check your guesses.

Understand the Ideas

In Chapter 9, you studied functions whose graphs were lines. They were called linear functions.

In the Explore above, you examined graphs of functions that were curves rather than simply lines. They are called **nonlinear functions.**

$f(x) = x^2$ is called a **quadratic function**

$f(x) = \sqrt{x}$ is called the **square root function**

$f(x) = |x|$ is called the **absolute value function**

These three functions can be used to build other nonlinear functions.

Example 1

Which of the three functions are used when defining the function $f(x) = \sqrt{|x - 2|}$?

Solution Both the square root function and the absolute value function

Try This

Which of the three functions are used when defining the function?

a. $f(x) = \sqrt{x^2 + 4}$ **b.** $f(x) = |x + 8|$

By substituting specific values for x into a function, you can calculate the corresponding values for $f(x)$. These values are recorded in a table.

Example 2

Evaluate $f(x) = 3x^2 - 2$ for the values given in the table. Copy and complete the table.

x	-3	-1	0	1	2	5
$f(x)$						

x	-3	-1	0	1	2	5
$f(x)$	25	1	-2	1	10	73

Solution

$f(-3) = 3(-3)^2 - 2 = 25$ $\quad f(-1) = 3(-1)^2 - 2 = 1$ $\quad f(0) = 3(0)^2 - 2 = -2$

$f(1) = 3(1)^2 - 2 = 1$ $\quad f(2) = 3(2)^2 - 2 = 10$ $\quad f(5) = 3(5)^2 - 2 = 73$

Try This

c. Evaluate $f(x) = 2\sqrt{x + 2}$ for the values given in the table. Copy and complete the table.

x	-2	2	7	14	23	34
$f(x)$						

Class Exercises

Use mental math to tell what value for x, if any, will make $f(x) = 0$

1. $f(x) = |2x + 6|$ **2.** $f(x) = 1 + x^2$ **3.** $f(x) = \sqrt{x^2}$

Discuss the Ideas

4. The equation $\sqrt{x^2} = |x|$ uses all three of the functions studied in this lesson. Do you think this equation is true for all values of x, some values of x, or no values of x? Explain.

Exercises

Practice and Apply

Which of the three functions are used when defining the function?

1. $f(x) = x^2 + \sqrt{x}$ **2.** $f(x) = |x^2 - 4|$ **3.** $f(x) = \sqrt{|5 - 2x^2|}$

For each function, complete the table of solutions.

4. $f(x) = |x - 2|$

x	-2	-1	0	1	2	3
$f(x)$						

5. $f(x) = 3\sqrt{x} - 2$

x	0	1	4	9	16	25
$f(x)$						

6. $f(x) = x^2 + 2x$

x	-2	-1	0	1	2	3
$f(x)$						

7. $f(x) = -2x^2 + 1$

x	-4	-2	0	2	4	6
$f(x)$						

8. The function $A(r) = \pi r^2$ gives the area (A) of a circle as a function of the radius (r). Find the area of a circular garden with a radius of 5.5 meters.

9. The length of the hypotenuse of a right triangle is a function of the lengths of the legs of the triangle. If a and b are the lengths of the legs of the triangle, we can write $H(a, b) = \sqrt{a^2 + b^2}$. Find the length of the hypotenuse when the lengths of the legs are 15 cm and 12 cm. Round to the nearest tenth if necessary.

Extend and Apply

10. Write to Learn Evaluate the function $f(x) = x^2 + 1$ for $x = -5, -4, -3, -2, -1, 0, 1, 2, 3, 4, 5$. Plot the points $(x, (f(x))$ on a coordinate grid and connect them. Write a paragraph that describes the shape of the graph.

Use Mathematical Reasoning

11. The graph at the right is the graph of the function $f(x) = 2x^2 - 4$. Use the graph to estimate the values for x that make $f(x) = 0$.

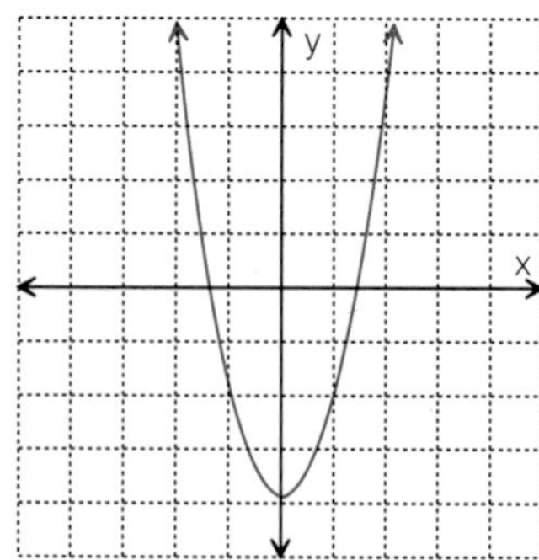

Mixed Review

Graph the equations to solve the system.

12. $x + y = 3, x - y = 1$

Find the x- and y- intercepts.

13. $x + y = -4$ **14.** $4x + 3y = 12$

Evaluate each expression.

15. $\sqrt{169 - 144}$ **16.** $\sqrt{104 - 79} + \sqrt{9}$

15-9 Trigonometric Ratios

Objective To find and use sine, cosine, and tangent.

Application

Cora needed to find the height of this building for a math project. She marked a point 40 feet from the base of the building and used the tangent ratio to finds its height. (See Example 2.)

Understand the Ideas

When you want to find a distance that cannot be measured directly, such as the height of a building, you can use an indirect method of measurement. One such method is to use trigonometric ratios.

Trigonometric ratios are ratios of lengths of sides of right triangles. Three of these ratios are called the **sine,** the **cosine,** and the **tangent.** They are defined for an acute angle A in a right triangle as follows:

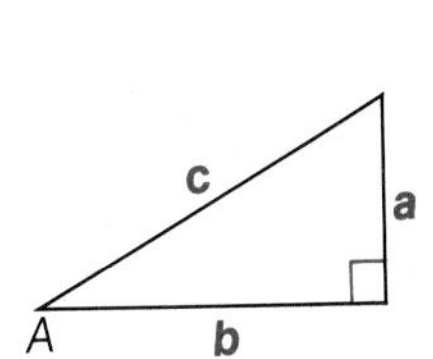

$$\text{sine of } \angle A \text{ or } \mathbf{sin}\ A = \frac{\text{length of side opposite } \angle A}{\text{length of hypotenuse}} = \frac{a}{c}$$

$$\text{cosine of } \angle A \text{ or } \mathbf{cos}\ A = \frac{\text{length of side adjacent to } \angle A}{\text{length of hypotenuse}} = \frac{b}{c}$$

$$\text{tangent of } \angle A \text{ or } \mathbf{tan}\ A = \frac{\text{length of side opposite } \angle A}{\text{length of side adjacent to } \angle A} = \frac{a}{b}$$

Since ratios of corresponding sides of similar triangles are equal, these three ratios have the same value for any acute angle congruent to angle A.

A scientific calculator has function keys for the sine, cosine, and tangent ratios. To find the sin of 72°, for example, use the following keystrokes.

72 [sin] 0.9510565

Example 1

Find sin A, cos A, and tan A for $\angle A$.

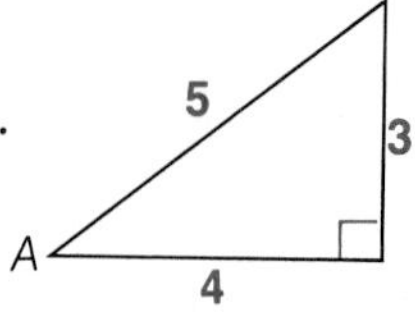

Solution

$\sin A = \frac{3}{5}$ Sine is the length of the opposite side divided by the length of the hypotenuse.

$\cos A = \frac{4}{5}$ Cosine is the length of the adjacent side divided by the length of the hypotenuse.

$\tan A = \frac{3}{4}$ Tangent is the length of the opposite side divided by the length of the adjacent side.

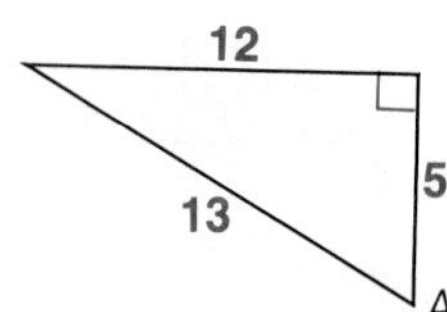

Try This

a. Find sin A, cos A, and tan A for $\angle A$.

Example 2

The measure of angle A is 62° at a point 40 feet from the base of the building shown in the application. Use a calculator to find the height of the building.

Solution $\tan 62° = \frac{h}{40}$

$h = 40(\tan 62°)$

$h = 40$ [×] 62 [tan]

$h \approx 75.23$ feet

The building is approximately 75.23 feet tall.

Try This **b.** Find the length of AB in the figure above.

Class Exercises

State whether each equation is true or false.

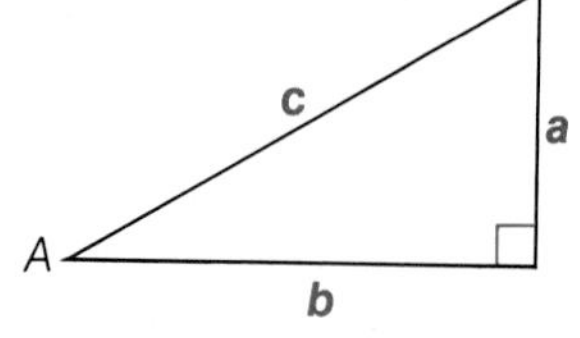

1. $\sin A = \frac{a}{b}$

2. $\cos A = \frac{b}{c}$

3. $\tan A = \frac{b}{a}$

4. $\sin A = \frac{a}{c}$

5. $\cos A = \frac{b}{a}$

6. $\tan A = \frac{a}{b}$

Discuss the Ideas

7. For what angle, if any, are the sine and cosine ratios equal? Explain.

Exercises

Practice and Apply

Find sin A, cos A, and tan A for $\angle A$.

1.

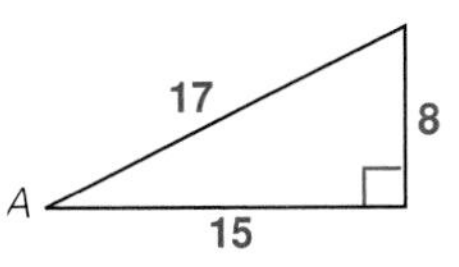

2.

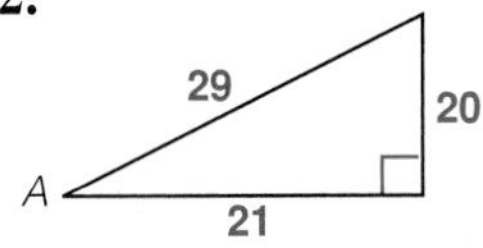

3.

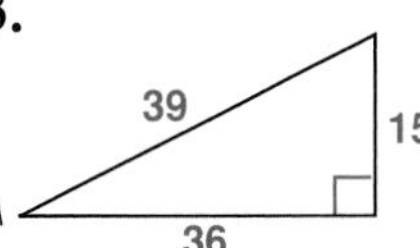

4.

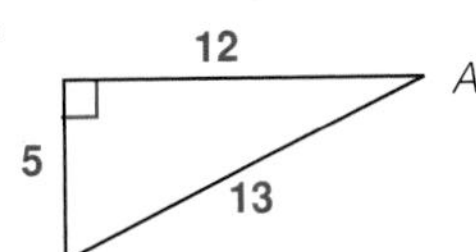

5.

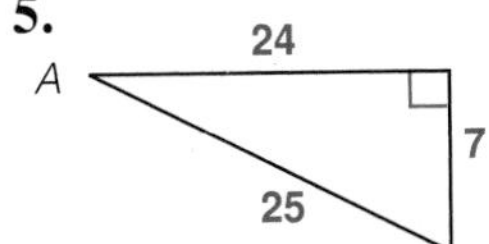

6.

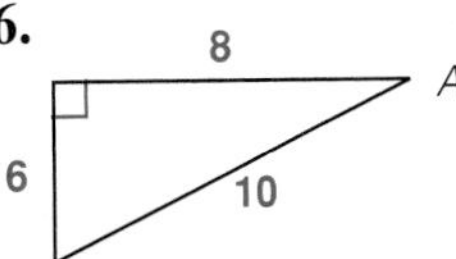

7. The angle from the ground to the top of the World Trade Center in New York City is 48° at a distance of 1,220 ft from the building. Use a calculator to find the height of the building.

8. Sears Tower in Chicago is 1,454 ft tall. Suppose point A is 1,000 ft from the base of the tower. What is the tangent of the angle at A formed by the ground and the line of vision to the top of the tower?

9. A surveyor measured BC to be 125 ft. Use a calculator to find the distance AB across the lake.

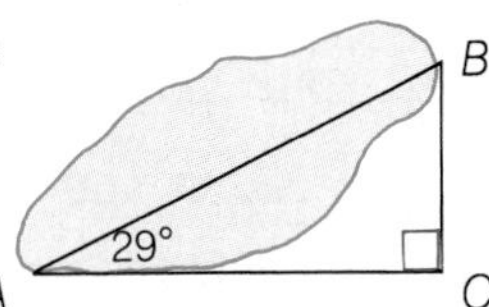

10. A surveyor wants to find the distance between mountain peaks A and B. He finds a point C, 228 ft from point A, so that $\angle ACB$ is a right angle. The measure of $\angle BAC$ is 89°. Use a calculator to find the distance AB.

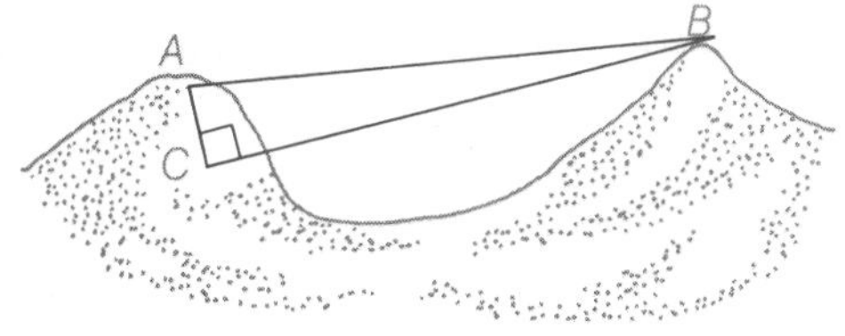

Extend and Apply

Draw a 45°-45° right triangle with legs of length 2. Draw a 30°-60° right triangle with a short leg of length 1. Find the lengths of all other sides. Use these figures to find the trigonometric ratios in Exercises 11–18. Leave your answer in radical form.

11. sin 30° **12.** tan 45° **13.** cos 60° **14.** tan 30°

15. cos 45° **16.** sin 60° **17.** sin 45° **18.** tan 60°

Use the Pythagorean Theorem to find x. Then, find $\sin A$, $\cos A$, and $\tan A$ for $\angle A$.

19. 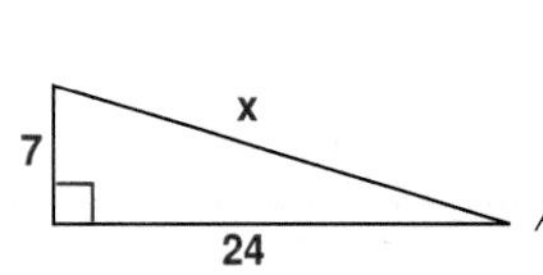

20. 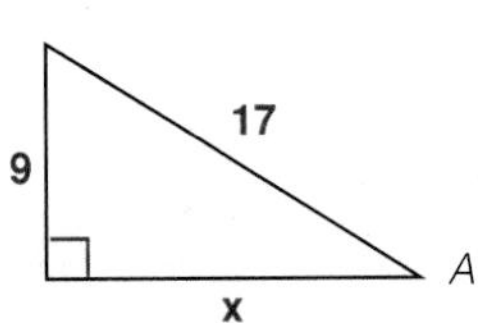

21. 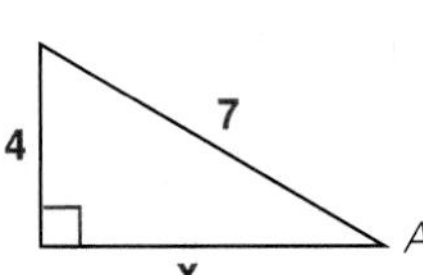

Use your answers to Exercises 11–18 to evaluate each expression.

22. $5 + x \sin 30°$ for $x = 4$

23. $y \cos 45°$ for $y = 4\sqrt{2}$

24. $x \tan 45° + 2x \sin 30°$ for $x = 5$

25. $5x \sin 30°$ for $x = 12$

Use Mathematical Reasoning

Use the results from Exercises 11–18 to solve the equations.

26. $\sin x = \frac{1}{2}$

27. $\cos x = \frac{\sqrt{2}}{2}$

28. $\tan x = \sqrt{3}$

29. $\sin 2x = \frac{\sqrt{3}}{2}$

30. $\tan 2x = 1$

31. $\cos 3x = \frac{1}{2}$

Mixed Review

Use the Counting Principle to find the total number of choices.

32. Select one soup and one salad from 4 soups and 5 salads.

Give the area. **33.** A square with one side of 4 cm.

34. A circle with diameter of 6 cm. Use 3.14 for π.

35. A triangle with base of 7 in., height = 8 in.

Give the mean. **36.** 12, 15, 17, 12, 13 **37.** 6, 2, 5, 4, 6, 0, 6

Give the least common multiple (LCM). **38.** 4, 5, 6, 12 **39.** 2, 3, 4, 8

Calculator Activity

A number is called a **perfect square** if its square root is an integer. Use a calculator to complete this table and discover a generalization.

	Value of x	Is x a perfect square?	$x + 1$	Is $x + 1$ a perfect square?
$x = 1 \cdot 2 \cdot 3 \cdot 4$	24	No	25	Yes
$x = 2 \cdot 3 \cdot 4 \cdot 5$				
$x = 3 \cdot 4 \cdot 5 \cdot 6$				
$x = 4 \cdot 5 \cdot 6 \cdot 7$				
$x = 5 \cdot 6 \cdot 7 \cdot 8$				

15-10 Problem Solving: Writing Equations

Practice Solving Problems

Objective To write and solve equations to solve word problems.

Problems

Practice and Apply

Solve by writing an equation.

1. Ms. Ericson bought a used car for \$175 more than half its original price. She paid \$2,465 for the car. What was its original price?
2. Sally has 8 more than twice as many coins in her collection as she did when her grandmother gave her the first coins in her collection. She now has 120 coins. How many did her grandmother give her?
3. A gasoline station charges \$1.16 per gallon of gas and \$2.50 for a car wash. Celia's total charge for gas and a wash was \$12.94. How many gallons of gasoline did she buy?
4. An amusement park had $\frac{1}{3}$ as many customers on Sunday as on Saturday. The total number of customers for the two days was 1,648. How many customers did the park have on each of the two days?

Extend and Apply

5. Tim and Ginny work in different restaurants. They both worked the same number of hours and earned the same amount last week. Tim worked for \$6 per hour and could keep no tips. Ginny worked for \$4 an hour, but was allowed to keep tips totaling \$76. How many hours did each work?
6. A three-member relay team ran the relay in 186 seconds. Lisa ran her lap in 9 seconds less than Sara. Kay took 3 seconds more than Sara to run her lap. What was the lap time for each runner?

Use Mathematical Reasoning

7. Write a word problem that could be solved using the equation
   a. $\frac{1}{2}x + 3 = 75$ **b.** $x + 7 = 12$

Mixed Review

Give the greatest common factor (GCF). **8.** 78, 54, 24 **9.** 9, 27, 15

Solve and check. **10.** $19 - 4m = 11$ **11.** $t + 0.9t = 9.5$

15-11 Problem Solving: Strategies

Practice Solving Problems

Objective To solve nonroutine problems.

Problems

Solve using the Strategies found on page 520.

1. A meeting room has a floor area of 625 ft^2 and an 8-foot high ceiling. Office guidelines recommend at least 200 ft^3 per person. What should be the maximum number of people allowed to meet in this room?
2. Doctors knew that a flu virus could spread very rapidly. They estimated that each person who had it would give it to 4 other people every day. On April 12th, the first case of the flu was reported. If the flu spread as the doctors predicted, when would about 20,000 people have had the flu?
3. Angie, Brenda, and Clara weighed themselves two at a time. Brenda and Clara weighed 208 lb together. Angie and Brenda weighed 222 lb, and Angie and Clara weighed 216 lb. How much did each one weigh?
4. A rich man left his money to two nieces and a nephew. To the older niece he gave half of his money. He gave the younger niece $\frac{1}{3}$ what he gave the older niece. He gave the nephew twice as much as he gave the younger niece. He gave the nephew $3.5 million. How much did he give to all three?

Group Decision Making

5. Work in a group. Discuss and decide.

   Situation The faucet in the restroom at school has been dripping for three months. You want to find out how much money has been wasted during that time because of the dripping faucet.

   a. What decision or decisions do you need to make in this situation?
   b. Formulate problems you need to solve to make the decision(s).
   c. List any assumptions you need to make to arrive at a decision.
   d. What data, if any, do you need to collect to make a decision?
   e. Write a paragraph summarizing what your group did, what decisions you made, and why.

Guidelines for Planning

- **Formulate Problems** you will need to solve.
- Discuss **Assumptions** you will make and **Data** you will need.

Extend Key Ideas

Sequences and Square Roots

Because the number $\sqrt{2}$ is an irrational number, it cannot be written exactly as a decimal or a fraction. The terms of the sequence below are approximations of $\sqrt{2}$. Each term of the sequence is a closer approximation than the term before it.

$$\frac{3}{2}, \frac{7}{5}, \frac{17}{12}, \frac{41}{29}, \frac{99}{70}, \ldots$$

$$\frac{99}{70} \rightarrow \frac{99 + 2(70)}{99 + 70} = \frac{239}{169}$$

You can use a calculator to confirm that the square of each term of this sequence is as shown.

$$\left(\frac{3}{2}\right)^2 = 2.25 \qquad \left(\frac{7}{5}\right)^2 = 1.96 \qquad \left(\frac{17}{12}\right)^2 = 2.0069$$

$$\left(\frac{41}{29}\right)^2 = 1.9988 \qquad \left(\frac{99}{70}\right)^2 = 2.00020$$

You can see that $\frac{99}{70}$ is approximately $\sqrt{2}$.

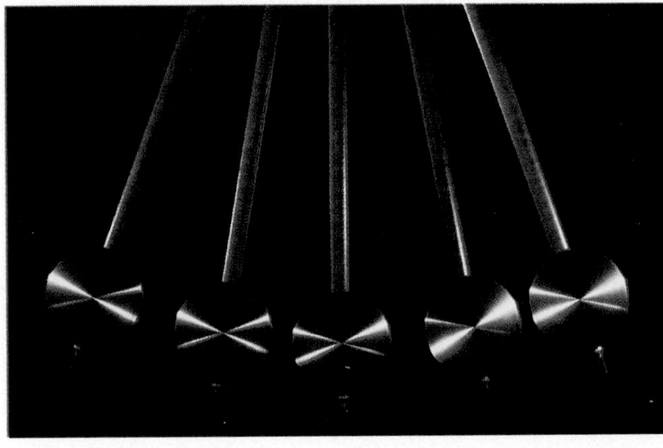

For a pendulum with length L, the time (T) of one period is given by the formula $T = 2 \cdot \sqrt{L}$.

Find the next term in each sequence. Then use a calculator to find what square root each sequence approximates.

1. $\frac{4}{3}, \frac{10}{7}, \frac{24}{17}, \frac{58}{41}, \frac{140}{99}, \ldots$
2. $\frac{3}{2}, \frac{9}{5}, \frac{24}{14}, \frac{66}{38}, \frac{180}{104}, \ldots$
3. $\frac{4}{3}, \frac{13}{7}, \frac{34}{20}, \frac{94}{54}, \frac{256}{148}, \ldots$
4. $\frac{2}{1}, \frac{5}{3}, \frac{14}{8}, \frac{38}{22}, \frac{104}{60}, \ldots$

Chapter 15 Review/Test

Understanding

True or False?

15-2 **1.** A square root is always a whole number.

15-3 **2.** The number $x = \sqrt{7}$ is the only solution to the equation $x^2 = 7$.

15-4 **3.** Given any triangle with sides of length a, b, and c, $a^2 + b^2 = c^2$.

15-6 **4.** Two polygons are similar if they are identical in shape but not necessarily identical in size.

15-7 **5.** If a 45°-45° right triangle has legs a units long, then the hypotenuse is $2a$ units long.

Skill

15-1 Evaluate each expression. **6.** $\sqrt{25} - \sqrt{121}$ **7.** $\sqrt{33 + 16}$

15-3 Solve and check. **8.** $x^2 = 81$ **9.** $x^2 = 43$.

15-4 Find the length of a to the nearest hundredth.

10.

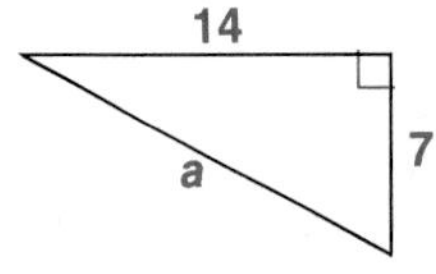

11.

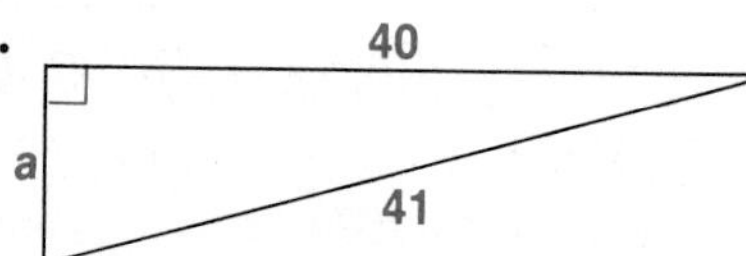

15-6 Use proportions to find the unknown lengths for these similar triangles.

12.

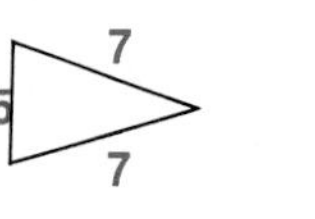

10.5
7.5
x

13.

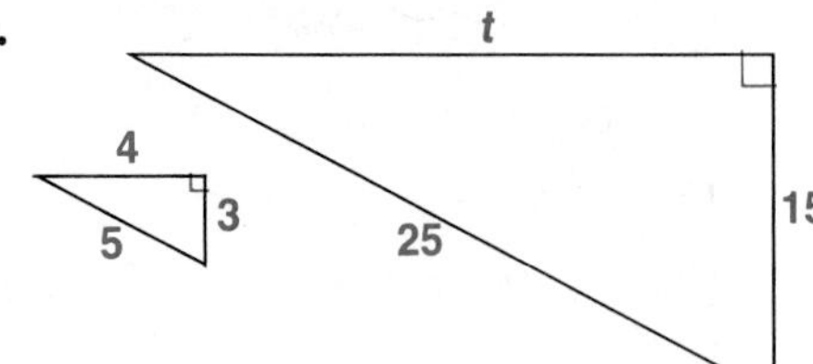

15-9 Find each ratio for $\angle A$.

14. sin A

15. cos A

16. tan A

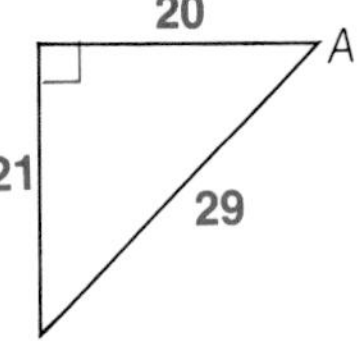

Application

15-4 **17.** A window is 6 ft wide and 4 ft high. What is the length of the diagonal of the window?

15-10 **18.** Solve by writing an equation. The Wilson family drove 623 miles to visit relatives. They drove 51 miles more than $\frac{1}{2}$ of the distance on the first day. How far did they drive the second day?

Cumulative Review

13-8 For problems 1–4, use 3.14 for π.

13-9 **1.** Find the volume of a cone with a radius of 6 in. and a height of 19 in.

2. Find the volume of a pyramid with a base area of 64 m^2 and a height of 20 m.

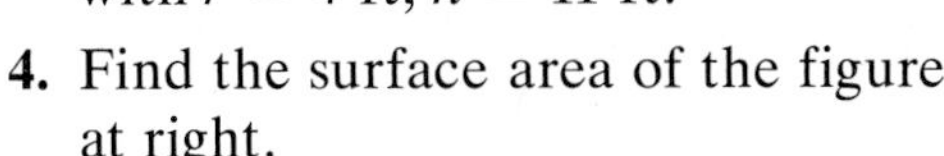

3. Find the surface area of a cylinder with $r = 4$ ft, $h = 11$ ft.

4. Find the surface area of the figure at right.

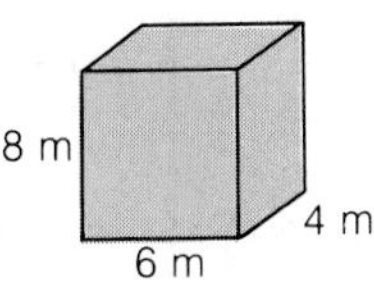

14-1 Use the counting principle to find the total number of outcomes.

5. T-shirt selection: one color and one size. Colors: blue, red, orange, green, black; Sizes: small, medium, large, extra large

14-2 Find the number of permutations.

6. t, u, e, s, d, a, y

7. stop, start, slow, fast

14-2 Solve.

8. Five drawings are entered in a drawing contest. How many ways can a winner and a runner-up be chosen?

14-6 Use the data to solve problems 9–12.
14-7 Points scored by Pamela in basketball games: 14, 14, 10, 18, 15, 14, 13

9. Find the range.

10. Find the mode.

11. Find the median.

12. Find the mean.

15-2 Between what two consecutive integers does each square root lie?

13. $-\sqrt{93}$

14. $\sqrt{34}$

15-2 Use a calculator with a $\sqrt{\ }$ key to find an approximation for each square root.

15. $\sqrt{28}$

16. $\sqrt{80}$

15-4 Find the length of a.

17.

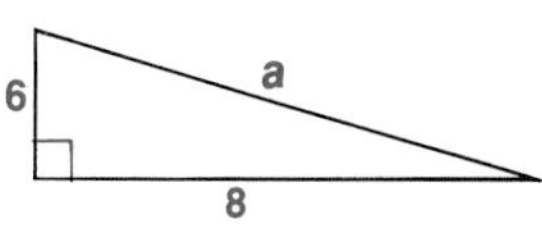

18.

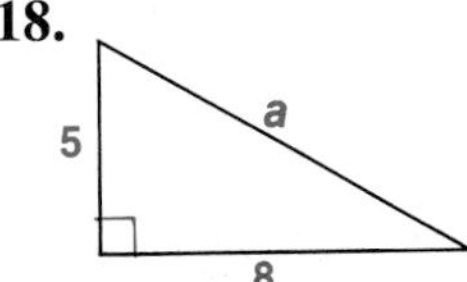

15-9 Find each ratio for angle A.

19. sin A

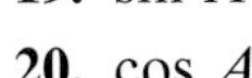

20. cos A

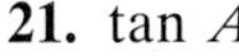

21. tan A

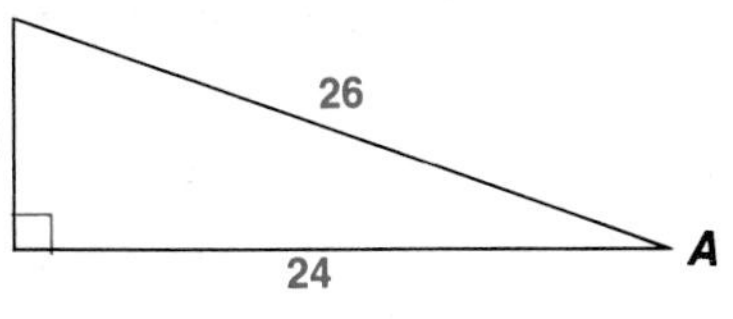

Tables

Table 1: Squares and Square Roots

N	N^2	$\sqrt{N}$	N	N^2	$\sqrt{N}$
1	1	1	51	2,601	7.141
2	4	1.414	52	2,704	7.211
3	9	1.732	53	2,809	7.280
4	16	2	54	2,916	7.348
5	25	2.236	55	3,025	7.416
6	36	2.449	56	3,136	7.483
7	49	2.646	57	3,249	7.550
8	64	2.828	58	3,364	7.616
9	81	3	59	3,481	7.681
10	100	3.162	60	3,600	7.746
11	121	3.317	61	3,721	7.810
12	144	3.464	62	3,844	7.874
13	169	3.606	63	3,969	7.937
14	196	3.742	64	4,096	8
15	225	3.873	65	4,225	8.062
16	256	4	66	4,356	8.124
17	289	4.123	67	4,489	8.185
18	324	4.243	68	4,624	8.246
19	361	4.359	69	4,761	8.307
20	400	4.472	70	4,900	8.367
21	441	4.583	71	5,041	8.426
22	484	4.690	72	5,184	8.485
23	529	4.796	73	5,329	8.544
24	576	4.899	74	5,476	8.602
25	625	5	75	5,625	8.660
26	676	5.099	76	5,776	8.718
27	729	5.196	77	5,929	8.775
28	784	5.292	78	6,084	8.832
29	841	5.385	79	6,241	8.888
30	900	5.477	80	6,400	8.944
31	961	5.568	81	6,561	9
32	1,024	5.657	82	6,724	9.055
33	1,089	5.745	83	6,889	9.110
34	1,156	5.831	84	7,056	9.165
35	1,225	5.916	85	7,225	9.220
36	1,296	6	86	7,396	9.274
37	1,369	6.083	87	7,569	9.327
38	1,444	6.164	88	7,744	9.381
39	1,521	6.245	89	7,921	9.434
40	1,600	6.325	90	8,100	9.487
41	1,681	6.403	91	8,281	9.539
42	1,764	6.481	92	8,464	9.592
43	1,849	6.557	93	8,649	9.644
44	1,936	6.633	94	8,836	9.695
45	2,025	6.708	95	9,025	9.747
46	2,116	6.782	96	9,216	9.798
47	2,209	6.856	97	9,409	9.849
48	2,304	6.928	98	9,604	9.899
49	2,401	7	99	9,801	9.950
50	2,500	7.071	100	10,000	10

Table 2: Values of Trigonometric Functions

Degrees	Sin	Cos	Tan	Degrees	Sin	Cos	Tan
0°	0.0000	1.0000	0.0000				
1°	0.0175	0.9998	0.0175	46°	0.7193	0.6947	1.0355
2°	0.0349	0.9994	0.0349	47°	0.7314	0.6820	1.0724
3°	0.0523	0.9986	0.0524	48°	0.7431	0.6691	1.1106
4°	0.0698	0.9976	0.0699	49°	0.7547	0.6561	1.1504
5°	0.0872	0.9962	0.0875	50°	0.7660	0.6428	1.1918
6°	0.1045	0.9945	0.1051	51°	0.7771	0.6293	1.2349
7°	0.1219	0.9925	0.1228	52°	0.7880	0.6157	1.2799
8°	0.1392	0.9903	0.1405	53°	0.7986	0.6018	1.3270
9°	0.1564	0.9877	0.1584	54°	0.8090	0.5878	1.3764
10°	0.1736	0.9848	0.1763	55°	0.8192	0.5736	1.4281
11°	0.1908	0.9816	0.1944	56°	0.8290	0.5592	1.4826
12°	0.2079	0.9781	0.2126	57°	0.8387	0.5446	1.5399
13°	0.2250	0.9744	0.2309	58°	0.8480	0.5299	1.6003
14°	0.2419	0.9703	0.2493	59°	0.8572	0.5150	1.6643
15°	0.2588	0.9659	0.2679	60°	0.8660	0.5000	1.7321
16°	0.2756	0.9613	0.2867	61°	0.8746	0.4848	1.8040
17°	0.2924	0.9563	0.3057	62°	0.8829	0.4695	1.8807
18°	0.3090	0.9511	0.3249	63°	0.8910	0.4540	1.9626
19°	0.3256	0.9455	0.3443	64°	0.8988	0.4384	2.0503
20°	0.3420	0.9397	0.3640	65°	0.9063	0.4226	2.1445
21°	0.3584	0.9336	0.3839	66°	0.9135	0.4067	2.2460
22°	0.3746	0.9272	0.4040	67°	0.9205	0.3907	2.3559
23°	0.3907	0.9205	0.4245	68°	0.9272	0.3746	2.4751
24°	0.4067	0.9135	0.4452	69°	0.9336	0.3584	2.6051
25°	0.4226	0.9063	0.4663	70°	0.9397	0.3420	2.7475
26°	0.4384	0.8988	0.4877	71°	0.9455	0.3256	2.9042
27°	0.4540	0.8910	0.5095	72°	0.9511	0.3090	3.0777
28°	0.4695	0.8829	0.5317	73°	0.9563	0.2924	3.2709
29°	0.4848	0.8746	0.5543	74°	0.9613	0.2756	3.4874
30°	0.5000	0.8660	0.5774	75°	0.9659	0.2588	3.7321
31°	0.5150	0.8572	0.6009	76°	0.9703	0.2419	4.0108
32°	0.5299	0.8480	0.6249	77°	0.9744	0.2250	4.3315
33°	0.5446	0.8387	0.6494	78°	0.9781	0.2079	4.7046
34°	0.5592	0.8290	0.6745	79°	0.9816	0.1908	5.1446
35°	0.5736	0.8192	0.7002	80°	0.9848	0.1736	5.6713
36°	0.5878	0.8090	0.7265	81°	0.9877	0.1564	6.3138
37°	0.6018	0.7986	0.7536	82°	0.9903	0.1392	7.1154
38°	0.6157	0.7880	0.7813	83°	0.9925	0.1219	8.1443
39°	0.6293	0.7771	0.8098	84°	0.9945	0.1045	9.5144
40°	0.6428	0.7660	0.8391	85°	0.9962	0.0872	11.4301
41°	0.6561	0.7547	0.8693	86°	0.9976	0.0698	14.3007
42°	0.6691	0.7431	0.9004	87°	0.9986	0.0523	19.0811
43°	0.6820	0.7314	0.9325	88°	0.9994	0.0349	28.6363
44°	0.6947	0.7193	0.9657	89°	0.9998	0.0175	57.2900
45°	0.7071	0.7071	1.0000	90°	1.0000	0.0000	

Table 3: Geometric Formulas

Rectangle
Area: $A = lw$
Perimeter: $P = 2l + 2w$

Parallelogram
Area: $A = bh$

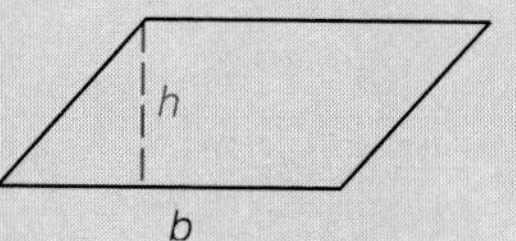

Square
Area: $A = s^2$
Perimeter: $P = 4s$

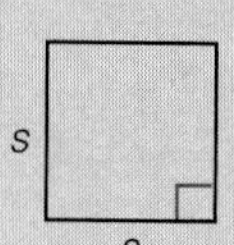

Trapezoid
Area: $A = \frac{1}{2}h(b_1 + b_2)$

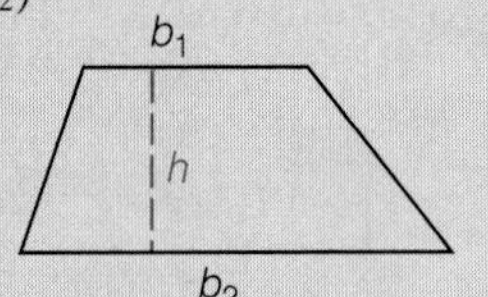

Triangle
Area: $A = \frac{1}{2}bh$
Sum of Angle Measures:
$A + B + C = 180°$

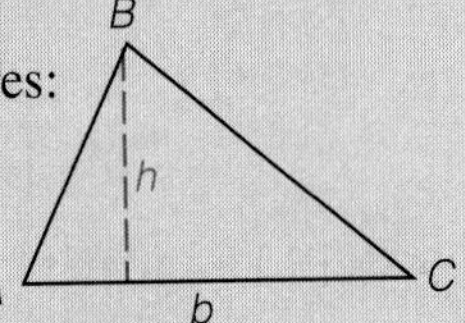

Circle
Area: $A = \pi r^2$
Circumference:
$C = \pi d = 2\pi r$

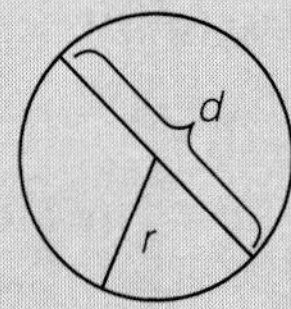

Right Triangle
Pythagorean Property:
$a^2 + b^2 = c^2$

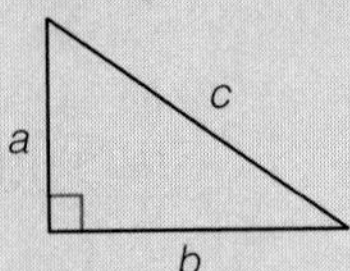

Rectangular Solid
Volume: $V = lwh$

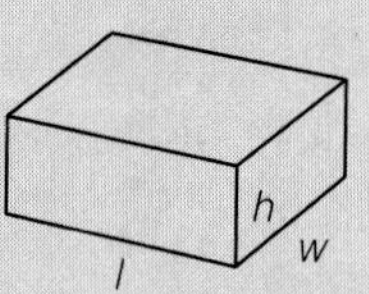

Pyramid
Volume $= \frac{1}{3}Bh$
B = base area

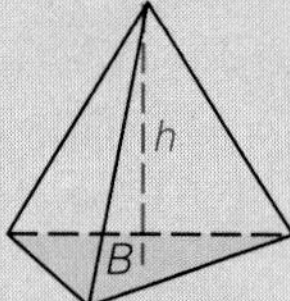

Cylinder
Volume: $V = \pi r^2 h$

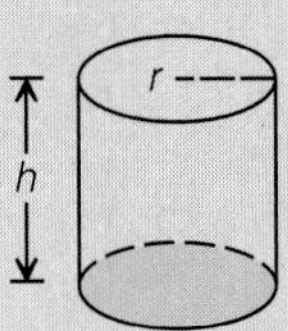

Prism
Volume: $V = Bh$
B = base area

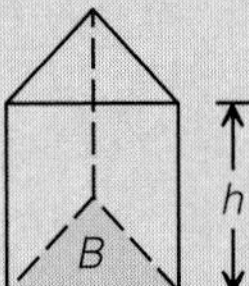

Cone
Volume: $V = \frac{1}{3}Bh$
B = base area

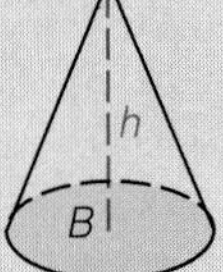

Chapter 1

Extra Practice

Evaluate each numerical or algebraic expression.

1. $(23 + 8) - 14$ **2.** $12 + (16 - 7)$ **3.** $9 + (21 - 13)$

4. $44 + (17 - 9)$ **5.** $b - 2$ for $b = 11$ **6.** $8 + v$ for $v = 5$

7. $3 + (x - 4)$ for $x = 7$ **8.** $(21 - t) + 2$ for $t = 4$

Look for a pattern. Copy and complete the table. Use the variable to write a rule that tells how to get the number in the bottom row.

9.

2	4	6	8	10	x
8	10	12	14		

10.

10	15	20	25	30	x
5	10	15	20		

Write as an algebraic expression.

11. 7 decreased by b **12.** 3 added to p **13.** 6 more than r

Write an expression for each question.

Chip rides his horse 11 miles every day. How far will he ride if

14. he rides 3 miles less? **15.** he rides m miles farther?

Use the basic properties to write an equivalent expression.

16. $z + 0$ **17.** $(2 + r) + 6$ **18.** $4 + b$

Solve the equation for the replacement set given.

19. $g - 8 = 5$ $\{12, 13, 14, 15\}$ **20.** $6 + b = 17$ $\{9, 10, 11, 12\}$

Solve and check.

21. $n - 18 = 7$ **22.** $x + 8 = 13$ **23.** $t - 9 = 4$

24. $43 + s = 72$ **25.** $t - 35 = 63$ **26.** $212 = x - 27$

27. $b + 345 = 567$ **28.** $111 = r - 343$ **29.** $654 = 321 + a$

30. Robin played tennis 2 hours less today than she did yesterday. She played for 3 hours today. How many hours did she play yesterday?

31. Bruce has 7 magazine subscriptions. Four of them were gifts. How many of them were not gifts?

Round to the nearest ten (t) or hundred (h) and estimate the value of the variable.

32. $a = 26 + 47$ (t) **33.** $67 + 234 = b$ (t) **34.** $z = 257 - 79$ (t)

35. $r = 968 + 497$ (h) **36.** $p = 423 + 1{,}254$ (h) **37.** $2{,}873 - 952 = t$ (h)

Use front-end estimation to estimate the value of the variable.

38. $768 + 269 + 548 = h$ **39.** $4{,}584 - (1{,}955 + 2{,}462) = k$

Chapter 2

Extra Practice

Evaluate each numerical or algebraic expression.

1. $3d$ for $d = 9$
2. $\frac{6w}{9}$ for $w = 3$
3. $a(4 + b)$ for $a = 7$
4. $\frac{8x}{z}$ for $z = 2$
5. $(f - g)$ for $f = 9, g = 4$
6. $t(10 - v)$ for $v = 9$

Look for a pattern. Copy and complete the table. Use the variable to write a rule that tells how to get the number in the bottom row.

7.

6	12	18	24	30	x
2	4	6	8		

8.

3	5	7	9	11	x
6	10	14	18		

Write as an algebraic expression.

9. 9 divided by s
10. 4 less than twice r
11. 7 multiplied by x
12. Suki has 6 books. How many would she have if she had x times as many?

Use the Commutative Property to write an equivalent expression.

13. rd
14. $m(3)$
15. $6s$

Use the Associative or Distributive Property to write an equivalent expression.

16. $13(3x)$
17. $(11b)t$
18. $(r6)7$
19. $d(4 + 7)$
20. $2(n + 9)$
21. $(x + 5)6$

Use the basic properties to simplify.

22. $12(3d)$
23. $5x(4)$
24. $17(a + 9)$
25. $4b + 3b$
26. $15z + z$
27. $24r - 7r$

Solve and check.

28. $9n = 63$
29. $\frac{56}{x} = 8$
30. $\frac{t}{4} = 6$
31. $6x = 72$
32. $121 = 11d$
33. $\frac{d}{13} = 4$
34. $\frac{207}{f} = 23$

Solve.

35. Nancy used 280 calories while exercising for 35 minutes. How many calories did she use each minute?
36. Jeffrey bought three T-shirts. The total cost was \$36. Solve the equation $3x = 36$ to find the cost per T-shirt.
37. Formula: $V = lwh$. V is the volume of a box in cubic units, l is the length of the box, w is the width of the box, and h is the height of the box. What is the volume of a box with length 5 cm, width 6 cm and height 8 cm?

Use rounding and choose compatible numbers to estimate each value.

38. $\frac{420}{38} = x$
39. $\frac{561}{82} = z$
40. $\frac{2{,}493}{52} = t$

Chapter 3

Extra Practice

Find the absolute value.

1. $|-23|$ 2. $|-14|$ 3. $|1|$

Use the symbols $<$ or $>$ to order from least to greatest.

4. 7, −6, 3 5. 0, 4, −12 6. 3, −3, −33

Find the sum or difference.

7. $-5 + (-5)$ 8. $-4 + 8$ 9. $-9 + 3$
10. $12 + (-6)$ 11. $14 + (-5)$ 12. $-17 + 6$
13. $9 - 14$ 14. $-5 - 7$ 15. $2 - 21$
16. $8 - (-5)$ 17. $-26 - 5$ 18. $14 - (-3)$

Evaluate.

19. $-15 + x$ for $x = -1$ 20. $s + (-8)$ for $s = 19$
21. $x - 9$ for $x = 4$ 22. $-17 - n$ for $n = -8$

Solve and check.

23. $b + 37 = 15$ 24. $25 + x = -2$ 25. $r - 47 = 35$
26. $43 = 78 + c$ 27. $d - (-56) = 77$ 28. $f + (-24) = 68$

Solve.

29. The temperature was −27°F and then it rose 36°. What was the temperature then?
30. Tom has \$235 in his checking account and \$450 in bills to pay. How much does he need to deposit to keep his account from being overdrawn?

Find the product or quotient.

31. 9(6) 32. 7(−3) 33. −4(−8)
34. −7(2) 35. 8(−6) 36. −9(−4)
37. $-9 \div 3$ 38. $-56 \div (-7)$ 39. $121 \div (-11)$
40. $92 \div (-4)$ 41. $-57 \div 3$ 42. $-18 \div (-6)$

Solve and check.

43. $75 = -3n$ 44. $-9y = 72$ 45. $12 = \frac{x}{-3}$ 46. $55 = -b$ 47. $-k = -1$
48. A plant grew 15 inches in 5 weeks. Solve the equation $x = \frac{15}{5}$ to find the plant's average growth per week.

Write an equation.

49. 17 multiplied by a number q is 85.
50. 34 less than a number p is 71.

Chapter 4

Extra Practice

Write as a decimal.

1. $8(10) + 6(1) + 3\left(\frac{1}{100}\right)$
2. $7\left(\frac{1}{100}\right) + 3\left(\frac{1}{1000}\right) + 2(1)$

Write <, >, or = for each □.

3. 3.23 □ 3.32
4. 7.41 □ 7.414
5. 5.05 □ 5.050

Round to the nearest whole number and estimate the value of x.

6. $x = 49.82 + 27.89$
7. $x = 64.79 + 575.13$
8. $x = 99.64 - 64.82$
9. $x = 749.86 - 244.91$

Round to the nearest tenth.

10. 41.046
11. 156.271
12. 22.96

Add or subtract.

13. $4.87 + 3.9$
14. $13.56 + 24.94 - 17.31$
15. $-5.3 + 8.44$
16. $72.4 + (-6.9) + 21.78$
17. $-21.65 + (-4.2)$
18. $74.68 - (-29.38)$

Solve and check.

19. $c - 2.96 = 3.84$
20. $13.62 + d = -4.85$
21. $m - 8.34 = -2.79$
22. $-41 + b = 17.32$
23. A tennis court is 12.3 meters long. How many centimeters long is this?
24. Kim's dog weighs 5500 grams. How many kilograms does it weigh?

Round to the nearest whole number and estimate the value of x.

25. $30.21 \times 4.7 = x$
26. $4.12 \times 24.89 = x$
27. $0.79 \times 19.8 = x$

Multiply or divide.

28. 4.2×11.83
29. 6.7×-5.92
30. $-0.429 \div (-0.03)$
31. $-3.752 \div 0.001$

Solve and check.

32. $3.6r = 194.4$
33. $-0.04x = 16$
34. $1.7s = 16.66$
35. $\frac{b}{0.23} = 5.9$
36. $\frac{f}{-1.4} = 13.8$
37. $\frac{d}{4.2} = -3.7$

Find the solution by writing and solving an equation.

38. A machine part is priced at \$0.455. What is the price of 100 parts?
39. Ivan got a \$13.79 discount on a baseball glove with an original price of \$54.98. How much did he pay for the glove?
40. Alan has 54.3 meters of insulation. He needs a total of 100 meters to insulate his attic. How much more insulation does he need to get?

Chapter 5

Extra Practice

Find all the factors of the given number.

1. 18 **2.** 42 **3.** 81

Give the first five nonzero multiples of each number.

4. 7 **5.** 20 **6.** 60

Tell whether the number is divisible by 2, by 3, and by 5.

7. 98 **8.** 12,345 **9.** 86

10. 156 **11.** 272 **12.** 985

Find the solution by writing and solving an equation.

13. Gloria is making 96 sandwiches for a party. Sandwich rolls come in packages of 8. How many packages does she need to buy?

14. Four equally-priced tickets to a football game cost $120. What is the price per ticket?

State whether the number is prime or composite.

15. 57 **16.** 79 **17.** 96

Write in expanded form. Simplify if possible.

18. 2^5 **19.** $(-4)^3$ **20.** r^7

Write using exponents.

21. $6 \cdot 6 \cdot 6 \cdot 6$ **22.** $b \cdot b \cdot b \cdot b \cdot b$ **23.** $(-8)(-8)(-8)$

Multiply. Give the answer in exponent form.

24. $x^2 \cdot x^3$ **25.** $7^4 \cdot 7^1$ **26.** $(-4)^4(-4)^5$

Simplify. **27.** $2^4 + 2^6$ **28.** $(-6)^2 + (-6)^3$ **29.** $3^3 \cdot 3^3$

Use exponents to show the prime factorization of each number.

30. 72 **31.** 210 **32.** 54 **33.** 225

Find the Greatest Common Factor (GCF) of each pair of numbers.

34. 42, 91 **35.** 21, 27 **36.** 70, 182

37. The Stopping Distance, S, is the Reaction Distance plus the Braking Distance: $S = R + 0.05R^2$, where R is the speed in miles per hour. If a car is traveling at 45 mi/h, how many feet will it go before it stops?

Find the Least Common Multiple (LCM) of each pair of numbers.

38. 5, 12 **39.** 18, 24 **40.** 7, 11

41. What is the shortest length of string that can be cut into either a whole number of 12-inch pieces or a whole number of 16-inch pieces?

Chapter 6

Extra Practice

Write an equivalent fraction by finding the value of the variable.

1. $\frac{4}{9} = \frac{x}{54}$ **2.** $\frac{m}{7} = \frac{35}{49}$ **3.** $-\frac{3}{11} = \frac{p}{66}$

Reduce each fraction to lowest terms.

4. $\frac{24}{36}$ **5.** $-\frac{11}{99}$ **6.** $\frac{105}{133}$

Solve.

7. In a survey, 24 out of 108 people said they had heard of a new product. Reduce $\frac{24}{108}$ to lowest terms to find what fraction this was.

Write each as an integer or mixed number.

8. $\frac{21}{8}$ **9.** $-\frac{41}{13}$ **10.** $\frac{246}{25}$

Write each as an improper fraction in lowest terms.

11. $6\frac{7}{8}$ **12.** $-4\frac{3}{8}$ **13.** $-5\frac{8}{10}$

14. Graph $-\frac{6}{4}, \frac{2}{3}, \frac{1}{4}$, and $\frac{3}{2}$ on a number line.

Write >, <, or = for each □.

15. $\frac{4}{8}$ □ $\frac{3}{7}$ **16.** $-\frac{2}{3}$ □ $-\frac{5}{9}$ **17.** $\frac{26}{39}$ □ $\frac{2}{3}$ **18.** $\frac{7}{11}$ □ $\frac{3}{4}$

Add or subtract. Reduce to lowest terms.

19. $\frac{6}{13} + \frac{3}{13}$ **20.** $-\frac{8}{18} + \frac{14}{18}$ **21.** $-\frac{8}{20} - \frac{7}{20}$

22. $\frac{1}{4} + \frac{1}{5}$ **23.** $\frac{4}{7} - \frac{1}{2}$ **24.** $-\frac{3}{8} - \left(-\frac{2}{5}\right)$

25. $3\frac{5}{6} - 2\frac{3}{8}$ **26.** $-5\frac{3}{4} + 1\frac{5}{12}$ **27.** $4\frac{2}{5} - 7\frac{3}{7}$

Solve.

28. Mr. Drucker walked $2\frac{7}{8}$ miles, stopped for a while, then walked $3\frac{1}{6}$ miles more. How far did he walk?

29. Alita had $6\frac{1}{2}$ buckets of paint. After she painted the living room, she had $2\frac{2}{3}$ buckets of paint left. How much did she use?

Solve and check.

30. $x - \frac{3}{8} = \frac{5}{12}$ **31.** $\frac{3}{7} + y = -\frac{3}{14}$ **32.** $\frac{9}{10} = b - \frac{2}{5}$

Find the solution by writing and solving an equation.

33. Ms. Gomez had 5 yards of material. She made a dress from some of it and then had $1\frac{5}{12}$ yards left. How much material did she use for the dress?

Chapter 7

Extra Practice

Multiply. Reduce to lowest terms.

1. $-\frac{3}{8}\left(\frac{4}{5}\right)$
2. $-\frac{5}{9}\left(-\frac{3}{5}\right)$
3. $-2\frac{3}{4}\left(-3\frac{4}{7}\right)$
4. $6\frac{4}{9}\left(-\frac{3}{4}\right)$

Divide. Reduce to lowest terms.

5. $\frac{5}{12} \div \left(-\frac{3}{4}\right)$
6. $-\frac{7}{10} \div \left(-\frac{5}{7}\right)$
7. $4\frac{1}{2} \div \left(-2\frac{3}{4}\right)$
8. $-6\frac{4}{7} \div 7\frac{2}{3}$

Solve and check.

9. $\frac{3}{x} = -\frac{18}{30}$
10. $\frac{1}{4}y = \frac{7}{8}$
11. $-4\frac{1}{5} = 1\frac{2}{5}m$
12. $\frac{2}{3}z = -\frac{5}{7}$

Find the solution by writing and solving an equation.

13. Maria lives $4\frac{8}{10}$ miles from school. She rode her moped $\frac{2}{3}$ of the way there before she ran out of gas. How far did she have to walk to get to school?

Solve.

14. If $\frac{2}{3}$ cup of soy sauce is used to make 2 cups of teriyaki sauce, how much soy sauce is used to make 10 cups of teriyaki sauce?
15. 18 links of a chain make a segment 42 inches long. What is the length of each link in this chain?
16. Selena received $9 off the price of a calculator that was on sale at $\frac{1}{4}$ off. What was the original price of the calculator?

Write each as a decimal. Use a bar for repeating decimals.

17. $\frac{3}{8}$
18. $\frac{4}{9}$
19. $\frac{7}{25}$

Simplify. Write the expression with exponents.

20. $\frac{9^7}{9^3}$
21. $\frac{(-6)^6}{(-6)^4}$
22. $\frac{x^8}{x^5}$

Write each expression without exponents.

23. 2^{-6}
24. $\frac{5^3}{5^7}$
25. $\frac{(-3)^5}{(-3)^3}$

Write each in scientific notation.

26. 4,270
27. 67,000
28. 200,000,000
29. 0.0035
30. 0.0001001
31. 0.246

Write each in standard form.

32. 3.9×10^4
33. 2.4×10^{-2}
34. 5.38×10^{-5}

Chapter 8

Extra Practice

Solve and check.

1. $4d - 3 = 45$
2. $33 = -2x + 3$
3. $5(7 + w) = -10$
4. $\frac{a - 11}{9} = -3$

Write an equation.

5. Erica's age, 7, is 1 less than twice Brian's age. How old is Brian?

Solve by writing an equation.

6. Steve had a box of spaghetti that was $\frac{2}{3}$ full. He used 4 oz, leaving 12 oz in the box. How many ounces did the box hold?

Evaluate the function for the values given.

7. $f(x) = 4x - (2 + 3)$ for $x = 4, 5, 6$ and 7.

Solve and check.

8. $2x + 7x = 54$
9. $-121 = 8p + 3p$
10. $108 = 17w - 5w$
11. $-11b - 12b = -92$
12. $3(x + 2) + 6x = 60$
13. $12d + (4 - 5d) = -52$
14. $8m + 6 - 2(3m) = 16$
15. $c + 5(3c - 5) = 23$
16. $156 - 9t = 4t$
17. $11z + 7 = 31 - z$
18. $6y + 11 = 5y$
19. $-6 + r = -20 - r$

Solve.

20. Margaret invited 3 more than $\frac{4}{5}$ of her class to a party. She invited 63 people to her party. How many people are in her class?
21. Smith's Tools rents a saw for a flat fee of \$8 plus \$6.50 per hour. Harrison's Rental rents the same saw for a flat fee of \$10 plus \$5.50 per hour. Solve $6.5h + 8 = 5.5h + 10$ to find the number of hours at which the two charges would be equal.
22. Marisa bought a camera for \$179, 2 rolls of 24-exposure print film at \$4.50 each and 2 rolls of 36-exposure slide film at \$5.75 each. What was the total cost before tax?

Add the polynomials.

23. $2x + 4x^2 + 2$ and $x - 2x^2 - 5$
24. $3a^2 + 4 - 2a$ and $-a^2 + 2 + 4a$

Solve and check.

25. $5d > 40$
26. $-3 + r < 12$
27. $17 < 4a - 3$
28. $-7b + 10b > -18$

Chapter 9

Extra Practice

Give the coordinates of each point.

1. A **2.** B

Graph the point on a pair of axes.

3. $C(2, -3)$ **4.** $D(-1, -1)$

5. Which of the ordered pairs $(-2, 3)$ or $(-3, -2)$ is a solution for the linear equation $2x - 3y = 0$?

Make a table of solutions for the equation.

6. $y = -2x + 1$ Use $x = -2, -1, 0, 1, 2, 3$

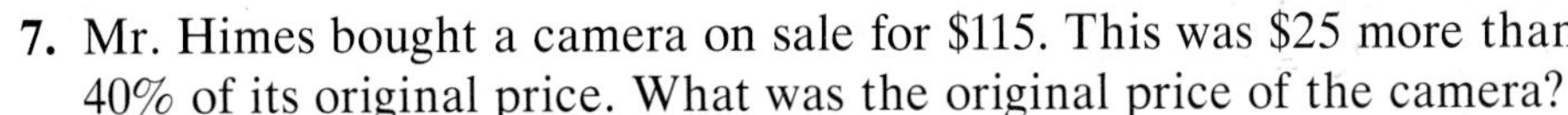

7. Mr. Himes bought a camera on sale for \$115. This was \$25 more than 40% of its original price. What was the original price of the camera?

Does y vary directly with x? If it does, find the value of k.

8.

x	y
1	2
2	4
3	6
4	8
5	10

9.

x	y
1	2
2	3
3	4
4	5
5	6

Does y vary inversely with x? If it does, find the value of k.

10.

x	y
1	9
2	7
3	5
4	3
5	1

11.

x	y
1	12
2	6
3	4
4	3
5	2.4

Find the slope of the line.

12. $3 - 7x = y$ **13.** $y = 4x + 1$

14. A line containing the points $A(3, 4)$ and $B(-2, -6)$.

15. Find the x- and y-intercept for the graph of $8 + 4y = x$.

16. Ace Carpet Cleaners charges \$75 to clean 3 rooms and \$20 for each additional room. How much would it cost to have 8 rooms cleaned?

Graph each solution on a number line.

17. $x \geq 0$ **18.** $2x - 2 < -6$

19. Graph the equations to solve the system. $x + y = 3, y - 3x = 3$.

20. Graph the inequality $y > x + 4$. Is the point $(-2, 2)$ a solution?

Chapter 10

Extra Practice

Write each ratio as a fraction in lowest terms.

1. 72 to 88
2. 12:21
3. $\frac{68}{16}$

Solve and check.

4. $\frac{9}{x} = \frac{27}{42}$
5. $\frac{y}{11} = \frac{30}{66}$
6. $\frac{3}{8} = \frac{27}{c}$

Simplify the rate.

7. $75/5 days
8. 217 km/3.5 h
9. 396 steps/18 floors

10. Florida and New York are 2,100 km apart. If it takes 3 hours to fly this distance, how fast does the plane travel?

Write an equation.

11. Connie used 288 tiles to tile her bedroom and kitchen floors. Her bedroom has twice the floor area of her kitchen. How many tiles did she use for each room?

Solve by writing an equation.

12. Juan had half the number of B's on his report card as he had A's. He was taking 6 courses all together, and got no grades lower than a B. How many of each grade did he get?

Find the scale dimensions of each. The scale is 1 cm = 0.5 m.

13. desk: 1 m × 2 m
14. bookcase: 1.5 m × 2.5 m

15. Grape juice costs $1.99 for the 32-ounce bottle and $2.69 for the 48-ounce bottle. Which size is the better buy?

Write each as a fraction in lowest terms.

16. 22%
17. 4%
18. 8.5%

Write as a decimal.

19. $14\frac{1}{4}\%$
20. 350%

Write as a percent.

21. 0.072
22. 9.68

23. Bank A offers an interest rate of $7\frac{3}{4}\%$. Bank B offers a rate of 7.71%. Which rate is higher?

Write each fraction as a percent.

24. $\frac{5}{8}$
25. $\frac{7}{25}$
26. $\frac{9}{5}$

Write each percent as a fraction or mixed number in lowest terms.

27. 175%
28. $\frac{4}{5}\%$
29. $3\frac{1}{2}\%$

Chapter 11

Extra Practice

Use a proportion or an equation to solve.

1. 60% of 185
2. 5% of 80
3. 4% of 55

Use a proportion or an equation to solve.

4. What percent of 90 is 27?
5. 63 is what percent of 105?
6. What percent of 160 is 120?
7. 9 out of 36 is what percent?

Use a proportion or an equation to solve. Round to the nearest tenth.

8. 14 is 7% of what number?
9. 40% of what number is 35?
10. 15% of what number is 45?
11. 22 is 25% of what number?

Solve by writing an equation.

12. A pair of jeans costs 75% as much as a pair of corduroy pants. What is the cost of each if the total cost for the jeans and cords is $42?
13. When Juanita was on vacation it rained 35% of the days. She was on vacation for 20 days. How many days did it rain?

Find the percent of increase or decrease.

14. Original amount = $75; new amount = $60.
15. Original amount = $60; new amount = $75.

Find the discount and sale price for each.

16. Regular price = $45
    Discount = 40%
17. Regular price = $2,450
    Discount = 6%

Find the commission.

18. Sale price = $11,250
    Commission = 4%
19. Sale price = $225
    Commission = 6%
20. The Chen family bought a new dishwasher priced at $300. There was $1\frac{1}{2}$ % local sales tax and 5% state sales tax. How much sales tax did they pay?

Find the interest and total amount.

21. $600 at 15% per year for 3 years
22. $800 at 12% per year for 4 months
23. $300 at 3% per month for 6 months
24. Make a circle graph to show the data in the table. Rackets Sold:

Badminton	Racquetball	Squash	Tennis	Other
5%	31%	19%	43%	2%

Chapter 12

Extra Practice

Estimate the length of each segment to the nearest centimeter.

1. $\overline{XY}$ **2.** $\overline{XZ}$

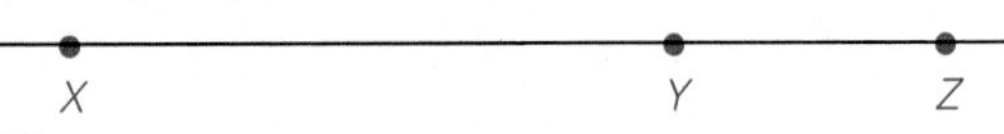

Refer to the figure for Exercises 3–13.

3. Name a point.

4. Name a line.

5. Name a plane.

6. Name a segment that includes Point *C*.

7. Name a ray.

8. Name an acute angle.

9. Name an obtuse angle.

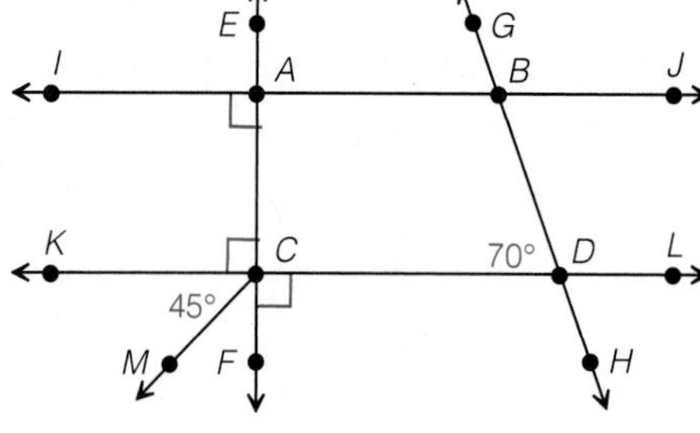

Find the measure of:

10. the complement of $\angle KCM$ **11.** the supplement of $\angle CDB$

12. $\angle ABG$ **13.** $\angle GBJ$

Classify each triangle by the measures of its angles and the lengths of its sides.

14. $\triangle ABC$ has a 120-degree angle and two sides equal in length.

15. $\triangle RST$ has three sides equal in length and three acute angles.

Name the polygon.

16.

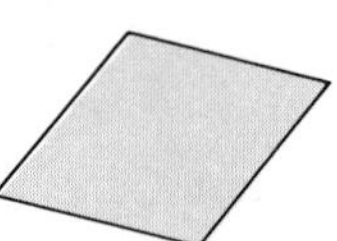

17. Find the measure of $\angle A$.

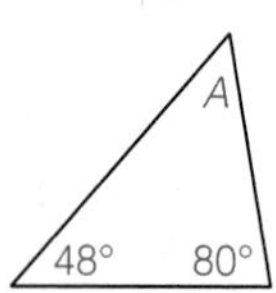

Solve. Use the formula *Distance* = *rate* × *time.*

18. Hans drove $4\frac{1}{2}$ hours and traveled 243 miles. What was his average speed?

Find the circumference of each circle. Use 3.14 for π.

19. radius = 4.3 cm **20.** diameter = 7 m

21. Find the diameter of a circle with circumference 25.12 cm.

Solve by writing an equation.

22. Joan and Harold each sold 23 tickets to the school play. Together they sold 40% of the total number of tickets sold to the play. How many tickets were sold in all?

Chapter 13

Extra Practice

Find the area of each figure.

1. Rectangle with length 15 m, width 6 cm
2. Triangle with base 38 ft, height 8 ft

Find the area of each quadrilateral.

3. Parallelogram with base = 11.2 m, height = 9.4 m
4. Trapezoid with $b_1 = 9$ cm, $b_2 = 5.5$ cm, $h = 13$ cm

Find the area of each circle. Use 3.14 for π.

5. $r = 6$ cm
6. $d = 5.8$ m

7. Find the area of the figure. Use 3.14 for π. Curved regions are semicircles.

Solve by writing an equation.

8. Linda bought 4 medium-sized drinks and 1 large drink for $3.20. If the large drink cost $0.80, how much did each medium-sized drink cost?

Find the volume of the prism or cylinder. Use 3.14 for π.

9.

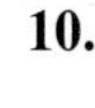

10.

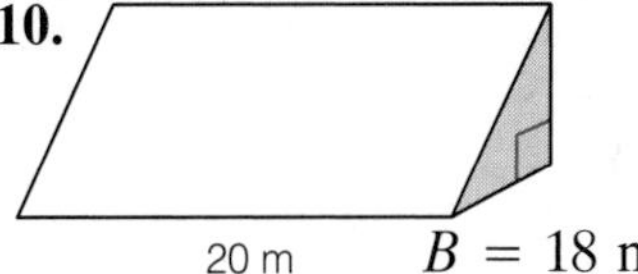

11. If concrete costs $30 per cubic yard, what is the cost of concrete for a foundation 38 feet long, 30 feet wide and 6 inches thick?

Find the volume. Use 3.14 for π.

12. Cone with a radius of 6 cm and a height of 14 cm
13. Pyramid with a base area of 45 square feet and a height of 12 feet

Find the surface area. Use 3.14 for π.

14.

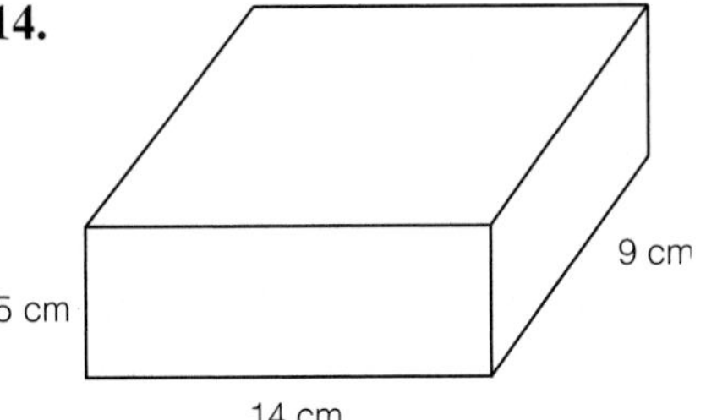

15.

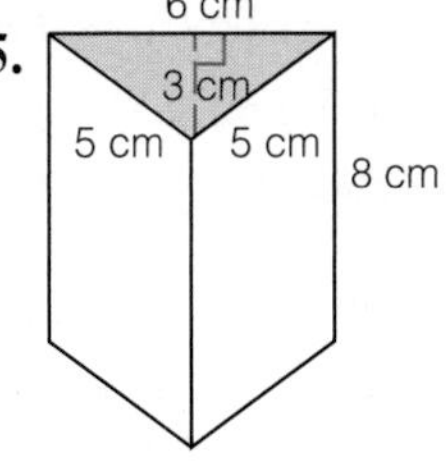

Chapter 14

Extra Practice

Use the counting principle to find the total number of outcomes.

1. Select 1 tennis racket. Composition: wood, metal, graphite, fiberglass. Head size: small, midsize, oversize. Grip size: $4\frac{3}{8}$, $4\frac{1}{2}$, $4\frac{5}{8}$.

Find the number of permutations.

2. m, a, t, h
3. 1, 2, 4, 5, 7, 8

There are 18 marbles in a bag. Six are clear, four are black, and eight are red.

4. *P*(black)
5. *P*(not clear)
6. *P*(clear or red)

Find the probability of each for one toss of two dice.

7. *P*(total of 2)
8. *P*(a number < 3, a number > 3)

There are 10 socks in a drawer. Six are blue and four are brown. Find each probability if you take one sock out and then, without replacing it, take another sock out.

9. blue then blue
10. brown then blue

Solve by writing an equation.

11. The length of a yard is 3 times its width. It takes 104 ft. of fencing to surround the yard. Find the dimensions of the yard.

Use this data to solve Exercises 12–15.
Test grades: 71, 75, 75, 78, 82, 83, 86, 89, 93

12. Find the range.
13. What is the mode?
14. What is the median?
15. Find the mean.
16. Make a bar graph for the data. Distance from Orlando in miles: Miami, 220; New York, 1,050; Raleigh, 600; Syracuse, 1,230.

Use the line graph for Exercises 17–19.

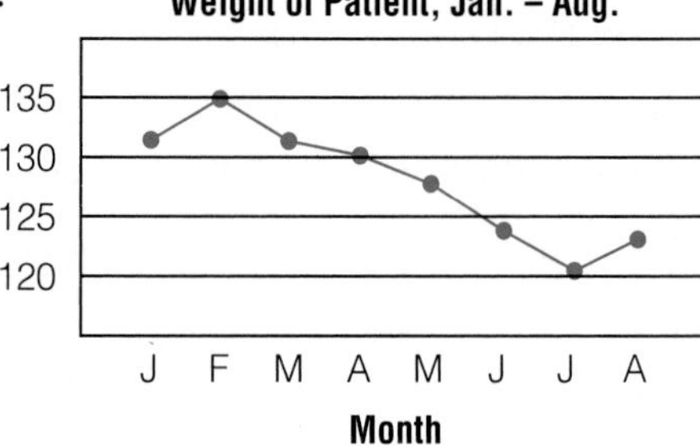

17. What is the range of weights for the patient in the time shown?
18. Between what months did the patient's weight increase?
19. By how much did the patient's weight decrease from April to July?
20. Make a pictogram for the data. Cars sold: January, 75; April, 150; July, 120; October, 90.

Chapter 15

Extra Practice

Evaluate each expression.

1. $\sqrt{36} - \sqrt{25}$ **2.** $\sqrt{(155 - 11)}$

Between what two consecutive integers does each square root lie?

3. $\sqrt{45}$ **4.** $\sqrt{8}$ **5.** $\sqrt{88}$

6. Find the time (t) in seconds it takes for an object to fall the distance (d) 2,400 feet. Use the formula $t = \sqrt{\frac{d}{16}}$.

Solve and check. **7.** $x^2 = 196$ **8.** $x^2 = 15$

Find the length of a to the nearest hundredth.

9.

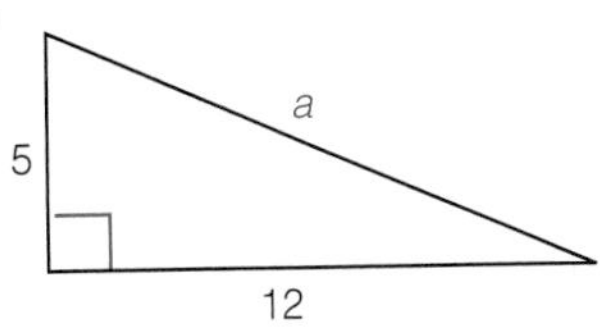

10.

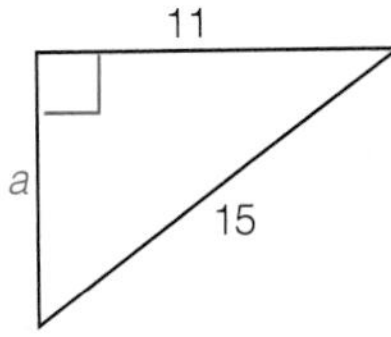

Solve.

11. A computer screen is 7 inches tall and 9 inches wide. What is the length of the diagonal of the screen?

Use proportions to find the unknown lengths for these similar triangles.

12.

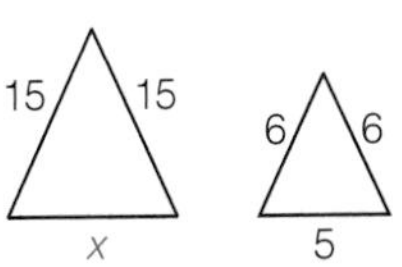

13.

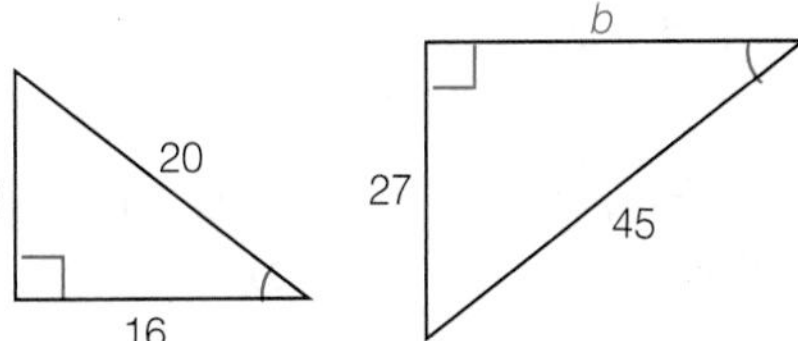

Find the unknown length.

14.

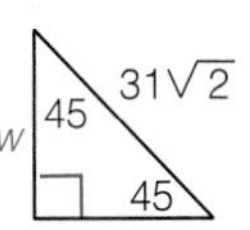

15.

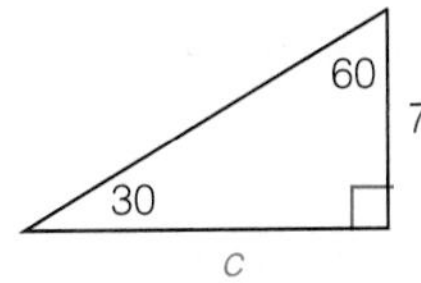

Function: $f(x) = |x^2 - 2x|$. Evaluate for the values given.

16. $x = -1$ **17.** $x = 0$ **18.** $x = 2$

Find each ratio for $\angle x$.

19. $\cos x$

20. $\sin x$

21. $\tan x$

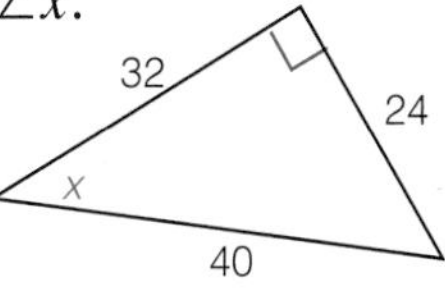

Glossary

Absolute value (p. 78) The absolute value of a number is its distance from 0 on a number line.
Absolute value function (p. 548) A function that can be described by the equation $f(x) = |x|$.
Acute angle (p. 41) An angle that has a measure less than 90°.
Acute triangle (p. 413) A triangle made up of three acute angles.
Addend A number to be added.
Addition Property of Equality (p. 25) For all numbers a, b, and c, if $a = b$, then $a + c = b + c$.
Addition Property of Inequality (p. 286) For all numbers a, b, and c, if $a > b$, then $a + c > b + c$.
Additive Identity (p. 14) Zero. When zero is added to a number, the result is that same number.
Additive Inverse Property (p. 82) See *Inverse Property.*
Algebraic expression (p. 4) An expression that contains at least one variable; for example, $n + 7$.
Angle (p. 413) Two rays with a common endpoint called the vertex.
Area (p. 451) The measure of a plane region in terms of square units.
Associative Property of Addition (p. 14) The sum of three or more numbers is the same regardless of the grouping:
$(a + b) + c = a + (b + c)$
Associative Property of Multiplication (p.50) The product of three or more numbers is the same regardless of the grouping:
$(a \cdot b) \cdot c = a \cdot (b \cdot c)$
Average (p. 508) See *Mean.*
Axes (p. 299) See *Rectangular coordinate system.*

Bar graph (p. 71) A type of statistical graph used to show data.
Base (geometry) (p. 452) Any side of a polygon may be referred to as a base.
Base (numbers) (p. 163) In exponential notation a^n, a is the base.
Binomial (p. 283) A polynomial with exactly two terms.
Boundary line (p. 332) A line that divides the plane of a rectangular coordinate system into two regions.

Centimeter (p. 129) $\frac{1}{100}$ of a meter.
Circle (p. 431) All the points in a plane that are a fixed distance from a point called the center.
Circle graph (p. 339) A type of statistical graph used to show the relationships of the parts to each other and to the total amount.
Circumference (p. 431) The distance around a circle.
Coefficient In any term, the coefficient is the numeric factor of the term of the number that is multiplied by the variable. For $-3x$, the coefficient is -3; for x^2, the coefficient is 1.
Combination (p. 552) A selection of a group of objects from a set without regard to order.
Common factor (p. 172) Any number that is a factor of each of the numbers in a set of numbers.
Commutative Property of Addition (p. 13) The sum of any two numbers is the same regardless of the order in which they are added:
$a + b = b + a$
Commutative Property of Multiplication (p. 49) The product of any two numbes is the same regardless of the order in which they are multiplied:
$a \cdot b = b \cdot a$
Complementary angles (p. 414) Two angles whose measures have a sum of 90°.
Composite number (p. 160) Any whole number greater than 1 that has more than two factors.
Cone (p. 473) A solid with exactly one circular base and exactly one vertex, not in the same plane as the base.
Congruent figures (p. 436) Two geometric figures are congruent if they have the same size and shape.
Constant (p. 283) A term with no variables.
Coordinate plane (p. 299) See *Rectangular coordinate system.*
Coordinates (p. 299) An ordered pair of numbers matched with a point in the coordinate plane.
Corresponding angles (p. 418) (1) In two similar triangles or congruent polygons, the angles with equal measures; (2) A pair of angles with equal measure, formed by the intersection of a transversal and a pair of parallel lines, with interiors on the same side as the transversal.
Corresponding parts (p. 436) The matching sides, angles, and vertices of congruent polygons.
Corresponding sides (p. 436) In two similar triangles or congruent polygons, the sides opposite the corresponding angles.

Cosine ratio (p. 551) For an acute angle A in a right triangle, the ratio of the length of the adjacent side to the length of the hypotenuse.
Counterexample (p. 204) An example that shows that a statement is false.
Counting Principle (p. 487) To find the total number of choices for an event, multiply the number of choices for each part.
Cross products (p. 188) For fractions $\frac{a}{b}$ and $\frac{c}{d}$, the products ad and bc.
Cubic units (p. 390) Units used for measuring volume.
Cylinder (p. 467) A solid having two congruent, circular bases in parallel planes.

Data (p. 70) Numerical information, usually about the real world.
Decimal system (p. 117) The place-value numeration system that uses the digits 0 through 9, and groups by tens.
Degree of an angle (p. 413) A unit used to measure angles. There are 90 degrees (90°) in a right angle.
Denominator (p. 187) For a fraction $\frac{a}{b}$, b is the denominator.
Dependent event (p. 499) An event whose outcome is influenced by the outcome of a previous event.
Diameter (p. 431) A segment that passes through the center of a circle and has endpoints on the circle.
Difference The answer to a subtraction problem.
Direct variation (p. 315) As the value of one variable increases at a constant rate, the value of a related variable also increases at a constant rate; described by the equation $y = kx$.
Distributive Property (p. 52) Connects multiplication and addition of whole numbers: $a(b + c) = a \cdot b + a \cdot c$
Dividend The number in a quotient that is being divided; in $a \div b$ or $\frac{a}{b}$, a is the dividend.
Divisible (p. 155) A number is divisible by a second number if the quotient of the first divided by the second is a whole number and the remainder is 0.
Divisor The number you divide by in a quotient; in $a \div b$ or $\frac{a}{b}$, b is the divisor.
Domain (p. 178) The domain of a function is the set of first coordinates.

Equation (p. 17) A statement of equality between two expressions.
Equilateral triangle (p. 422) A triangle with all three sides equal in length.
Equivalent expressions (p. 13) Two algebraic expressions are equivalent if (and only if) they have the same value for any number that replaces the variable.
Estimate (p. 29) To find an approximate solution.
Evaluate an expression (p. 3) To evaluate an expression is to replace each variable in the expression with a given value and simplify the result.
Even numbers (p. 152) All whole numbers that are multiples of 2.
Event (p. 495) An outcome or combination of outcomes.
Expanded form (factored form) (p. 162) A number represented as the product of factors.
Exponent (p. 162) In exponential notation a^n, n is the exponent. The exponent tells how many times a, called the base, is used as a factor.
Expression See *Algebraic expression, Numerical expression.*

Factor (p. 151) A number that is multiplied by another number to yield a product.
Factor completely (p. 166) To express a number as the product of prime factors.
Formula (p. 66) An equation that shows a relationship between two or more variables.
Fraction (p. 187) A symbol in the form $\frac{a}{b}$, where a is the numerator and b is the denominator and $b \neq 0$.
Frequency table (p. 71) A collection of data organized to show numbers of distinct responses.
Function (p. 178) A relationship between two variables that pairs every member of one set, the *domain,* with one and only one member of another set, the *range.*

Generalization (p. 205) A statement that says something is always true for every member of a specified set.
Glyph (p. 440) A picture or symbol that shows selected data at a glance.
Gram (p. 129) The basic unit of mass in the metric system.
Greatest common factor (GCF) (p. 169) The greatest whole number that is a factor of two or more given numbers.
Grouping symbols (p. 39) Parentheses ( ), brackets [ ], and the fraction bar (a division symbol) are grouping symbols, and indicate the order in which operations should be done.

Height of a trapezoid (p. 456) The distance between the bases of a trapezoid.

Height of a triangle (p. 455) The perpendicular distance from a vertex to a base.
Hexagon (p. 425) A six-sided polygon.
Horizontal line A line that is parallel to the x-axis.
Hypotenuse (p. 535) The longest side of a right triangle, opposite the right angle.

Identity Property for Addition (p. 13) The sum of an addend and zero is the addend: $a + 0 = 0 + a = a$
Identity Property for Multiplication (p. 50) The product of a factor and one is the factor: $a \cdot 1 = 1 \cdot a = a$
Improper fraction (p. 192) A fraction whose numerator is greater than or equal to its denominator.
Independent event (p. 499) An event whose outcome is not influenced by the outcome of a previous event.
Inequality (p. 286) A statement that uses the symbols $>$ (greater than), $<$ (less than), $\geq$ (greater than or equal to), or $\leq$ (less than or equal to), to compare two expressions.
Inequality symbols (p. 78) The symbols $<$, $>$, $\leq$, and $\geq$.
Integers (p. 77) The whole numbers and their additive inverses.
Interest (p. 393) A charge for the use of money, paid by the borrower to the lender.
Intersecting lines (p. 417) Lines in the same plane that are not parallel.
Inverse operations (p. 25) Operations that can undo each other; addition and subtraction; multiplication and division.
Inverse Property of Addition (p. 82) The sum of any number and its additive inverse is 0: $a + (-a) = 0$; $-a + a = 0$
Inverse Property of Multiplication (p. 236) The product of any rational number and its multiplicative inverse is 1:

$$\frac{a}{b} \cdot \frac{b}{a} = \frac{b}{a} \cdot \frac{a}{b} = 1$$

Inverse variation (p. 316) As the value of one variable increases at a constant rate, the value of a related variable decreases and the product of the variables is a constant; described by the equation

$$y = \frac{k}{x}.$$

Irrational number (p. 190) A real number that cannot be expressed as the quotient of two integers. Irrational numbers have nonrepeating decimal representations.

Isosceles triangle (p. 422) A triangle with two sides equal in length.

Least common denominator (LCD) (p. 208) The smallest positive number that is a multiple of each denominator of two or more fractions.
Least common multiple (LCM) (p. 175) The smallest nonzero number that is a multiple of two or more given numbers.
Legs of a triangle (p. 535) The two sides of a right triangle that form the right angle.
Like terms (p. 56) Terms having exactly the same variables with exactly the same exponents.
Line (p. 407) A set of points determined by two points, and extending endlessly in both directions.
Line graph (p. 513) A type of statistical graph used to show changes over time.
Linear equation (p. 303) An equation that can be written in the form $y = ax + b$.
Line segment (p. 407) See *Segment.*
Liter (p. 129) The basic unit of capacity in the metric system.
Lowest terms (p. 189) A fraction is in lowest terms when the only common factor of the numerator and the denominator is 1.

Mean (p. 508) The average; the sum of a set of numbers divided by the number of members in the set.
Median (p. 508) The middle number in a list of numbers given in order.
Meter (p. 129) The basic unit of length in the metric system.
Metric system (p. 129) The system of measurement that uses the meter as the basic unit of length, the liter as the basic unit of capacity, and the gram as the basic unit of mass.
Midpoint (p. 302) The midpoint of a segment is the point that divides the segment into two segments of equal length.
Minuend The number you are subtracting from; in $a - b$, a is the minuend.
Mixed number (p. 192) A numeral that has a whole number part and a fraction part.
Mode (p. 504) In a list of numbers, the number that occurs most frequently.
Monomial (p. 283) An expression that is either a numeral, a variable, or the product of numerals and variables.
Multiple (p. 151) The product of two whole numbers is a multiple of each of the whole numbers.
Multiplication Property of Equality (p. 61) For all numbers a, b, and c, if $a = b$, then $ac = bc$.

Multiplication Property of Inequality (p. 287) For all numbers a, b, and c,
where c is positive: if $a > b$, then $ac > bc$
where c is negative: if $a > b$, then $ac < bc$

Multiplicative Identity (p. 50) One. When a number is multiplied by 1, the result is that same number.

Multiplicative Inverse Property (p. 236) See *Inverse Property.*

Mutually exclusive events (p. 496) Two events that cannot occur at the same time.

Natural numbers The numbers we use for counting. They are 1, 2, 3, 4, and so on.

Negative number (p. 77) Any number that is less than zero.

Nonlinear functions (p. 548) Functions whose graphs are not straight lines.

Numerator (p. 187) For each fraction $\frac{a}{b}$, a is the numerator.

Numerical expression (p. 3) A number, or two or more numbers together with operation signs.

Obtuse angle (p. 413) An angle with measure greater than 90° and less than 180°.

Octagon (p. 425) An eight-sided polygon.

Odd numbers (p. 152) All whole numbers that are not multiples of 2.

Open sentence (p. 19) An equation or inequality that contains at least one variable.

Opposites (p. 77) Numbers, such as 4 and -4, that are the same distance from 0 but are on opposite sides of 0 on the number line.

Order of operations (p. 39) A rule for the order in which operations should be done. The order of operations is: (1) compute within grouping symbols; (2) compute powers; (3) multiply and divide in order from left to right; and (4) add and subtract in order from left to right.

Ordered pair (p. 299) A pair of numbers in a particular order; the coordinates of a point in a plane.

Origin (p. 299) The point at which the axes of a graph cross; the point $(0, 0)$ in the coordinate plane system.

Parallel lines (p. 417) Lines in the same plane that do not intersect.

Parallelogram (p. 425) A quadrilateral with both pairs of opposite sides parallel.

Pentagon (p. 425) A five-sided polygon.

Percent (p. 355) Literally, "per one hundred"; represented by the symbol %.

Perfect square (p. 525) An expression whose square root can be written as an integer.

Perimeter (p. 410) The sum of the lengths of the sides of a polygon.

Permutation (p. 491) An arrangement of objects in a particular order.

Perpendicular lines (p. 417) Two intersecting lines that form right angles.

Pi (π) (p. 431) The ratio of the circumference of a circle to its diameter. The decimal for π is unending and does not repeat. $\pi = 3.14159\ldots$

Pictogram (p. 517) A type of statistical graph using pictures to present data.

Place value (p. 117) The value given to the place a digit occupies in a numeral. In the decimal system, each place of a numeral has ten times the value of the place to its right.

Plane (p. 407) The geometric figure determined by three points that are not on the same line.

Point (p. 408) The simplest geometric figure; it shows a location.

Polygon (p. 425) A closed plane figure formed by three or more segments that intersect only at their endpoints so that exactly two segments meet at each point.

Polynomial (p. 283) A monomial or a sum of monomials.

Positive number (p. 77) Any number that is greater than zero.

Power (p. 162) A product in which each factor is identical; for example, 32 is the fifth power of 2.

Prime factorization (p. 166) The expression of a composite number as the product of prime factors.

Prime number (p. 160) A whole number greater than 1 that has exactly two factors, itself and 1.

Principal (p. 393) An amount of money that is borrowed or invested.

Prism (p. 467) A solid that has a pair of parallel, congruent bases and rectangular sides that are parallelograms.

Probability (p. 495) The ratio of the number of times a certain outcome can occur to the number of total possible outcomes.

Product The answer to a multiplication problem.

Proper fraction (p. 192) A fraction whose numerator is less than its denominator.

Property of Equivalent Fractions (p. 188) Multiplying or dividing both the numerator and denominator of a fraction by the same nonzero integer results in an equivalent fraction: for all numbers a, b, and c, $(b \neq 0, c \neq 0)$, $\frac{a}{b} = \frac{a \cdot c}{b \cdot c}$ and $\frac{a}{b} = \frac{a \div c}{b \div c}$

Property of −1 (p. 106) The product of −1 and a number is the opposite of the number.

Proportion (p. 344) An equation stating that two ratios are equal.

Protractor (p. 413) An instrument used to measure angles.

Pyramid (p. 473) A solid that has three or more triangular sides and a polygon as a base.

Pythagorean Theorem (p. 535) In a right triangle, the square of the length of the hypotenuse is equal to the sum of the squares of the lengths of the other two sides.

Quadrant One of the four regions into which the coordinate axes divide a plane.

Quadratic function (p. 548) A second degree function: $f(x) = ax^2 + bx + c$, where $a \neq 0$.

Quadrilateral (p. 425) A four-sided polygon.

Quotient The result obtained when dividing two numbers.

Radical sign (p. 525) The symbol $\sqrt{}$ is called a radical sign and is used to indicate a square root.

Radius (p. 431) Any segment that joins the center to a point on a circle.

Range (p. 504) The difference between the greatest number and the least number in a set of data.

Range of a function (p. 178) The set of second coordinates of the ordered pairs.

Ranked stem-and-leaf diagram (p. 144) A stem-and-leaf diagram in which the values are arranged in order from least to greatest.

Rate (p. 348) A ratio that compares two different units.

Ratio (p. 341) A comparison of one number to another, expressed as a quotient.

Rational number (p. 195) Any number that can be written in the form $\frac{a}{b}$ where a and b are integers, $b \neq 0$.

Ray (p. 407) A part of a line that has one endpoint and extends endlessly in one direction.

Real numbers (p. 330) The rational numbers and the irrational numbers. There is a real number for each point on the number line.

Reciprocal (p. 236) Two numbers are reciprocals if their product is 1. A reciprocal is also called a multiplicative inverse.

Rectangle (p. 425) A quadrilateral with two pairs of parallel sides and four right angles.

Rectangular coordinate system (p. 299) A plane containing two intersecting perpendicular number lines called axes; used for graphing ordered pairs.

Regular polygon (p. 425) A polygon in which all sides have the same measure and all angles have the same measure.

Repeating decimal (p. 198) A decimal with a sequence of digits that repeats endlessly.

Replacement set (p. 19) The set of numbers from which replacements for the variable in an equation are selected.

Rhombus (p. 425) A quadrilateral with all sides of the same length.

Right angle (p. 413) An angle that measures 90°.

Right triangle (p. 545) A triangle with a right angle.

Rise (p. 319) The difference between the y-coordinates of two points; used to find the slope of a line.

Run (p. 319) The difference between the x-coordinates of two points; used to find the slope of a line.

Scale (p. 350) The constant ratio with which actual dimensions are represented in a map or drawing.

Scalene triangle (p. 422) A triangle with no two sides equal in length.

Scatterplot (p. 328) A display of ordered pairs of data used to determine a correlation between variables.

Scientific notation (p. 251) A system of writing a number as the product of a power of 10 and a number greater than or equal to one but less than 10.

Segment (p. 407) Part of a line; two points and all the points between them.

Sequence (p. 113) A set of numbers in a particular order.

Similar polygons (p. 541) Polygons that are the same shape but not necessarily the same size.

Simple interest (p. 393) A percentage of an amount of money paid by the borrower to the lender.

Simplify an expression (p. 55) To replace an algebraic (or numerical) expression with the simplest equivalent expression.

Sine ratio (p. 551) For an acute angle A in a right triangle, the ratio of the length of the opposite side to the length of the hypotenuse.

Slope (p. 319) The ratio of rise to run in the graph of any linear equation.

Solution set (p. 19) The collection of all the solutions to a given equation.

Solve an equation (p. 19) Find all the solutions to an equation.
Square (geometry) (p. 425) A quadrilateral with sides of equal length and four right angles.
Square (numbers) (p. 162) The product of a number multiplied by itself is called the square of that number.
Square root (p. 525) If $a^2 = b$, then a is a square root of b.
Square root function (p. 549) A function that can be described by the equation $f(x) = \sqrt{x}$.
Standard form (p. 251) A number such as 100 or 3.21 written in its decimal form.
Statistics The branch of mathematics that deals with the collection, organization, display, and interpretation of data.
Stem-and-leaf diagram (p. 144) A method of displaying data that shows certain digits as "stems" and the remaining digit(s) as "leaves."
Subtrahend In the subtraction $a - b$, b is the subtrahend.
Sum The answer to an addition problem.
Supplementary angles (p. 414) Two angles whose measures have a sum of 180°.
Surface area (p. 476) The area of the surfaces of a solid figure.
Survey (p. 70) A technique used for collecting data involving fact or opinion.
System of equations (p. 325) Two or more equations for which a common solution is sought.
System of inequalities (p. 333) Two or more linear inequalities for which a common solution is sought.

Tangent ratio (p. 551) For an acute angle A in a right triangle, the ratio of the length of the opposite side to the length of the adjacent side.
Term of a polynomial (p. 283) In a polynomial, each monomial is a term.
Terminating decimal (p. 198) A decimal with a finite number of digits; for example, 0.375.
Terms (p. 56) The parts of an algebraic expression that are separated by an addition or subtraction sign.
Transversal (p. 418) A line that intersects two or more lines.
Trapezoid (p. 425) A quadrilateral with one pair of parallel sides.
Triangle (p. 422) A three-sided polygon.
Trigonometric ratios (p. 551) Ratios of lengths of sides of right triangles. Three of these ratios are called the sine, the cosine, and the tangent.
Trinomial (p. 283) A polynomial with exactly three terms.

Variable (p. 7) A letter or other symbol used to reserve a place for a number in an expression or equation.
Venn Diagram (p. 36) A drawing used to show logical relationships among members of a set.
Vertex (p. 413) The point that the two rays of an angle have in common.
Vertical angles (p. 417) The two pairs of angles formed by the intersection of two lines.
Vertical line A line that is parallel to the y-axis.
Volume (p. 467) The measure of a solid region in terms of cubic units.

Whole number (p. 13) Any number in the set $\{0, 1, 2, 3, 4, 5, \ldots\}$.

x-axis (p. 299) The horizontal axis in a rectangular coordinate plane system.
x-coordinate (p. 299) The first number in an ordered pair; used to plot a point in a coordinate plane system.
x-intercept (p. 321) The x-coordinate of the point where a line crosses the x-axis.

y-axis (p. 299) The vertical axis in a rectangular coordinate plane system.
y-coordinate (p. 299) The second number in an ordered pair; used to plot a point in a coordinate plane system.
y-intercept (p. 321) The y-coordinate of the point where a line crosses the y-axis.

Zero Property of Multiplication (p. 50) The product of any number and zero is zero:
For all whole numbers a, $a(0) = 0$, $0(a) = 0$

Selected Answers

Chapter 1

Expressions and Equations: Addition and Subtraction

Lesson 1-1

Try This **a.** 9 **b.** 16 **c.** 14 **d.** 450 m **e.** 24 **f.** 11 **g.** 4

Exercises **1.** 58 **3.** 33 **5.** 18 **7.** 10 **9.** 43 **11.** 12 **13.** 74 **15.** 50 **17.** 27 **19.** 90 **21.** 4 **23.** 10 **25.** 59°F **27.** 17 cm **29.** 20 **31.** $9 + 9 - 1 = 17$ **33.** $7 + 7 - 6 = 8$ **35.** $6 + 6 - 9 = 3$ **37.** 406 ft **39.** 30 **41.** 125 **43.** 7,303 **45.** 12,192 **47.** 61,426

Calculator Activity **1.** 3,775 **3.** 2,355

Lesson 1-2

Try This **a.** 6, 7, 22 **b.** 13, 27, $n - 3$ **c.** 17, 19, 29, $p + 9$

Exercises **1.** 7, 8, 13 **3.** 50, 60, $x + 10$ **5.** 1, 6, 11, 16, 21 **7.** \$31, \$45.95, \$25.50, \$36.75, \$51 **9.** 41 **11.** 27 **13.** 7

Lesson 1-3

Try This **a.** $10 - 6$ **b.** $8 + 7$ **c.** $9 - 2$ **d.** $n + 5$ **e.** $n - 8$ **f.** $n + 7$ **g.** $n - 5$ **h.** $23 + 9$ **i.** $23 + y$ **j.** $23 - 14$ **k.** $23 - t$

Exercises **1.** $8 + 6$ **3.** $9 + 7$ **5.** $6 + 7$ **7.** $12 + 8$ **9.** $x + 6$ **11.** $n + 7$ **13.** $r + 8$ **15.** $y - 5$ **17.** $s - 9$ **19.** $n + 6$ **21.** $n + 16$ **23.** $45 + 7$ **25.** $45 - 4$ **27.** $75 + 45$ **29.** $75 - 37$ **31.** $n + 1$ **33.** $n + 2$ **35.** $x + y = 31, x - y = 3, x = 17, y = 14$ **37.** 993 **39.** 43 **41.** 728, 376 **43.** 50, 50

Mental Math **1.** 343 **3.** 325 **5.** 7,633

Lesson 1-4

Try This **a.** $x + 45$ **b.** $5{,}138 + a$ **c.** $t + 479$ **d.** $n + (145 + 68)$ **e.** $(125 + 75) + a$ **f.** t **g.** a **h.** z **i.** 0

Exercises **1.** $b + 137$ **3.** $y + 507$ **5.** $z + (16 + 34)$ **7.** x **9.** 0 **11.** y; Identity **13.** $x + 57$; Commutative **15.** $x + y$; Identity **17.** $d + (30 + 35)$; Associative **21.** 1,492 **23.** 144 **25.** 0 **27.** 2 **29.** 157 **31.** 25 **33.** two thousand seventeen **35.** six thousand nine hundred six

Lesson 1-5

Try This **a.** $n + 4 = 10$; 6 counters

Exercises **1.** $n + 3 = 7$; 4 counters **3.** $9 = n + 5$; 4 counters **5.** 4 **7.** 7 **9.** 8 **11.** 8 **13.** $2n + 4 = 24$; 10 counters **15.** 57

Lesson 1-6

Try This **a.** 6 **b.** 2 **c.** 4 **d.** 0 **e.** no solution **f.** no solution

Exercises **1.** 9 **3.** no solution **5.** no solution **7.** no solution **9.** all whole numbers **13.** $7 - 6$

Lesson 1-7

Try This **a.** 50 **b.** 4 **c.** 8 **d.** 30 bowling balls **e.** 48 **f.** 1,104 **g.** 667

Exercises **1.** 6 **3.** 2 **5.** 11 **7.** 21 **9.** 13 **11.** 158 **13.** 155 **15.** 1,651 **17.** 1,127 **19.** 3 frames **21.** 7 boards **23.** $x = 7{,}247 + 638; x = 7{,}885$ **25.** $z = 6{,}079 + 2{,}346; z = 8{,}425$ **27.** 152,054 **29.** 75,975 **33.** 1,061 **35.** 8,756 **37.** 61,671 **39.** 20 **41.** 20

Lesson 1-8

Try This **a.** $x + 5 = 13; x = 8$ **b.** 317 **c.** 36 **d.** 234 **e.** 235

Exercises **1.** $x + 4 = 9; x = 5$ **3.** $x + 4 = 25; x = 21$ **5.** 36 **7.** 63 **9.** 215 **11.** 197 **13.** 252 **15.** 864 **17.** 133 lb **19.** 54 **21.** 126 **23.** $x + 2 + 14 = 27, x = 11$; $12 + 9 + y = 27, y = 6$; $n + 16 + 7 = 27, n = 4$ **25.** $b + a$ **27.** $n + 125$ **29.** 243 **31.** 6

Lesson 1-9

Try This **a.** 14,000 **b.** 72,000 **c.** 1,700 **d.** 6,500

Exercises **1.** 150 **3.** 170 **5.** 960 **7.** 1,200 **9.** 1,600 **11.** 6,000 **13.** 15,000 **15.** 1,800,000 **17.** 94,000 mi **19.** 74,999 and 65,000 **21.** 300; 325 **23.** 78 + (65 + 135) **25.** 27 **27.** 92 **29.** 2,423 **31.** 32,948 **33.** 460,994

Lesson 1-10

Problems **1.** $2,207 **3.** $1,819 **5.** $12,412

Lesson 1-11

Problems **1.** 18 this week, 12 last week **3.** 35 **5.** Gil is 24, Phil is 25, Will is 26

Chapter 1 Review/Test

1. false **3.** true **5.** true **7.** 24 **9.** 4 **11.** $p + 5$ **13.** $7 + n$ **15.** $n + (5 + 4)$ **17.** 3 **19.** 53 **21.** 1,200 **23.** $x - 26 = 143$ **25.** 28,000 mi

Chapter 2

Expressions and Equations: Multiplication and Division

Lesson 2-1

Try This **a.** 3 **b.** 16 **c.** 33 **d.** 36 **e.** 240 **f.** 9 **g.** 1 **h.** 2

Exercises **1.** 19 **3.** 96 **5.** 18 **7.** 9 **9.** 29 **11.** 1,088 **13.** 96 **15.** 225 **17.** 60 **19.** 9 **21.** $6(5) - 30 = 0$ **23.** $12 \div 3 + 18 \div 3 = 10$ **25.** 9 **29.** 15 **31.** $27 - x$ **33.** 6,500

Calculator Activity **1.** 569 **3.** 208 **5.** 40

Lesson 2-2

Try This **a.** 20, 25, 30, $\frac{n}{2}$ **b.** 210, 287, 315, $7p$

Exercises **1.** 8, $\frac{x}{3}$ **3.** 175, 455, $7p$ **5.** 36, $6x$ **7.** 4, 8, 16, 33 **11.** 14, 17, $3x + 2$ **13.** 38 **15.** 480 **17.** 78

Lesson 2-3

Try This **a.** $24 \div 6$ **b.** $2 \cdot 8$ **c.** $12 \cdot 7$ **d.** $3 \cdot 4$ **e.** $6n$ **f.** $2n$ **g.** $n \div 5$ **h.** $5 + 2n$ **i.** $7(n + 4)$ **j.** 84(2) **k.** $84 \div 4$ **l.** $84s$

Exercises **1.** $8 \cdot 7$ **3.** $2 \cdot 46$ **5.** $48 \div 4$ **7.** $9n$ **9.** $n \div 5$ **11.** $35 + 2n$ **13.** $\frac{n}{10} - 1$ **15.** $3n - 24$ **17.** 36(9) **19.** $36 \div 4$ **21.** 48(4) **23.** $48 \div 12$ **25.** $2n$, $2n + 2$ **27.** Eagles 12, Cougars 5 **29.** 454 **31.** 26

Lesson 2-4

Try This **a.** yx **b.** $6z$ **c.** $p(24)$ **d.** $n(12 \cdot 7)$ **e.** $(25 \cdot 4)a$ **f.** $6(a \cdot b)$ **g.** 0 **h.** n **i.** 0 **j.** $6r + 24$ **k.** $5n + 3n$ **l.** $27 \cdot 10 = 270$ **m.** $1,000 \cdot 58 = 58,000$ **n.** $354 \cdot 100 = 35,400$

Exercises **1.** $4y$ **3.** dc **5.** $n(3 \cdot 8)$ **7.** $(8 \cdot 5)a$ **9.** y **11.** 1 **13.** $4x + 12$ **15.** $6y + 9y$ or $15y$ **17.** 260 **19.** 5,600 **21.** $2L + 24$ **23.** yes, 117 **25.** 24 **27.** 100 **31.** 8,648 **33.** 29,165 **35.** 5,192 **37.** 19 **39.** 17

Numbers to Algebra **1.** $2(a + b)$ **3.** $6(n + 7)$ **5.** $p(3 + n)$

Lesson 2-5

Try This **a.** $30x$ **b.** $63b$ **c.** $96y$ **d.** $n + 32$ **e.** $z + 20$ **f.** $11n$ **g.** $40b$ **h.** $41z$ **i.** $6x$

Exercises **1.** $208c$ **3.** $48p$ **5.** $z + 70$ **7.** $y + 203$ **9.** $12a$ **11.** $123c$ **13.** $y + 14$ **15.** $7x + 56$ **17.** Monday 8, Tuesday 16, Wednesday 24, Thursday 32 **19.** $6x - 9$ **21.** 328

Mental Math **1.** 68 **3.** 92 **5.** 258

Lesson 2-6

Try This **a.** 36 **b.** 8 **c.** 27 **d.** 150 lb **e.** 364 **f.** 23 **g.** 608

Exercises **1.** 9 **3.** 72 **5.** 30 **7.** 20 **9.** 210 **11.** 2 **13.** 13 **15.** 9 **17a.** $x = 42 \cdot 28$; 1,176 **17b.** $n = 53 \cdot 24$; 1,272 **17c.** $z = 17 \cdot 125$; 2,125 **19.** $36,280 **21.** 24, 6 **23.** 9 **25.** 19 **27.** 27

Lesson 2-7

Try This **a.** $3n = 12, n = 4$ **b.** 13 **c.** 24 **d.** 72 **e.** 32

Exercises **1.** $3n = 21$; $n = 7$ **3.** $4n = 8$; $n = 2$ **5.** 49 **7.** 17 **9.** 2,100 **11.** 9,882 **13.** 1,444 **15.** 805 **17.** $\frac{m}{9} = 5, m = 45$ **19.** 3 **21.** 4,860 **23.** 70 **25.** 1,776 **27.** $(6 \cdot 9) + 13$ **29.** 22

Lesson 2-8

Problems **1.** 270 **3.** 910 **5.** 385 **7.** 9

Lesson 2-9

Try This **a.** 135 **b.** 170 lb

Exercises **1.** 140 **3.** 86 **5.** 272 **7.** 51 miles **9.** \$280 **11.** 16 **13.** 4 **17.** $g = \frac{P - f}{2}$ **19.** 19

Lesson 2-10

Try This **a.** 72,000 **b.** 30 **c.** $720 \div 9 = 80$ **d.** $1{,}600 \div 40 = 40$

Exercises **1.** 2,400 **3.** 1,600 **5.** 150,000 **7.** 4 **9.** 8 **11.** 5 **13.** 6 **15.** 40 **17.** 408,900 **19.** 24,111 **21.** estimate 9 hours; 8.68932 hours **23.** 2,197 **25.** 16 **27.** 30

Lesson 2-12

Problems **1.** 18 cm **3.** 45 ft **5.** Randy's class = 9, Mark's class = 17, Sam's class = 34 **7.** 4 hours

Chapter 2 Review/Test

1. true **3.** false **5.** true **7.** 52 **9.** 45 **11.** 16 **13.** $6 \div r$ **15.** $n + 12$ **17.** $7r$ **19.** 4 **21.** 13 **23.** 12,000 **25.** 400 **27.** 15 spaces

Chapter 3

Integers

Lesson 3-1

Try This **a.**

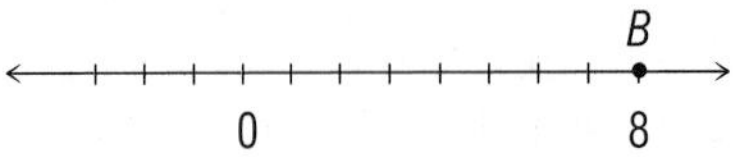

b. 9 **c.** 85 **d.** $^-16 < ^-8 < 6$ **e.** $^-3 < 0 < |^-6| < 9$

Exercises **1.** 2 **3.** 5 **5.** 8 **7.** 5 **9.** 123 **11.** 36 **13.** $^-7 < 0 < 7$ **15.** $^-24 < ^-23 < 8$ **17.** $^-13 < ^-4 < 6 < 12 < |^-18|$ **19.** $^-6° < ^-4° < ^-1° < 5°$ **21.** $^-124$ **23.** $^-12$ **25.** 8 **27.** $M = 10°, A = 25°, E = ^-5°, N = ^-20°$ **29.** positive **31.** positive **33.** greater **35.** 32, 47, 62 **37.** $^-5$, $^-11$, $^-17$ **39.** 3,536 **41.** 131 **43.** $2n$ **45.** $33a$ **47.** 16 **49.** 5

Lesson 3-2

Try This **a.** $^-11$ **b.** 3 **c.** $^-2$ **d.** 15 **e.** $^-13$ **f.** 2 **g.** 4 **h.** $^-30$ **i.** 64 **j.** $^-60$ **k.** 2 **l.** 16 **m.** 2 **n.** 60

Exercises **1.** $^-2$ **3.** $^-10$ **5.** 2 **7.** 6 **9.** 8 **11.** 8 **13.** $^-9$ **15.** $^-24$ **17.** $^-2$ **19.** $^-12$ **21.** 26 **23.** 52 **25.** $^-5$ yards **27.** $^-6$ pins **31.** 35 **33.** $^-6 < ^-1 < 0 < 1 < 4$

Numbers to Algebra **1.** $^-8$ **3.** 24

Lesson 3-3

Try This **a.** 11 **b.** $^-1$ **c.** 7 **d.** $^-8$ **e.** $^-13$ **f.** $^-6$ **g.** −5 **h.** −10 **i.** −11 **j.** 6 **k.** 12 **l.** 14 **m.** −7 **n.** −6 **o.** 6 **p.** 30 **q.** −37

Exercises **1.** 11 **3.** 4 **5.** −4 **7.** −15 **9.** 6 **11.** −6 **13.** −6 **15.** −14 **17.** −22 **19.** 13 **21.** 25 **23.** 14 **25.** −15 **27.** −6 **29.** 16 **31.** −431 **33.** 192 **35.** −\$54 **37.** −13 **39.** −2 **41.** −3 **43.** $3 - 2 = 1$, but $2 - 3 = -1$ **45.** 14,776 ft **49.** 27 **51.** −2 **53.** −8

Lesson 3-4

Try This **a.** $n = -8$ **b.** $n = -3$

Exercises **1.** $n = 10$ **3.** $n = 4$ **5.** $n = 3$ **7.** $n = -9$ **9.** 15 pounds **11.** −19 **13.** 12 **15.** 16 **17.** $n - 2 = 6$ **19.** $-7n$ **21.** −1

Lesson 3-5

Try This **a.** −66 **b.** −118 **c.** 13°F **d.** 28 **e.** −16 **f.** −58 **g.** 69

Exercises **1.** −111 **3.** −253 **5.** 200 **7.** −209 **9.** −311 **11.** 581 **13.** $n = -59$ **15.** $A = 17, B = 7$ **17.** −7 **19.** $2(7 + n)$

Mental Math **1.** 28 **3.** 210

Lesson 3-6

Problems **1.** −6 **3.** \$23.50 **5.** adult, 53 **7.** 75°

Lesson 3-7

Problems **1.** \$46 **3.** \$663 **5.** \$159 **7.** \$200

Lesson 3-8

Try This **a.** 54 **b.** 56 **c.** 45 **d.** −20 **e.** −48 **f.** −36 **g.** −21 **h.** −1,081 **i.** −11,214 **j.** 68,440 **k.** 1,599,156

Exercises **1.** 63 **3.** 32 **5.** 36 **7.** 14 **9.** 56 **11.** −45 **13.** 0 **15.** −81 **17.** −476,088 **19.** −16,701,630 **21.** −20 in. **25a.** negative **25b.** positive **27.** 21,600 **29.** −255 **31.** −41 **35.** −28°C **37a.** 12, −24, 15 **37b.** −10, −14, −18 **39.** −7 **41.** 50

Mental Math **1.** 687,000 **3.** −57,900 **5.** 9,600

Lesson 3-9

Try This **a.** 5 **b.** 5 **c.** 9 **d.** −6 **e.** −5 **f.** −8

Exercises **1.** 7 **3.** 5 **5.** −9 **7.** −8 **9.** −9 **11.** 6 **13.** −9 **15.** 6 **17.** −8°F **19.** 3 **21.** 7 **23.** −753 **25.** 32 **27.** −10 **29.** 77 **31.** 16 **33.** $125w$

Mathematical Reasoning

1. The midpoints of the sides of a quadrilateral form a parallelogram.

Lesson 3-10

Try This **a.** −17 **b.** −26 **c.** −15° **d.** −432 **e.** −200

Exercises **1.** −12 **3.** 15 **5.** −23 **7.** 12 **9.** −153 **11.** 186 **13.** −270 **15.** −506 **17.** −3,900 **19.** 18 **21.** 6 **23.** 6 **25.** 37, −37 **27.** 137, −137 **29.** 40 **31.** −18 **33.** −11

Lesson 3-11

Try This **a.** i **b.** $x - 9 = 54$ **c.** $y + 47 = -112$

Exercises **1.** b **3.** a **5.** b **7.** $c - 17 = 101$ **9.** $x + 56 = 104$ **11.** $\frac{n}{25} = -12$ **13.** $9y = -171$ **15.** $x - 17 = 15$ **17.** $6n = 91$ **19.** $x + 9 = 72$ **21.** $34t = 272$ **23.** $c - 600 = 19{,}820$ **25.** $t + 19 = 56$ **27.** $375 = p - 49$ **29.** $12 = 5 + f$ **31.** $67 = t - 18$
33. A number increased by 9 is 23.
35. A number multiplied by −8 is 72.
37. A number increased by 12 is 65.
39. A number divided by 12 is 5. **41.** $r = 9 \cdot 6$ **43.** $f = 89 - 17$ **45.** $5x + 7y = 110$; (8,10) **47.** −50 **49.** −36 **51.** 3 **53.** 36

Lesson 3-12

Problems **1.** 465 members **3.** 55, 89, 144, 233, 377 **5.** 13 years old **7.** January 1, 1790

Chapter 3 Review/Test

1. false **3.** true
5. Multiply both sides of the equation by −3.
7. 5 **9.** −5 **11.** 3 **13.** −17 **15.** −105 **17.** −48 **19.** −8 **21.** −6 **23.** 22 **25.** $140

Cumulative Review

1. $g + 9$ **2.** $k - 3$ **3.** $v + 10$ **4.** $\frac{m}{2}$ **5.** $7y$ **6.** $\frac{9}{w}$ **7.** $16 - r$ **8.** $16 + b$ **9.** 4 **10.** 5 **11.** 47 **12.** 11 **13.** 2 **14.** 4 **15.** 64 **16.** 4 **17.** 18 **18.** −8 **19.** 25 **20.** −9 **21.** −10 **22.** 14 **23.** 15 **24.** $6y$ **25.** qp **26.** $z + 12$ **27.** $(20 \cdot 8)p$ **28.** $5(fn)$ **29.** $y + (2 + 9)$
30. $3 \cdot c + 3 \cdot 4$; $3c + 12$
31. $8 \cdot a + 9 \cdot a$; $8a + 9a = 17a$
32. $7 \cdot 8 + b \cdot 8$; $56 + 8b$ **33.** $10t$ **34.** $24k$ **35.** $30d$ **36.** $8g$ **37.** $6v$ **38.** $75p$ **39.** −4 **40.** −96 **41.** −2 **42.** 17, $3x - 1$

Chapter 4

Decimals

Lesson 4-1

Try This **a.** 24.36 **b.** 470.093 **c.** −2.74 **d.** 2.75 **e.** > **f.** > **g.** =

Exercises **1.** 2.26 **3.** 540.76 **5.** 748.07 **7.** 578.3 **9.** 0.1 **11.** −0.34 **13.** = **15.** > **17.** < **19.** 3.069, 3.07, 3.7 **21.** 6.010, 6.0101, 6.101 **23.** −5.404, −5.044, −5.040 **33.** −221 **35.** −25 **37.** −6

Lesson 4-2

Try This **a.** 7.09 **b.** 0.9 **c.** 11.7 **d.** 73.5 **e.** 0.25 **f.** 22 + 11 = 33 **g.** 350 − 150 = 200

Exercises **1.** 147 **3.** 35 **5.** 1,000 **7.** 1.7 **9.** 8.3 **11.** 4.59 **13.** 3.01 **15.** 1.00 **17.** 15 **19.** 160 **21a.** 8.3 cm **21b.** 0.9 m **23.** 31 **25.** 8 for $1.05 **27.** 2.113, 3.421, 5.534 **29.** −18 **31.** −126 **33.** $-72m$

Mental Math **1.** 27.75 **3.** 15.1 **5.** 14.4

Lesson 4-3

Try This **a.** 293.58 **b.** 43.595 **c.** 57.9 **d.** 0.4 **e.** −4.95 **f.** 14.04

Exercises **1.** 48.12 **3.** 8.84 **5.** −121.88 **7.** 11.1 **9.** 8.69 **11.** 40.158 **13.** 40.7274 **15.** −76.26 **17.** 4.27 km **19.** $8.76 million **21.** 11.2, 8.38, 13 **23.** 61.7; 46.9 **25.** 12.5 hours **27.** −18 **29.** 2 **31.** −6

Numbers to Algebra **1.** $7x + 6y$

Lesson 4-4

Try This **a.** −17.24 **b.** 1.953 **c.** 17.24 **d.** 3.107

Exercises **1.** 7.9 **3.** 4.73 **5.** 113.2 **7.** −28.44 **9.** −5.53 **11.** 0.67 **13.** 2.04 lb; 1.54 lb **15.** −130.32 **17.** 66.9 **19.** $x = 1, y = 0.5$ **21.** 68 **23.** −24

Mental Math **1.** 17 **3.** 40.45

Lesson 4-5

Problems **1.** 1.5 km **3.** 8 cm **5.** 1.9 cm **7.** 2 mm **9.** 1,000,000

Lesson 4-6

Try This **a.** 120 **b.** 1,000 **c.** 800 **d.** 20,000 **e.** 8.652 **f.** 0.146 **g.** 9.527 **h.** −16.137

Exercises **1.** 100 **3.** 4 **5.** 250 **7.** 0.189 **9.** 3.46 **11.** −0.3504 **13.** 258.03 **15.** 10.2453 **17.** 47.502 m **19.** 1,700.18 **21.** 2.948 **23.** 0.0103 **25.** 19.26 **27.** 61.36 **29.** 62.6°F **31.** 134.06°F **33.** 24 **35.** $43c$ **37.** $-63k$ **39.** 12

Lesson 4-7

Try This **a.** 3 **b.** 8 **c.** 21.25 **d.** 9.3 **e.** 0.0025 **f.** −0.33 **g.** 0.045 **h.** 7.1

Exercises **1.** 5 **3.** 3 **5.** −0.0087 **7.** 0.0798 **9.** −4.19 **11.** 2,190 **13.** 3.4 **15.** 16 **17.** \$69.63 **19.** $8.\overline{33}$ **21.** $1.\overline{6}$ **23.** 4 **25.** $0.0\overline{5}$; $0.\overline{08}$; $0.\overline{123}$ **27.** −0.43 **29.** $-0.3\overline{6}$ **31.** $n + 0.95$ **33.** $\frac{8.3}{n}$

Lesson 4-8

Try This **a.** 19

Exercises **1.** a, c **3.** 1,989 **5.** 70 cars **7.** record was 24.80 seconds **9.** 19 hours **11.** appraised value of movie theater **13.** −0.237 **15.** 1 **17.** −4.5

Calculator Activity **1.** \$76.49 **3.** \$133.33

Lesson 4-9

Try This **a.** 150 **b.** −920 **c.** 0.728 **d.** −18.56

Exercises **1.** 5.3 **3.** −7 **5.** −19.09 **7.** −15 **9.** −12 **11.** 20 **13.** −5.976 **15.** −17.28 **17.** 4.6 s **19.** −18 **21.** 17.5 **23.** 15.91 **25.** 113.82 **27.** $x = 220$ **31.** 5.3 **33.** $(2.3 + 4.6)x = 36.57$ **35.** −4.2 **37.** 6.6 **39.** −12

Lesson 4-11

Problems **1.** \$4,095,000,000 **3.** Giants 64, Lions 39

Chapter 4 Review/Test

1. false **3.** true **5.** false **7.** 400.86 **9.** $x = 500$ **11.** $x = 76$ **13.** 49.219 **15.** $g = 36.05$ **17.** $w = 15.96$ **19.** 200 **21.** 0.5 km **23.** 74.7 m

Chapter 5

Number Theory

Lesson 5-1

Try This **a.** no **b.** yes **c.** yes **d.** 1, 2, 3, 6, 9, 18 **e.** 1, 2, 4, 8, 16, 32 **f.** 1, 2, 3, 4, 6, 8, 12, 16, 24, 32, 48, 96 **g.** 7, 14, 21 **h.** 9, 18, 27, 36, 45

Exercises **1.** yes **3.** yes **5.** yes **7.** 1, 2, 4, 5, 10, 20 **9.** 1, 2, 3, 4, 6, 7, 12, 14, 21, 28, 42, 84 **11.** 1, 2, 3, 4, 5, 6, 10, 12, 15, 20, 30, 60 **13.** 1, 2, 3, 5, 6, 9, 10, 15, 18, 30, 45, 90 **15.** 1, 2, 3, 4, 5, 6, 8, 10, 12, 15, 20, 24, 30, 40, 60, 120 **17.** 1, 2, 3, 5, 6, 7, 9, 10, 14, 15, 18, 21, 30, 35, 42, 45, 63, 70, 90, 105, 126, 210, 315, 630 **19.** 5, 10, 15, 20 **21.** 11, 22, 33, 44 **23.** 100, 200, 300, 400 **25.** 137, 274, 411, 548, 685 **27.** 599; 1,198; 1,797; 2,396; 2,995 **29.** 1,056; 2,112; 3,168; 4,224; 5,280 **31.** no **33.** 1×18, 2×9, 3×6 **35.** 91; 18, 91 **37.** 4, 9, 25, 49; squares of prime nos. **43.** factors: 1, 2, 4, 7, 14, 28; $1 + 2 + 4 + 7 + 14 = 28$ **45.** −6.6 **47.** −0.1 **49.** $2m + 2$

Lesson 5-2

Try This **a.** 2 **b.** 5 **c.** neither **d.** 2, 5 **e.** 2, 5 **f.** 2 **g.** 2 **h.** yes **i.** no **j.** yes **k.** yes **l.** no **m.** no

Exercises **1.** no **3.** yes **5.** yes **7.** yes **9.** yes **11.** no **13.** yes **15.** yes **17.** no **19.** no **21.** no **23.** yes **25.** no **27.** no **29.** yes **33.** 70; other divisors: 2, 10, 14, 35, 70 **35.** > **37.** = **39.** −44.793 **41.** 26.163

Mental Math **1.** yes **3.** yes

Lesson 5-3

Try This **a.** \$504

Exercises **1.** a, b **3.** \$9.64 **5.** 42 **7.** less than \$300 **9.** 672 boxes, 56 crates **13.** -20 **15.** 2 **17.** 18 **19.** -12 **21.** 51.52 **23.** 56.58

Lesson 5-4

Try This **a.** 17, 19, 23

Exercises **1.** composite; 2, 3 **3.** composite; 3 **5.** composite; 2, 3, etc. **7.** prime **9.** composite; 2, 4, etc. **11.** composite; 2, 17 **13.** 51 **15a.** 4 **15b.** 6 **21.** 0.6125 **23.** 0.3

Lesson 5-5

Try This **a.** $3 \cdot 3 \cdot 3 \cdot 3 = 81$ **b.** $(-2)(-2)(-2)(-2) = 16$ **c.** $a \cdot a \cdot a$ **d.** $10 \cdot 10 \cdot 10 \cdot 10 = 10{,}000$ **e.** 64 **f.** 32 **g.** 144 **h.** 10^3 **i.** $(-2)^2$ **j.** b^4 **k.** $(-5)^6$ **l.** 10^7 **m.** x^5 **n.** $100 + 1{,}000 = 1{,}100$ **o.** $25 + 625 = 650$

Exercises
1. $10 \cdot 10 \cdot 10 \cdot 10 \cdot 10 \cdot 10 \cdot 10 = 10{,}000{,}000$ **3.** $7 \cdot 7 \cdot 7 = 343$ **5.** $9 \cdot 9 \cdot 9 = 729$ **7.** $8 \cdot 8 = 64$ **9.** $n \cdot n \cdot n \cdot n$ **11.** 5^4 **13.** 10^4 **15.** 9^4 **17.** 3^6 **19.** 10^{10} **21.** 12 **23.** 125 **25.** $5^8 = 5 \cdot 5 \cdot 5 \cdot 5 \cdot 5 \cdot 5 \cdot 5 \cdot 5 = 390{,}625$ **27.** 10^2 **29.** 10^4 **31.** 65,536 **33.** 78,125 **35.** 123 **37.** $-2, 4, -8, 16$ **39.** positive **41a.** 100 **41b.** a googol, or 10^{100} **43.** -0.75 **45.** 7.25 **47.** 2 **49.** 2.3

Estimation **3.** 10^9

Lesson 5-6

Try This **a.** $2 \cdot 2 \cdot 2 \cdot 5$ **b.** $2 \cdot 3 \cdot 3 \cdot 3$ **c.** $2^2 \cdot 7$ **d.** $2^3 \cdot 3^2$ **e.** $2 \cdot 3 \cdot 7$ **f.** $3 \cdot 3 \cdot 5 \cdot 7$

Exercises **1.** $2 \cdot 2 \cdot 3 \cdot 3$ **3.** $2 \cdot 3 \cdot 5 \cdot 7$ **5.** $2 \cdot 2 \cdot 2 \cdot 2 \cdot 3$ **7.** $2 \cdot 2 \cdot 5 \cdot 7$ **9.** $2^2 \cdot 3$ **11.** $3^2 \cdot 5$ **13.** $3^2 \cdot 5 \cdot 13$ **15.** $2^2 \cdot 3^3$ **17.** 5^4 **19.** Jenny **21.** 5 **23.** 1,125 **25.** 137,200 **27.** repeats the age **29.** $2 \cdot 3 \cdot 5 \cdot 7 \cdot 11 \cdot 13 = 30{,}030$ **31.** $9(12 + n) = 135$ **33.** -15.5

Lesson 5-7

Try This **a.** 1, 2, 3, 6, 9, 18; GCF = 9 **b.** 1, 2, 3, 4, 6, 12; GCF = 4 **c.** 5 **d.** $12 = 2 \cdot 2 \cdot 3$, $16 = 2 \cdot 2 \cdot 2 \cdot 2$; GCF = 4 **e.** $24 = 2 \cdot 2 \cdot 2 \cdot 3$, $42 = 2 \cdot 3 \cdot 7$; GCF = 6 **f.** 27 **g.** 16 **h.** 19 **i.** 113

Exercises **1.** 1 **3.** 8 **5.** 12 **7.** 16 **9.** 8 **11.** 1 **13.** 15 **15.** 24 **17.** 21 **19.** 2 **21.** 72 **23.** 26 **25.** 23 **27.** 37 **29.** 14 **31.** 6 **33.** 6 **35.** 8 **37a.** yes **37b.** yes **37c.** yes **39.** 6 ft × 6 ft **41.** 15m **43.** 12c **45.** 30 **47.** 9

Numbers to Algebra **1.** xy **3.** $6xy^2$ **5.** $8x^2z^2$

Lesson 5-8

Problems **1.** 80 ft **3.** 65 ft **5.** about 3 times **7.** braking 151.25 ft, stopping 206.25 ft **9.** 146.25 ft **11.** 95 miles

Lesson 5-9

Try This **a.** LCM = 18 **b.** LCM = 24 **c.** $2 \cdot 2 \cdot 3 \cdot 5 = 60$ **d.** $2 \cdot 2 \cdot 2 \cdot 3 \cdot 5 = 120$

Exercises **1.** 12 **3.** 12 **5.** 45 **7.** 90 **9.** 180 **11.** 108 **13.** 120 **15.** 240 **17.** 60 **19.** 1,680 **21.** 540 **23.** 1,260 **25.** 24 hours **27.** x^4 **29.** -4 **31.** 12.6

Numbers to Algebra **1.** a^2b^2 **3.** $6m^2n^2$

Lesson 5-10

Try This **a.** **(1)** gallons in pool, number of hours **(2)** gallons in pool is function of number of hours pump is on **(3)** A; gallons decrease with more hours

Exercises **1.** graph C **3.** graph A **9.** the greater the cost, the higher the quality **11.** -252 **13.** 69 **15.** -28 **17.** 2.589 **19.** 0.321 **21.** -6.848 **23.** 2.172 **25.** $m - 4.50$

Computer Activity **1.** 252

Lesson 5-11

Problems **1.** 24 arrangements. MAT, HAT, TAM, HAM are words. **3.** 25 **5.** The squares of 1 through 30. They alone have an odd number of factors.

Chapter 5 Review/Test

1. false **3.** false **5.** false **7.** increase **9.** no, yes, yes **11.** $7 \cdot 7 \cdot 7 \cdot 7 = 2{,}401$ **13.** $r \cdot r \cdot r \cdot r \cdot r \cdot r \cdot r$ **15.** b^6 **17.** $(-2)^8$ **19a.** $2^4 \cdot 3$ **19b.** $3 \cdot 5 \cdot 7$ **21.** 6 **23.** 90 **25.** 2.5 hours

Chapter 6

Rational Numbers: Addition and Subtraction

Lesson 6-1

Try This **a.** $x = 36$ **b.** $y = 35$ **c.** $c = 3$ **d.** yes **e.** yes **f.** $\frac{1}{2}$ **g.** $\frac{2}{3}$

Exercises **1.** 14 **3.** 3 **5.** 1 **7.** 50 **9.** 65 **11.** 7 **13.** 35 **15.** 12 **17.** no **19.** yes **21.** yes **23.** yes **25.** $\frac{10}{13}$ **27.** $\frac{4}{7}$ **29.** $\frac{17}{19}$ **31.** $\frac{2}{3}$ **33.** $\frac{13}{14}$ **35.** $t = 16$ **37.** $\frac{3}{4}$ **43.** no **45.** yes **47.** 180 ninth graders **49.** false **53.** $5m$ **55.** $14r - 10$ **57.** $3t$ **59.** a^3 **61.** 5 **63.** -5.35 **65.** 6.56

Numbers to Algebra **1.** $\frac{2}{3}$ **3.** $\frac{7a}{8b}$ **7.** $\frac{4a}{bc}$ **9.** $\frac{3}{7}$ **11.** $\frac{12}{35a}$

Lesson 6-2

Try This **a.** $3\frac{2}{3}$ **b.** 6 **c.** $5\frac{1}{7}$ **d.** $\frac{19}{4}$ **e.** $\frac{16}{3}$ **f.** $\frac{73}{10}$

Exercises **1.** $4\frac{1}{6}$ **3.** 17 **5.** $8\frac{3}{11}$ **7.** 11 **9.** $11\frac{3}{5}$ **11.** $3\frac{1}{2}$ **13.** $\frac{31}{8}$ **15.** $\frac{41}{16}$ **17.** $\frac{52}{9}$ **19.** $\frac{26}{3}$ **21.** $\frac{11}{2}$ **23.** $4\frac{3}{5}$ **25.** $4\frac{5}{17}$ **27.** $13\frac{1}{5}$ **29.** 21 **31.** $a\frac{b}{c} = \frac{ac + b}{c}$ **33.** $3 \cdot 3 \cdot 3$ **35.** 8.625 **37.** composite

Computer Activity **1.** $\frac{1}{11}$ **3.** $\frac{1,950}{17}$

Lesson 6-3

Try This **a.** $-\frac{5}{6}, \frac{-5}{6}, \frac{5}{-6}$ **b.** $-\frac{7}{3}, \frac{-7}{3}, \frac{7}{-3}$ **c.** $-\frac{11}{12}, \frac{-11}{12}, \frac{11}{-12}$

d. −2 −1 0 1 2

↑ −2 ↑ $-\frac{3}{8}$ ↑ $\frac{1}{8}$ ↑ $\frac{5}{8}$ ↑ $\frac{9}{8}$

Exercises **1.** $\frac{-3}{8}, -\frac{3}{8}, \frac{3}{-8}$ **3.** $\frac{-11}{16}, -\frac{11}{16}, \frac{11}{-16}$ **5.** $-\frac{5}{2}, \frac{-5}{2}, \frac{5}{-2}$ **7.** $-\frac{3}{2}, \frac{-3}{2}, \frac{3}{-2}$ **17.** left **19.** $-\frac{3}{x}$ **21.** $\frac{h}{2}$ **23.** $\frac{6}{n}$ **25.** $\frac{12}{m}$ **27.** $\frac{3}{5}$ **29.** $\frac{15}{2}$ or $7\frac{1}{2}$ **31.** $\frac{43}{52}$ **33.** $\frac{34}{51}$ **35.** $\frac{22}{53}$ **37.** $-\frac{1}{13}, \frac{1}{15}, -\frac{1}{17}$ **39.** $4m + 8n$ **41.** -3.781

Estimation **1.** 5 **3.** 0 **5.** -4

Lesson 6-4

Try This **a.** $0.\overline{2}$ **b.** $0.1\overline{6}$

Exercises **1.** 0.575 **3.** 0.375 **5.** 0.64 **7.** $2.\overline{6}$ **9.** $3.6\overline{1}$ **11.** 12.375 **13.** 33 **15.** 219 **17.** $0.4, 0.4\overline{29}, 0.4\overline{3}, 0.44, 0.45, 0.4\overline{5}$ **19.** $0.\overline{09}, 0.\overline{18}, 0.\overline{27}, 0.\overline{36}, 0.\overline{45}, 0.\overline{54}, 0.\overline{63}, 0.\overline{72}$ **21.** 12 **23.** 4.2

Lesson 6-5

Try This **a.** $>$ **b.** $<$ **c.** $>$ **d.** $<$ **e.** $>$ **f.** $>$

Exercises **1.** $<$ **3.** $>$ **5.** $<$ **7.** $>$ **9.** $=$ **11.** $>$ **13.** $<$ **15.** $<$ **17.** $<$ **19.** $<$ **21.** $<$ **23.** $>$ **25.** $>$ **27.** $>$ **29.** Freedom Bank **31.** $\frac{1}{5}, \frac{1}{4}, \frac{1}{3}$ **33.** $\frac{4}{9}, \frac{6}{12}, \frac{2}{3}$ **35.** $-\frac{3}{4}, -\frac{5}{12}, -\frac{6}{15}$ **37.** $>$ **39.** $=$ **41.** $<$ **43.** $>$ **45.** $=$ **47.** $\frac{5}{12}, \frac{5}{9}, \frac{5}{8}, \frac{5}{6}, \frac{5}{5}, \frac{5}{4}, \frac{5}{3}, \frac{5}{2}$ **49.** 55 **51.** 3 **53.** 5.22

Mathematical Reasoning

1. Find someone who does not have a portable television. **3.** false **5.** true

Lesson 6-6

Try This **a.** $\frac{3}{4}$ **b.** $\frac{2}{7}$ **c.** $-1\frac{1}{9}$ **d.** $\frac{1}{3}$ **e.** $\frac{1}{2}$ **f.** $-\frac{1}{4}$

Exercises **1.** $\frac{1}{2}$ **3.** $\frac{3}{11}$ **5.** $1\frac{1}{3}$ **7.** -1 **9.** 0 **11.** $\frac{1}{4}$ **13.** $\frac{5}{9}$ **15.** $\frac{2}{7}$ **17.** $\frac{7}{12}$ **19.** $\frac{11}{z}$ **21.** $\frac{12}{x}$ **23.** $\frac{42}{u}$ **25.** $7\frac{1}{2}$ **27.** $\frac{1}{2}$ cup **29.** $t = 1, 2, 3, 4, 6, 8, 12, 24$ **31.** $\frac{1}{4}, \frac{1}{4}$ **33.** 1.982 **35.** 14 **37.** n^9

Lesson 6-7

Try This **a.** $1\frac{13}{60}$ **b.** $\frac{7}{10}$ **c.** $\frac{11}{15}$ **d.** $\frac{23}{24}$ **e.** $-\frac{9}{10}$ **f.** $\frac{1}{12}$

Exercises **1.** $\frac{7}{8}$ **3.** $-\frac{7}{12}$ **5.** $\frac{7}{12}$ **7.** $\frac{1}{4}$ **9.** $1\frac{8}{15}$ **11.** $\frac{7}{9}$ **13.** $-2\frac{1}{6}$ **15.** $3\frac{1}{4}$ **17.** $\frac{5}{28}$ **19.** $-\frac{3}{10}$ **21.** $-\frac{5}{36}$ **23.** $1\frac{1}{4}$ lb **25.** $1\frac{5}{18}$ yd **27.** $-1\frac{1}{12}$ **29.** $-\frac{11}{24}$ **31.** $1\frac{5}{12}$ cup **33.** $\frac{1}{15}$ **35.** $-\frac{2}{5} + \frac{3}{4} = \frac{7}{20}$ **37.** 1, 5, 25 **39.** 7, 7 **41.** estimate = 28, $M = 26$ **43.** -37.71

Estimation **1.** 2 **3.** $\frac{1}{4}$ **5.** 0

Lesson 6-8

Try This **a.** $1\frac{3}{4}$ **b.** $9\frac{17}{40}$ **c.** $7\frac{1}{5}$ **d.** $12\frac{1}{4}$ **e.** $2\frac{1}{4}$ **f.** $1\frac{1}{15}$ **g.** $4\frac{1}{4}$

Exercises **1.** $1\frac{1}{15}$ **3.** $2\frac{16}{21}$ **5.** $4\frac{1}{60}$ **7.** 6 **9.** $12\frac{1}{12}$ **11.** $3\frac{9}{20}$ **13.** $-6\frac{4}{7}$ **15.** $-5\frac{35}{48}$ **17.** $-1\frac{3}{4}$ **19.** $\frac{7}{8}$ ft **21.** $\frac{3}{8}$ mi **23.** 3 **25.** -4 **27.** 7 **29.** 15 **31.** 36 **33.** Monday, $5\frac{1}{4}$ hrs **37.** 120 **39.** 0

Mental Math **1.** 0 **3.** $9\frac{5}{6}$ **5.** $\frac{5}{12}$

Lesson 6-9

Problems **1.** $31\frac{3}{4}$ **3.** $15\frac{3}{4}$ **5.** $2\frac{7}{8}$ **7.** increased by $\frac{1}{8}$ **9.** $1,975 **11.** increase; $2\frac{1}{4}$

Lesson 6-10

Try This **a.** $-\frac{1}{3}$ **b.** $\frac{1}{12}$ **c.** $\frac{5}{8}$ **d.** $1\frac{7}{15}$ **e.** $\frac{13}{24}$ mi **f.** $-\frac{19}{24}$ **g.** $-\frac{11}{45}$ **h.** $2\frac{7}{10}$ mi

Exercises **1.** $1\frac{1}{9}$ **3.** $-\frac{7}{30}$ **5.** $-\frac{13}{30}$ **7.** $\frac{1}{8}$ **9.** $-\frac{1}{4}$ **11.** $-\frac{47}{50}$ **13.** $\frac{1}{2}$ **15.** $-\frac{14}{15}$ **17.** $-\frac{13}{40}$ **19.** $\frac{1}{24}$ **21.** $\frac{8}{15}$ **23.** $-\frac{13}{35}$ **25.** $\frac{5}{8}$ lb **27.** $\frac{17}{45}$ **29.** $1\frac{11}{36}$ **31.** $-\frac{7}{12}$ **33.** $-\frac{1}{2}$ **39.** 36 **41.** -9.2 **43.** 1, 3, 9 **45.** $(-4)^4$

Mental Math **1.** $3\frac{1}{4}$ **3.** $7\frac{1}{3}$ **5.** $5\frac{2}{3}$

Lesson 6-11

Try This **a.** $1\frac{5}{8}$ yards

Exercises **1.** c **3.** $\frac{7}{8}$ in. **5.** $\frac{17}{40}$ mi **7.** 25 **9.** $1.25 **11.** $\frac{5}{24}$ in. **13.** $7 **17.** $2 \cdot 17$ **19.** 42 **21.** x^2y^2 **23.** $3c$ **25.** 36

Lesson 6-12

Problems **1.** Ned, Jefferson; Mary, Stoverton; Steve, Millerville; Jack, Newville **3.** 66 **5.** 60

Chapter 6 Review/Test

1. true **3.** false **5.** 66 **7.** 96 **9.** $-\frac{2}{15}$ **11.** $6\frac{1}{3}$ **13.** $-\frac{47}{11}$ **15.** $0.6\overline{1}$ **17.** $0.\overline{2}$ **19.** $>$ **21.** $<$ **23.** $7\frac{7}{8}$ **25.** $1\frac{1}{2}$ **27.** $6\frac{3}{4}$ **29.** $-\frac{11}{12}$ **31.** $5\frac{3}{4}$ lb **33.** $1\frac{5}{6}$ gallons

Cumulative Review

1. 47.8 **2.** 200.69 **3.** 5.17 **4.** 0.379 **5.** $=$ **6.** $<$ **7.** $>$ **8.** $>$ **9.** $>$ **10.** $<$ **11.** 80 **12.** 7,000 **13.** 300 **14.** 20,000 **15.** 60 **16.** 230 **17.** 60 **18.** 900 **19.** 200 **20.** 3,600 **21–27.** Possible answers are given. **21.** 10 **22.** 350 **23.** 50 **24.** 100 **25.** 28 **26.** 49 **27.** 7 **28.** 4, 8, 12, 16, 20 **29.** 7, 14, 21, 28, 35 **30.** 30, 60, 90, 120, 150 **31.** 1, 2, 4, 8, 16, 32 **32.** 1, 2, 3, 6, 7, 14, 21, 42 **33.** 1, 2, 3, 4, 5, 6, 10, 12, 15, 20, 30, 60 **34.** yes **35.** yes **36.** no **37.** no **38.** yes **39.** yes **40.** yes **41.** yes **42.** no

Chapter 7

Rational Numbers: Multiplication and Division

Lesson 7-1

Try This **a.** $\frac{5}{16}$ **b.** $\frac{16}{27}$ **c.** $\frac{3}{8}$ **d.** $3\frac{1}{5}$ **e.** $-6\frac{1}{6}$

Exercises **1.** $\frac{9}{20}$ **3.** $\frac{5}{32}$ **5.** $-\frac{5}{6}$ **7.** $-\frac{7}{10}$ **9.** $\frac{7}{9}$ **11.** $1\frac{1}{4}$ **13.** $\frac{5}{24}$ **15.** $1\frac{1}{5}$ **17.** $14\frac{5}{8}$ **19.** $6\frac{3}{4}$ **21.** $-12\frac{8}{9}$ **23.** $23\frac{4}{7}$ **25.** $-1\frac{2}{5}$ **27.** 22 **29.** 52 ft **31.** $9\frac{1}{3}$ hour **33.** $\frac{9}{10}$ acre **35.** -16 **37.** $2\frac{7}{16}$ **39.** $-\frac{11}{36}$ **41.** $\frac{1}{2}$ **43.** $-2\frac{2}{5}$ **45.** $-\frac{3}{8}$ **47.** 35 **49.** 80 **51.** 7 **53.** 8 **55.** $x = 48$ **57.** 8 **59.** $2c + 3t$ **61.** 1 **63.** $-\frac{1}{5}$ **65.** $-\frac{34}{5}$ **67.** $\frac{87}{16}$ **69.** -0.06 **71.** $\frac{7}{8}$ **73.** $\frac{4}{15}$

Mental Math **1.** 28 **3.** -46 **5.** 34 **7.** 101 **9.** $-9\frac{2}{15}$

Lesson 7-2

Try This **a.** -4 **b.** $\frac{1}{24}$ **c.** $-2\frac{2}{15}$ **d.** $1\frac{1}{2}$

Exercises **1.** 3 **3.** $\frac{5}{7}$ **5.** $-\frac{5}{12}$ **7.** $-\frac{3}{16}$ **9.** 4 **11.** $3\frac{5}{21}$ **13.** $1\frac{2}{5}$ hr **15.** $-\frac{67}{128}$ **17.** $\frac{1}{8}$ in.
19a. 19
19b. There are 19 ways 4 stamps can be connected.
19c. Make an organized list **21.** -2.2

Estimation **1.** >14 **3.** >3 **5.** <3

Lesson 7-3

Try This **a.** 24 **b.** −2 **c.** $\frac{1}{16}$ **d.** $\frac{1}{10}$ **e.** 832 **f.** $1\frac{2}{13}$ **g.** $-1\frac{29}{55}$

Exercises **1.** $\frac{3}{16}$ **3.** $6\frac{1}{4}$ **5.** 5 **7.** −9 **9.** $\frac{6}{7}$ **11.** −8 **13.** $\frac{6}{11}$ **15.** $1\frac{17}{26}$ **17.** $12 **19.** $18 **21.** 48 oz **23.** $1\frac{1}{7}$ **25.** $-1\frac{7}{27}$ **27.** 0 **29.** $\frac{1}{2}$ **31.** about 16 gallons **33.** $8\frac{1}{2}$ in. by 11 in. **35.** 10 **37.** $x = \frac{1}{2}, x = -\frac{1}{2}$ **39.** $10x - 16$ **41.** 288 **43.** $13\frac{3}{4}$

Computer Activity **1.** no **3.** Invert the divisor and continue as in multiplication.

Lesson 7-4

Try This **a.** $\frac{7}{8}x = 21; x = 24$; 3 people

Exercises **1.** a **3.** $16\frac{1}{2}$ lb **5.** 2,208 **7.** 12 mi/h **9.** $96 **13.** $-\frac{3}{22}$ **15.** −3.7 **17.** 27.13 **19.** $-\frac{7}{20}$ **21.** $2\frac{1}{10}$ **23.** $\frac{6}{13}$ **25.** $-\frac{3}{5}$ **27.** $1\frac{3}{4}$ pounds

Lesson 7-5

Problems **1.** 13 in. **3.** 35 in. **5.** $149\frac{1}{2}$ in. **7.** 4,884 **9.** 18

Lesson 7-6

Try This **a.** 5^3 **b.** $(-3)^3$ **c.** 10^3 **d.** y^5 **e.** m^4 **f.** z **g.** $\frac{1}{125}$ **h.** $\frac{1}{4}$

Exercises **1.** 3^3 **3.** $(-4)^2$ **5.** 10^4 **7.** 8^4 **9.** t^2 **11.** g **13.** x^5 **15.** n^2 **17.** $\frac{1}{16}$ **19.** $\frac{1}{16}$ **21.** $\frac{1}{10{,}000}$ **23.** $\frac{1}{25}$ **25.** $\frac{1}{10^{12}}$ **27.** 10^{-9} **29.** 4^3 **31.** a^2 **33.** 3 **35.** z^{-3} **37.** −3 **39.** $64x^6$ **41.** 9 **43.** 4 **45.** 8.15 **47.** −48

Numbers to Algebra **1.** xy^2 **3.** $\frac{6n^2}{5m}$

Lesson 7-7

Try This **a.** 0.00018 **b.** 655.6 **c.** 0.04 **d.** 4.567×10^3 **e.** 2.34×10^5 **f.** 5×10^7 **g.** 2.06×10^{-2} **h.** 8×10^{-6} **i.** 2.004×10^{-1}

Exercises **1.** 35,000 **3.** 405,000 **5.** 1.35×10^2 **7.** 3.45×10^5 **9.** 1.24×10^3 **11.** 4.55×10^6 **13.** 9.9×10^4 **15.** 7.8×10^{-2} **17.** 6.77×10^{-4} **19.** 1×10^{-6} **21.** 4.05×10^{-5} **23.** 1.01×10^{-1} **25.** 5.5×10^6 **27.** 0.00012 kg **29.** 8.0×10^7 **31.** 3.0×10^1 **33.** 1.5×10^8 km **35.** 9×10^3 **37.** $\frac{1}{5}$ **39.** $\frac{3}{35}$ **41.** $\frac{7}{15}$ **43.** $10t$

Calculator Activity **1.** 4.029×10^{18} **3.** 1.7192×10^{14} **5.** 1.53×10^{16}

Lesson 7-8

Problems **1.** 1,340 **3.** $3\frac{2}{5}$ **5.** 272 **7.** 187 **9.** $8.18 **11.** 20,518 **13.** $2.75 **15.** yes **17.** yes; 168 students **19a.** 30¢ **19b.** A weekday paper costs about 30¢.

Lesson 7-9

Problems **1.** 48; Ned 18, Gary 9, Kris 13 **3.** Jana could have bought 5 granola bars and 6 carob chews, or 6 granola bars, 2 honey drops, and 3 carob chews, or 7 granola bars and 4 honey drops.

Chapter 7 Review/Test

1. false **3.** true **5.** true **7.** $\frac{-2}{5}$ **9.** $1\frac{1}{9}$ **11.** $-5\frac{1}{7}$ **13.** $\frac{7}{15}$ **15.** 9^4 **17.** p^4 **19.** 0.009 **21.** $7.9 \cdot 10^{-3}$ **23.** 9.9×10^7 **25.** $1\frac{3}{4}$ in. **27.** 498 bricks

Chapter 8

Equations and Inequalities

Lesson 8-1

Try This **a.** 16 **b.** −17 **c.** 18 **d.** 80 grapefruit **e.** 34 **f.** −9 **g.** 23 **h.** 45

Exercises **1.** 7 **3.** 10 **5.** 5 **7.** 80 **9.** 648 **11.** −62 **13.** 56 **15.** 24 **17.** 9 **19.** 20 **21.** 5 **23.** 16 m **25.** 180 cm **27.** 8 km **29.** 13 **31.** $-\frac{5}{6}$ **33.** $-\frac{1}{15}$ **35.** −1.87

Lesson 8-2

Try This **a.** $2J + 5 = 39$ **b.** $3s - 4 = 65$

Exercises **1.** $2j + 25 = 200$ **3.** $37 = 2v + 3$ **5.** $125 = \frac{p}{3} - 5$ **7.** $3s + 15 = 180$ **9.** $56 = 2j + 8$ **11.** $564 = \frac{1}{4}n + 36$ **13.** Three more than twice a number is 13. **17.** 4 **19.** $9\frac{3}{8}$ **21.** $10t + 800$

Lesson 8-3

Try This **a.** $2a + 5 = 83$; 39
Exercises **1.** 100 **3.** 80 ounces **5.** 2,844 gallons **9.** 3.3 **11.** −1.25

Lesson 8-4

Try This **a.** 1, 5, 9, 13 **b.** 36 mi **c.** $f(x) = x^2$
Exercises **1.** −4, −1, 2, 5 **3.** 6, 8, 10, 12 **5.** 21, 26, $5x + 1$; $f(x) = 5x + 1$ **7.** 100; 200; 260 **9.** 46, 54, 70, 86 **11.** $f(x) = 5 + 2x$ **17.** $-2\frac{7}{9}$

Lesson 8-5

Try This **a.** 74 **b.** 30 **c.** −6.5 **d.** 9
Exercises **1.** 12 **3.** 4 **5.** −12 **7.** 5 **9.** 5 **11.** 16 **13.** 43 g **15.** −8 **17.** 3 **19.** yes **21.** 75¢ **23.** 9 **25.** 9.6
Computer Activity **1.** 3

Lesson 8-6

Try This **a.** 13 **b.** −4 **c.** 12 **d.** −7
Exercises **1.** −9 **3.** $20\frac{1}{2}$ **5.** 4 **7.** $6\frac{3}{4}$ **9.** 9 helmets **11.** 8 **13.** $-3\frac{1}{2}$ **15.** 45 **17.** Juana is 26. Mary is 78. **19.** $9, $11, $13 **21.** 149 **23.** 0.875 **25.** 0.9 **27.** 17
Numbers to Algebra **1.** $x - 5$ **3.** $5t - 7$ **5.** $-2b + 15$

Lesson 8-7

Try This **a.** 36 **b.** 3
c. $h = 5$; The prices are the same for 5 hours. For less than 5 hours, $6 per hour is better. For more than 5 hours, the other price is better.
d. $\frac{2}{3}$ **e.** 1
Exercises **1.** 2 **3.** 3 **5.** 6 **7.** 12 **9.** 10 **11.** −2 **13.** −32 **15.** 12 **17.** 3 hours **19.** $-\frac{1}{2}$ **21.** 12 **23.** −32 **25.** 30 checks **27.** 12 **29.** $<$ **31.** 73 **33.** $-\frac{9}{10}$ **35.** r^2
Mental Math **1.** 3,599 **3.** 6,399 **5.** 4,896

Lesson 8-8

Problems **1.** $450.48 **3.** $3.87 **5.** $124.92 (includes processing) **7.** 6 rolls of each type **9.** 5 rolls

Lesson 8-9

Try This **a.** binomial **b.** trinomial **c.** trinomial **d.** monomial **e.** $-2n^2 - 2n + 5$ **f.** $-2x^2 + 2$
Exercises **1.** monomial **3.** trinomial **5.** trinomial **7.** $2a^2 + 5a$ **9.** $d^2 - 3d - 5$ **11.** $3n^2 + 5n + 2$
17. yes; model with a cube and squares
19. −7.15 **21.** 8

Lesson 8-10

Try This **a.** $n \le 1$ **b.** $x < 1\frac{1}{2}$ **c.** $b > 16$ **d.** $p < -5$
Exercises **1.** $a < 6$ **3.** $c < 5$ **5.** $p > 21$ **7.** $s > 9$ **9.** $n > 7$ **11.** $m \le \frac{5}{12}$ **13.** less than $12 **15a.** $s > 55$ **15b.** $s < 40$ **17.** 5 **19.** $s >$ $46,000 **21.** 0.25 **23.** 0.8 **25.** −0.5

Lesson 8-11

Try This **a.** $n > 20$ **b.** $a \ge 4\frac{1}{2}$ **c.** $t > 7$ **d.** $r < -4$ **e.** $x > 3$ **f.** $b < 1$ **g.** $c \le -\frac{1}{7}$
Exercises **1.** $a > 3$ **3.** $s < -1$ **5.** $n < 18$ **7.** $y > -6$ **9.** $c < -18$ **11.** $c < -6$ **13.** $x > 12\frac{1}{2}$ **15.** $n < -10$ **17.** >$5 **19.** $x < 1$ **21.** $2n - 9 < 57$ **23.** $\frac{2}{3}n + 6 < 40$
25. smallest possible integer is 43
27. smallest yearly income is $30,000 **31.** 45
33. m^6n^4

Mathematical Reasoning

1. correct **3.** incorrect

Lesson 8-12

Problems **1.** 8 **3.** 5:00 p.m. **5.** 729

Chapter 8 Review/Test

1. subtraction then division
3. Distributive Property
5. reverse the inequality sign **7.** 23
9. $3t + 2 = 38$ **11.** 4 **13.** −8 **15.** 8
17. −35 **19.** $f < 10$ **21.** $n < -14$
23. $28 = \frac{3}{4}a + 4$; 32

Chapter 9

Graphs of Equations and Inequalities

Lesson 9-1

Try This **a.** $(D, 1)$
b. $D(-3, -5)$ $E(5, 2)$ $F(5, -2)$ $G(-4, 2)$
c.

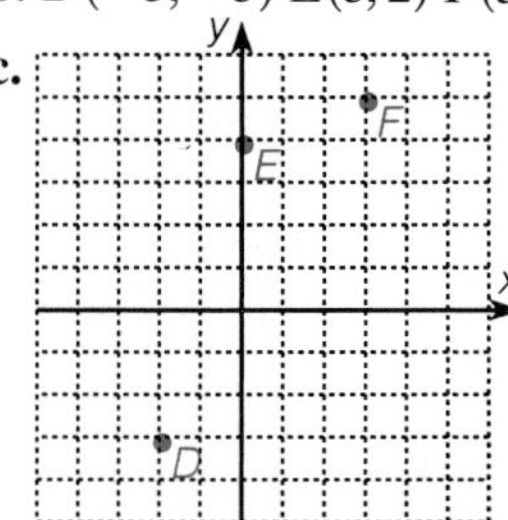

Exercises **1.** (C, 2) **3.** (3, 2) **5.** $(-2, -4)$
7. $(3, -4)$ **9.** $(-6, -3)$ **11.** $(-6, 4)$ **13.** $(4, 0)$
27. $(-2, 4)$ **29.** $(-1, -3)$ **31.** forms letter M
33. forms letter T **35.** forms letter I
37. forms letter F **39.** forms letter N
41. $(2, 3)$ **43.** $-12, -3x$ **45.** -4.9

Numbers to Algebra **1.** $(5, 4)$ **3.** $(2, 2)$

Lesson 9-2

Try This **a.** $(2, -3)$ **b.** $y = 2x - 3$

x	y
-3	-9
-2	-7
-1	-5
0	-3
1	-1

c.

$y = 2x - 1$

x	y
-2	-5
-1	-3
0	-1
1	1
2	3

d.

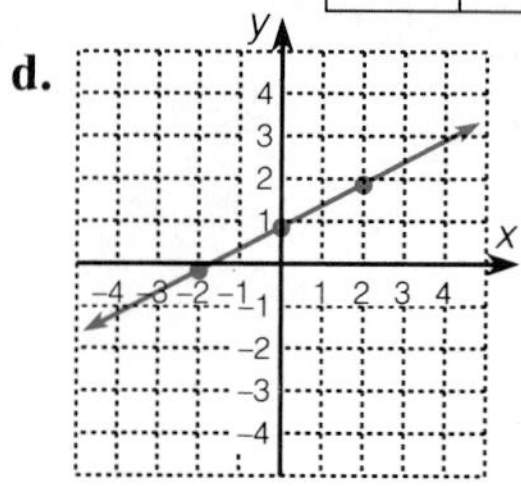

Exercises **1.** $(2, 3)$ **3.** $(-3, 4)$
21. $y = -4x + 4$ **23.** $y = -2x + 8$
25. $y = \frac{3}{2}x - 2$ **29.** $3x - 5$ rises, $2 - x$ falls
31. $(2, 0)$ $(0, 3)$ **33.** 2 **35.** 4

Computer Activity **1.** a, c, e, f

Lesson 9-3

Try This **a.**

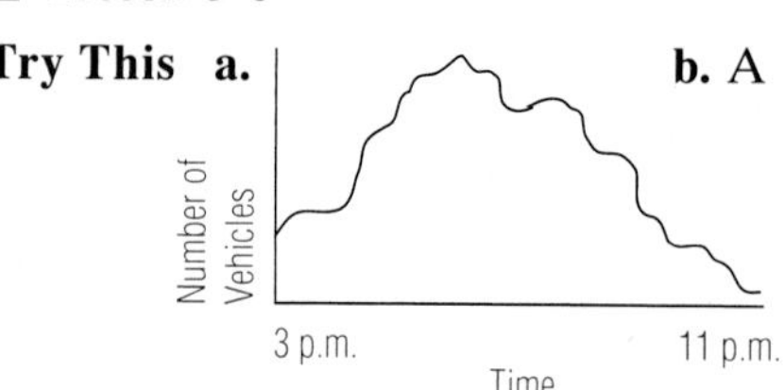

b. A

Exercises **1.** D **3.** B **11.** $\frac{11}{20}$ **13.** $d > -7$

Lesson 9-4

Try This **a.** d **b.** $3d$ **c.** $n + 2n = 24$

Exercises **1.** $c = k + 7$ **3.** $\frac{g}{2}$ **5.** $2s$ **7.** $\frac{9p}{2}$
9. $2g + 8 = 64$ **11.** $s + 2s = 110$
13. $f + (f + 25) = 297$ **15.** $2f + f = 111$
17a. seats in middle section **17b.** $2s + s + s$
17c. $2s + s + s = 96$ **21.** $a - 18$ **23.** -2
25. 6

Lesson 9-5

Try This **a.** 12 are girls.

Exercises **1.** 138 were occupied.
3. 145 are male; 209 are female. **5.** The large holds 32 oz; the regular holds 8 oz. **7.** Fred collected 9; Jerry collected 18; Tom collected 21. **9.** 120 **11.** $\frac{19}{30}$ **13.** $\frac{7}{30}$

Lesson 9-6

Try This **a.** yes, $k = 5$
b. no, $k = -2$ (not positive) **c.** no **d.** no
e. yes, $k = 1$

Exercises **1.** yes, $k = 1$ **3.** no **5.** no
7. yes, $k = 2$ **9.** inversely **11a.** 20, 40, 60
11b. 320, 160, $106\frac{2}{3}$ **13.** 30 **15.** 90 **17.** 2.4

Lesson 9-7

Try This **a.** $\frac{7}{12}$ **b.** slope $= 2$ **c.** slope $= \frac{1}{4}$
d. -2 **e.** $\frac{2}{3}$

f. x-intercept $= -3$, y-intercept $= 6$
g. x-intercept $= \frac{10}{3}$, y-intercept $= -5$
Exercises **1.** slope $= \frac{2}{5}$ **3.** slope $= -2$
5. slope $= \frac{1}{7}$ **7.** slope $= 3$ **9.** 2 **11.** 2
13. $\frac{-1}{3}$ **15.** x-intercept $= 5$, y-intercept $= 5$
17. x-intercept $= 6$, y-intercept $= -2$
19. x-intercept $= 5$, y-intercept $= 4$ **25.** 12 ft
27. 28 **29.** 3

Lesson 9-8

Problems **1.** \$8.40 **3.** \$4.80 **5.** \$3.60
7. \$22.80 **9.** \$0.20 **11.** about 1.4¢

Lesson 9-9

Try This **a.** yes **b.** (2, 1)
Exercises **1.** yes **3.** no **5.** yes **7.** (1, 0)
9. (−1, 1) **11.** (2, 1) **13.** infinite **15.** infinite
17. $\left(\frac{1}{3}, \frac{10}{3}\right)$ **19.** $k = 0$
21. More-for-Your-Money, 100 miles
23. 13 **25.** −40 **27.** 5 **29.** $-\frac{8}{9}$ **31.** 60 cm

Lesson 9-10

Exercises **7.** yes
9. total wins vs. wins against right-handers
11. total wins vs. wins on grass

Lesson 9-11

Try This **a.** $x > -\frac{8}{3}$ **b.** $x < 1$ **c.** $x \le 2$
d. $x \le 1$
Exercises **3.** $x > \frac{1}{2}$ **5.** $x \le -5$ **7.** $x > 3$
9. $x \le 1$ **11.** $x < 9$ **13.** $x < 15.25$
19. $2 < x < 8$ **21.** 6 **23.** $t = 4$

Lesson 9-12

Try This

a. $y > 2x - 1$

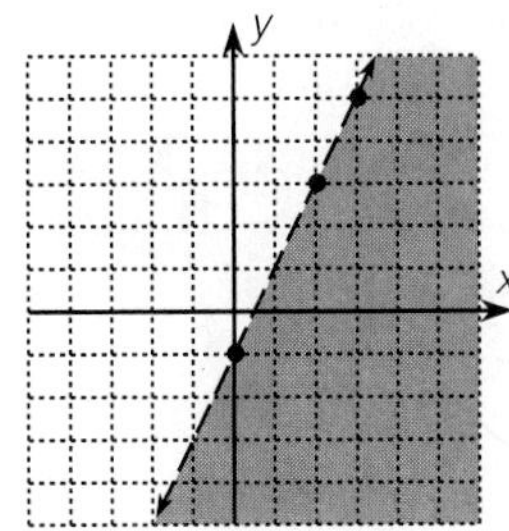

b. $y \le \frac{1}{2}x + 1$

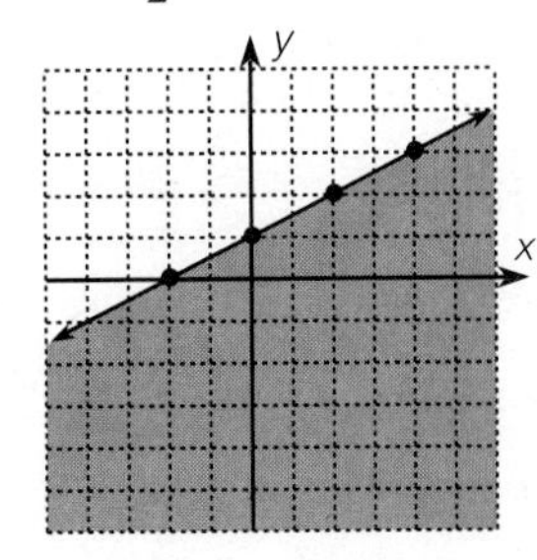

Exercises **17.** $5x + 7y \le 500$ **21.** −1

Lesson 9-13

Problems **1.** 65 **3.** 3 at \$5 and 5 at \$7

Chapter 9 Review/Test

1. true **3.** false **5.** true **9.** −2 **11.** (−1, 1)
13. no **15.** \$420

Cumulative Review

1. 59,049 **2.** 1,296 **3.** $t \cdot t \cdot t$ **4.** 9^4 **5.** c^7
6. $(-2)^3$ **7.** 4^5 **8.** $(-5)^{10}$ **9.** v^4 **10.** 30 **11.** 32
12. $2 \cdot 2 \cdot 2 \cdot 3 \cdot 3$ **13.** $5 \cdot 5$ **14.** $2 \cdot 5 \cdot 11$
15. $2 \cdot 2 \cdot 2 \cdot 5 \cdot 5$ **16.** 4 **17.** 6 **18.** 15 **19.** 30
20. 24 **21.** 60 **22.** $0.\overline{6}$ **23.** 0.875 **24.** $0.\overline{45}$
25. 5^5 **26.** $(-7)^4$ **27.** $\frac{1}{r^3}$ or r^{-3} **28.** $\frac{1}{8}$ **29.** $\frac{1}{9}$
30. $\frac{1}{36}$ **31.** $4.14 \cdot 10^2$ **32.** $3.3 \cdot 10^4$ **33.** $1.2 \cdot 10^7$
34. $5.0 \cdot 10^{-2}$ **35.** $2.25 \cdot 10^{-5}$ **36.** $8.9 \cdot 10^{-3}$
37. 27,800 **38.** 0.00003 **39.** 0.00708 **40.** −1
41. −4

Chapter 10

Ratio, Proportion, and Percent

Lesson 10-1

Try This **a.** $\frac{1}{3}$ **b.** $\frac{3}{2}$ **c.** $\frac{5}{4}$ **d.** $\frac{36}{1}$
Exercises **1.** $\frac{3}{2}$ **3.** $\frac{4}{9}$ **5.** $\frac{3}{8}$ **7.** $\frac{12}{7}$ **9.** $\frac{3}{2}$ **11.** $\frac{8}{5}$
13. $\frac{4}{1}$ **15.** $\frac{16}{9}$ **17.** $\frac{5}{18}$ **19.** $\frac{1}{2}$ **21.** $\frac{7}{3}$ **23.** $\frac{11}{2}$
25. 3:1,000 **27.** 24:425 **29.** $y:x$
31. $\frac{s+t}{p}$; $(s + t):p$ **33.** $\frac{a+b}{a-b}$; $(a + b):(a - b)$
35. 12 **37.** −7.5 **39.** $z < -9$ **41.** $t > 7$
43. 0.05 **45.** $\frac{1}{2}$

Lesson 10-2

Try This **a.** ≠ **b.** = **c.** 15 **d.** 63 **e.** 30
Exercises **1.** = **3.** ≠ **5.** ≠ **7.** = **9.** =
11. = **13.** 18 **15.** 9 **17.** 18 **19.** 11 **21.** 35
23. 7 **25.** $15\frac{3}{4}$ **27.** 50 **29.** 20 **31.** 102 lb
33. $\frac{5}{12} = \frac{25}{60}$ **35.** $\frac{42}{90} = \frac{84}{180}$ **37.** 399 **39.** 60 more
41. $\frac{5}{7}$ **43.** $\frac{6}{11}$ **45.** 8,000 **47.** 6 **49.** 20

Numbers to Algebra **1.** 7 **3.** 25

Lesson 10-3

Try This **a.** 8.7 km/L **b.** 375 words/minute **c.** $18.75

Exercises **1.** $8/hr **3.** 250 words/minute **5.** 937.5 km/h **7.** $5.50/h **9.** 13 players/team **11.** $2.70 **13.** 44 **15.** $\frac{a+b}{b} = \frac{a}{b} + 1$ and $\frac{c+d}{d} = \frac{c}{d} + 1$ **17.** 1.5 **19.** -0.928 **21.** -0.08

Lesson 10-4

Try This **a.** 1.2 m **b.** 0.4 m **c.** 0.8 m **d.** 18 cm

Exercises **1.** 600 km **3.** 900 km **5.** 720 km **7.** 555 km **9.** 10 mm × 12.5 mm **11.** 2.5 mm × 7.5 mm **13.** 3.5 mm × 1.65 mm **15.** 5.375 m **17.** 3.625 m **19.** 11.6 cm × 6.4 cm **21.** c or d **23.** 21 m **25.** $4t + 8$ **27.** $-\frac{2}{15}$ **29.** $5^2 = 25$ **31.** $7^4 = 2,401$ **33.** $-\frac{33}{5}$

Lesson 10-5

Problems **1.** 0.832, 0.81; Bob's **3.** 1.50, 1.20; Bob's **5.** 2.50, 2.75; A & B **7.** Jones, $16.67 each **9.** Bob's, 0.85 to 0.90 per liter **11.** about 1¢ more **13.** $1.60

Lesson 10-6

Try This **a.** $\frac{11}{20}$ **b.** $\frac{1}{25}$ **c.** $\frac{21}{100}$ **d.** $\frac{11}{200}$ **e.** $\frac{11}{400}$ **f.** $\frac{1}{15}$ **g.** 96% **h.** 40% **i.** 15%

Exercises **1.** $\frac{9}{20}$ **3.** $\frac{1}{20}$ **5.** $\frac{1}{5}$ **7.** $\frac{1}{10}$ **9.** $\frac{1}{1}$ **11.** $\frac{23}{400}$ **13.** $\frac{39}{400}$ **15.** $\frac{149}{1,000}$ **17.** 60% **19.** 25% **21.** 72% **23.** 80% **25.** 60% **27.** 34 **29.** 25% prime, 74% composite **31.** English **33.** -6 **35.** -2 **37.** 1.5

Estimation **1.** ≈50% **3.** ≈$33\frac{1}{3}$% **5.** ≈$66\frac{2}{3}$%

Lesson 10-7

Try This **a.** 0.05 **b.** 0.0825 **c.** 1.25 **d.** 60% **e.** $8\frac{1}{2}$% **f.** 214% **g.** 16.7% **h.** 37.5% **i.** 11.1%

Exercises **1.** 0.4 **3.** 0.05 **5.** 0.02 **7.** 1.5 **9.** 0.12 **11.** 0.34 **13.** 0.0075 **15.** 0.05625 **17.** 62% **19.** 5% **21.** 80% **23.** $\frac{1}{10}$% **25.** $1\frac{1}{2}$% **27.** $12\frac{1}{2}$% **29.** 438% **31.** $\frac{3}{5}$% **33.** 33.3% **35.** 83.3% **37.** 18.8% **39.** 10.05% and 10.5%; 10.5% is greater **41.** $x(0.01)$ **43.** $\frac{17}{25}$, 68% **45.** $\frac{19}{50}$, 0.38 **47.** $\frac{49}{400}$, 12.25% **49.** 35.6% **51.** 85.7% **53.** 11 **55.** 3 **57.** -2 **59.** $4 < r$ **61.** -3 **63.** 0.375 **65.** 4

Lesson 10-8

Try This **a.** $102 = \frac{1}{2}x + x, x = 68$ customers

Exercises **1.** 19 books **3.** 20 customers **5.** The jeans were $31.50. **7.** She made $90. **11.** -1 **13.** $5 \cdot 5 \cdot 5$ or 125 **15.** $\frac{1}{-6 \times (-6)}$ or $\frac{1}{36}$

Estimation **1.** ≈30 km/L **3.** ≈$4

Lesson 10-9

Try This **a.** 125% **b.** 115% **c.** 150% **d.** 0.75%, $\frac{3}{4}$% **e.** 0.8%, $\frac{4}{5}$% **f.** 0.15% **g.** $2\frac{1}{4}$ **h.** $1\frac{16}{25}$ **i.** $\frac{1}{200}$ **j.** $\frac{1}{800}$

Exercises **1.** 175% **3.** 225% **5.** 320% **7.** $\frac{4}{5}$% **9.** $\frac{3}{5}$% **11.** $1\frac{3}{4}$ **13.** $2\frac{1}{2}$ **15.** $\frac{1}{500}$ **17.** $\frac{3}{800}$ **19.** 125% **21.** 165% **23.** yes **25.** 8 × 2 units **27.** 4 **29.** $8\frac{2}{3}$ **31.** $8\frac{3}{8}$

Lesson 10-10

Problems **1.** no solution **3.** 0 **5.** 642

Chapter 10 Review/Test

1. true **3.** false **5.** false **7.** $\frac{4}{5}$ **9.** 18 **11.** 20 **13.** $125/day **15.** 3 cm × 2 cm **17.** 240% **19.** 37.5% **21.** $\frac{1}{100}$ **23.** $3\frac{1}{4}$ **25.** $\frac{1}{40}$ **27.** 0.122 **29.** $2\frac{1}{2}$% **31.** $15

Chapter 11

Applying Percent

Lesson 11-1

Try This **a.** $100 **b.** 10 **c.** 180 **d.** 6 **e.** 90 **f.** 3.6 **g.** 78 **h.** 3.375 **i.** 102 **j.** $0.60 **k.** $95

Exercises **1.** 16 **3.** 135 **5.** 120 **7.** 385 **9.** 12 **11.** 24 **13.** 45 **15.** 5.4 **17.** 8 **19.** 2.5 **21.** 0.378 **23.** 9.72 **25.** 50 **27.** 2.7 **29.** about $111 **31.** $14,787.50 **33.** 8.25 **35.** 18 **37.** ≈60 **39.** 50% **41.** 75% **43.** -2 **45.** -5

Mental Math **1.** 45 **3.** 70 **5.** 15 **7.** 12 **9.** 10

Lesson 11-2

Try This **a.** 20% **b.** $33\frac{1}{3}$% **c.** $8\frac{1}{3}$% **d.** 50.8$\overline{3}$% **e.** $33\frac{1}{3}$% **f.** $13\frac{1}{3}$%

Exercises **1.** 15% **3.** 60% **5.** 20% **7.** $33\frac{1}{3}$% **9.** 80% **11.** $2\frac{1}{2}$% **13.** 46% **15.** 26% **17.** 22% **19.** $26\frac{2}{3}$% **21.** 25, 50 **23.** Art and Kathy, Brent and Nicki, Chuck and Lynn, Darin and Michaelia **25.** 0.8 **27.** 0.19 **29.** 4

Lesson 11-3

Try This **a.** 60 **b.** 200 **c.** 62.9 **d.** 200

Exercises **1.** 32 **3.** 160 **5.** 300 **7.** 283.3 **9.** 266.7 **11.** 400 **13.** 18 **15.** 800 students **17.** 180 yd^3 **19.** 38.33 **21.** 3,069.31 **23.** 21.04 **25.** 60 students **27.** 32 **29.** 28 **31.** 400 ml **33.** $\frac{3}{4}$, 75% **35.** 5, 500% **37.** $\frac{9}{2}$, 450% **39.** $r = \frac{25}{8}$

Critical Thinking

Exercises **1.** no **3.** no

Lesson 11-4

Problems **1.** 6 ft $3\frac{3}{4}$ in. **3.** popcorn $0.95, juice $0.70 **5.** $12.50 **7.** $140 **9.** 2.4 **11.** −2

Lesson 11-5

Try This **a.** 12.5% **b.** 48%

Exercises **1.** 25% **3.** 20% **5.** 75% **7.** 57.9% **9.** 50% increase **11.** 43.8% decrease **13.** $16\frac{2}{3}$% **15.** $9\frac{41}{51}$% or approximately 9.8% **17.** $650 **19.** $74.25 **21.** 0.8 **23.** 2.$\overline{6}$ **25.** 0.3125 **27.** $\frac{5}{16}$ **29.** $\frac{3}{38}$ **31.** −2 **33.** −1

Lesson 11-6

Try This **a.** discount = $450, sale price = $1,800 **b.** $12

Exercises **1.** $0.33, $11.67 **3.** $32.50, $227.50 **5.** $103.49, $586.46 **7.** $571.25, $3,998.75 **9.** $1.35 **11.** $0.71 **13.** $23.39 **15.** 23.5% **17.** 16.8% **19.** $\frac{7}{20}$ **21.** $\frac{5}{4}$ **23.** 2

Computer Activity **1.** $37.50, $337.50 **3.** $473.95, $9,005.05

Lesson 11-7

Problems **1.** $75.00 **3.** $375 **5.** $7,987.50 **7.** $200 **9.** $14.44 **11.** $257.82

Lesson 11-8

Try This **a.** $75, $325 **b.** $22.50, $97.50 **c.** $15, $140

Exercises **1.** $3.60, $123.60 **3.** $121.63, $816.63 **5.** $96, $496 **7.** $456.30, $1,301.30 **9.** $72, $872 **11.** $806.25 **13.** $938.97 **15.** $936.30, $14.05, $950.35 **17.** $761.61, $561.61, $8.43, $570.04 **19.** $175.60, $2.64, $178.24 **21.** $78.24 **23.** P = $104.17 **25.** 13 · 0.25 · 4 or 25 · 0.13 · 4 **27.** 2.4 **29.** 18 **31.** $\frac{c}{2}$ or t **33.** $\frac{1}{3}t$ or r

Numbers to Algebra **1.** $t = \frac{D}{r}$ **3.** $C = \frac{F - 32}{1.8}$ **5.** $W = \frac{P - 2L}{2}$

Lesson 11-9

Problems **1.** 53.76 **3.** about $33\frac{1}{3}$% **5.** $33\frac{1}{3}$% **7.** about $15,000 **9.** 25, 41.25, 50, 60, 82.5, 125 **11.** about 375,000 **13.** 24% **15.** 90

Lesson 11-10

Try This **a.** 4-year college, 180°; work, 99°; 2-year college, 54°; armed services, 18°; undecided, 9° **b.** no **c.** 2-year college and armed services

Exercises **1.** adventure, 180°; science fiction, 72°; children's, 54°; comedy, 36°; other, 18° **3.** walk, 162°; bus, 108°; bicycle, 61°; car, 29° **9.** $\frac{7}{20}$ **11.** 3

Lesson 11-11

Problems **1.** 23, 7, 19, 9 or 23, 5, 9, 21 or 27, 5, 7, 19 or 21, 19, 13, 5 **3.** 5 ways

Chapter 11 Review/Test

1. true **3.** false **5.** false **7.** 16 **9.** 28% **11.** 60 **13.** 63 **15.** $2.80 **17.** $42 **19.** birthday, 90°; anniversary, 54°; graduation, 36°; special occasion, 108°; other, 72°

Chapter 12

Equations in Geometry

Lesson 12-1

Try This **a.** points: X, Y, Z; lines: $\overleftrightarrow{WY}$, $\overleftrightarrow{WZ}$, $\overleftrightarrow{XZ}$; segments: $\overline{YW}$, $\overline{ZW}$, $\overline{XY}$, $\overline{YZ}$, $\overline{XZ}$; rays: $\overrightarrow{YW}$, $\overrightarrow{YZ}$, $\overrightarrow{WX}$, $\overrightarrow{XW}$, $\overrightarrow{WY}$, $\overrightarrow{XY}$, $\overrightarrow{ZY}$, $\overrightarrow{WZ}$, $\overrightarrow{ZW}$, $\overrightarrow{XZ}$, $\overrightarrow{ZX}$

Exercises **1.** A, B, C, D, E **3.** ACD, AED, BCD, etc. **5.** $\overleftrightarrow{AC}$, $\overleftrightarrow{DC}$, $\overleftrightarrow{BC}$ **7.** $\overline{AE}$, $\overline{AB}$, $\overline{AD}$ **9.** $\overline{AB}$, $\overline{BC}$, $\overline{CD}$, $\overline{DA}$, $\overline{FG}$, $\overline{EA}$, $\overline{FB}$, $\overline{GC}$, $\overline{HD}$, $\overline{EF}$, $\overline{GH}$, $\overline{HE}$ **11.** 15, 21, 28 **13.** 33.5 **15.** $x > 7$ **17.** $x > -1$

Lesson 12-2

Try This **a.** 3 **b.** 2 **c.** $BC = 15.8$ m **d.** 15 cm **e.** $x = 4.3$

Exercises **1.** 3.2 cm **3.** 6.1 cm **5.** 7.2 cm **7.** $x = 6.4$ **9.** $z = 4$ **11.** 35.8 cm **13.** 35 cm **15.** 178 cm **17.** $y = 16.4$ cm **19.** $x = 4$; sides are 4 cm, 4 cm, 6 cm **21.** $x = 12$, $3x = 36$ **23.** $x = 2$, $y = 6$, $P = 70$ **25.** $1\frac{2}{5}$ **27.** $1\frac{2}{25}$ **29.** $\frac{37}{100}$ **31.** 0.3 **33.** 150%

Lesson 12-3

Try This **a.** $\angle CBA$, $\angle DAB$, $\angle DAC$, $\angle DCA$ **b.** $\angle ADC$ and $\angle ADB$ **c.** 37° **d.** 16° **e.** 61° **f.** 42°

Exercises **1.** $\angle AOB = 45°$, $\angle AOC = 150°$, $\angle AOD = 180°$, $\angle BOC = 105°$, $\angle BOD = 135°$, $\angle COD = 30°$ **3.** $\angle BDC$ **5.** 56° **7.** 17° **9.** 13° **11.** 20.5° **13.** 66° **15.** 37° **17.** 27° **19.** 22.5° **21.** $m\angle y = 15°$ **23.** 69° **25.** $\frac{7}{20}$ **27.** 1.5

Estimation **1.** 15° **3.** 40°

Lesson 12-4

Try This **a.** 61° **b.** $m\angle 5 = 38°$, $m\angle 6 = 38°$, $m\angle 7 = 38°$, $m\angle 8 = 142°$

Exercises **1.** $m\angle 1 = 52°$, $m\angle 2 = 38°$ **3.** $m\angle 1 = 90°$, $m\angle 2 = 40°$ **5.** $m\angle 1 = m\angle 2 = m\angle 3 = m\angle 4 = 100°$ **7.** $m\angle 1 = 95°$, $m\angle 2 = 95°$, $m\angle 3 = 85°$, $m\angle 4 = 95°$ **9.** south **11.** $\angle 5$ has a 135° angle as a supplement. **13.** $m\angle 3 = 135°$, $m\angle 4 = 45°$ **15.** $\angle 4$ and $\angle 5$ are alternate interior angles **17.** $m\angle ABC = 60°$ **21.** $x = 56\frac{1}{3}°$; $m\angle ABC = 71\frac{1}{3}°$ **23.** 12.5% **25.** 60% **27.** 149.5

Mathematical Reasoning

1a. true **1b.** true **1c.** false **1d.** false

Lesson 12-5

Try This **a.** $\triangle XYZ$ is right and scalene; $\triangle BCD$ is obtuse and scalene. **b.** $x = 51$

Exercises **1.** obtuse isosceles **3.** right scalene **5.** 85° **7.** 95° **9.** 78° **11.** 130° **13.** 62°, 93° **15.** $x = \frac{180 - n}{2}$ **17.** 85%

Lesson 12-6

Try This **a.** trapezoid, not regular **b.** octagon, not regular **c.** $m\angle A = 130°$

Exercises **1.** pentagon, not regular **3.** octagon, not regular **5.** 118° **7.** 49° **9.** 60°, 90°, 90°, 120° **11.** 60°, 60°, 120°, 120° **13.** 110°, 60°, 85°, 105° **17.** 4 **19.** 150%

Numbers to Algebra **1.** 1,800°

Lesson 12-7

Problems **1.** 27 miles **3.** 39 miles **5.** yes **7.** approximately $4\frac{1}{2}$ hr **9.** $960 **11.** 1,310 mi

Lesson 12-8

Try This **a.** 10.048 cm **b.** 51.496 cm **c.** 131.95 ft **d.** 1.91 m **e.** 5.73 cm

Exercises **1.** 15.7 cm **3.** 62.8 cm **5.** 38.308 m **7.** 1.59 cm **9.** 3.82 m **11.** 71.4 cm **13.** 1.43 cm **15.** 2.39 cm **17.** 16.42 m **19.** 87.92 in. **21.** 26.84 **23.** approximately $7\frac{1}{3}$ feet; 720 revolutions **25.** A cat could walk under. **27.** 16.67%

Computer Activity **1.** 52 **3.** 1,000

Lesson 12-9

Problems **1.** 36 hours **3.** 45°, 90°, 45° **5.** 1,264 cans **9.** −1 **11.** 9

Lesson 12-10

Try This **a.** $\angle A \cong \angle G$, $\angle B \cong \angle H$, $\angle C \cong \angle I$, $\angle D \cong \angle J$, $\angle E \cong \angle K$, $\angle F \cong \angle L$; $\overline{AB} \cong \overline{GH}$, $\overline{BC} \cong \overline{HI}$, $\overline{CD} \cong \overline{IJ}$, $\overline{DE} \cong \overline{JK}$, $\overline{EF} \cong \overline{KL}$, $\overline{FA} \cong \overline{LG}$ **b.** $\angle C \cong \angle W$, $\overline{AC} \cong \overline{UW}$, $\angle A \cong \angle U$, $\triangle ABC \cong \triangle UVW$ by ASA property

Exercises **1.** $\angle U$ **3.** $\angle T$ **5.** $\angle R$ **7.** $\overline{VW}$ **9.** $\angle B$ **11.** $\overline{TU}$ **13.** $\overline{AB}$ **15.** SSS **17.** ASA **19.** $\triangle ABC \cong \triangle FED$ **21.** $\triangle AFE$; SSS or SAS **23.** $\triangle BCE, \triangle CDA, \triangle DEB, \triangle EAC$ **25.** 0.1875 **27.** 3.5 **29.** 0.2 **31.** 1.25

Estimation **1.** no **3.** no

Lesson 12-12

Exercises **21.** 5 **23.** 4 **25.** 19

Lesson 12-13

Problems **1.** Dec. 31

Chapter 12 Review/Test

1. between **3.** point in common **5.** angle and side measures **7.** $\overleftrightarrow{DC}$, $\overleftrightarrow{DE}$, $\overleftrightarrow{EB}$, $\overleftrightarrow{BC}$, etc. **9.** $\angle ABE, \angle ACD, \angle CBF, \angle AEB, \angle ADC$ **11.** $\overleftrightarrow{DC}$, $\overleftrightarrow{EB}$ **13.** obtuse, isosceles **15.** rhombus **17.** 20 games

Cumulative Review

1. $x = 9$ **2.** $f = 4$ **3.** $d = -25$ **4.** $k = 2$ **5.** $p < 13$ **6.** $m < -8$ **7.** $n > 5$ **8.** $w > 54$ **9.** -8 **10.** no **11.** $\frac{7}{17}$ **12.** $\frac{3}{4}$ **13.** $\frac{4}{1}$ **14.** $a = 10$ **15.** $y = 49$ **16.** $p = 24$ **17.** 54 inches **18.** 12 trombones **19.** 53 km/h **20.** \$120/day **21.** 64 beats/min **22.** \$18/h **23.** 34 mi/gal **24.** 21 **25.** 60 **26.** 9 **27.** 45% **28.** 20% **29.** 25% **30.** 15% **31.** 140 **32.** 80 **33.** 76 **34.** 48

Chapter 13

Area and Volume Formulas

Lesson 13-1

Try This **a.** 427 yd^2 **b.** 216 m^2 **c.** 2,487.45 cm^2

Exercises **1.** 224 cm^2 **3.** 150 cm^2 **5.** 82.94 cm^2 **7.** 0.3588 km^2 **9.** the soccer field **11.** 100 cm^2 **13.** 54 cm^2 **15.** 14 m **17.** 4.7 mm **19.** 5 in. **21.** \$384 **23.** $l = 25$, $w = 25$; A square has the greatest area of all rectangles with the same perimeter. **25.** $-\frac{4}{15}$ **27.** $1\frac{1}{12}$ **29.** $116\frac{2}{3}$% **31.** 87.5%

Lesson 13-2

Try This **a.** 20 cm^2 **b.** 33 cm^2 **c.** 464 m^2 **d.** 231 m^2

Exercises **1.** 31.5 cm^2 **3.** 63 cm^2 **5.** 103.5 m^2 **7.** 34 m^2 **9.** 81 m^2 **11.** 57.5 m^2 **13.** 12 cm **15.** n^2 **17.** -1

Numbers to Algebra **1.** $h = \frac{A}{b}$

Lesson 13-3

Try This **a.** 28.26 ft^2 **b.** 50.24 m^2

Exercises **1.** 78.5 cm^2 **3.** 78.5 cm^2 **5.** 47.76 m^2 **7.** 7,850 cm^2 **9.** 7.065 m^2 **11.** 113.04 mm^2 **13.** 50.24 $in.^2$ **15.** 860,852.85 cm^2 **17.** 633.1496 cm^2 **19.** 15.89625 m^2 **21a.** 50.24 $in.^2$ **21b.** 19.625 $in.^2$ **21c.** 9.61625 $in.^2$ **23.** 12π **25.** $144 + \frac{25\pi}{2}$ **27.** 25 times **29.** \$1.80 **31.** $\frac{6}{25}$ **33.** $\frac{11}{100}$ **35.** 12 **37.** -66 **39.** 1.12

Estimation **1.** $\frac{9}{36} = \frac{1}{4}$ **3.** $\frac{49}{100} \approx \frac{1}{2}$

Lesson 13-4

Try This **a.** 239 m^2 **b.** 76.13 m^2

Exercises **1.** 108 m^2 **3.** 48 m^2 **5.** 119.28 cm^2 **7.** 72 ft^2 **9.** 188 ft^2 **13.** 320.11 m^2 **15.** 0.16 **17.** 1.2 **19.** $\frac{3}{4}$

Lesson 13-5

Exercises **1.** \$5.25 **3.** \$10.38 **5.** \$525 **7.** \$6.75 **9.** $<$ **11.** 4

Lesson 13-6

Try This **a.** 1,528.8 cm^3 **b.** 628 cm^3 **c.** 141.3 cm^3

Exercises **1.** 352 cm^3 **3.** 2,009.6 ft^3 **5.** 300 cm^3 **7.** 504 ft^3 **9.** approximately 3,356 cm^3 per gallon **11.** 72,000 cm^3 **13.** 28.98 m^3 **15.** 7,218.86 m^3 **17.** 602.88 dm^3 **19.** 1,969,408 cm^3 **21.** 565.2 cm^3 **23.** 100 cm^2 **25.** 497.6 cm^3 **27.** 34 cubic units **29.** 3 **31.** -1.75 **33.** $0.\overline{3}$ **35.** 300% **37.** 70% **39.** 6.5 **41.** 5 **43.** \$255.60

Lesson 13-7

Problems **1.** 604.4 yd^3 are moved. Cost: \$785.78 **3.** 15.4321 yd^3; \$694.45 **5.** \$3,318.75 **7.** \$3,360

Lesson 13-8

Try This a. 198 cm^3 **b.** 188.4 m^3

Exercises 1. 209.3 cm^3 **3.** 339.12 cm^3 **5.** 150.72 $in.^3$ **7.** 1,013.2 cm^3 **9.** 235.5 dm^3 **11.** 158.3 cm^3 **13.** 188 m^3 **15.** 0.0062 $in.^3$ **17.** 24π **19.** 72 **21.** 144 **23.** 6.9 **25.** 2 times greater **27.** 288π cm^3 **29.** 176.868π m^3 **31.** 30, 55, 91 **33.** 1.35 **35.** 0.194 **37.** 1.6×10^{-4} **39.** $-\frac{9}{8}$

Lesson 13-9

Try This a. 533.8 cm^2 **b.** 1,155.52 m^2 **c.** 1,872 cm^2

Exercises 1. 527.52 cm^2 **3.** 427.04 cm^2 **5.** 1,004.8 cm^2 **7.** 22.0428 m^2 **9.** 439.6 dm^2 **11.** 3,165.12 m^2 **13.** 87.92 ft^2 **15.** 114 cm^2 **17.** 136 cm^2 **19.** 2,612.48 cm^2 **21.** 12.56 m^2 **23.** 300 ft^2 **25.** $\frac{9}{25}$ **27.** $\frac{13}{50}$ **29.** 8 **31.** −12

Computer Activity 1. 3.98089172

Lesson 13-10

Problems 1. 15 g **3.** Jane: 36; Sally: 18; Al: 35 **5.** 9 tables of 6, 15 tables of 4

Chapter 13 Review/Test

1. true **3.** true **5.** true **7.** 252 cm^2 **9.** 5,256 mm^2 **11.** approximately 50.24 m^2 or 16π m^2 **13.** approximately 769.3 $in.^3$ **15.** 1,130.4 ft^2 **17.** \$1,955.56 **19.** $523.\overline{3}$ tons

Geometry Review

1. A, B, C, or D **2.** $\overleftrightarrow{AB}, \overleftrightarrow{AD}, \overleftrightarrow{DC}, \overleftrightarrow{BC}$ **3.** ABC, ABD, ACD, BCD **4.** $\overline{AB}$ or $\overline{BC}$ **5.** $\overrightarrow{AB}$ or $\overrightarrow{AD}$ **6.** acute, equilateral **7.** right, isosceles **8.** ASA **9.** 97.92 m^2 **10.** 98 cm^2 **11.** 254.34 m^2 **12.** 9.0746 km^2 **13.** 216 m^3 **14.** 6,908 ft^3 **15.** 21 yd^3 **16.** 506.59 ft^3 **17.** $170.\overline{6}$ dm^3 **18.** 1,909.12 cm^2

Chapter 14

Probability, Statistics, and Graphs

Lesson 14-1

Try This a. 12

Exercises 1. 9 **3.** 12 **5.** 12 **7.** 50 **9.** 30 **11.** 700 **13.** 54 **15.** 5 **17.** 80% **19.** 30% **21.** 30, 36, $2n$

Lesson 14-2

Try This a. 120 **b.** 6 **c.** 12

Exercises 1. 120 **3.** 120 **5.** 24 **7.** 336 **9.** 120 **11.** 16 **13.** 3,276,000 **15.** 800 **17.** 1,680 **19.** 5,040 **21.** $3m$ **23.** $9n$ **25.** $6(x - y)$ **27.** 15.7 **29.** 20 **31.** −2 **33.** −4

Numbers to Algebra 1. $(n + 1), (n + 2), (n + 3), (n + 4)$ **3.** $(y - 2), (y - 4)$

Lesson 14-3

Try This a. $\frac{3}{6} = \frac{1}{2}$ **b.** 1 **c.** $\frac{5}{12}$ **d.** $\frac{9}{12} = \frac{3}{4}$

Exercises 1. $\frac{1}{2}$ **3.** $\frac{1}{13}$ **5.** $\frac{1}{13}$ **7.** $\frac{1}{52}$ **9.** $\frac{3}{26}$ **11.** $\frac{4}{15}$ **13.** $\frac{1}{3}$ **15.** $\frac{3}{5}$ **17.** $\frac{11}{16}$ **19.** $\frac{3}{8}$ **21.** $\frac{9}{16}$ **23.** $\frac{3}{8}$ **25.** $\frac{1}{8}$ **27.** $\frac{1}{9}$ **29.** 30 **31.** $m < 2$ **33.** 18 cm

Computer Activity 1. 25

Lesson 14-4

Try This a. $\frac{9}{20}$ **b.** $\frac{1}{5}$ **c.** $\frac{8}{33}$ **d.** $\frac{8}{33}$

Exercises 1. $\frac{1}{48}$ **3.** $\frac{5}{48}$ **5.** $\frac{1}{12}$ **7.** $\frac{1}{2,652}$ **9.** $\frac{4}{663}$ **11.** $\frac{1}{56}$ **13.** $\frac{1}{42}$ **15.** $\frac{15}{1,024}$ **17.** $\frac{1}{72}$ **19.** $\frac{5}{24}$ **21.** 60% **23.** 60% **25.** 3

Calculator Activity 1. 58%

Lesson 14-5

Exercises 1. \$40 **3.** $1.8\overline{3}$ m and $4.1\overline{6}$ m **5.** 16 ft, 17 ft, 18 ft **9.** −8 **11.** $2^3 \cdot 3^2 \cdot 7$

Lesson 14-6

Try This a. range = 3, mode = $16\frac{1}{2}$

Exercises 1. range = 9, mode = 31 **3.** range = 12, mode = 3 **5.** range = 34, mode = 35 **7.** range = \$5, mode = \$1–\$2.99 **9.** 24 **11.** $c > 4$ **13.** $-\frac{1}{2}$ **15.** 25% **17.** 16 **19.** −4 **21.** −30 **23.** neither **25.** inversely; $k = 24$

Estimation Range ≈ 14, mode = 4-year college; 20, 13, 16, 9, 6

Lesson 14-7

Try This **a.** mean: 14.6, median: 12

Exercises **1.** mean: 48, median: 56 **3.** 5.4 **5.** 17.9 **9.** 0.414 **11.** 60, 65, 70, 75, 80 **13.** 37.5% **15.** 87.5% **17.** $\frac{1}{2}$ **19.** $\frac{2}{3}$ **21.** <

Lesson 14-8

Problems **1.** 20% **3.** 55% **5.** 77.5% **7.** 8 **9.** 1988: 98; 1990: 101 **11.** 40% **13.** $150 **15.** $400

Lesson 14-9

Try This

a.

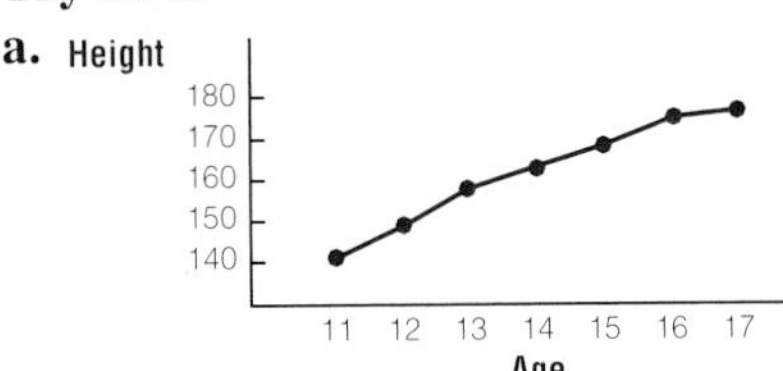

b.

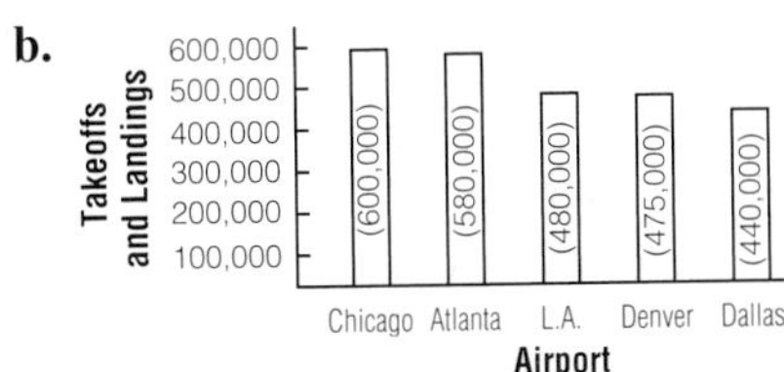

Exercises **7.** $9n - 9$ **9.** 4 **11.** −7 **13.** 7 **15.** −4 **17.** 10 **19.** 24 m **21.** 37.5 cm

Lesson 14-10

Try This

a.

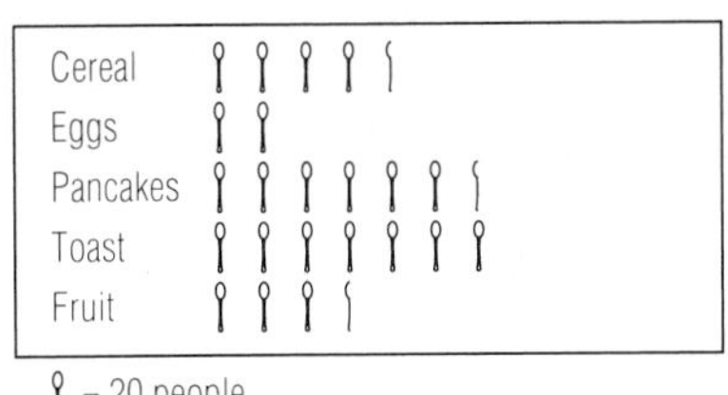

Exercises **7.** mean ≈ 6,500,000; median ≈ 7,500,000 **9.** < **11.** = **13.** = **15.** 4.2 **17.** 31.25%

Lesson 14-11

Problems **1.** $295.31 ≤ x ≤ $393.75 **3.** 6 sessions **7.** 24

Chapter 14 Review/Test

1. permutations **3.** true **5.** 18 **7.** $\frac{8}{10} = \frac{4}{5}$ **9.** $\frac{1}{36}$ **11.** mean 23; median 23; mode 20 **13.** 18 choices

Chapter 15

Square Roots and Special Triangles

Lesson 15-1

Try This **a.** −5 **b.** 9 **c.** $\frac{4}{3}$ **d.** $-\frac{3}{8}$ **e.** 18 **f.** 9

Exercises **1.** 5 **3.** 2 **5.** 12 **7.** −4 **9.** 4 **11.** $\frac{1}{3}$ **13.** $-\frac{4}{7}$ **15.** $-\frac{12}{5}$ **17.** 4 cm **19.** 6 **21.** 10 **23.** 11 **25.** −1 **27.** 12 **29.** 0 **31.** < **33.** < **35.** 9 **37.** $\sqrt{5^6} = 125$, $\sqrt{6^6} = 216$, $\sqrt{n^6} = n^3$ **39.** $\frac{1}{52}$

Numbers to Algebra **1.** 8 **3.** 12 **5.** 10 **7.** 9

Lesson 15-2

Try This **a.** $5 < \sqrt{28} < 6$ **b.** $7 < \sqrt{53} < 8$ **c.** 4 s **d.** 7.9 s **e.** 18.2 s **f.** 3.873 **g.** 3.317

Exercises **1.** 2,3 **3.** 4,5 **5.** 6,7 **7.** −6, −7 **9.** 5,6 **11.** 4,5 **13.** 9,10 **15.** 10,11 **17.** 87 mi **19.** 188 mi **21.** 6.3 s **23.** 15 s **25.** 5.8 s **27.** 7.7 s **29.** 2.236 **31.** 4.123 **33.** 3.162 **35.** 9.644 **37.** < **39.** < **41.** > **43.** < **45.** < **47.** > **49.** $D = 11$ **53.** 4 **55.** 64 cm^2 **57.** $\angle CBD$ and $\angle DBE$ **59.** $m = 40$ **61.** 9 **63.** 0.5 **65.** 3

Computer Activity **1.** 2.0 **2.** 8.9

Lesson 15-3

Try This **a.** ±7 **b.** ±10 **c.** $\pm\sqrt{39}$, ±6.245 **d.** $\pm\sqrt{73}$, ±8.544 **e.** ±3 **f.** ±4

Exercises **1.** ±4 **3.** ±9 **5.** ±11 **7.** $\pm\sqrt{56}$, ±7.483 **9.** $\pm\sqrt{132}$, ±11.489 **11.** $\pm\sqrt{53}$, ±7.28 **13.** ±5 **15.** ±10 **17.** ±7 **19.** ±7 **21.** ±9 **23.** 11 **25.** $\pm\sqrt{55}$, ±7.416 **27.** $\pm\sqrt{30}$, ±5.477 **29.** $\pm\sqrt{32}$, ±5.657 **31.** −1, 2 **33.** 55% **35.** 20% **37.** 2 **39.** 12 yd^3

Estimation **1.** ≈6 **3.** ≈10 **5.** ≈4

Lesson 15-4

Try This **a.** 13 **b.** $\sqrt{274}$ **c.** $\sqrt{161}$ **d.** $\sqrt{160}$
Exercises **1.** 15 **3.** $\sqrt{130}$ **5.** 17 **7.** 41 **9.** $\sqrt{261}$ **11.** $\sqrt{19}$ **13.** $\sqrt{133}$ **15.** $\sqrt{56}$ **17.** $\sqrt{205}$ **19.** $\sqrt{924}$ or 30.4 ft **21.** no **23.** no **25.** no **27.** yes **29.** 17 mi **31.** 20.19 ft **33.** yes **35.** yes **37.** $3c - 12$ or $3(c - 4)$ **39.** 0.5
Mental Math **1.** 3,025 **3.** 5,625 **5.** 9,025

Lesson 15-5

Problems **1.** yes **3.** 12 **5.** 136.01 yd **7.** ≈14.40 yd ($\sqrt{207.25}$)

Lesson 15-6

Try This **a.** $\frac{x}{15} = \frac{12}{18}$, 10 **b.** $\frac{y}{13} = \frac{18}{12}$, 19.5
Exercises **1.** 14 **3.** 15 **5.** 48 ft **7.** $e = 32$; $a = 5$ **9.** $p = 9\frac{1}{3}$; $u = 40\frac{1}{2}$ **11.** $d = 90$ m **13.** $AB = 66$ m **15.** area $\triangle ABC = 150$; area $\triangle PQR = 600$ **17.** $\frac{3}{14}$ **19.** $\frac{5}{7}$ **21.** 10 **23.** $12\frac{1}{4}$ hours

Lesson 15-7

Try This **a.** $x = 5\sqrt{2}$ **b.** $x = 2.5$; $y = 2.5\sqrt{3}$
Exercises **1.** $x = 3\sqrt{2}$ **3.** $x = 3\sqrt{3}$; $y = 3$ **5.** $5\sqrt{2}$; $4.3\sqrt{2}$ **7.** 127.28 ft **9.** 3.464 **11.** $\sqrt{2}$ **13.** 5 **15.** $\frac{3}{2}$ **17.** −2

Lesson 15-8

Try This **a.** quadratic, square root **b.** absolute value **c.** 0, 4, 6, 8, 10, 12
Exercises **1.** quadratic, square root **3.** quadratic, square root, absolute value **5.** −2, 1, 4, 7, 10, 13 **7.** −31, −7, 1, −7, −31, −71 **9.** 19.2 cm **11.** ±1.4 **13.** x-intercept = −4; y-intercept = −4 **15.** 5

Lesson 15-9

Try This
a. $\sin A = \frac{12}{13}$; $\cos A = \frac{5}{13}$; $\tan A = \frac{12}{5}$
b. $AB^2 = 40^2 + 75.23^2$, $AB \approx 85.20$

Exercises
1. $\sin A = \frac{8}{17}$; $\cos A = \frac{15}{17}$; $\tan A = \frac{8}{15}$
3. $\sin A = \frac{5}{13}$; $\cos A = \frac{12}{13}$; $\tan A = \frac{5}{12}$
5. $\sin A = \frac{7}{25}$; $\cos A = \frac{24}{25}$; $\tan A = \frac{7}{24}$
7. $h = 1{,}354.95$ ft **9.** $AB = 257.84$ ft **11.** $\frac{1}{2}$ **13.** $\frac{1}{2}$ **15.** $\frac{1}{\sqrt{2}}$ or $\frac{\sqrt{2}}{2}$ **17.** $\frac{1}{\sqrt{2}}$ or $\frac{\sqrt{2}}{2}$
19. $\sin A = \frac{7}{25}$; $\cos A = \frac{24}{25}$; $\tan A = \frac{7}{24}$; $x = 25$
21. $\sin A = \frac{4}{7}$; $\cos A \approx \frac{5.74}{7}$; $\tan A \approx \frac{4}{5.74}$; $x = 5.74$ **23.** 4 **25.** 30 **27.** $x = 45°$ **29.** $x = 30°$ **31.** $x = 20°$ **33.** 16 cm² **35.** 28 in.² **37.** 4.14 **39.** 24

Lesson 15-10

Problems **1.** $4,580 **3.** 9 gal **5.** 38 hours **9.** 3 **11.** 5

Lesson 15-11

Problems **1.** 25 **3.** Angie, 115 lb; Brenda, 107 lb; Clara, 101 lb

Chapter 15 Review/Test

1. false **3.** false **5.** false **7.** 7 **9.** $\pm\sqrt{43}$ **11.** $a = 9$ **13.** 20 **15.** $\frac{20}{29}$ **17.** approximately 7.2 ft

Cumulative Review

1. 715.92 in.³ **2.** $426\frac{2}{3}$ m³ **3.** 376.80 ft³ **4.** 208 m² **5.** 20 **6.** 5,040 **7.** 24 **8.** 20 **9.** 8 **10.** 14 **11.** 14 **12.** 14 **13.** −9 and −10 **14.** 5 and 6 **15.** 5.29 **16.** 8.94 **17.** 10 **18.** $\sqrt{89}$ or ≈9.43 **19.** $\frac{5}{13}$ **20.** $\frac{12}{13}$ **21.** $\frac{5}{12}$

Extra Practice

Chapter 1 Extra Practice

1. 17 **3.** 17 **5.** 9 **7.** 6 **9.** 16; $x + 6$ **11.** $7 - b$ **13.** $r + 6$ **15.** $11 + m$ **17.** $2 + (r + 6)$ **19.** 13 **21.** 25 **23.** 13 **25.** 98 **27.** 222 **29.** 333 **31.** 3 **33.** 300 **35.** 1,500 **37.** 1,900 **39.** Possible answer: 170

Chapter 2 Extra Practice

1. 27 **3.** $28 + 7b$ **5.** 5 **7.** 10; $x \div 3$ **9.** $\frac{9}{s}$ **11.** $7x$ **13.** dr **15.** $s(6)$ **17.** $11(bt)$ **19.** $4d + 7d = 11d$ **21.** $6x + 30$ **23.** $20x$ **25.** $7b$ **27.** $17r$ **29.** 7 **31.** 12 **33.** 52 **35.** 8 calories **37.** 240 cm³ **39.** Possible answer: 7

Chapter 3 Extra Practice

1. 23 **3.** 1 **5.** $-12 < 0 < 4$ **7.** −10 **9.** −6 **11.** 9 **13.** −5 **15.** −19 **17.** −31 **19.** −16

21. -5 **23.** -22 **25.** 82 **27.** 21 **29.** 9°F
31. 54 **33.** 32 **35.** -48 **37.** -3 **39.** -11
41. -19 **43.** -25 **45.** -36 **47.** 1
49. $17q = 85$

Chapter 4 Extra Practice

1. 86.03 **3.** < **5.** = **7.** 640 **9.** 505 **11.** 156.3
13. 8.77 **15.** 3.14 **17.** -25.85 **19.** 6.8 **21.** 5.55
23. 1,230 cm **25.** 150 **27.** 20 **29.** -39.664
31. $-3{,}752$ **33.** -400 **35.** 1.357 **37.** -15.54
39. \$41.19

Chapter 5 Extra Practice

1. 1, 2, 3, 6, 9, 18 **3.** 1, 3, 9, 27, 81
5. 20, 40, 60, 80, 100 **7.** 2 **9.** 2 **11.** 2
13. $8p = 96$; 12 **15.** composite **17.** composite
19. $(-4)(-4)(-4) = -64$ **21.** 6^4 **23.** $(-8)^3$
25. 7^5 **27.** 80 **29.** 729 **31.** $2 \cdot 3 \cdot 5 \cdot 7$
33. $3^2 \cdot 5^2$ **35.** 3 **37.** 146.25 ft **39.** 72
41. 48 inches

Chapter 6 Extra Practice

1. 24 **3.** -18 **5.** $-\frac{1}{9}$ **7.** $\frac{2}{9}$ **9.** $-3\frac{2}{13}$ **11.** $\frac{55}{8}$
13. $-\frac{29}{5}$ **15.** > **17.** = **19.** $\frac{9}{13}$ **21.** $-\frac{3}{4}$ **23.** $\frac{1}{14}$
25. $1\frac{11}{24}$ **27.** $-3\frac{1}{35}$ **29.** $3\frac{5}{6}$ buckets **31.** $-\frac{9}{14}$
33. $3\frac{7}{12}$ yards

Chapter 7 Extra Practice

1. $-\frac{3}{10}$ **3.** $9\frac{23}{28}$ **5.** $-\frac{5}{9}$ **7.** $-1\frac{7}{11}$ **9.** -5
11. -3 **13.** $1\frac{3}{5}$ miles **15.** $2\frac{1}{3}$ inches
17. 0.375 **19.** 0.28 **21.** $(-6)^2$ **23.** $\frac{1}{64}$ **25.** 9
27. 6.7×10^4 **29.** 3.5×10^{-3} **31.** 2.46×10^{-1}
33. 0.024

Chapter 8 Extra Practice

1. 12 **3.** -9 **5.** $2b - 1 = 7$
7. $f(4) = 11, f(5) = 15, f(6) = 19, f(7) = 23$
9. -11 **11.** 4 **13.** -8 **15.** 3 **17.** 2 **19.** -7
21. 2 hours **23.** $2x^2 + 3x - 3$ **25.** $d > 8$
27. $a > 5$

Chapter 9 Extra Practice

1. $(-4, 1)$ **5.** $(-3, -2)$ **7.** \$225 **9.** no
11. yes; $k = 12$ **13.** 4 **15.** x-int: 8, y-int: -2
17.

Chapter 10 Extra Practice

1. $\frac{9}{11}$ **3.** $\frac{17}{4}$ **5.** 5 **7.** \$15/day **9.** 22 steps/floor
11. $x + 2x = 288$ **13.** 2 cm × 4 cm
15. 48-ounce
17. $\frac{1}{25}$ **19.** 0.1425 **21.** $7\frac{1}{5}\%$ **23.** $7\frac{3}{4}\%$
25. 28% **27.** $1\frac{3}{4}$ **29.** $\frac{7}{200}$

Chapter 11 Extra Practice

1. 111 **3.** 2.2 **5.** 60% **7.** 25% **9.** 87.5 **11.** 88
13. 7 days **15.** 25% increase **17.** \$147; \$2,303
19. \$13.50 **21.** \$270; \$870 **23.** \$54; \$354

Chapter 12 Extra Practice

1. 4 cm **3.** *A*, *B*, *C*, etc. **5.** *ABC*, *ICB*
7. $\overrightarrow{GB}$, $\overrightarrow{DL}$, etc. **9.** $\angle GBJ$, etc. **11.** 110°
13. 110° **15.** acute, equilateral **17.** 52°
19. 27.004 cm **21.** 8 cm

Chapter 13 Extra Practice

1. 0.9 m^2 or 9,000 cm^2 **3.** 105.28 m^2
5. 113.04 cm^2 **7.** 158.13 m^2 **9.** 863.5 ft^3
11. \$633.33 **13.** 180 ft^3 **15.** 146 cm^2

Chapter 14 Extra Practice

1. 36 **3.** 720 **5.** $\frac{2}{3}$ **7.** $\frac{1}{36}$ **9.** $\frac{1}{3}$
11. $2w + 2(3w) = 104$; $w = 13$ ft, $l = 39$ ft
13. 75 **15.** 81.3 **17.** 120 lb – 135 lb
19. 10 pounds

Chapter 15 Extra Practice

1. 1 **3.** 6 and 7 **5.** 9 and 10 **7.** ± 14 **9.** 13
11. 11.4 inches **13.** 36 **15.** $7\sqrt{3}$ **17.** 0 **19.** $\frac{4}{5}$
21. $\frac{3}{4}$

Milestones in Mathematics

Gauss called mathematics the Queen of the sciences. Clearly then, mathematicians are her courtiers. To fully enjoy mathematics, you need a sense of its development and of the people of genius who have devoted their lives to its exploration. **Milestones in Mathematics** is a partial list of important events in mathematical history. You may want to find additional information in the library to learn more about these and other mathematicians and their contributions to the field of mathematics.

Milestones in Mathematics

c. 30,000+BC	The knucklebones of animals were used as dice in games of chance.
c. 20,000+BC	A wolfbone with 55 notches in two rows divided into groups of five was used for counting (discovered at Vestonice in Czechoslovakia).
c. 8,000 BC	First evidence of recorded counting.
c. 2,000 BC	The Egyptians had arrived at the value for pi of $\pi = 4(8/9)^2$.
c. 1,900 BC	Babylonian scholars used cuneiform numerals to the base 60 in the oldest-known written numeration for place value.
c. 1,700 BC	Sumerian notation was used to solve quadratic equations by the equivalent of the formula we use today.
c. 800 BC	Queen Dido founded the great city of Carthage by solving the geometric "Problem of Dido." A rigorous proof of this problem—what closed curve of specified length will enclose a maximum area—did not come until the nineteenth century.
c. 700 BC	Zero appeared in the Seleucid mathematical tables.
c. 550 BC	Pythagoras developed a logical, deductive proof of the Pythagorean theorem.
c. 300 BC	Euclid wrote the first geometry text, *Elements*.
c. 250 BC	Archimedes wrote *On Mechanical Theorems, Method* for his friend Eratosthenes.
c. 250 AD	An initial-letter shorthand for algebraic equations was developed.
c. 300 AD	Pappus of Alexandria discussed the areas of figures with the same perimeter in the *Mathematical Collection*.
c. 375 AD	Earliest known Mayan Initial Series inscriptions for expressing dates and periods of time.
c. 400 AD	Hypatia, the foremost mathematician in Alexandria, lectured on Diophantine algebra.
595	Date of an Indian deed on copper plate showing the oldest known use of the nine numerals according to the place value principle: the first written decimal numeration with the structure used today.

825 A treatise on linear and quadratic equations was published by Mohammed Al-Khwarizmi.

850 Mahavira contributed to the development of algebra in India.

1202 Leonardo of Pisa, also called Fibonacci, wrote *Liber abaci,* introducing Arabic numbers to Europe. This book contains his "rabbit problem" involving the numbers we now call Fibonacci.

1261 Yang Hui of China wrote on the properties of the binomial coefficients.

1557 The equal sign (=) came into general use during the 16th century, A.D. (The twin lines as an equal sign were used by the English physician and mathematician Robert Recorde with the explanation that "noe .2. thynges, can be moare equalle.")

1614 John Napier invented logarithms.

1639 René Descartes published his treatise on the application of algebra to geometry (analytic geometry).

1654 Blaise Pascal described the properties of the triangle we now call Pascal's triangle.

1657 Major contributions to number theory were made by Pierre de Fermat including his formulation of the "Pell" equation.

1670 G. Mouton devised a decimal-based measuring system.

1688 The calculus was published by Isaac Newton in *Principia Mathematica.*

1735 Graph theory was originated by Leonard Euler in his paper on the problem, "The Seven Bridges of Konigsberg."

1784 Maria Agnesi developed new ways to deal with problems involving infinite quantities in her book, *Analytical Institutions.*

1799 The fundamental theorem of algebra was delineated by Carl Friederich Gauss, who also developed rigorous proof as the requirement of mathematics.

1816 Sophie Germain published equations which stated the law for vibrating elastic surfaces.

1832 Evariste Galois wrote the theorem stating the conditions under which an equation can be solved.

1854 George Boole developed the postulates of "Boolean Algebra" in *Laws of Thought.*

1854 Mary Fairfax Somerville wrote books to popularize mathematics and extend the influence of the work of mathematicians.

1859 George F. B. Reimann published his work on the distribution of primes; "Reimann's Hypothesis" became one of the famous unsolved problems of mathematics.

1886	Modern combinatorial topology was created by Henri Poincare.
1888	Sonya Kovalesvskaya was awarded the Prix Bordin for her paper "On the Rotation of a Solid Body About a Fixed Point."
1897	David Hilbert published his monumental work on the theory of number fields and later clarified the foundations of geometry.
1906	Grace Chisholm Young and William Young published the first text on set theory.
1914	Srinivasa Ramanujan went to England to collaborate with G. H. Hardy on analytic number theory.
1925	Hermann Weyl published fundamental papers on group theory.
1931	Gödel showed that there must be undecidable propositions in any formal system and that one of those undecidable propositions is consistency.
1932	A completely general theory of ideal numbers was built up, on an axiomatic basis, by Emmy Noether.
1936	The minimax principle in probability and statistics was developed by Abraham Wald.
1937	Goldbach's conjecture that every even number is the sum of two primes ($12 = 5 + 7$, $100 = 3 + 97$) was established by I. M. Vinogradov for every sufficiently large even number that is the sum of, at most, four primes.
1938	Claude E. Shannon discovered the analogy between the truth values of propositions and the states of switches and relays in an electric circuit.
1942	Jacqueline Ferrand created the concept of preholomorphic functions, using these to produce a new methodology for mathematical proofs.
1951	Elizabeth Scott, Jerzy Newyman, and C. D. Shane applied statistical theories to deduce the existence of clusters of galaxies.
1953	Maria Pastori extended the usefulness of the tensor calculus in the pure mathematical investigation of generalized spaces.
1960	Advances in the application of probability and statistics were made by Florence Nightingale David.
1976	Four color problem proved using electronic computing in concert with human deduction.
1985	A new algorithm for factoring large numbers by using elliptic curves was developed by Hendrik W. Lenstra, Jr.
1985	David Hoffman discovered a fourth minimal surface, the first new minimal surface discovered since the 1700s.
????	"Fermat's Last Theorem" on the impossibility of separating any power above the second into two powers of the same degree is proved.

INDEX